ENCYCLOPEDIA OF
FIREARMS

Edited by
HAROLD L. PETERSON

E. P. DUTTON AND COMPANY INC.,
NEW YORK

First published in the U.S.A. 1964
by E. P. Dutton & Co. Inc.

First Edition

Printed in The Netherlands

This book was designed and produced by George Rainbird
Ltd, 2 Hyde Park Place, London W2, England, for
E. P. Dutton & Co. Inc., 201 Park Avenue South, New
York 3. The engravings for the color and monochrome
plates were made by Austin Miles Ltd, London. The text
and monochrome plates were printed by N.V. Drukkerij
Koch & Knuttel, Gouda, Holland. The color plates were
printed by Robert Maclehose & Co. Ltd, Glasgow.
The endpapers and jacket were printed by L. van Leer &
Co. N.V., Amsterdam. The paper was supplied by Mar-
shall Feddern & Co. Ltd, London. The book was bound
by Van Rijmenam N.V., The Hague.

CONTENTS

723

COLOR PLATES

PREFACE

A bibliography of three thousand books on any given subject would normally indicate that it has been explored with at least a fair degree of thoroughness. Yet the most conservative estimates indicate that the number of gun books has already reached this figure, and more are being published every year. Most of these volumes are specialized studies of a specific type of firearm or of the guns of a given area or nation, or even of a single manufacturer, and they have appeared in all the major European languages and some of the minor ones. Only a specialist with world-wide contacts and unusual linguistic abilities can possibly be familiar with all of the literature in the field. The novice or the curator of a small general museum is faced with a bewildering plethora of titles, but with no way of sorting the good from the bad, the current from the obsolete.

This is the situation that has called the present volume into being. Good general references on firearms are extremely few, and by their very nature are of more value for background than for specific reference. There has never been a true firearms encyclopedia to provide the non-specialist with a brief synopsis of the facet of the subject in which he is interested and to direct him to the best readily available sources for further information should he require more data.

It is hoped that the *Encyclopedia of Firearms* will perform these functions. Leading students throughout Europe and America have contributed articles on their specialities, some of them presenting new information as well as synthesizing the best of previously published data. To all of them the editor is deeply indebted. Most of the articles are followed by a select bibliography which indicates the best sources for further information – if, indeed, anything worthwhile has been published on the subject. Generally, these bibliographic references have been confined to reasonably available books in English. Rare volumes, foreign language publications, and articles in periodicals have been included only when they are of exceptional importance or when nothing else is available. The student who wishes to read widely in a subject will normally be led to the more esoteric sources through those which are cited here.

In any encyclopedia, be it one volume or many, it is necessary to select the topics to be covered and to apportion the total wordage among them. This is the most difficult task faced by the editor.

His decisions must reflect his conception of the scope and purpose of the book, and all errors of judgment are directly attributable to him. In view of this, a few comments about the basic principles which have guided the creation of this particular book may be in order.

First of all, the subject matter has been restricted primarily to small arms with a few excursions into the field of light ordnance such as machine guns and swivel guns. Heavy ordnance would have broadened the scope too greatly for compression into single-volume form, which was considered the most practical and useful. Within this subject range the emphasis has been on history and development, since it was felt that these were the aspects of the subject for which most readers would consult an encyclopedia. Use and theory, however, have not been entirely overlooked. In addition, ammunition, major accessories and accoutrements, famous armories and important persons have been included. In selecting the men whose biographies appear, the principal criterion was their contribution to the development of firearms. Generally speaking, they are inventors, rather than fine or prolific gunsmiths. The reader who is interested in obtaining information on a maker as a means of identifying a specimen is referred to Gluckman and Satterlee: *American Gun Makers*, Støckel: *Haandskyderaabens Bedømmelse*, or one of the other historical directories of gunsmiths already in print. There has been no attempt to duplicate their manifold listings here.

Finally, since this is an encyclopedia, the topics are mostly broad and the treatment discursive and expository, in contrast to the dictionary approach with its myriad short definitions.

HAROLD L. PETERSON

CONTRIBUTORS

A. G. **Colonel Arcadi Gluckman**
Colonel, U. S. Army (retired). Author of *United States Martial Pistols and Revolvers* (1939) and *United States Muskets, Rifles and Carbines* (1959); co-author with L. D. Satterlee of *American Gun Makers* (1953).

A. H. **Dr. Arne Hoff**
Curator, Firearms Department, Tøjhusmuseet (Royal Arsenal Museum), Copenhagen. Author of *The Rasmussen Revolving Guns* (1946), *Aeldre Dansk Bøssemageri* (1957), and other books. Contributor to *Armes Anciennes, The Journal of the Arms and Armour Society*, and other periodicals. Editor of *Vaabenhistoriske Aarbøger* (year books of the Danish Arms and Armor Society).

A. N. K. **A. N. Kennard**
Assistant Master of the Armouries, Tower of London. Fellow of the Society of Antiquaries. Contributor to the *Burlington Magazine, The Connoisseur*, and *The Journal of the Arms and Armour Society*.

B. R. L. **Colonel Berkeley R. Lewis**
Colonel, U. S. Army (retired). Author of *Small Arms and Ammunition in the United States Service* (1956). Contributor to *The American Rifleman* and *Ordnance*.

B. W. M. **Bluford W. Muir**
Photographic Consultant, U.S. Forest Service. Fellow of the Company of Military Historians. Contributor to *The American Rifleman*. Responsible for photography in many firearms books and periodicals.

C. B. **Claude Blair**
Assistant Keeper of the Metalwork Department, Victoria and Albert Museum, London. Fellow of the Society of Antiquaries. Author of *European Armour* (1958) and *European and American Arms* (1962). Hon. Editor of and contributor to *The Journal of the Arms and Armour Society*. Contributor to *Archaeologia, The Connoisseur*, and other periodicals.

C. E. H. **Charles E. Hanson, Jr.**
Consulting Director, Museum of the Fur Trade, Chadron, Nebraska. Author of *The Northwest Gun* (1956) and *The Plains Rifle* (1960). Contributor to *The Gun Digest, The Missouri Archaeologist*, and other periodicals.

C. H. R. **Dr. C. H. Roads**
Research student in firearms and military history, University of Cambridge. Contributor to *Guns Review* and *The Journal of the Arms and Armour Society*.

CL. B.   Clement Bosson
Staff member of the Museum of Art and History, Geneva. Co-editor of *Armes Anciennes*. Contributor to various firearms periodicals.

C. R. G.   Craddock R. Goins, Jr.
Associate Curator, Smithsonian Institution, Washington, D.C. Author of a forthcoming book on the Hall breech-loading system.

C. W.   Colin Willock
Head of Anglia TV Natural History Unit. Author of *Gun Punt Adventure* (1948), *Duck Shooting* (1962), and other books. Editor of *The Farmer's Book of Field Sports* (1961).

D. B. W.   Donald B. Webster, Jr.
Author of *Suicide Specials* (1958). Contributor to *Gun Report*, *Ordnance*, and other periodicals.

E. A. S.   Edouard A. Stackpole
Curator, Mystic Seaport, Mystic, Conn. (Marine Historical Association Museum). Author of *The Sea Hunters, the first two centuries of whaling* (1953), *Scrimshaw, American Whaling Folk Art* (1957), and other books.

E. E.   Egon Eriksen
Curator on the staff of the Tøjhusmuseet (Royal Arsenal Museum), Copenhagen. Author of *Danske Orgelespingoler* [Danish organ espignolles], *1850–1877* (1945), and other books. Contributor to various periodicals.

E. G. W.   Eldon G. Wolff
Curator of History, Milwaukee Public Museum. Author of *Ballard Rifles in the Henry J. Nunnemacher Collection* (1945), *Air Guns* (1958), and other publications. Contributor to various firearms periodicals.

F. A.   F. Askgaard
Curator and librarian on the staff of the Tøjhusmuseet (Royal Arsenal Museum), Copenhagen. Author of books on the Swedish-Danish wars of 1657–60 and on other topics. Contributor to *Vaabenhistoriske Aarbøger* (year books of the Danish Arms and Armor Society), and other periodicals.

G. B. J.   Colonel G. B. Jarrett
Colonel, U.S. Army (retired); Chief, U.S. Army Ordnance Museum, Aberdeen Proving Ground, Maryland. Fellow of the Company of Military Historians.

G. E. B.   G. E. Bennett
Founder Member and Hon. Treasurer of the Arms and Armour Society. Contributor to *The Journal of the Arms and Armour Society*.

G. M. C.   Colonel George M. Chinn
Colonel, U.S. Marine Corps (retired); Director, Kentucky Historical Society. Author of *The Machine Gun* (4 vols, 1951–5).

H. C. L.   Herschel C. Logan
Past President, American Society of Arms Collectors. Fellow of the Company of Military Historians. Author of *Hand Cannon to Automatic* (1944), *Cartridges* (1948), *Underhammer Guns* (1960), and other books. Contributor to *The American Rifleman*, *Hobbies*, and other periodicals.

H. J. K.   Henry J. Kauffman
Author of *Early American Gunsmiths, 1650–1850* (1962) and *The Pennsylvania-Kentucky Rifle* (1960). Contributor to various periodicals.

H. L. B.   Howard L. Blackmore
Fellow of the Society of Antiquaries; President of the Arms and Armour Society. Author of *British Military Firearms, 1650–1850* (1961). Contributor to *The American Rifleman*, *The Connoisseur*, and *The Journal of the Arms and Armour Society*.

H. L. P.   Harold L. Peterson
Staff Historian, U.S. National Park Service. President of the Company of Military Historians; a director of the National Rifle Association of America. Author of *The American Sword, 1775–1945* (1954), *Arms and Armor in Colonial America, 1526–1783* (1956), *American Knives* (1958), *The Treasury of the Gun* (1962), and other books. Contributor to *The Concise Encyclopedia of American Antiques* (1958), the *Encyclopedia Britannica*, and various firearms periodicals. Sometime lecturer at The Metropolitan Museum of Art, New York, The New-York Historical Society, and elsewhere. Editor of this encyclopedia.

H. W.   Harry Wandrus
Museum Preservation Specialist, U.S. National Park Service. Fellow of the Company of Military Historians. Formerly firearms editor of *Hobbies* magazine. Contributor to various periodicals.

J. C. M. **John C. McMurray**
Co-author with C. Meade Patterson of "United States Military Wall Guns" in *Muzzle Blasts* (August-November 1953).

J. D. L. **James Duncan Lavin**
Author of a forthcoming history of Spanish firearms.

J. E. P. **John E. Parsons**
Author of *The Peacemaker and Its Rivals* (1950), *Henry Deringer's Pocket Pistol* (1952), *The First Winchester* (1955), *Smith & Wesson Revolvers* (1957), and *West on the 49th Parallel* (1963). Contributor to various firearms periodicals and historical journals.

J. E. S. **Joseph E. Smith**
Chief, Firepower Group, Weapons System Analysis, U.S. Army Foreign Science and Technology Center. Editor of *The Book of Rifles* and *Small Arms of the World*.

J. F. H. **J. F. Hayward**
Deputy Keeper in the Department of Woodwork, Victoria and Albert Museum, London. Author of *European Firearms* (1957), *The Art of The Gunmaker* (2 vols, 1962–4), and other books. Contributor to *The Concise Encyclopedia of Antiques*, and to *The Connoisseur*, *The Journal of the Arms and Armour Society*, and other periodicals.

J. J. G. **James J. Grant**
Author of *Single-shot Rifles* (1947) and *More Single-shot Rifles* (1959).

J. R. P. **J. R. Partington**
Emeritus Professor, University of London. Author of *A History of Greek Fire and Gunpowder* (1960) and other books.

J.S. DU M. **John S. du Mont**
Vice President, the du Mont Corporation. Co-author with John E. Parsons of *Firearms in the Custer Battle* (1953). Contributor to *The American Rifleman*, *The Gun Digest*, *The Military Collector & Historian*, and other periodicals.

J. S. H. **James S. Hutchins**
Assistant Coordinator of Studies, National Armed Forces Museum Advisory Board, the Smithsonian Institution. Fellow of the Company of Military Historians. Contributor to *The Military Collector & Historian* and other periodicals.

L. A. W. **Lee A. Wallace, Jr.**
Staff Historian, U.S. National Park Service. Managing Associate Editor of *The Military Collector & Historian*. Contributor to various firearms periodicals.

L. J. **LaDow Johnston**
Member of the Ohio Academy of Science, a director of the National Muzzle-loading Rifle Association, and President of the Ohio Gun Collectors Association and of the Kentucky Rifle Association. Contributor to the *Ohio Archaeologist* and other publications.

L. W. **Lewis Winant** (d. 1963)
Author of *Pepperbox Firearms* (1952), *Firearms Curiosa* (1955) and *Early Percussion Firearms* (1959). Contributor to *The American Rifleman*, *The Gun Collector*, and other periodicals.

P. J. W. **Paul J. Wolf**
Contributor to *The American Arms Collector*, *The Journal of the Arms and Armour Society*, and *The Journal of the Ontario Arms Collectors' Association*.

P. W. **Captain Paul J. Westergard**
Captain, U.S. Army (retired). Contributor to W. H. B. Smith's *Gas, Air and Spring Guns* and other publications.

R. L. M. **Robert L. Miller**
Fellow of the Company of Military Historians. Associate Editor of *The Military Collector & Historian*.

R. R. **Ray Riling**
Author, bookseller, and publisher. Fellow of the Company of Military Historians. Author of *Guns and Shooting, a bibliography* (1951) and *The Powder Flask Book* (1953). Contributor to various firearms periodicals.

S. J. G. **S. James Gooding**
Head, Museum Section, Department of Northern Affairs and National Resources, Ottawa, Canada. Author of *Canadian Gunsmiths* (1962). Contributor to *The American Rifleman*, *The Missouri Archaeologist*, the *Ontario Arms Collectors' Association Bulletin*, and other periodicals.

T. M. H. **T. M. Hamilton**
Compiler of *Indian Trade Guns* (1962). Contributor to *The Missouri Archaeologist*.

T. T. H. **Dr. Thomas T. Hoopes**
Curator, City Art Museum, St. Louis, Missouri. Author of *Armor and Arms* (1954). Contributor to *A Miscellany of Arms and Armor* (1927) and to various periodicals. Sometime Carnegie Foundation research fellow in arms at the Kunsthistorisches Museum, Vienna.

W. A. A. **William A. Albaugh, III**
Author of *Handbook of Confederate Swords* (1951), *The Original Confederate Colt* (1952), *The Confederate Brass-framed Colt and Whitney* (1954), *Confederate Arms* (1958), *Tyler, Texas, C.S.A.* (1959), *Confederate Edged Weapons* (1960), and *Confederate Handguns* (1963). Contributor to *The American Gun Collector*, *Army Ordnance*, *The Gun Digest*, and other periodicals.

W. R. **William Reid**
Assistant, The Armouries, Tower of London. Fellow of the Society of Antiquaries of Scotland. Contributor to *The American Rifleman*, *The Antiquaries' Journal*, *The Connoisseur*, *The Journal of the Arms and Armour Society*, the *Scottish Art Review*, and other periodicals.

THE
ENCYCLOPEDIA

A

ACCESSORIES

The sportsman using the early hand cannon or matchlock gun was faced with many difficulties, not only in firing his gun but in loading it and keeping it in serviceable condition. He needed a bullet bag and two powder flasks, a large one to hold the powder for the main charge in the barrel, and a smaller one, known as a touchbox or priming flask, for the finer-grain powder which was applied to the priming pan. To fire his charge a length of slow match was necessary, and, as a protection against the weather or to conceal the position of a soldier at night, the glowing end of the match was housed in a matchbox. This was a perforated tube of tin or brass, about a foot long. It was also necessary to gauge the right amount of powder to put in the barrel. This could be done accurately by a powder measure, an iron or brass tube with a pull-out base giving numbered readings, but it was normally sufficient for the main powder flask to be fitted with a measured nozzle. Another method was to carry separate charges in boxes of wood or horn strung on to a belt slung from the shoulder, called a bandolier.

Bullets and powder had to be properly rammed down the barrel, so each gun had a ramrod or "scowring stick headed at one end with Rammers of Horne suitable to the bore of the Piece and at the other with boxes of iron in which to screw their wormes." The ramrod and its accompanying tools were an important part of the gunner's equipment, as the crude gunpowder used soon clogged up the barrel and made the bullet jam. To remedy these accidents, two, or sometimes three, small tools, which screwed into the end of the ramrod, were carried: a loop or jag to hold a piece of cloth, and a worm, something like a single or double corkscrew, whose steel points bit into the wadding so that it could be withdrawn, together with the loose-fitting ball. If a bullet stuck in the bore, a ball screw or ball drawer was used to dig into the soft lead of the bullet to withdraw it. A small piece of wire known as a priming iron or pricker was also required to keep the touchhole clear. If necessary, of course, the sportsman carried a bullet mold and a circular punch to cut wads. As if all these accessories were not enough, the soldier firing the heavy, cumbersome musket was also burdened with a rest "of Ash wood or other tough wood with iron Pikes in the neather end and halfe hoopes of Iron above to rest the musquet on."

When the complicated wheel lock was introduced an additional tool became essential: a key or spanner to wind up or "span" the mechanism. The piece of iron pyrites

which set off the spark in the pan was held between two screw-held jaws of the cock, and so the wheel lock key was usually shaped as a screwdriver at one end. It was often an object of great artistic merit, the steel being delicately chiseled with floral decoration. Sometimes it was combined with a flask or powder measure. This attempt to reduce the number of accessories was assisted by the introduction of paper cartridges, carried in a container known as a patron, thus dispensing with the need for flasks, bandoliers and bullet bags.

The adoption of the flintlock did away with the wheel lock key, but in the late seventeenth century a type of flintlock pocket pistol became popular which had a "turn-off" barrel requiring another form of key. This could be better described as a barrel wrench or ring spanner which fitted over a stud on the barrel to unscrew it for loading. This loose tool was sometimes replaced by a hinged lever fitted on to the barrel itself. In the case of pairs of all-steel pistols a hole could be cut in the grip which served the same purpose as the wrench. Another method was to cut grooves, often mistaken for rifling, in the muzzle and to file a square projection on the handle of the bullet mold which keyed into the grooves.

The soldier of the eighteenth and early nineteenth centuries, however, needed only three tools to keep his musket in order: a turnkey or multiple screwdriver with which to change a broken flint; a worm for his ramrod; and a brush and pricker to keep the pan and touchhole clear. He was discouraged from taking any further action such as dismantling the lock or gun, as this was considered the responsibility of the regimental or ship's armorer. The armorer in the field was supplied with a portable forge and suitable tools, but some armorers appear to have made a pocket set of tools, perhaps as a symbol of office. The finest example of these, engraved with the name of the maker, "J. Delpire, Armurier du 7m Regt Suisse de la Garde Royale, Paris," includes two punches or drifts (to knock out pins or nails), a hammer, a file, a spring clamp, a pair of pliers and various screwdrivers, jags and worms, all ingeniously screwing together.

A set of tools often carried by the sportsman was a pair of pliers with a hammer fitting on the head and a worm, pricker and whistle (for his dogs) screwed on to the handles. A striking example of pocket tools was made by the London gunmaker Andrew Dolep to go with a fine flintlock fowling piece commissioned by a member of the Medici family, whose arms adorn it. It consists of a small steel box, shaped like a scent bottle and nicely engraved, which contains a set of plain but beautifully made tools which clip into the neck of the box, the latter acting as a handle. The gun is in the Armeria Reale, Turin, and the tools are in the Tower of London.

From the middle of the eighteenth century, a cased pair

of pistols, whether used for dueling or as a traveling safeguard, was an important part of every gentleman's wardrobe. The case was usually of mahogany or oak with brass fittings and handles and lined with felt or velvet. Accessories supplied were a powder flask, sometimes with a compartment for bullets and another for flints, a bullet mold, a screwdriver, an oil bottle and a separate ramrod with worm and jag. In contrast, the pistol of the traveler in the Near East was rarely cased and was never fitted for a ramrod. This was carried separately, hung from the belt. Called a *suma*, it took the form of a hollow steel rod whose handle unscrewed to display a pair of tongs or a poinard. A decorative object, often inlaid with gold and silver or colored ivory, it was accompanied by a powder measure, *wazna-i-barut*, similarly adorned.

The percussion lock, although a simpler form of lock, presented another problem. Not only was it necessary to devise cap magazines and dispensers (see CAPPER) to handle the tiny copper cap, but a nipple key was needed to replace broken nipples. This key was often incorporated in a T-shaped or Y-shaped combination tool. The two prongs formed screwdrivers, the body was hollowed out as an oil bottle and one end was cut into the proper shape to fit the nut of the nipple. A hook-shaped projection on the side acted as a main spring cramp (spring vise). Some sportsmen also carried nipple primers to help clear clogged nipples under field conditions. The cased pair of pistols reached its zenith in the percussion era, some of the cases made by French and Belgian gunmakers being extravagantly fitted and embellished with every conceivable form of tool, including mallets and ladles. With the stocks of pistols and the handles of the tools carved from ebony or ivory, these suites of arms and accessories make an imposing sight. An interesting feature of nearly all cased guns is the printed trade label stuck on the inside of the lid, giving the maker's name and address and information about his business.

The multi-shot guns brought some interesting types of powder and ball chargers. The famous Colt Paterson revolver was supplied with a brass and copper cylinder with five nozzles which dispensed balls and powder to the chambers in two quick operations. In similar style was the seven-nozzle charger supplied with the seven-barreled volley gun made by Forsyth & Company now in the Tower of London. Another interesting accessory developed by Samuel Colt in 1857 was his patent lubricator, a small metal tube which screwed on the end of the ramrod and automatically oiled the bullet during the loading process. Such a refinement was due to the increasing efforts being made to give the muzzle-loading rifle the required accuracy. To avoid damaging the grooves at the muzzle, the target rifle was provided with a false muzzle, which was clipped to the barrel during loading.

The introduction of the breechloader using a metallic cartridge did not immediately mean the end of all these accessories, for the cartridge was not easily obtainable. With the early breechloaders of Pauly, Robert, Lefaucheux, and others, a set of reloading tools, which could de-cap the spent case, fit a new primer, load the powder, shape the bullet and crimp the case tight, was a worthwhile investment. As the metal cartridge and its gun improved, the soldier was relieved of all his former paraphernalia, and his cleaner (a weighted piece of string with a loop, known as a pull-through) and his oil bottle could be carried in the butt trap of his rifle. The armorer of the British Army, however, was still supplied with an official combination tool of clever design which rejoiced in the name of "Implement, action, Sergeant Armourers for the use of."

It is a curious thing that, although there is little need for it, the modern sportsman and target shooter still loves to surround himself with a mass of equipment and accessories, often casting his own bullets and measuring his powder with a micrometer balance.   H.L.B.

Illustrations: pages 111, 338, 344–50.

See also: BANDOLIER; BULLET MOLD; CAPPER; FALSE MUZZLE; NIPPLE PRIMER; POWDER FLASK AND POWDER HORN; SHOT POUCH; SPANNER.

ADAMS, JOHN

John Adams, who at first assisted his brother Robert, began his own activities as a gunmaker in 1857, with a patent for an improved rifle sight and another for a revolver with a complicated action. The action was not a success, but in 1861 his patent for a revolver which could be used as a muzzle-loader or breechloader aroused some interest, as the conversion of muzzle-loading firearms was under active consideration. Although his revolver was not adopted officially, he was encouraged to form the Adams Patent Small Arms Company Ltd., specialising in conversion work on revolvers and the promotion of his own patent revolvers. Business commenced at 391 Strand, London, in 1865. Two more patents in 1866 and 1867 related to metallic-cartridge conversions, and in 1872 came a patent for a simple cartridge ejector which was fitted to numerous British and foreign revolvers and brought large orders for the Model 1872 Adams revolver. In the same year the business was transferred to 9 Finsbury Place South and the name altered to Adams & Co. In 1886 another move took place, to 32 Finsbury Pavement, where the firm continued for another ten years.   H.L.B.

See also: ADAMS, ROBERT.

ADAMS, ROBERT

The revolver patented by Robert Adams in 1851 was the English challenge to the Colt revolver, but unlike the latter it was made with a solid frame and a self-cocking action. This 1851 model had no rammer, but, using special wadded bullets, its five chambers could be loaded and fired twice in two minutes. The second model, introduced probably in 1853, was fitted with a Rigby-type rammer. Both these patterns were made for officers serving in the Crimea and the colonies by Deane, Adams & Deane of 30 King William Street, London. In 1855 Adams secured the rights of Frederick Beaumont's patent double-action mechanism, by which the hammer of a revolver could be raised either by the thumb or by the trigger. The Ordnance showed immediate interest and two sizes of revolver were ordered, one of 38 bore weighing 2 lb 15½ oz and a smaller model of 54 bore weighing 2 lb 6½ oz. In the following year, Adams helped form the London Armoury Company to manufacture the Beaumont-Adams revolver, as it is known to collectors. A factory was built at Bermondsey, and rifling machinery, patented by Adams in 1854, was installed. The inventor acted as manager of the company until 1859, when he started his own business at 76 King William Street. In 1865 he moved to 40 Pall Mall, but after only a year at that address he appears to have retired. He did, however, take out two more firearms patents in 1867.   H.L.B.

Illustration: page 174.

See also: ADAMS, JOHN; REVOLVER.

AFGHAN STOCK

When British troops entered Sind in the 1840's they found the natives using a long gun with a sharply curved stock and a high thin butt terminating in a straight or slightly curved line. Because Sind had been ruled by Afghanistan, they called this distinctive stock form the Afghan stock. Actually, the jezail with its slender stock was more common in Afghanistan proper.   H.L.P.

Illustration: page 210.

Egerton, Wilbraham, *An Illustrated Handbook of Indian Arms*, London, 1880.
Stone, George Cameron, *A Glossary of the Construction, Decoration and Use of Arms and Armor in All Countries and in All Times together with some Closely Related Subjects*, Portland, Me., 1934.

See also: ASIATIC FIREARMS; JEZAIL.

AFRICAN FIREARMS

The firearms found in Africa present a varying picture, differing from place to place but showing very little trace of development through the four centuries preceding ours.

Originally, firearms seem to have gone to the Africans by three routes: through the Turks, by European influence in North Africa, and as imports on the African West Coast, especially from England and the Netherlands.

The Turks in their perpetual wars with Europeans during the fifteenth century had learnt the use of firearms and rapidly became very capable in both their production and use. When in 1517 the sultan Selim I beat the Mamelukes in Egypt, this country came under Turkish domination and thus came under the influence of Turkish culture. Probably soon afterwards firearms of Turkish type came into use over a widespread area of North Africa as well as the Middle East. Single elements of such firearms were also incorporated in arms of other types.

Turkish gun barrels are usually finely damascened and often decorated with inlays in silver or niello. A very typical ornament is a kind of pointed trefoil on a long stem coming up from a triple arch. Among other ornamental elements are more or less intricately interlaced knots. An impressive touch is also created by the incrustation of precious or semiprecious stones, in the case of more common barrels generally corals. The chamber is always distinctly divided from the rest of the barrel by a molding. The breech screw has a convex comb with a sighting notch, or more often a series of peepholes corresponding to different ranges. Not infrequently, the muzzle part is sculptured as a dragon's head or a flower calyx, or simply reinforced by a ring.

The stock has a rather conspicuous form with a pentagonal straight butt set at an angle to the fore-stock. The butt plate, which may be rather thick, is of ivory or white bone. The trigger is of knob form and has no trigger guard. The barrel is attached to the stock by means of capucines, metal bands passing round both barrel and stock. Turkish capucines are generally broader on the upper side.

The lock of the Turkish gun was originally a matchlock, but, at least after the middle of the seventeenth century, this was superseded by a miquelet lock with a characteristic long bridle connecting the cock screw with the pancover screw. The cock is more streamlined than that of the usual miquelet lock. This type of lock was probably developed in Spain, and then spread all over the Mediterranean coast.

The European influence in North Africa is also of an early date. In 1517 some chronicles mention the use of arquebuses in Morocco. Later, Christian slaves are said to have worked in the arsenals there, making firearms of the common European types. Only the wheel lock is never found in Africa. More important than the production of firearms in North Africa itself, no doubt, was the import of firearms from Europe, mostly of gun barrels and locks. A letter from the sultan of Morocco to Louis XIV of France in 1684 mentions a load of a thousand gun locks brought back from Europe.

The most popular lock in Northwest Africa, especially in Morocco, is a Dutch snaphance type. This lock has a movable pan cover of wheel lock type and a separate steel. The mainspring is placed on the inside of the lock plate and acts on a tumbler. As the lock is safe when the steel is turned to its forward position, there is no half cock. Full cock is obtained by a stud on the sear projecting through the lock plate over the tail of the cock. The forward movement of the lock is limited by a buffer fastened to the lock plate with one or usually two screws. A very conspicuous detail is a circular fence on the end of the pan. Snaphances of this type were common in the Netherlands in the second half of the sixteenth and the beginning of the seventeenth centuries. Later they were probably made in Liège for export to Africa. A typical feature of the Dutch snaphances made in North Africa was a lock plate considerably thicker than the original Dutch ones.

Another lock of European origin is the so-called Kabyl lock, a type developed in Spain, where it is found at the beginning of the seventeenth century. The Kabyl lock is a miquelet lock with all or most of the external parts plated in brass. The lock plate is rather curved and has a tiny cock with enormous jaws. Full cock is created by a stud protruding into a slot in the body of the cock, while half cock is obtained by a dog catch engaging in a notch in the cock. The strong and dominating mainspring acts on the toe of the cock. The cock screw has a head with horizontal holes for a turning lever, and two horn-like fingergrips for cocking the lock. The steel and the pan cover form one member, and a single spring acts on them.

The quality of the European barrels exported to North Africa was usually so poor that it is difficult to distinguish them from the African copies. Very often the export barrels were unsigned, or provided only with a sequence of letters without meaning, intended to give the impression of a signature. In Africa they were decorated in the native style and frequently provided with a brass back sight consisting of two walls with a very tiny aperture between them.

A European influence can also be traced among the gun stocks used in North Africa. A popular type has a stock very like, and no doubt developed from, the musket stock of western Europe of about 1600, with a rather flat triangular butt and a fairly deep-cut thumb rest at the neck. But, in contrast to the European prototype, the African stock has a thick butt plate of ivory or bone, often consisting of several layers. The trigger guard has a very narrow arch around the trigger and rather long fore and back branches. The tang screw is almost always inserted from below, just in front of the arch of the trigger guard.

Another type of gun stock is of more primitive form, with a curved butt of oval section and no butt plate. The entire stock may be decorated with inlays of bone or brass, or simply incised ornamentation. Often the neck has a transverse hole for a gun sling, the fore-end of the sling being fastened in a loop around the barrel and stock.

In south Morocco a special gun stock is found which has a flat, downward curving butt with a very pronounced concavity at the end. The butt plate has here degenerated into a bend along the ridge of the butt, ending in a spur accentuating the concavity of the butt end.

A common feature of all North African guns is the use of capucines to keep the barrel and stock together. Capucines are found in many different kinds of metal – silver, brass, copper and iron. Normally there is a rather broad one around the breech and a number of smaller ones towards the muzzle.

While the guns in North Africa were partly imported from Europe and partly produced locally, the guns in Central and South Africa were almost exclusively cheap European trade guns, resembling our military guns but of very inferior quality.

Such guns mostly came from England and Belgium, to some extent also from France, Holland, Spain and other countries. On the Gold Coast the term "Dane gun," today meaning only an obsolete gun, recalls an eighteenth-century Danish trade gun of high reputation.   A.H.

Illustrations: page 208.

Stöcklein, Hans, "Orientalische Waffen aus der Residenz-Büchsenkammer im Ethnographischen Museum, München" in *Münchner Jahrbuch der bildende Kunst*, Vol. 1914–15.
Stone, George Cameron, *A Glossary of the Construction, Decoration and Use of Arms and Armor in All Countries and in All Times together with some Closely Related Subjects*, Portland, Me., 1934.

See also: ASIATIC FIREARMS; TRADE GUNS.

AIR GUN

An air gun is a gun in which the propellant is compressed air. Usually this compression is created before the actual shooting, the compressed air being stored and used for a number of shots. In a few constructions, however, the compression is created immediately before shooting. In the seventeenth and eighteenth centuries, air guns were called wind guns, and the term air gun first appeared about 1800.

The propulsory force of compressed air and the possibility of obtaining a compression were known by several of the mechanical writers of ancient Egypt. Thus Ktesibios from Alexandria in about 250 B.C. describes a double air gun of catapult type. When during the Renaissance the study of ancient literature was again taken up, there also developed an interest in pneumatic experiments, resulting in the re-invention of various engines of more or less practical value. Among these was the air gun.

The oldest air guns still preserved are of the type where the air compression is created immediately before shooting. Two such guns in the Kunsthistorisches Museum, Vienna, from the last quarter of the sixteenth century, have in the stock a hollow chamber in which is housed a cylinder with a piston. This is connected to the mainspring of the lock by means of a rack. Thus the pulling of the trigger will release the piston, which is then driven violently forward, creating a strong pressure of air which in turn pushes out a small projectile. Another almost contemporary gun in the Royal Armory, Stockholm, has small cylindrical bellows also worked by the mainspring.

Guns of this kind are found occasionally during the eighteenth century, and about 1800 and even later a type is found in south Germany and Austria where the butt contains fairly large, flat bellows, which by pressure on the trigger are squeezed together by two strong springs located over and under the bellows. These bellows guns are usually breechloaders, the breech end of the barrel being tipped up by a spring when a release button is pressed.

A late development of these air guns are the so-called gallery guns, of which the United States, especially, has produced a number of types. They became very popular in the second half of the nineteenth century and are still found in use in amusement parks all over the world.

Guns where the compression was made just before shooting had, of course, only comparatively small pressure. It was probably for this reason that guns were constructed where the air could be stored and far greater pressure thus obtained. Such guns are known to have existed as early as the first decade of the seventeenth century. The French gunmaker Marin le Bourgeoys, probably the inventor of the flintlock proper, had at this time made an air gun which used darts of wood with iron points, and had in the rear end a twist of paper in which the air pressure worked. This gun, unfortunately, no longer exists, but a number of air guns are preserved dating from about fifty years later.

Almost all existing seventeenth-century air guns of this kind are of a type where the barrel consists of two tubes, one inside the other. The inner tube is the barrel proper, while the space between the inner and outer tubes acts as an air reservoir. A pressure pump, not unlike the one used for modern bicycles, is built into the butt. Oldest among this kind of air gun are two guns in the Royal Armory, Stockholm, and two in the National Museum, Copenhagen, from 1644 and 1645 respectively. They were all made by one Hans Köhler of Kitzing, a small place near Würzburg in Germany. It is an interesting fact that in the town of Würzburg in about 1630–40 there lived a professor of mathematics and physics called Athanasius Kirchner, who in one of his works describes an air gun, although of a more primitive type.

The lock of the Köhler guns was extremely simple, consisting only of a lever which held the valve open as long as the trigger was pressed. From the middle of the century we have a number of air guns with more complicated systems, where the cock gives the opening valve a short but vigorous blow. Only a portion of the compressed air is released by this. All these guns seem to be of German origin. A most interesting air gun in Skokloster castle in Sweden, signed by Johan Kock of Cologne in 1654, has engravings on the lock plate showing the pumping up of an air gun. The man manipulating the air gun holds the handle of the pump with his foot and is moving the whole gun up and down. This way of pumping was no doubt necessary owing to the very heavy resistance of the valve to be overcome when a strong compression was to be created.

At about the same time, we first hear of air guns in connection with Britain. During the Commonwealth period a conspirator against Cromwell's life was said to have bought an air gun in the Netherlands. It had an air capacity corresponding to seven shots and could be used at a distance of 150 paces. No doubt it was chosen because of its being almost noiseless.

When the Royal Society for the Improving of Natural Knowledge was founded in London in 1660, the question of air guns was taken up in one of the first meetings, and in 1663 an air gun was given to the Society by Dr. Wilkins and a series of experiments undertaken. Later in the century several makers of air guns in London are mentioned, among them William Bull, trumpet-maker to the Court.

Although the air guns with a reservoir around the barrel were still seen in the eighteenth century, two other types were more often found. In the first, the air was held in a globe of brass or copper, screwed to the gun under – or, rarely, over – the breech end of the barrel. The neck of the globe was fitted with a pin valve which, when struck by a lever of the lock, would release part of the compressed air. Guns of this type were made all over Europe until just after 1800. Of course, guns of the globe type were unwieldy and used only for target shooting or as curios. A much more practical solution was to have the air reservoir in the hollowed butt, with a screw socket for a pump concealed by the butt plate. About the middle of the eighteenth century, the system was improved by cutting off the butt and replacing it with an air flask of metal covered with leather or cloth. Thus it was possible to carry spare flasks of air which could easily replace the one in use when its air pressure had declined too much. As it was impossible to see on an air flask how great the pressure was, air guns were sometimes given a numerator. Each time the lock mechanism was fired, a disc with figures would turn showing the number of shots since the numerator was set at zero.

Most of the eighteenth-century air guns had a lock which had the outward appearance of a flintlock. When the cock hit forward, a projecting lug either on the cock itself or on the tumbler would strike the opening valve for a moment, thus releasing the air. Owing to this type of lock, many guns have been considered dual-purpose guns which could be used either with gunpowder or with air. This is a misunderstanding, as can easily be seen from the absence of a touchhole (vent) in the barrel. There are, however, double-barreled guns where one barrel is for powder and the other uses air compression.

A number of late air guns have ball magazines. In fact, the air gun is more easily adapted to the magazine system, as there is no danger of the ignition setting fire to the entire powder magazine, as so often happened to magazine guns using gunpowder. In 1779 Girardoni, an Italian inventor in Austrian service, after an accident while experimenting with powder magazine guns, constructed a magazine air gun. It was of the flask-butt type with a tube ball magazine lying along the side of the barrel and a coiled spring pressing the balls backwards. The square, transverse breechblock, which also closed the ball magazine, had in its center a recess for the ball. A simple pressure on the side of the breechblock would make it slide over, so that the recess received a ball, whereafter a strong spring brought the breechblock back to normal position. Thus, as long as there were balls in the magazine and enough air pressure in the flask-butt, the shots would follow each other with only a few seconds' interval.

The Girardoni air gun was introduced into the Austrian Army as the Model 1780 and used by some Jägers. Soon after 1800 it was, however, again abandoned. (During the Second World War certain experiments were made with air guns for commando troops and partisans, owing to the very feeble noise of the air guns, but in the end other ways were followed.)

The caliber of the Girardoni air gun was about .50. With a fully loaded air flask which required 2,000 strokes of the pump, the muzzle velocity was about 325 yards per second. The first ten shots were effective at a distance of about 150 paces, the next ten at 120–125 paces, the next ten again at 100 paces, and the rest only at very short distances. No doubt this rapid decrease of the trajectory, which forced the soldier not only to count his shots, but also to know how to correct his aiming-point at each stage, was one of the decisive drawbacks of the system.

Probably the air gun was only rarely considered to be anything other than a toy or a gun for target shooting. Various eighteenth-century authors of books on fowling or deer shooting express their disapproval of air guns. Nevertheless, the Landgrave Louis VIII of Hesse (1691–1768) is reported to have killed a very considerable number of game with his air gun, among them a magnificent stag weighing 480 lb.

One of the most outstanding features of the air gun was that it was almost noiseless. This quality made it very suitable for assassins and poachers. Often, therefore, the use or possession of air guns seems to have been forbidden by law.

Several types of innocent-looking air guns were invented for poaching, among them the cane gun. This was usually a thin tube of iron or brass, painted like a cane or covered with wood. About half the length of the tube was the barrel, while the other half formed the air reservoir. The trigger was mostly of the folding type and was also used to cock the lock mechanism.   A.H.

Illustrations: page 273.

Hoff, Arne, "Luftbøsser fra 1600-årene" [Seventeenth-century Airguns], in *Svenska Vapenhistoriska Sällskapets Skrifter*, edited by Nils E. Hellsten, 2nd series, Vol. 4, Stockholm, 1955.

Smith, Walter H. B., *Gas, Air and Spring Guns of the World*, Harrisburg, Pa., 1957.

Wesley, L., *Air-Guns and Air-Pistols*, New York and London, 1955.

Wolff, Eldon G., *Air Guns* (Milwaukee Public Museum Publications in History, No. 1), Milwaukee, 1958.

See also: CANE GUN; GALLERY GUN; LÖBNITZ, NICOLAI JOHAN.

ALARM GUN

An alarm gun is a self-acting device that may be set to fire and sound an alert. The gunpowder explosion may by itself give warning or it may accompany other warning signals; and the notice given may be of the presence of an intruder, or simply a signal such as an automatic timer will give.

An example of an alarm gun that does no more than announce the hour is the sundial gun, which comprises a burning glass and a small cannon. The cannon's touchhole is long and runs parallel to the bore. Because the sun's position changes with the seasons, both the glass and the gun must be movable through an arc in the plane of the shadow-casting vertical plate (the gnomon) on the sundial. With the sundial placed in position at the exact latitude and longitude for which the time lines are cut on its face, this saluting cannon will fire when the sun's rays focus through the glass on the train of gunpowder.

Another alarm gun, set to fire a 16-gauge pin-fire cartridge at a predetermined time, has a mechanism like that of a kitchen timer, with a pointer on the dial set for the number of hours to elapse before the alarm sounds. There is a short arm that turns as the dial hand turns and slowly moves a long, heavy striker until, at the intended time, force of gravity makes the striker drop on the pin of the cartridge.

An early and complicated gun made to warn of an attempted entry was a flintlock door alarm. The ingenious mechanism permitted those knowing the secret to draw the bolt – by an unusual procedure in turning the doorkey – without discharging the piece, although normal turning of the key exploded the charge.

The further back in time, the more elaborate were the alarm guns. One alarm employed clockwork, with a hand set to trip a lever at a desired time. When the lever moved, a wheel lock fired a pistol, a bell rang, a door in a tower opened and a princess came through, while a knight struck a dragon with his lance.

With percussion caps and metallic cartridges came simplicity, and a price well under a dollar. Often made to be fastened to a door jamb or window, these alarms fired when a cocked spring-driven hammer was released by movement of the door or window.

Several makes were designed not only to sound an alarm but to light a match which "exposes the burglar and at once shows the location of the attempted entry," as one inventor put it.

One good, rugged and loud-voiced alarm, that came in a fitted leather case, was of solid bronze. After its barrel was filled with black powder, its nipple capped, and its hammer drawn back to be held by a catch, it was placed on the floor at the edge of a closed door, as we hold a door with a wedge. Two prongs were at the muzzle end, to dig in if the door were pushed. Pressure on the door by an intruder forced down a long sloping trigger, to release the hammer. The same doorstop form was later applied to a more cheaply constructed and less vociferous alarm that fired a .22 blank. In this case, pressing the door along the inclined top of the alarm caused two prongs to move backward and so release a striker.

Quite different was the drop alarm. This was designed to be dislodged and fall when a door opened – with a shape slightly reminiscent of a plumb bob. Made of two loosely fitted parts, it was suspended by a cord that had at its top a wire to be inserted between the frame and the top rail of the door. The upper part of the alarm held a .32 Smith & Wesson blank with its base down; the loosely attached lower part contained a sharp pin capable of detonating the cartridge primer. When the door opened the wire was freed and the alarm, heavy base down, plunged to the floor, with the firing pin driving up to explode the cartridge. This alarm could be used as well on a window as on a door.

A minority of the alarm guns were made to warn specifically of a disturbance to a locked drawer, or desk, or trunk. When a drawer or lid was prised open, a lever moved to cause a small explosion of gunpowder, and usually to sound a long-ringing bell.

Some alarm guns were also trap guns.   L.W.

Illustrations: page 274.

Logan, Herschel C., *Hand Cannon to Automatic*, Huntingdon, W.Va., 1944.
Winant, Lewis, *Firearms Curiosa*, New York, 1955, 2nd edition 1961, and London, 1956.

See also: TRAP GUN/TRIP GUN.

ALLEN, ETHAN

Ethan Allen was born in Bellingham, Massachusetts, on September 2, 1808; although he bore the same name as the hero of the American War of Independence, there was apparently no relationship. The Allens were well established in Massachusetts, and family ties were strong; almost all Allen's business ventures, in fact, were family affairs. His first partner, Charles Thurber, was his brother-in-law; Thomas P. Wheelock of Allen & Wheelock was another brother-in-law; then, after Wheelock's death in 1864, two of Allen's sons-in-law, S. Forehand and H. C. Wadsworth, were admitted to the firm.

Allen's first venture, after leaving Bellingham, was to establish a gunsmithing business in Grafton, Massachusetts, near Worcester. There he formed his partnership with Thurber, and, as Allen & Thurber, set about making pistols, especially pepperboxes. In 1842 the company moved to Norwich, Connecticut, then, in 1847, back to Worcester. Thurber retired in 1856, and the firm of Allen & Wheelock was established. This partnership continued until Wheelock's death in 1864. Shortly thereafter, with Forehand and Wadsworth joining the organization, the name was changed to Ethan Allen & Company.

During his various partnerships, Allen manufactured many different kinds of firearms. The pepperboxes were the most famous, but there were also single-shot pistols, rifles, and double-barreled pistols. These had started as percussion arms, but by the time of his death the firm was manufacturing a complete line of cartridge guns. All arms were sporting or personal defense weapons. Allen never made any military guns.

In the field of development, Allen's first patent was granted in 1837 for a double-action lock. The patent itself described a single-shot pistol, but its principal application in practice was to the pepperbox. In a fully developed Allen specimen, a single pull on the trigger cocked the hammer, revolved the barrel block, and fired the gun. It made the Allen the fastest firing gun of its day, far better known and more popular than the Colt Paterson revolver which was its contemporary. In 1845 Allen obtained a second patent, this time specifically relating to pepperboxes. It covered a mechanism to improve the rotation of the barrels and a device by which the pistol could be fired either single- or double-action. It was too late to make any appreciable difference in the history of the pepperbox, however. Within a few years the revolver began to gain rapidly in popularity, and during the 1850's it completely outstripped the multi-barreled pistol. Allen continued to manufacture pepperboxes throughout the 1860's, but after his death on January 7, 1871, the firm switched to the single-barrel revolver.   H.L.P.

Illustration: page 169.

See also: PEPPERBOX.

ALLIN, ERSKINE S.

Born at Enfield, Connecticut, on February 3, 1809, E. S. Allin spent his entire career as a gunsmith and designer at the nearby Springfield Armory. He was apprenticed at the Water Shop there in 1829, became Master Armorer in 1847, and retained that position until his retirement in 1878. He died on September 11, 1879.

Allin's greatest contribution to firearms development was his design for a breech-loading system that could be applied to existing muzzle-loading arms in a relatively simple operation. It consisted of a hinged "trapdoor" breech block with a locking latch, an extractor and a firing pin. A section was milled from the top of the breech of an existing gun, the new block attached, the percussion hammer replaced by one designed to strike the new firing pin, and the conversion was complete. Allin's alteration was adopted by the United States government, and 5,000 percussion rifle muskets were directed to be converted with it in 1865. In 1866 the extractor was improved, and 25,000 more arms were directed to be altered. These Model 1866 rifles also underwent a second alteration which reduced their caliber from .58 to .50 by brazing a liner in the bore.

With further refinements, the Allin breechloading system was adopted for new arms, including both rifles and carbines, and it remained the standard system for most United States martial long arms until 1892 when it was replaced by the Krag-Jørgensen magazine repeater.

                                                    H.L.P.

Illustration: page 47.

Gluckman, Colonel Arcadi, *United States Muskets, Rifles and Carbines*, Harrisburg, Pa., 1959.

Hicks, Captain (later Major) James Ernest, *Notes on United States Ordnance*, 2 vols, Mount Vernon, N.Y., 1940.

See also: BREECHLOADERS; SPRINGFIELD.

ALL-METAL ARMS

Among the very earliest examples of hand firearms of which we have knowledge are all-metal arms. These very early arms include such examples as the "Vedelspang Gun," at the Tøjhusmuseet, Copenhagen, dating from about 1400. It consists of a short, crudely made tube with a metal bar for a stock and a hook to hang over a wall or window sill to take the recoil; this match-ignited arm has no lock. It was found in the ruins of the fortress of Vedelspang, in Schleswig, which was razed in 1426. Other similar guns have survived.

Early wheel lock pistols were made in the all-metal style as well. A considerable number of these pistols exist, the earliest dating from before 1550. In many cases these arms were highly decorated – which, of course, added to their chance of survival – usually by etching, often with added enrichment by gilding, and are considered to be military weapons, for field and parade use, the etching being similar to that of the etched elements of armor. Nuremberg and Augsburg produced many of these, as the town and makers' marks attest. Most of the larger public and national collections exhibit examples. The Armeria Reale at Turin has an all-metal wheel lock pistol of the Holy Roman Emperor Charles V, a three-barreled revolving pistol constructed to fire darts. This piece dates from ca.1530. There is a group of more than twenty-five single-barreled, ball-butted, all-metal pistols at the Doge's Palace, Venice. Made, apparently, for the Doge's bodyguard, these weapons bear the pine-cone mark of Augsburg, and they can be dated to the third quarter of the sixteenth century.

Many all-metal wheel locks differ from conventional wheel lock arms only in that their stocks are of iron, rather than the more usual wood.

The seventeenth century saw a continuation of the use of metal for stocks, some of the surviving French wheel lock petronels being exquisite examples both of fine gunsmithing and of sophisticated decoration. The school of Eisenschneiders that flourished at Munich under the patronage of the Electors, the family of the Sadelers – Daniel and Emanuel – and Caspar Spät, produced some noteworthy pieces. An especially fine weapon, now in the Metropolitan Museum of Art, New York, may be dated by the arms on the butt to 1624, and was made for the Elector Maximilian I of Bavaria.

Later in the seventeenth century, Brescian pistols – a number made by Stephano Scioli (also spelled Cioli and Sioli) who specialized in metal stocks – followed the conventional form, with the usual walnut stock replaced by ornately chiseled, chased, and engraved iron stocks. A fine piece of this type, signed on the lock PIETRO FIORINTIN and on the barrel PIETRO PALINO, is now in the Walters Art Gallery, Baltimore.

Another interesting seventeenth-century variation is the type with exposed lock parts. These seem to have originated in Germany, but few bear signatures or marks. There are also a number of iron-stocked pistols with normal flintlocks, signed JAN CLOETER, who worked both at Mannheim, Germany, and at Grevenbroich, Germany, in the third quarter of the century.

Beginning towards the end of the sixteenth century, and continuing into the nineteenth, the Scots produced their distinctive weapons (see SCOTTISH FIREARMS). These are probably the most widely known all-metal pistols, and spring instantly to mind whenever the subject is raised. There is an extensive literature on them.

Coming to the eighteenth century, we find the small all-metal box lock flint pistols. These popular civilian pocket arms were a variation that saw wide use, the earliest of them dating from about the middle of the century. They were made well into the nineteenth century, the last of them being either original percussion or conversions from flintlock.

Most of these pistols originated in Liège, Belgium, no matter what name or place is engraved on the pistols themselves. The Liège makers, who, in the middle of the eighteenth century, operated 70–80 "factories" employing 6,000–7,000 workers, were so modest as to believe that their products would sell better, and appeal more to prospective purchasers, if they were signed with a name and place indicating that they were made in London, Paris, or Dublin, or were at least signed with a famous name.

There are a few authentic English all-metal pistols of the eighteenth century, which will be discussed later in this article, but by far the largest number of such pistols originated in Liège. Once in a while, a specimen is found bearing the name of a Liège maker and the proper place of origin, but this is the exception. Many bear no signature or place of manufacture at all. Others are signed LONDON and some variation of SEGALAS, or with a name that is usually not to be found in the rolls of the Company of Gunmakers. Such a name may be that of an ironmonger, clothier, hardware merchant or other vendor, rather than that of the actual maker.

The Liège box locks are found in three basic varieties: single-barreled, double-barreled, and four-barreled pieces. There are a very, very few three-barreled examples. Each of these types may be further sub-divided.

Single-barreled pistols

Single-barreled pistols are found with bulging butts (the most usual type), with flat butts of similar form, with flat butts pierced for use as barrel wrenches, with trigger guards, and with folding triggers without trigger guards. There is one reference to a single all-metal pistol, of the usual box lock type, with ball trigger and no trigger guard.

The most usual form of safety was that of the movable trigger guard. A pin operating through a hole in the front of the thickened flash fence engaged a hole at the bottom of the frizzen to hold it firm against the accidental fall of the cock. Pistols with folding triggers usually had a safety stud underneath, behind the trigger, to lock the cock; occasionally an example is found with a safety on top of the body, in the rear of the cock, moving forward to engage a slot in the back of the cock. This last type is more commonly found on the four-barreled arms.

The greatest number of these arms are 5½-6 inches long, with an average caliber of .32, which was small for the flintlock era, compared to the .45 and .50 calibers of the sturdy English pocket pistols of the same period.

Critical examination of typical pistols of this genre can be quite enlightening. Most of them are well finished as to externals and embellished with tasteful engraving, but the interior parts are crude in the extreme, roughly filed to shape, with no apparent effort to finish them, and the screws have uneven and shallow threads. Comparison with genuine English pistols of good quality shows that the English gunsmiths put much time and effort into finishing the interior lockparts, and the threading of the screws was uniform and careful. The lockparts of English weapons were made of steel, while the Liège pieces are of softer metal.

Some few all-metal pistols exist that are better made, larger, longer, and of heavier caliber. Some of these will be found, on critical examination, to be authentically English. Such a piece is the all-brass single pistol signed J. MOORE, LONDON, which bears the proof mark of the Tower of London (crowned crossed sceptres).

Double-barreled pistols

These, too, are to be found in more than one basic design. The Liège box locks are most frequently found in side-by-side doubles, with two cocks and two frizzens, the trigger guard being movable to lock the cocks internally. These are to be found with both bulging and flat butts in the same fashion as the single-barreled arms, as well as others with a decorative molding at the change of shape from the square body to the rounded bulging butt. Lengths vary from about 5½ to as much as 8½ inches, with pistols about 6 inches in length being most numerous.

In addition, there are over-and-under double pistols of two basic designs. The first of these uses two side locks, and most examples of this type are small, usually about 5 inches over-all, beautifully made, well engraved, often stocked in silver, sometimes gilt. Most of the doubles of this pattern bear some variation of the Niquet family signatures, and have no trigger guards. The Niquet family, which we know from surviving pistols to have included Arnold, Claude, and others who signed themselves NI-QUET A LIEGE and NIQUET LE JEUNE A LIEGE, were members of a leading Liège family of eighteenth-century gunsmiths. It is, of course, possible that more than the four members mentioned above produced arms.

Other pistols, otherwise similar, usually have trigger guards, and bear signatures such as PARIS (on a superb pair at the Palace of Capodimonte, Naples), or RICH-ARD, LYONS, as on a fine example in the Scott Collection, Glasgow.

The last type of double pistol employs the tap action, and is larger, heavier, and of greater caliber than the usual Belgian pistol. Several of these tap-action superposed doubles seem to be the work of ASPINALL, LONDON, a gunmaker variously described as being of Birmingham and/or London. In any event, one pistol signed by him has authentic London proof marks. Other pistols by this maker, of the same type, are known.

Three-barreled pistols

There seem to be very few three-barreled all-metal pistols. One was listed in the *Fifty Years' Scrapbook of Vari-Type Firearms*, the catalogue of the Bivens Collection, sold by F. Theodore Dexter in 1960, which seemed to be a strange wedding of a side-by-side double, with side locks, having above the double barrels a third single barrel with its own centrally hung box lock. There were three triggers to release the various locks. The practicality, to say nothing of the genuineness, of such an arm, is open to serious doubt, at the very least.

Another three-barreled all-metal pistol is in the George F. Harding Museum, Chicago. It, too, is an unusual piece. The basic pistol body is an English three-barreled tap action of normal construction, with engraving of the sort usually found on English pocket pistols of the late eighteenth century, which has been fitted with a brass and silver butt of typical Scottish scroll-butted form. There is no trigger guard, and the ball trigger matches the pricker

in shape. The barrel group is also unusual, there being three straight tubes, with moldings at the muzzles. The barrels are numbered 4, 5 and 6, showing that this was the second of a pair.

A recent addition to this short list, bringing the total to three, is a three-barreled tap action, with steel barrels, brass body and grip, and folding trigger, signed TWIGG. This was in a sale at Christie's, London, in May 1963. Examination has proved it to be genuinely English.

Four-barreled pistols

Four-barreled all-metal box lock pistols, like the single- and double-barreled types, are to be found in several variations. These arms typically have two cocks and triggers. Each barrel has its own pan and frizzen, and the barrels, as a block of four, revolve as a unit, held by a catch activated by the trigger guard.

There are two basic varieties, the difference being in the form of the barrel latch. In the first type, the rear of the trigger guard is pressed into the pistol body to release the barrel assembly. In the second type, the trigger guard moves toward the butt of the pistol to achieve the same result. This type may be quickly identified as there is a spur on the front of the trigger guard to aid in pressing it to the rear to release the barrel block. This is necessary, because when the frizzens of the two lower barrels are in battery they effectively mask the front of the trigger guard.

The first type is further subdivided into the usual flat and bulging butt examples, plus a third flat-butted type in which the butt is rather larger than the others. The second type, typically, is flat-butted, and features the spur on the front of the trigger guard.

All the four-barreled pistols of the types under consideration are of Liège origin, although there are, as usual, a number of signatures to be seen designed to suggest English, French, or even Irish, manufacture. It is the opinion of the present writer that these signatures are all frauds. The usual variations on SEGALAS are common; MICHEL LE PAGE is engraved on an excellent example of the bulging-butted type, MICHEL appearing on one side, LE PAGE on the other! No place of origin is mentioned, and there are, of course, no proof marks. Another was sold in 1958 signed BARBAR, LONDON. It would be very interesting indeed to be able to know for certain whether this pistol ever really passed through Barbar's hands, even as a sales piece. A well-known Texas collector has a fine example engraved GALTON, LONDON, and the Parezo-Boss sale catalogue (New York, 1938) listed a four-barrel as by DAMOUR, A LIEGE. Further, a pair was sold some years ago signed GRENEL, PARIS, and a specimen engraved SEGLAS, DUBLIN, was in the Schott sale, New York, 1918.

In addition to the standard types which have been

discussed above, there are a number of interesting arms that seem to be unique, although that is hard to prove and dangerous to state. No sooner has one gone on record as saying that something is unique, than another specimen comes out of hiding. Discussion of the more unusual pieces, however, is outside the scope of this brief article. It may be said, though, that the all-metal box locks of the eighteenth century are comparatively scarce, especially in fine condition, and even a type collection cannot be readily assembled in a short period.

In the nineteenth century, the coming of the percussion era did not do away with the demand for all-metal arms. In addition to the box locks previously discussed, which were widely used in the earlier part of the century, other types found favor. Officers serving in India found that all-metal stocks, especially "white metal," were less affected by the tropics and the conditions of high humidity, heat, and dampness, that were hard on the usual wooden stocks and caused fast deterioration. A number of these sturdy, well-made pistols, usually singles, but a few in side-by-side double form, exist, both by English makers and from arsenals in India. These pistols have side locks, the later ones back-action, and they are often of military caliber. There are also pairs with saw handles, a form usually associated with dueling pistols.

After the switch to breech-loading arms, which was accelerated by the American Civil War, such all-metal pistols as Moore's Deringer, Colt's Number One Deringer and the "My Friend" knuckle-duster were popular. But even these were not the last; the ornate "Tiffany" silver stocks brought Colt revolvers into the category, and in the twentieth century the Second World War saw the liberator pistol, a single-shot made of hurried stampings under the pressures of modern war, meant to be used and thrown away.
P.J.W.

Illustrations: pages 107–9, and endpapers.

Wolf, Paul J., "Some Segalas Variations" in *Journal of the Arms and Armour Society*, Vol. 3, No. 8, London, December 1960.

See also: FLINTLOCK; LIBERATOR PISTOL; SAFETY DEVICE; SCOTTISH FIREARMS; WHEEL LOCK.

AMMUNITION

The necessary ingredients for discharging a firearm constitute ammunition – basically, propellant and projectile. An ignition system is usually included. Ammunition has been classified as separate-loading, semi-fixed, and fixed. In separate-loading types, the powder and projectile are carried and loaded separately, as in muzzle-loaders and large cannon. In semi-fixed types, the charges are packaged in metallic, paper or cloth cases, which may include the primer. Fixed ammunition – the type in general use today – combines all elements in a watertight, usually metallic, case.
B.R.L.

See also: BULLET; CARTRIDGE; GUNPOWDER; PRIMER; SHOT; SMOKELESS POWDER.

AMUSETTE

The term "amusette" referred originally to a light, long-barreled field cannon, but later was also used to designate a large stocked musket or rifle. Herman Maurice, Comte de Saxe (1696–1750), Marshal of France (1744), applied the term to a gun of his invention in his *Reveries, or Memoirs Upon the Art of War* (English translation, London, 1757). Marshal Saxe introduces his description of the gun as follows:

"Every century is to be furnished with a piece of ordnance of my own invention, called an *Amusette*, which carries above four thousand paces with extreme velocity; the field pieces used by the Germans and Swedes will scarcely carry a fourth part of that distance: this is also much more true [accurate]; is drawn and worked with ease by two or three men; carries a half-pound ball, and is made with convenience to hold a thousand; all which must render it of great service on numberless occasions in war."

A century comprised ten companies of fifteen men each, and totaled 184 men including officers. Saxe further describes the application of the gun:

". . . Before an engagement these *Amusettes* are to be advanced in front, along with the light-armed troops: as they can be fired two hundred times in an hour with ease, and carry above three thousand paces, they will be of great use to gall an enemy, when forming after they have passed any wood, defile or village; when marching in column; or drawing up in order of battle, which last requires time: every century is to have but one; nevertheless, those of both lines may be joined upon occasion, and the whole collected upon any eminence, in which situation they must do prodigious execution. They will carry further and much more true than our cannon, and the captains-at-arms must be taught by constant practice to work them with dexterity and judgement: the sixteen belonging to a legion planted together in an engagement will be sufficient to silence any battery of the enemy's in an instant."

An accompanying plate shows a muzzle-loading cannon having conventional moldings, dolphins, and trunnions with a bore of about $1\frac{1}{2}$ inches and a length of about nine feet. No carriage is shown in this reference, but it is certain that a light wheeled carriage was used.

The original amusette, considered as a cannon, was exceptionally long in terms of its caliber – approximating to a length of seventy calibers. General Lallemand, in *A Treatise on Artillery* (New York, 1820), said that "the proper length for the bore of guns has never yet been settled" and guns ranged from eleven calibers to twenty-six calibers in length. He said that the usual lengths were: field pieces 17, mountain 11, and "22 and 24 in smaller pieces intended for garrisons and sieges."

The British evidently adopted, or at least experimented with, one-pounder amusettes in three lengths: five, six, and seven feet, these corresponding in caliber lengths to 29.7, 35.6, and 41.5 respectively. These are listed in a tabulation of English Brass Guns in William Duane's *Military Dictionary* (Philadelphia, 1810) and were no doubt taken from a British publication. These guns weighed respectively 292 lb., 347 lb., and 376 lb., with bores of 2.019 inches for a one-pounder iron ball of 1.923 inches. It was noted that they were "not used since 1795 on general service." The same reference listed ranges of these guns, based upon experiments in 1793. With eight ounces of powder, the seven-foot amusette was fired at elevations of 1°, 2°, and 3°; the first graze of shot ranging 656 yards, 830 yards, and 1,000 yards respectively. The five-foot amusette was tested only at 1° and 2°, giving ranges of 604 yards and 800 yards respectively.

The application of the name "amusette" to a stocked weapon having a flintlock is suggested by usage during the American War of Independence and by its definition in Charles James's *Military Dictionary* (London, 1810):

"Amusette, a species of offensive weapon which was invented by the celebrated Marshal Saxe. It is fired off in the same manner as a musquet, but it is mounted nearly like a cannon. It was found of considerable use during the late war, especially among the French who armed their horse artillery with it; and found it superior to the one adopted by the Prussians. The ball with which it is loaded is from one pound and a half to two pounds weight of lead."   J.C.M.

Illustration: page 282.

Lallemand, Henri Dominique, *A Treatise on Artillery*, English translation by James Renwick, New York, 1820.
Peterson, Harold L., *Arms and Armor in Colonial America, 1526–1783*, Harrisburg, Pa., 1956.

See also: SWIVEL GUN.

APACHE PISTOL

See: COMBINATION WEAPON.

ARISAKA RIFLE

A series of bolt-action magazine-fed rifles developed by Colonel Nariake Arisaka, superintendent of the Tokyo Arsenal. The first Arisaka was the 6.5 mm. Type 30 (M1897). This weapon has a two-piece bolt somewhat similar to the Mannlicher, with a five-round Mauser-type staggered box magazine. It can be distinguished visually from later Arisaka designs by its hook-shaped safety.

The 6.5 mm. Type 38 (M1905) Arisaka has a modified Mauser bolt, but is otherwise similar to Type 30. It is far more common than Type 30. The bolt is one-piece and has forward-mounted dual-locking lugs. The safety is engaged by pushing in the cap at the rear end of the bolt and rotating it a one-eighth turn clockwise. The Type 38 rifle weighs 9.06 lb. and is 50.19 inches long with a 31.44-inch barrel. It has a muzzle velocity of approximately 2,400 feet per second. The stock is of rather unusual construction, having a two-piece butt. The rifle uses a knife bayonet.

There are two carbine versions, Type 38 and Type 44. Type 38 uses a knife bayonet and Type 44 has a folding bayonet. In 1939, Japan introduced a new series of Arisaka rifles chambered for the 7.7 mm. Type 99 rimless cartridge. The Type 99 rifle is similar to Type 38 except for the weight, the anti-aircraft "lead" bars on the rear sight, and the folding wire mount. The Type 99 short rifle has a 25.8-inch barrel, as does the Type 2 paratroop rifle. The 7.7 mm. Type 99 cartridge has a muzzle velocity of 2,400 feet per second.   J.E.S.

Illustration: page 106.

Smith, Walter H. B. and Joseph E., *The Book of Rifles*, 3rd edition, Harrisburg, Pa., 1963.
Smith, Walter H. B. and Joseph E., *Small Arms of the World*, 6th edition, Harrisburg, Pa., 1960.

ARQUEBUS/HARQUEBUS

The term arquebus has had several different meanings during its period of use. Generally, however, it has meant a light portable firearm with a stock enabling it to be held against the cheek, chest or shoulder. In the beginning it was also distinguished from the hand cannon by having a serpentine to hold the lighted match by which it was fired.

Victor Gay, in his *Glossaire Archéologique* (Vol. 1, p.73), quotes a Latin document of 1417, concerning the term "arcubusariis" and another of 1475, in French, mentioning the terms "hacquebusies" and "arquebuse de fer." The term "l'archibusio" was referred to in the work, written in 1465, of an Italian, Francesco de Giorgio Martini (1423–1506), and quoted by Colonel Favé (*Etudes sur le Passé et l'Avenir de l'Artillerie*, Paris, 1862, Vol. 3).

The first arquebuses were little different in appearance from the hand cannon, according to a text of 1478: ". . . paid to Perrinot Poinsard, for the price of three francs each, twelve arquebuses (*harquebuches*), six with iron butts and the others with wooden butts." (cited by V. Gay, *Glossaire* 1, p. 73).

As time passed, the word arquebus came to have different meanings which varied according to the time and the nationality of the person using it. After the musket became popular about the middle of the sixteenth century, the term arquebus, at least in English-speaking countries, was used to denote a lighter arm that could be fired without a rest. In other instances, it was used to indicate a wheel lock as opposed to a matchlock, but after 1550 it almost always referred to a light firearm, whether for military or sporting purposes. CL.B.

Illustrations: pages 33–5.

Blair, Claude, *European and American Arms*, London, 1962.

Bosson, Clement. "Que sait-on de l'Haquebute?" in *Armes Anciennes*, Vol. 2, No. 1, Geneva, 1957.

Peterson, Harold L., *Arms and Armor in Colonial America, 1526–1783*, Harrisburg, Pa., 1956.

Peterson, Harold L., *The Treasury of the Gun*, New York, 1962 (*The Book of the Gun*, London, 1963)

See also: HACBUTT; MATCHLOCK; MUSKET.

ASIATIC FIREARMS

Firearms in Asia developed in a pattern entirely different from those made in Europe or America. Greater isolation of areas created a much wider range of local types which were made without change for longer periods of time. Whereas European guns passed through several different ignition systems, Asiatic firearms normally started as matchlocks and either continued to be made as such until modern times or at best shifted to one of the various flint forms. The wheel lock was ignored, and, generally speaking, the percussion system was attempted only in Japan during the mid-nineteenth century. And in that country the flint ignition had been passed by completely. Because of this situation, the only logical approach to Asiatic firearms in a short article is by areas and spheres of influence.

The Asiatic area with the longest firearms history is the Near East. Close contact with Europe, especially on the part of the Turks, brought guns to this sphere very early. The huge cannon known as the Dardanelles Gun, now at the Tower of London, was cast during the mid-fifteenth century, and small arms were also well known and in some use at the same time. As a distinctive style developed, the typical Turkish gun had a thick, relatively straight, stock with a sharp step down in the top line directly behind the lock. The butt was pentagonal in cross section. The earliest guns were matchlocks, but the miquelet became popular, apparently during the middle of the seventeenth century, and it remained the standard ignition system until modern times. Both rifles and smoothbores were made, and the rifles normally boasted heavy vertical peep sights at the breech with a number of different apertures for varying ranges. The same style of gun is found in the Caucasus along with local variants in the shape of the stock, which tends to be lighter, with graceful curves and often a fishtail butt. Almost always these were miquelet. In Persia the Turkish type was also dominant, along with the slender Arab forms from Africa. Persian workmanship, however, tended to be finer than that of the other areas within this general sphere of influence. Pistols also were made, always miquelets except when European parts were used, with varying butt forms. In Turkey and Persia the pistol was most often a small copy of the long gun but with a butt more closely resembling the European shape with a comb at the top. Some slender butts terminating in pointed bulbs were used, and, especially in the Caucasus, the heavy ball butt was popular. Ramrods were almost always carried separately, and so there were neither channels nor pipes for them on the pistols.

A second major sphere of influence included the modern nations of India, Pakistan, Afghanistan, and their neighbors. Firearms apparently first came to this area overland through Persia, for the most common stock forms suggest the Turkish design even to the sharp step-down behind the lock and the butt with its pentagonal section. Others follow the same silhouette but are rounded in section. Still others used by the Coorgs on the southwestern coast are thin and flat while retaining a similar outline. Also encountered, however, are the slender curved stocks of the jezail and the deep, sharply curved butts of the so-called Afghan stock used primarily in Sind in modern Pakistan. Finally, there is a most unusual stock shape also favored by the Coorgs, which tapers to a point and hooks back. Except for an occasional specimen using a European flintlock, all of these forms were normally made as matchlocks of a simple and crude construction. The serpentine moved forward away from the shooter, activated by pressure on a blade trigger which was pushed up into a recess in the stock. There was no trigger guard. Barrels were normally attached to the stocks with wire or rawhide wrappings, sometimes fastened over silver saddles. Occasionally solid bands were used. These barrels varied considerably. Those guns with the Turkish-style stocks usually had light barrels. Those with jezail stocks were normally very heavy at the breech. Both types often had heavy moldings at the muzzle, and the better specimens frequently were made with a fine "Damascus" twist. Some barrels were square externally, and a few are even encountered with square bores. Almost all Indian guns were single-shot muzzleloaders, but a few matchlock revolving long arms exist.

The island of Ceylon, off the southern tip of India, represents a small but entirely individual area in regard to firearms design. Its guns were usually finely made, and boasted a miquelet lock with a dog catch mounted on the left hand side of the arm instead of on the right as is usual. These were the only flint arms made east of Persia, all other areas preferring the matchlock. The stocks terminated in a scrolled butt, often inlaid with elaborately carved ivory or tortoiseshell traceries. They were unusual among Asiatic firearms in normally having trigger guards. The Portuguese landed in Ceylon in 1505, and it would seem that the knowledge of firearms came primarily from this European contact and that this explains the pronounced difference between the guns of Ceylon and those of neighboring India.

Another primary sphere of influence in which a knowledge of firearms was derived primarily from Portuguese contact comprised the islands of Japan. According to tradition, the introduction occurred in 1542, and the skilled Japanese workmen soon set about producing their own copies and adaptations of the guns they had seen and acquired by trade. Interestingly enough, this was a snapping matchlock of a type that had had very limited popularity in Europe. The serpentine was cocked against a spring. When released by pressure on the button or stud trigger, it snapped forward. Only within the Japanese sphere of influence are these snapping matchlocks encountered. All other Asiatic matchlocks operate on the more common European principle in which pressure on the trigger depresses the serpentine against the resistance of a spring. When the trigger pressure is removed, the spring raises the serpentine again and holds it away from the pan. The stocks are slender and slightly curved with very little enlargement at the butt. A crudely made Japanese-style gun is a great rarity and gives rise to the suspicion that it was made either in Malaya or possibly Burma rather than in Japan itself. Most Japanese firearms were very well made, and many are finely decorated with lacquered stocks and inlaid barrels. Once again, the single-shot muzzleloader was standard, with specimens ranging from a few inches in length to huge pieces weighing as much as fifty pounds. A length of four feet was average. As in India, revolving arms are occasionally encountered. After Japan was opened to outsiders during the 1850's, some matchlocks were converted to percussion, and a very few original percussion arms were made before Japan began to modernize its gun industry with the latest breech-loading cartridge arms at the end of the century. The Japanese sphere of influence extended throughout Indo-China and Malaya, and into Assam and the Burmese hills where the snapping matchlock shared popularity with the Indian form.

The early Chinese guns were among the roughest and simplest of Asiatic firearms. They were matchlocks of the Indian type with short, pistol-grip butt stocks designed so that the piece would be held in both hands and fired from the hip. Sighting would be impossible in this position, but many of the Chinese guns have two or three sights which are seldom in line. Tibetan guns normally utilized iron parts made in China, but had straight stocks, often covered with hide from a wild ass. A flap of leather frequently served also as a pan cover, and a forked rest similar to those found on the jezail and other central Asian arms was normally attached to a pivot on the bottom of the stock near the muzzle.

These were the principle stylistic areas of firearms production in Asia in the years prior to the general introduction of western guns in the present century. In assigning a place of origin to an Asiatic firearm, the primary guide is the shape of the stock; second, the lock; and third, the type and style of decoration. Except for the Japanese, almost all used bands or wrappings to fasten barrel and stock together, and almost all were some form of matchlock or miquelet. H.L.P.

Illustrations: pages 209–11.

Egerton, Wilbraham, *An Illustrated Handbook of Indian Arms*, London, 1880.

Kimbrough, Robert E., "Japanese Firearms" in *The Gun Collector*, No. 33.

Stöcklein, Hans, "Orientalische Waffen aus der Residenz-Büchsenkammer im Ethnographischen Museum, München" in *Münchner Jahrbuch der bildende Kunst*, Vol. 1914–15.

Stone, George Cameron, *A Glossary of the Construction, Decoration and Use of Arms and Armor in All Countries and in All Times together with some Closely Related Subjects*, Portland, Me., 1934.

Van Zandt, H. F., "Firearms in Feudal Japan" in *The American Rifleman*, November 1953.

See also: AFGHAN STOCK; JEZAIL.

AUTOMATIC ARMS

An automatic weapon is one in which the process of feeding, firing, extracting and ejecting is carried out by the mechanism of the weapon, after a primary manual, electrical or pneumatic cocking, as long as the trigger is held to the rear and the supply of ammunition in the belt, feed strip or magazine lasts. A semi-automatic or self-loading weapon is one in which the same processes are carried out by the weapon mechanism, but only one shot is fired for each squeeze of the trigger; pressure on the trigger must be relaxed to fire another shot.

A number of different operating systems exist for automatic and semi-automatic weapons:

Recoil operation. The barrel is movable and upon discharge the barrel and locked bolt move to the rear together. If the bolt unlocks from the barrel within a distance less than the length of the complete cartridge used, it is called a short recoil system. If the distance of locked recoil is longer than the distance of the complete cartridge used, it is called a long recoil system.

Gas operation. Gas produced by the combustion of the propellent charge is tapped off the barrel and used to function the mechanism of the weapon. There are a number of variations of this system; the most common is that in which the gas is bled from the barrel into a cylinder and drives a piston to the rear, the piston causing the bolt to unlock either through direct action or by moving a bolt carrier to the rear. In a variant of this system, the piston is dispensed with and the gas is channeled through a tube to strike a bolt carrier. Another gas system is that in which a trap at the muzzle collects gas which is then led to the cylinder. Most weapons take the gas from the barrel at a considerable distance from the chamber, because of pressure problems. There is, however, the so-called "short gas take-off" in which the gases are taken off a short distance from the chamber and force a captive piston rearwards: this piston strikes an operating rod which unlocks the bolt.

Blowback. The weapon has a fixed barrel and no positive lock. The cartridge is confined merely by the inertia of the bolt and the bolt return spring. This system is usable only with cartridges of relatively low pressure – usually pistol cartridges – and is sometimes called an inertia-locking or spent-case projection system.

Delayed blowback. The weapon has a fixed barrel and no positive lock, but the rearward thrust of the cartridge case has to overcome some mechanical disadvantage such as a toggle joint or elbow-type action. These systems when used with high-pressure cartridges require a fluted chamber or lubricated ammunition, since they have no provision for slow initial extraction of the case. These systems are sometimes called hesitation locking systems.

Combined systems. There are some weapons which have combined gas and blowback operation or combined recoil

and blowback. As an example, the Hispano Swiza 20 mm. Type 404 is unlocked by gas operation before the chamber pressure has completely dropped, and the rearward thrust of the cartridge case helps to operate the gun mechanism.

Primer setback. This system has not been used in any weapon produced in quantity. The primer "sets back" against the bolt, forcing a plunger mounted in the bolt face to the rear. The plunger operates the unlocking mechanism.

The first practical automatic weapon was the short recoil operated Maxim machine gun which was patented by Hiram Maxim in 1884. Maxim had patented a recoil operated modification of the Winchester rifle in 1883. Maxim's machine gun was belt fed and water cooled and had a toggle-type lock. It was adopted by the British Army in 1889, originally in .450 caliber, later in .303 caliber. The weapon still in the British Army as the Vickers Mark I is only a modification of that original Maxim machine gun. The Maxim was used by the Germans in the First World War (MG 08, MG 08/15, and MG 08/18) and by the Russians in the Russo-Japanese War and the First and Second World Wars, Model 1905 and 1910; the 1910 was also used by the North Koreans in the Korean War. The Maxim has been used by every major country in the world.

John M. Browning submitted a gas-operated machine gun to Colt in 1890. It was perfected by 1895 and was known as the Colt "potato digger," owing to the gas lever arm which rotated in a vertical plane below the gun. Browning developed a short recoil operated gun which was patented in 1901; from this design grew the United States M1917 water cooled and M1919 air cooled machine guns, and the later Browning aircraft guns which were the mainstay of the United States and British air forces in the Second World War. Over sixty-five different models of Browning recoil operated machine guns have been produced.

The Hotchkiss gas-operated gun was based on the design of an Austrian, Baron Adolph Von Odkolek. Lawrence Benét, an American, and Henri Mercié, a Frenchman, adopted Odkolek's idea of operation by a piston housed under the barrel, thereby designing a practical and very successful machine gun – the 1895 Hotchkiss. This air cooled weapon had fins on the barrel to draw off heat and was fed by strips of cartridges rather than by a belt. The Model 1914 Hotchkiss was the main French heavy machine gun in the First World War. In 1909 the light Hotchkiss machine gun appeared.

The Madsen, a recoil operated gun developed in Denmark, can be considered one of the first light machine guns. This magazine-fed gun appeared in 1903, and in modified form is still in service in many countries, the latest model being the 1950. Other light machine guns used in the First World War were the gas-operated, drum-fed Lewis (developed by Colonel I. N. Lewis of the United States) and the long recoil operated French M1915 Chauchat.

After the First World War, the accent was on the lightening of machine guns and increasing sustained rate of fire. Advances in metallurgy allowed a decrease in weight and the introduction of the quick-change barrel allowed an increase in the sustained rate of fire. The Czech-designed and produced 7.92 mm. magazine-fed ZB-26 was the first widely known machine gun to have a quick-change barrel. This weapon in modified form was adopted by the British in 1935 (the Bren), and is still in service. Germany developed a recoil operated, belt-fed, quick-change barrel weapon – the MG 34. The Germans started to replace MG 34's with the MG 42 during the war. MG 42 is a recoil operated, belt-fed gun composed mainly of stampings and, like the MG 34, was one of the first of a new type of machine gun – the general purpose gun which could serve as a light machine gun on a bipod or as a heavy machine gun on a tripod. Before the war, in 1927, the U.S.S.R. had developed the 7.62 mm. Degtyarev (DP) drum-fed light machine gun. This gas-operated gun later evolved into the belt-fed RP-46 which is currently in Soviet service.

In the Second World War few guns were developed, but the period immediately afterwards saw the development, among many others, of the Soviet RPD, chambered for the 7.62 mm. intermediate-sized cartridge, and at present the lightest belt-fed gun in the world (19.42 lb. with a 100-round belt). Belgium's Fabrique Nationale FN Type MAG gas-operated, belt-fed, general-purpose machine gun is a notable postwar development. Having a modified Browning automatic rifle action, this weapon was adopted by Sweden in 1958 in 6.5 mm. and has since been adopted by Belgium and Britain in 7.62 mm. NATO.

The United States adopted the 7.62 mm. M60 general-purpose machine gun. This weapon is gas-operated and belt-fed and like almost all postwar weapons has a quick-change barrel.

For some obscure reason, self-loading or semi-automatic pistols have always been called "automatic" pistols in the United States. There have been a number of pistols which could be fully automatic as well as semi-automatic, but the greater number of "automatic" pistols are actually semi-automatic. The first self-loading pistol made in any quantity was the design of Hugo Borchardt, and was produced by Ludwig Loewe in Berlin in 1893. This recoil operated, toggle action weapon was the first to use a detachable box magazine inserted in the grip. The Borchardt was developed by George Luger into the Luger pistol and was in manufacture from 1898 to 1942. Theodore Bergmann introduced the first of a series of self-loading pistols in 1892; an unusual feature of his early pistols was the

sliding plate magazine cover. The cartridge clip was inserted from the right side of the gun where the cover was opened. Bergmann produced both blowback and recoil operated designs. Maxim developed a blowback operated pistol in 1896, but it was not a commercial success. In 1895 the first model of the 7.63 mm. recoil operated Mauser pistol appeared. The Mauser is one of the outstanding self-loading pistols; in most models the magazine is non-detachable and is loaded by a ten-round charger from the top of the receiver. The Mauser has been made in over thirty models, the last being the M1932 which is a selective-fire weapon with a removable magazine.

In 1897, John Browning entered the self-loading pistol field. His first designs were blowbacks chambered for the .32 caliber automatic pistol cartridge and were produced by the Fabrique Nationale, Liège. In 1900 Colt introduced a recoil operated Browning in .38 caliber. This weapon evolved through several stages into the .45 caliber Model 1911 United States Army service pistol. This weapon, in very slightly modified form, is still the standard arm of the United States. The FN 9 mm. Hi-Power pistol is also a Browning design, and is the service pistol of Canada, Britain and many other countries. The following recoil operated pistols are all modified Brownings and use the parallel rule locking system of the Browning: 9 mm. Polish Radom, 9 mm. French M1950, 7.62 mm. Soviet Tokarev, 7.65 mm. French models 1935A and 1935S, 9 mm. Swiss Model 1949 and .45 caliber Argentine Ballister Molina.

Mannlicher produced several self-loading pistol designs, both recoil and blowback operated; only the 7.65 mm. M1901 was made in quantity. Webley entered the self-loading pistol field in the early 1900's with several blowback pistols after having produced a small quantity of the Gabbett "Fairfax Mars" pistols. In 1904 the first recoil operated .455 Webley appeared, and evolved by 1909 into the weapon adopted by the Royal Navy in 1912. The 9 mm. Steyr, or Steyr Hahn as it is sometimes called, was adopted by the Austrians in 1912. This recoil operated pistol had a barrel which rotated to lock and unlock. This system was later used by the Mexican Obregon pistol and in a slightly modified form by the Savage pistols.

The Walther PP, introduced in 1929, and the PPK introduced in 1931 are famous, as is the Walther 9 mm. P38, for their double-action firing system which allowed the firing of the pistol, with the hammer in the down position and a cartridge in the chamber, by pulling through on the trigger as with a double-action revolver. Automatic pistols since the Second World War are mainly modifications of early designs such as the Colt Commander, a light-weight version of the Colt M1911A1. The Beretta 9 mm. M1951, a locked breech version of the earlier Berettas, also uses an aluminum alloy receiver. The Soviet Union has two new automatic pistols, the Makarov and the Stechkin; both are blowback operated weapons chambered for a 9 mm. pistol cartridge of Soviet design. The Makarov is similar to the Walther PP and the Stechkin, has a shoulder stock holster and has selective fire. The Czech 7.62 mm. Model 1952 pistol is recoil operated and has a roller locking mechanism similar to the German MG42 machine gun.

Although innumerable designs of automatic pistols have appeared since the 1890's, the weapons which are still in manufacture and use are of remarkably few basic types; of these types, the Browning blowback and recoil or modified Brownings are by far the most numerous.

During the First World War, the need for a light-weight fully automatic weapon suitable for short-range use was clearly shown. The Italians introduced a blowback weapon of rather peculiar appearance, chambered for the 9 mm. Parabellum cartridge. The Villar Perosa, which appeared in 1915, consisted of two guns fed by two 25-round box magazines, the whole commonly mounted on one bipod. The Germans produced the first true submachine gun in the MP18, which was produced by Bergmann and is sometimes called the Bergmann Musquete. This blowback operated, magazine-fed shoulder weapon was chambered for the 9 mm. Parabellum cartridge. The Thompson submachine gun appeared in 1919, the first production model being the Model 1921. This weapon was the first to be called a "submachine gun" and was a delayed blowback, chambered for the .45 caliber automatic pistol cartridge. This weapon was produced in a number of other models, the best known being the Model 1928A1 and two models developed during the Second World War, the M1 and M1A1, which were blowback designs using only a box magazine rather than the drum or box used on earlier models. The Thompson, in common with many other guns developed between the First and Second World Wars, was rather heavy and extremely expensive to manufacture.

A large number of submachine guns appeared in the period 1925–39. Outstanding among these were the Bergmann Model 34, the Schmeisser 28 II, the Beretta Model 38, the Hungarian Model 39, and the Schmeisser Model 38. All were blowback operated with the exception of the Hungarian Model 39, which was delayed blowback. The Schmeisser Model 38 – MP38 – introduced a new concept: the light-weight cheaply constructed submachine gun. All the major nations followed this in their submachine guns during the Second World War, as illustrated by the British 9 mm. Sten guns, the Soviet 7.62 mm. PPSh M1941 and PPS1943, the German Schmeisser MP40 and the United States .45 caliber M3 and M3A1 submachine guns.

Postwar submachine gun improvements have for the most part been confined to lightening, increasing safety, and increasing ease of maintenance by the provision of easily removable components. As an example the Madsen M46, M50 and M53 submachine guns have a hinged receiver which can be opened for maintenance. A novel operating feature is the provision of a partially hollowed-out bolt which telescopes the barrel. This allows the use of a relatively long barrel in a weapon of short overall length. The Czech Model 23, Israeli Uzi and Beretta Model 12 submachine guns all currently use this system.

During the Second World War, the submachine gun started to evolve into a new weapon – the assault rifle chambered for the "intermediate" sized cartridge, i.e. a cartridge between the pistol and rifle cartridges in size and power.

Although a Finnish Suomi assault rifle using a shortened version of the 7.62 mm. rimmed cartridge was produced in limited quantities in the late thirties, the first assault rifles used in quantity were the German MKb42(H) and MKb42(W). These were gas-operated, selective-fire, magazine-fed weapons chambered for a shortened version of the standard German 7.92 mm. cartridge. These weapons were followed by the MP43 series which evolved from the MKb42 (H).

Since the Second World War, a large number of assault rifles have appeared; outstanding among these are the 7.62 mm. Soviet AK, a gas-operated weapon fed by a 30-round box magazine and of heavy construction, and the German-Spanish CETME assault rifle. The CETME was under development in Germany at the end of the Second World War, and development was completed in Spain. Although originally developed for an intermediate sized cartridge, CETME's currently in service in Spain and Germany are chambered for the 7.62 mm. NATO cartridge. They are delayed blowback, magazine-fed weapons.

Although designs for semi-automatic and automatic rifles appeared in the late nineteenth century, none were successful, owing to their weight and complexity. The Mexican-designed, Swiss-made Mondragon was the first semi-automatic rifle to be used extensively in war, being used by the Germans on aircraft before the adoption of aircraft machine guns. In 1916, the Germans introduced a limited number of Mauser semi-automatic rifles. The French followed in 1917, with the Saint-Étienne gas-operated semi-automatic. Browning had developed a recoil operated rifle for medium-power cartridges before the First World War (Remington Model 8), and the gas-operated Browning automatic rifle was adopted by the United States in 1918.

After the First World War a large number of semi-automatic rifle designs appeared: among these were the Thompson, the Liu, the Hatcher, the Bang (an improvement on a 1911 design), the Berthier, the Garand, the Simonov, the Tokarev, the Czech ZH 29 and the Walther.

During the Second World War, the United States was

the only country to have its troops equipped mainly with semi-automatic rifles (the M1 Garand) and a semi-automatic carbine.

The Germans introduced three gas-operated rifles, the G 41 (M), G 41 (W) and G 43 (sometimes called Kar 43). Only the G 43 was made in quantity. The U.S.S.R. used the Simonov M1936, the Tokarev M1938 and Tokarev M1940 – all gas-operated weapons. Sweden adopted the 6.5 mm. gas-operated Ljungman semi-automatic rifle in 1942.

After the Second World War, all the major nations rushed to develop and adopt new semi-automatic or selective-fire rifles. The U.S.S.R. adopted the SKS gas-operated semi-automatic weapons chambered for the intermediate 7.62 mm. M1943 cartridge. This weapon has now been replaced in the Soviet Army by the AK assault rifle. The British, after developing the gas-operated .280 EM2, adopted the Fabrique-Nationale (FN) developed "FAL" (light automatic rifle) in 7.62 mm. caliber NATO. This gas-operated rifle, which is designated L1A1 by the British, comes in selective-fire or semi-automatic versions and has been adopted by many countries.

The United States has adopted the 7.62 mm. M24 rifle; the M24 has a bolt mechanism similar to the M1 but has a different gas and magazine system and is capable of selective fire.   J.E.S.

Illustrations: pages 176, 201–7.

Allen, Major W. G. B., *Pistols, Rifles and Machine Guns*, London, 1953.

Chinn, Colonel George M., *The Machine Gun*, 4 vols, Washington, D.C., 1951–55.

Datig, Fred, *The Luger Pistol*, revised edition, Beverley Hills, Cal., 1958.

Smith, Walter H. B. and Joseph E., *The Book of Rifles*, 3rd edition, Harrisburg, Pa., 1963.

Smith, Walter H. B. and Joseph E., *Small Arms of the World*, 6th edition, Harrisburg, Pa., 1960.

See also: GARAND RIFLE; LUGER PISTOL; MACHINE GUN; PEDERSEN DEVICE.

B

BACK-ACTION LOCK

Back-action is a descriptive term applied to a percussion lock in which the mainspring is located behind the hammer, instead of in front of it as was the case with the standard side lock. A secondary feature is that the mainspring usually exerts its force upwards against the tumbler rather than downwards as it does in those locks in which it is located ahead. The principal advantage of the back-action lock lay in the fact that it could be mortised into the wrist of the stock, thus allowing the fore-stock to be lightened, an important factor in the design of pistols and double-barreled shotguns. The first locks of this form seem to have appeared in the early 1830's. They had become common by 1850.   H.L.P.

See also: LOVELL, GEORGE.

BAKER, EZEKIEL

After serving an apprenticeship to Henry Nock, Ezekiel Baker first worked for his master and then, in 1794, became an arms contractor to the British Board of Ordnance. In a small workshop near the Minories, he was employed mainly on minor work on barrels and locks. In 1800, however, a rifle made to his specification was chosen for the British Rifle Corps then being formed, and soon afterwards he published his *Remarks on Rifle Guns*. The fame of his rifle, for which he received large orders from the Ordnance and the East India Company, and the publicity from his book brought him to the attention of the sporting world and the Prince of Wales. After a short partnership with another lockmaker, James Negus, he set up business on his own, in 1805, at 24 Whitechapel Road. Behind the shop was a warehouse which he converted into a factory and proofhouse. Here, with the encouragement of his royal patron, his clients' guns were subjected to a special "Fire, Water and Target" proof and were stamped with special proof marks. His friendship with the Prince, who was Colonel of the 10th Dragoons, led to the adoption of his cavalry rifle, a smaller edition of the infantry weapon, by several regular and volunteer regiments. An appointment as court gunmaker followed, and many of his finely decorated arms, and others converted or embellished by him, formed part of the Carlton House Collection now in Windsor Castle. He was responsible for many minor improvements in firearms – special locks, bayonets, rammers, pistol grips, etc. – and his safety locks and bullet mold were awarded three silver medals by the Society for the Encouragement of Arts and Manufactures. Although he failed to persuade the Ordnance to adopt a musket, carbine and pistol of his design, he presented them with an inscribed set of these arms which is still in the Tower of London. He never liked the new percussion firearms introduced during his lifetime, and at the age of seventy-five he helped design the last British flintlock arm, the Pattern 1833 carbine. After his death, in 1836, his business was continued by his son, Ezekiel John.   H.L.B.

See also: BAKER RIFLE.

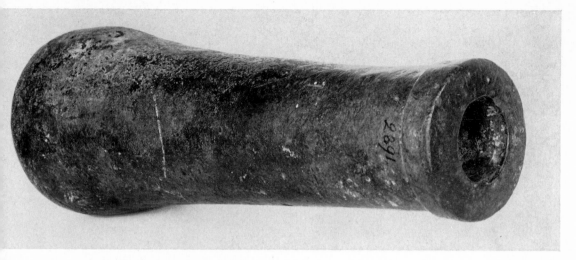

Hand cannon of *ca.*1350, found near Loshult, Sweden.
National Historical Museum, Stockholm.

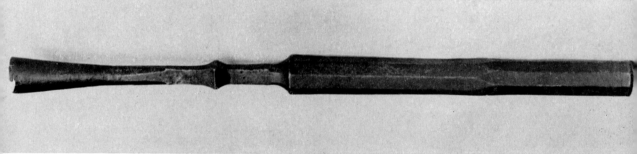

Hand cannon, *ca.*1450; the tiller fitted into the socket at the left.
Museum of Art and History, Geneva.

Hacbutt or large arquebus with a hook and without a priming pan, *ca.*1470.
Museum of Art and History, Geneva.

Arquebuses, *ca.*1500, from *Codex Monacensis 222.*

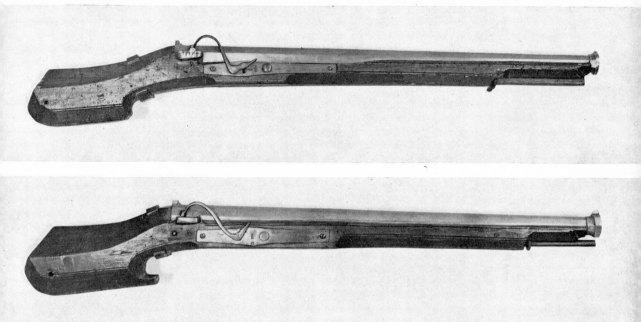

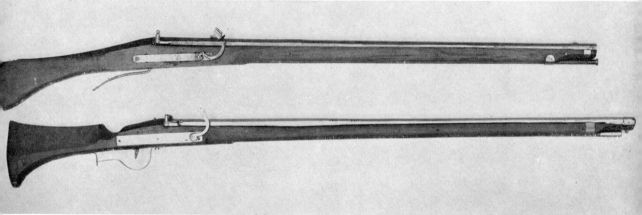

Two arquebuses with snapping matchlocks, *ca.*1500. *Basle Historical Museum.*

Italian matchlock musket with lever trigger, *ca.*1580, and German matchlock musket with sear trigger, *ca.*1590–1620. *Collection of Harold L. Peterson.*

Wheel lock arquebus with the arms of Bavaria, mid-sixteenth century. *Bavarian State Museum, Munich.*

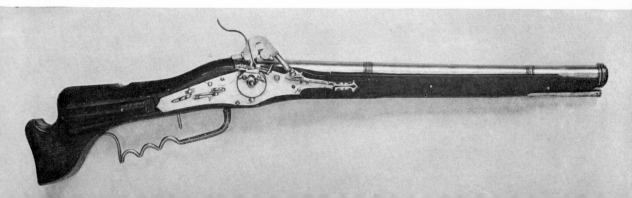

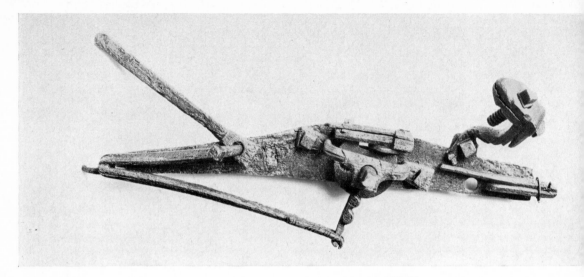

Early wheel lock with external mainspring. *Budapest National Museum* (Inv. 17/1906B).

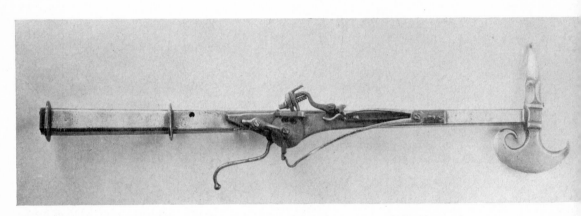

Early sixteenth-century combination of wheel lock pistol and battleaxe, external view (ABOVE) and internal view (BELOW).
Doge's Palace Museum, Venice (Inv. Q7).

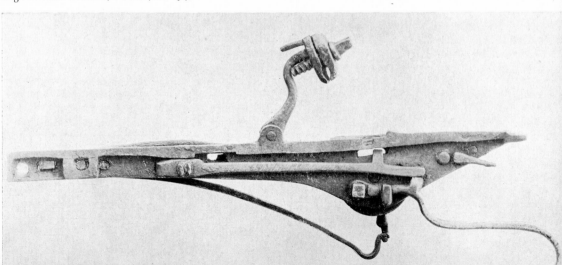

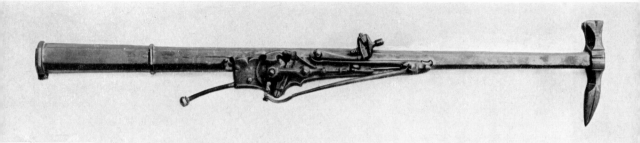

Early sixteenth-century combination of wheel lock
and battle hammer, with external and internal views of the lock.
Ferdinandeum Museum, Innsbruck (Inv. 1035).

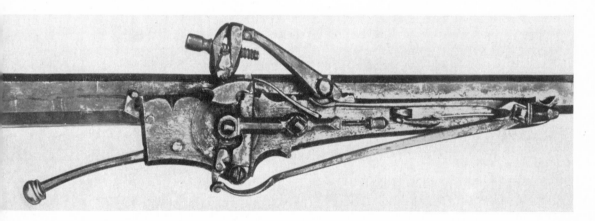

Early sixteenth-century wheel lock pistol combined with
crossbow; the bow is not shown in the picture.
Doge's Palace Museum, Venice (Inv. Q3).

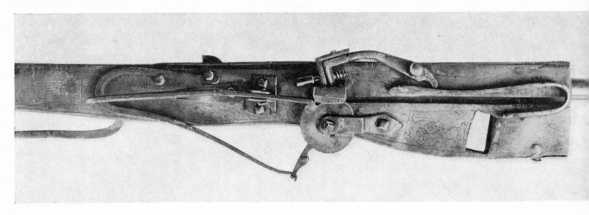

Wheel lock tschinke,
the walnut stock inlaid with engraved staghorn.
City Art Museum, St. Louis, Missouri.

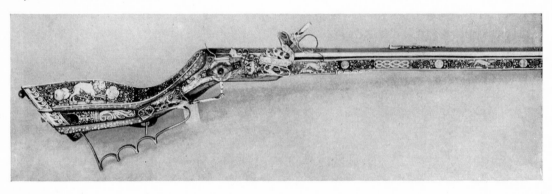

Saxon wheel lock holster pistol, early seventeenth century;
the wooden stock stamped to resemble staghorn and inlaid with engraved horn;
the lock plate etched with a monster amidst foliage. *British Museum.*

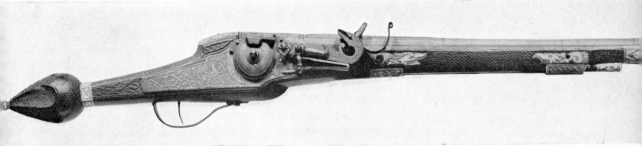

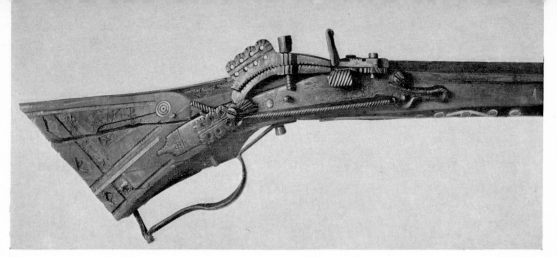

A typical North Scanian border gun, with Swedish snap lock. *Tøjhusmuseet, Copenhagen.*

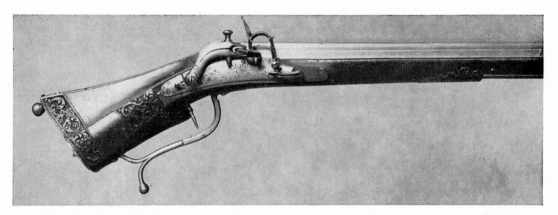

A fine quality Swedish snap lock rifle, *ca.*1680, the stock carved with scrollwork in low relief. *Royal Armory, Stockholm.*

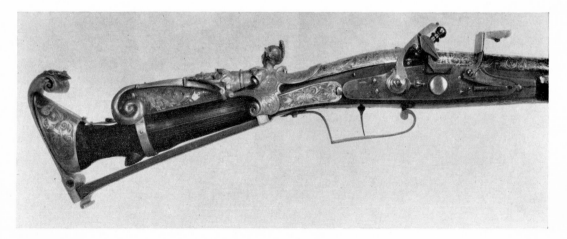

Flintlock gun by Marin le Bourgeoys. *Hermitage Museum, Leningrad.*

Brass-barreled blunderbuss with spring bayonet mounted above the barrel and heavy moldings at the muzzle, *ca.*1800. *Armouries, Tower of London.*

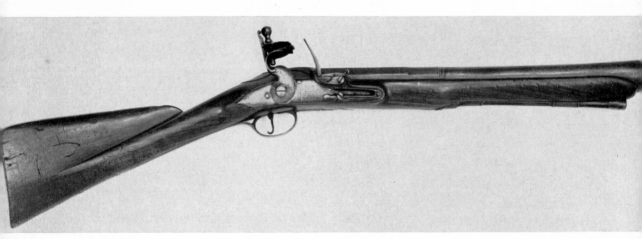

Flintlock blunderbuss with flaring muzzle, made by Hatcher of London, *ca.*1750.
Armouries, Tower of London.

The first model "Brown Bess," or Long Land musket, with wooden ramrod, and India pattern "Brown Bess."
Armouries, Tower of London.

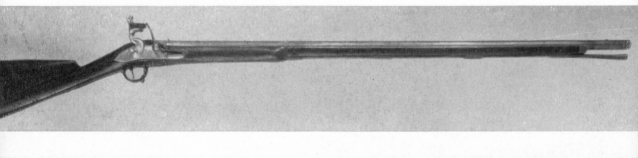

Cartmell
Doncaster
patch lock
with detachable
striker.
*Collection of
W. Keith Neal.*

Forsyth
scent-bottle
pistol.
*Collection of
Henry M. Stewart.*

Billinghurst revolving
pill-lock combination
rifle and shotgun.
Collection of Mark Aziz.

Heurteloup gun, showing
the breech open.
Collection of Lewis Winant.

Breech-loading fowling piece with the
badges and initials HR of Henry VIII,
showing the breech open. The lock is missing.
Armouries, Tower of London.

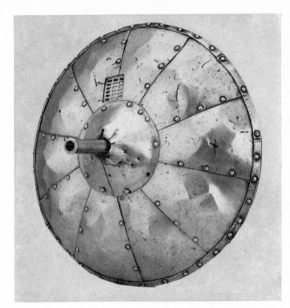

Breech-loading pistol shield made for
Henry VIII, *ca.*1540–50.
Armouries, Tower of London.

La Chaumette breech-loading flintlock
fowling piece made by Bidet of London,
the lock and barrel chiseled with scrollwork,
the stock carved with foliate scrolls
and inlaid with silver wire.
Collection of H.R.H. the Duke of Brunswick.

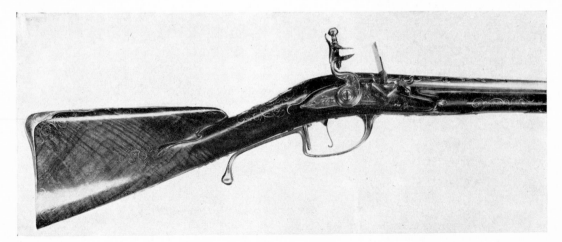

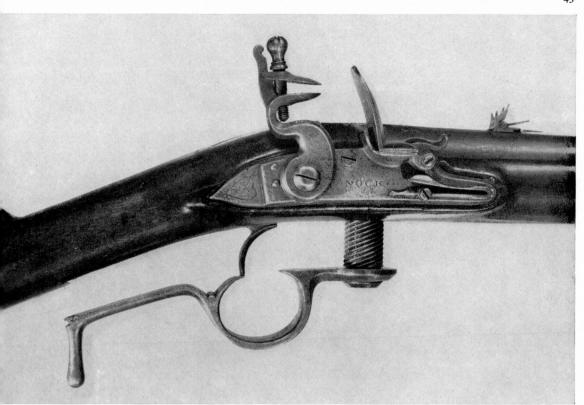

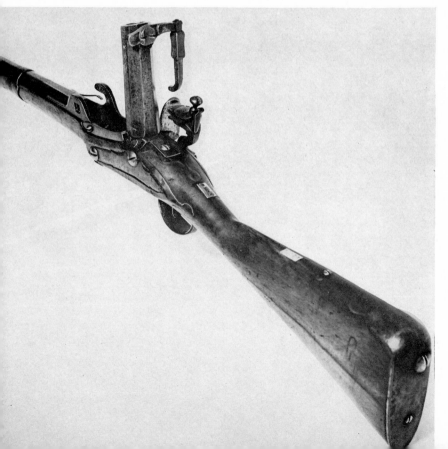

ABOVE A Ferguson rifle
made for the
East India Company by
Henry Nock, dated 1776;
the breech plug open,
showing the screw plug.
*Collection of
Howard L. Blackmore.*

Austrian flintlock
breechloader of so-called
Crespi system, *ca.*1770.
Armouries, Tower of London.

Hall breech-loading carbine, Model 1843, with North-Savage side lever for raising breechblock. *Smithsonian Institution.*

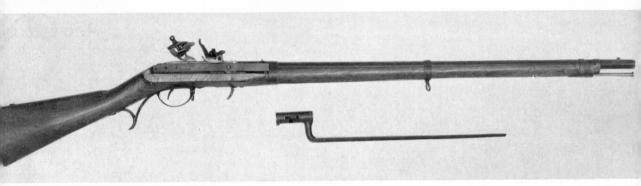

Hall rifle and bayonet, Model 1819. *Smithsonian Institution.*

Norwegian breech-loading rifle Pattern 1842, invented by F. W. Scheel. *Tøjhusmuseet, Copenhagen.*

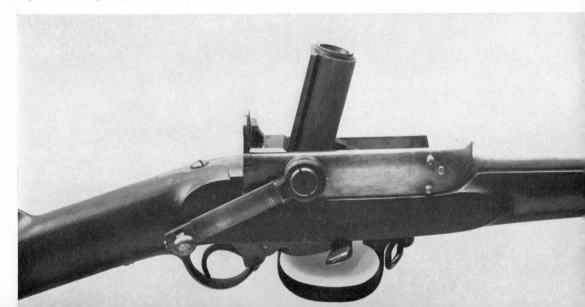

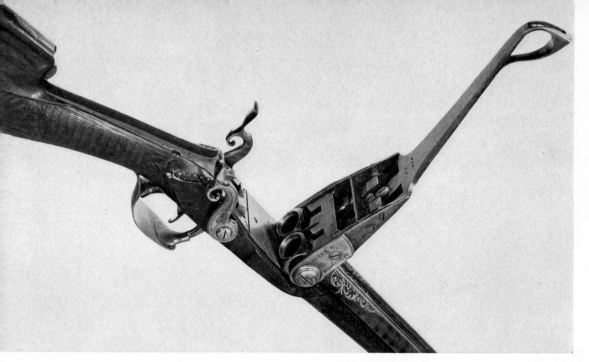

A Paris-made Pauly sporting gun with lifting breech action, *ca.*1815; the lock and
furniture engraved, the twist barrels damascened with gold. *Armouries, Tower of London.*

Pauly breech-loading center-fire pistol made on the system patented in 1812.
Armouries, Tower of London.

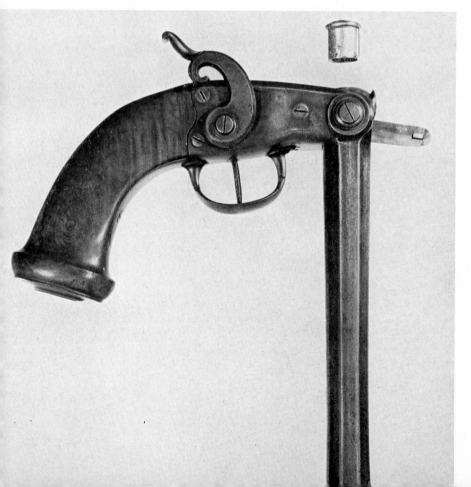

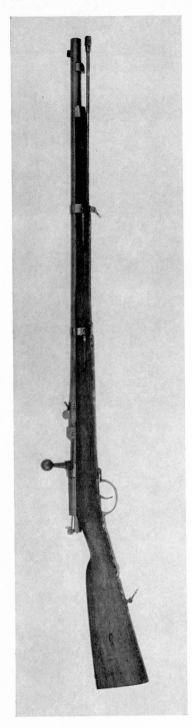

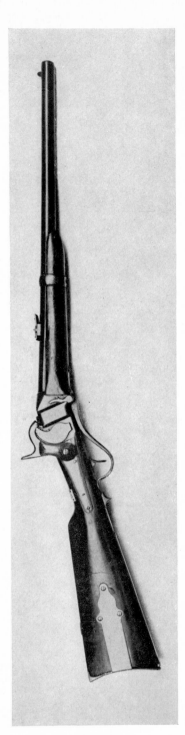

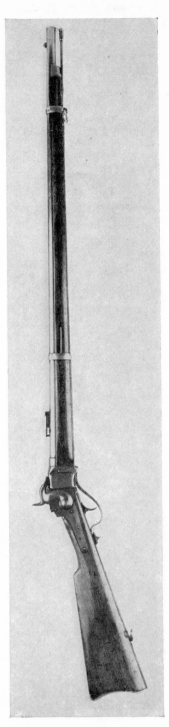

Dreyse bolt-action needle gun.
*Winchester Repeating
Arms Company.*

American Sharps carbine,
Model 1855.
Armouries, Tower of London.

Sharps Army rifle altered
for metallic cartridges.
West Point Museum Collections.

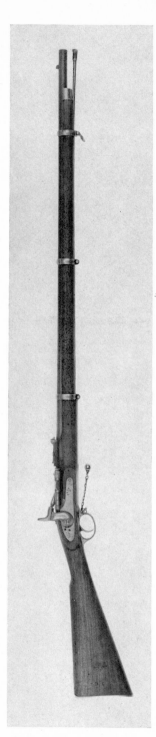

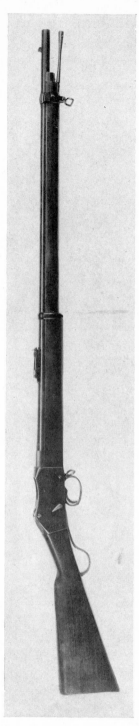

Springfield .45-70 rifle,
Model 1873. *Winchester Repeating
Arms Company.*

Snider Enfield rifle.
*Winchester Repeating
Arms Company.*

Martini-Henry rifle.
*Winchester Repeating
Arms Comp.ny.*

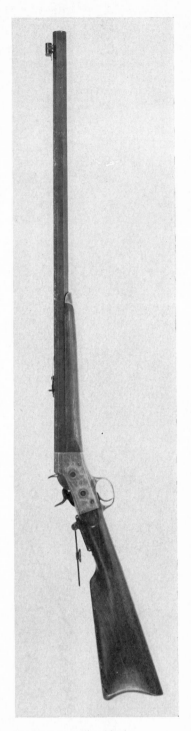

German Mauser rifle,
Model 1871.
Smithsonian Institution.

Maynard breech-loading percussion
carbine, caliber .50.
Smithsonian Institution.

Remington rolling-block
sporting rifle. *Winchester
Repeating Arms Company.*

BAKER RIFLE

In February 1800, after a series of trials at Woolwich, the barrel made by Ezekiel Baker, thirty inches long with a quarter-turn seven-groove rifling, was adopted for the first issue British rifle. Its general design copied the German Jaeger model. Fully stocked, it was fitted with a cheek rest and a brass pistol-grip trigger guard to assist the aim, and a brass butt box to hold the bullet patches and rammer tools. At first some rifles were made to take the ordinary musket ammunition, but these heavy rifles, which needed a wooden mallet to hammer down the charge, were soon discarded. The standard rifle had a carbine bore or caliber of .625 and weighed approximately nine pounds.

The first Baker bayonet was a sword with a flat single-edged blade twenty-three inches long. A brass handle with knuckle bow clipped on to a bar on the side of the barrel near the muzzle. Weighing two pounds, it made the rifle difficult to fire when fixed, and in 1815 it was replaced by a light socket bayonet. The necessary conversion proved costly and slow, and finally, in 1823, a spike bayonet consisting of the old brass handle armed with the triangular blade of a musket bayonet was substituted.

The quality of Baker rifles varied considerably, depending on the type of flintlock used and whether they were assembled in London or Birmingham, but generally they gave good service and were accurate up to two hundred yards. Production continued until 1838, when they were superseded by the percussion Brunswick rifle.   H.L.B.

Illustrations: page 104.

Baker, Ezekiel, *Remarks on Rifle Guns*, 11th edition, London, 1835.
Blackmore, Howard L., *British Military Firearms, 1650–1850*, London, 1961.

See also: BAKER, EZEKIEL; RIFLES AND RIFLING.

BALLARD, C. H.

C. H. Ballard, of Worcester, Massachusetts, received a United States patent, identified as "Improvement in Breech-Loading Fire Arms," on November 5, 1861 (Patent No. 33,631). The device consisted of a lever-operated, dropping-breech, single-shot arm. Subsequently a percussion device, adapted to the Ballard action, was patented by Joseph Merwin and Edward P. Bray, of New York, on January 5, 1864 (Patent No. 41,166). John M. Marlin, of New Haven, Connecticut, received a patent covering a reversible firing pin on February 9, 1875 (Patent No. 159,592) for use with rim- or center-fire ammunition,

adapting the same to the rifle. These dates are noted on the arms.

The Ballard rifle was produced almost continuously over a period of about thirty years by the following makers: Ball & Williams, Worcester, Massachusetts, 1861–66; The Merrimack Arms and Manufacturing Company, Newburyport, Massachusetts, 1866–69; The Brown Manufacturing Company, Newburyport, 1869–73; J. M. Marlin, New Haven, Connecticut, 1875–81; the Marlin Fire Arms Company, New Haven, Connecticut, 1881–*ca.*1892.

Following the Brown Manufacturing Company after an interval of two years, J. M. Marlin at first produced substantially the older arm, which was characterized by a manually operated extractor. This was followed shortly afterwards by an expanding series of models with a mechanical extractor which survived to the end of the Ballard production.

Shop numbers were continuous from the first products to the advent of Marlin, the highest number observed being 21,723. This has been broken down into the following observed numbers: Ball & Williams to 15,664; Merrimack to 19,985; Brown to 21,723. The combined Marlin products, commencing a new series, are: J. M. Marlin to 16,498; Marlin Fire Arms Company to 36,396. Thus, over 58,000 pieces were produced over a span of thirty years or more.

Previous to the J. M. Marlin production, all Ballards were rim-fire, some with the addition of Merwin & Bray's auxiliary percussion nipple in the block, usable with reloaded, base-perforated, rim-fire cases. Several Ball & Williams and Merrimack models are so equipped. J. M. Marlin introduced the center-fire cartridge to the Ballard.

In spite of its popularity, contemporary literature on the Ballard is rare. Its military history is short-lived. During the Civil War the United States government purchased 1,059 Ballards, identified as carbines, for $35,140, and 35 rifles for $1,262.

The government test of 1866 showed that the Ballard could be shot at the rate of eighteen times per minute. Advertisements claimed that the state of Kentucky had 20,000 Ballards in active service as late as 1865.

Inasmuch as the Ballard rifle had been, since its origin, constantly gaining favor as a sporting arm, manufacturers determined to produce that type only. As a result, highly specialized models were developed. Some were for general use while others were identified as hunting or target rifles, all being considered very desirable and used widely.

In all, forty-seven models have been listed. Recognition is occasionally difficult inasmuch as there is evidence of custom assembly, the parts being interchangeable. Specialized elements such as stocks and barrels may also be present, many of the latter being the products of famous makers. Certain models were recognized for their outstanding quality and finish.

292063

Aside from use as a hunting arm, the Ballard was famed for target use. Two basic forms were recognized, the Creedmoor for back-prone shooting and the Schuetzen for offhand use.   E.G.W.

Wolff, Eldon G., *Ballard Rifles in the Henry J. Nunnemacher Collection* (Bulletin of the Public Museum of the City of Milwaukee, Vol. 18, No. 1), 2nd edition, Milwaukee, 1961.

BALLISTICS

Ballistics is the study of the natural laws relating to the performance of gunpowder and projectiles in firearms, and the means for predicting such performance.

Understanding of the nature of ballistics was very sketchy in the early years of firearms. Guns were aimed for the most part by rule of thumb, in which experience played a major role. Gunpowder varied so greatly in strength, even in the same barrel, that it was very difficult to obtain adequate data on which to base scientific theories.

When first studied, a projectile's flight was considered to be in three parts. The first was straight horizontal flight, then a part following a parabola, finally a vertical drop. Though Galileo had stated the flight to be a parabola, this was true only in a vacuum – the effect of air resistance was not recognized for many years. Newton made the first experiments on air resistance in 1710. The Englishman Benjamin Robins was one of the first to state sound ballistics theories, in his *New Principles of Gunnery*, 1742. His ballistic pendulum provided necessary data. Yet another century passed before the scientific study of ballistics began in earnest.

The study of ballistics is conveniently divided into three parts. Interior ballistics is the theory of the motion of the projectile within the gun barrel. Exterior ballistics covers the path from the gun to the target. Terminal ballistics considers the effect of the projectile on the target.

The special problems of shot ballistics, and forensic ballistics (the study of recovered projectiles), have also to be considered.

Interior ballistics

The time during which the projectile is influenced by interior ballistics is very short. From the release of the firing pin to the moment the sound of the shot can be heard as it leaves the muzzle occupies only about 0.01 seconds, in a modern rifle. Special devices are required to measure such time intervals with accuracy. The cap or primer detonates when struck, releasing very hot gases and hot particles. The powder begins to burn and the pressure inside the cartridge rises rapidly. Almost at once the bullet is pushed from the case mouth. At first, the sides of the bullet are forced outward to make a firm contact with the bore, so that the gas cannot leak by. As the bullet moves down the barrel, the available combustion space is increased. The powder burns progressively, at first increasing its burning rate faster than the space increases. As long as this condition continues, the pressure (and the bullet velocity) continues to rise. The maximum pressure is soon reached, when the two rates are momentarily equal. Thereafter the pressure drops till the bullet leaves the muzzle, accompanied by the usual report. If there is leakage of gas past the bullet, the barrel is eroded quite rapidly. A little space is left just ahead of the cartridge neck in which the rifling has been reamed away. This space, called "lead" or the "forcing cone," allows the bullet to expand so that it will fit the rifling properly.

The well-known kick of a firearm is influenced by two factors, the energy of recoil and the rate of the rise of velocity. The energy of recoil can be computed by equating the mass times the velocity of the projectile, plus mass times velocity of the propellant (which is also expelled from the muzzle), to the mass times velocity of the firearm. There are three elements contributing to the recoil energy: the reactions to the mass of the bullet accelerated to its muzzle velocity and that of the powder (as a gas) to about half that velocity, plus the rocket-like reaction of the gases as they rush out of the muzzle. Actual calculations of these values are usually based on workable approximations, obtained from experimental data. As the velocities are squared to obtain energies, it can be seen that reducing the muzzle blast (as by a muzzle brake) can have a substantial effect in reducing total recoil. The rate of rise of velocity depends on the type of powder used and other factors. If it is very high the kick becomes much sharper. Another effect usually associated with recoil is jump. The recoil force is exerted in line with the axis of the bore. As the butt of the firearm is usually located below this axis, there is a turning movement developed which makes the muzzle jump upwards during recoil. In a "straightline" stock such as is found on some light machine guns, the center of the butt is on a prolongation of the bore, hence there is no jump or "climb," which is the tendency for the muzzle to keep on rising during automatic fire. Such stocks have not been popular for sporting arms, as aiming with them is unnatural, the eye coming too high above the barrel and sights.

A subject associated with interior ballistics is that of bore erosion and fouling of various kinds. Gas erosion has been mentioned. Some types of powder burn at much higher temperatures than others, hence are more destructive to the gun barrel. Erosion is caused by a combination of temperature and velocity. Hence cool-burning powders that have low peak pressures are usually preferred. Material for bullet jackets is selected to provide the optimum gas seal with minimum metal fouling. Some of the metals formerly in general use, such as cupro-nickel, left small deposits in the bore, which eventually had to be removed by special solvents.

Residues left from primer combustion can seriously affect the cartridge case or the barrel itself. When primers contain fulminate of mercury, finely divided metallic mercury is left in the brass case. This forms an amalgam which makes the brass brittle and unsuitable for re-use. When the primer contains chlorates, these leave a deposit of potassium chloride in the bore. This substance is deliquescent, which means it has the property of attracting water. The result is eventual rusting, unless this fouling is removed. The salt being soluble in water, cleaning with hot water, followed by drying and oiling, is the simplest and most effective way to prevent damage. Modern primers do not use either mercury compounds or chlorates.

A by-product of interior ballistics is the subject of barrels and actions that burst when fired. The former are most often caused by obstructions which cause the pressure to rise above safe limits. The obstruction might be water, mud, grease, a bullet lodged in the bore, or a bullet too large for the bore. Burst actions may be caused by defective heat treatment of the receiver or bolt, but most often are caused by overloads or by improper head space. By this is meant the fit between the bolt face and the cartridge head. The brass case is only to provide a gas-tight powder container – it must depend on the steel bolt to hold against the powder pressure. If the head space is too large, the head of the cartridge is unsupported. This can result in a failure at that point, which releases high-pressure gas into the action. Such leakage might seriously injure the eyes or other parts of the shooter's anatomy, but is most likely to cause a spectacular rupture of the receiver and/or stock in that area.

Exterior ballistics

The flight of most bullets does not exceed thirty seconds at maximum range, which for almost any firearm is obtained at an elevation of about thirty-three degrees. This flight can be divided into three distinct parts for study. During the first, which lasts for only a few yards, the bullet is recovering from the initial shock of firing. It is wobbly. The second or normal period of flight extends for several hundred yards. During this time it travels as it should, point first, with its axis of rotation nearly on the trajectory. This part of the flight can be calculated quite accurately from suitable ballistic tables. The final period of flight is after the bullet has started to lose both velocity and spin. It again begins to wobble and finally tips over or tumbles in an unpredictable manner.

The basis for calculating a bullet's flight is a large number of experimental firings by which the relative performances of various bullet shapes have been established. From such data comes a series of "form factors" from which one is selected which is as near as possible to that for the shape of the bullet being considered. The section density of the bullet is obtained by dividing its weight in pounds by the square of its diameter in inches. This result divided by the form factor provides the "ballistic coefficient," usually shown by the letter C. This value will always be the same for a given bullet. With it, data on performance can be extracted from ballistic tables.

Rifle bullets require spin to make them stable in flight. The proper amount of spin depends on the size and weight of the bullet and its velocity. The spin imparted by the rifling, besides making the bullet fly point foremost, also causes it to "drift," which in the case of a rifle having a right-hand spin makes the bullet go slightly to the right of the line of sight. The bullet's center of gravity travels along a parabolic course, the trajectory. But the point is kept about on the line of sight by the gyroscopic action of the spin. It is the resulting couple which moves the bullet to the right. At extreme ranges when the bullet is falling quite rapidly, the point is still being held up by this gyro effect, so that the bullet is finally traveling somewhat sideways through the air. This is called yaw.

Wind also causes a bullet to move to the side, in the direction the wind is moving. It makes a smaller but still appreciable difference in range, also. The wind deflection is in proportion to: (*a*) cross-wind speed, (*b*) range, and (*c*) delay of the bullet in its flight. The cross-wind speed is proportional to the cosine of the wind's angle to the line of sight. The delay is that caused by air resistance, and may be calculated by subtracting the time figured from the muzzle velocity if fired in a vacuum, from the actual observed time of flight. The formula for wind deflection is $D = W (T - T_v)$, in which W is the cross-wind in feet/second, T is the time of flight for the range used, and T_v the time for flight in a vacuum.

Many modern rifles have sights which can be adjusted to correct for "windage," the term used for the correction required for wind effect. With fixed sights the shooter has to estimate the displacement that will be caused by the wind and aim that distance into the wind from his target. This is often called "Kentucky windage" from the habit of frontiersmen using Kentucky rifles "held off" in this manner for wind correction.

Terminal ballistics

Terminal ballistics are important to both sportsman and military. In order to deliver all the potential energy of the bullet to the game target, hunting bullets usually have soft lead tips, or other complex design which makes them expand on impact. Military bullets cannot have such characteristics in accord with international conventions. Their penetration is of prime interest. Penetration is important also in determining safety requirements for target backstops. At two hundred yards an average military rifle projectile will penetrate about twenty-four inches of loam, fourteen inches of oak, seven inches of dry sand or four inches of concrete.

Modern caliber .22 rifles have an extreme range of about one mile, which is also about the maximum range of most pistol and revolver ammunition. Military and sporting rifles of larger calibers have danger zones of several thousand yards.

Shot ballistics

The muzzle velocity of a shotgun is about half that of a center-fire rifle, and shot loses speed more rapidly than a conical bullet. Shot with "high velocity" powder charge has a muzzle velocity of around 1,300 feet per second. With No. 6 shot this represents an average velocity at 40 yards of only 975 feet per second. Shot in flight has "string" and "pattern." The load strings out while moving through the barrel, and at 40 yards the average string is 12 feet long. Pattern is the percentage of shot pellets that strike a 30-inch circle at 40 yards.

Unlike the rifle, the shotgun requires that aim be ahead of the target. The target is usually rising as well as moving away, so both vertical and horizontal leads must be used. The first shotguns had cylinder bores uniform in diameter throughout their length. Gunmakers found that a slight restriction, or choke, at the muzzle improved the pattern. Commonly, a short section of reduced diameter joins the main part by a conical taper. A swaged choke has a simple conical section at the muzzle. The recessed choke has a slightly enlarged portion of barrel, with conical sections fore and aft. Full chokes are used for long-range shooting, modified chokes or cylinder bores for upland birds and skeet shooting.

Shot pellets being spherical projectiles, their sectional density increases with diameter. Thus large shot will retain velocity better than a smaller size, besides having greater striking energy. No. 2 shot has at least 50 f/s more velocity at 50 yards than No. 6. Higher average velocity requires less lead, minimizing pointing errors. All things being equal, large shot gives more kills at longer ranges than small shot, but the statement is true only *per shot pellet*. No. 6, with many more pellets per load than No. 2, gives a better pattern, hence more hits. Thus the load must be a compromise.

Before choke bores were generally available, many ideas were advanced for concentrating the shot in flight. They involved little wire or mesh baskets, metallic containers which separated in flight, or paper tubes. Modern manufacturers have done much research to provide better patterns and reduced shot string.

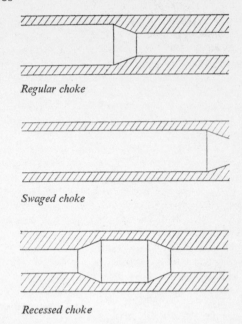

Regular choke

Swaged choke

Recessed choke

Forensic ballistics

Forensic ballistics is the study of recovered projectiles to identify the firearms which fired them. It would be better termed firearms identification. The evidence thus obtained is generally accepted in criminal court trials to establish use or possession of a certain weapon.

Formerly, all that an "expert" could testify in court concerning a bullet recovered from the scene of a crime was that it was a certain type and caliber. Thus a caliber .38 bullet could not have been fired in a caliber .45 revolver. Linking the bullet to a specific revolver was not then possible. About 1920, great advances began to be made in identifying firearms by their fired bullets and/or cartridge cases, and, for the first time, formal criminology courses were offered by universities to train individuals in the techniques of forensic ballistics. Colonel Calvin H. Goddard was a leader in this effort. The most important tool used was the comparison microscope, a binocular instrument so arranged that two similar objects can be compared in detail simultaneously, with corresponding surfaces adjacent.

When a bullet is fired, it acquires marks or scratches from the bore surfaces. These marks, from irregularities left by the tool cuts or caused by wear and rust, are reproducible by firing another bullet through the same barrel. The bullet in evidence and the second bullet can then be compared for match. The pattern obtained is comparable to a finger print, thus making coincidence of identical patterns from two different guns most unlikely, if not impossible. A complication is that, as yet, there has been no system devised to classify such patterns, as there is with fingerprints.

When a cartridge is fired it is pressed forcibly against the breech, thereby receiving an impression of any tool marks on the breech. The firing pin also leaves its mark on the fired cartridge, and abnormalities such as a chipped edge will show up. All these marks can be compared by the microscope, and a fired case can thus be linked to a specific weapon. B.R.L.

Gunther, Jack D. and Charles O., *Identification of Firearms*, New York and London, 1935.

Hall, A. R., *Ballistics in the Seventeenth Century*, London, 1952.

Hatcher, Major General Julian S., *Hatcher's Notebook*, Harrisburg, Pa., 1947.

Hatcher, Major General Julian S., *Textbook of Firearms Investigation, Identification, and Evidence*, Plantersville, S.C., 1935.

Mathews, Dr. J. Howard, *Firearms Identification*, 2 vols, Madison, Wis., 1962.

Textbook of Small Arms, H.M. Stationery Office, London, 1929.

See also: AMMUNITION; BULLET; CARTRIDGE.

BALTIC LOCK

See: SCANDINAVIAN SNAP LOCK.

BANDOLIER

The bandolier is a device for carrying separate charges of ammunition on a belt. Early European forms consisted of a leather strap or baldric from which were suspended a number of cylinders, each of which contained sufficient powder for one charge. These cylinders varied in number, although twelve was about average. They were made of several different materials: wood was probably the most popular, but copper, tin, pewter and jacked leather were also used. With these bandoliers, and usually attached to them, it was customary to carry a priming flask and a bullet pouch. The bandolier is generally believed to have developed in the Low Countries during the first half of the sixteenth century. From there it spread rapidly throughout western Europe, except in Spain, where it was apparently viewed with little favor. The bandolier was also used in America, Africa and Asia.

Although these early bandoliers offered a convenient way of carrying separate, ready-measured charges, they suffered from several serious drawbacks, which were noted by contemporary military writers. When matchlock muskets were used, there was a danger that one or more of the cylinders might be set off by the match or by the flash of the priming; they sometimes tangled with the bandolier of an adjacent soldier; and their rattling made considerable noise. These defects, plus the growing popularity of the

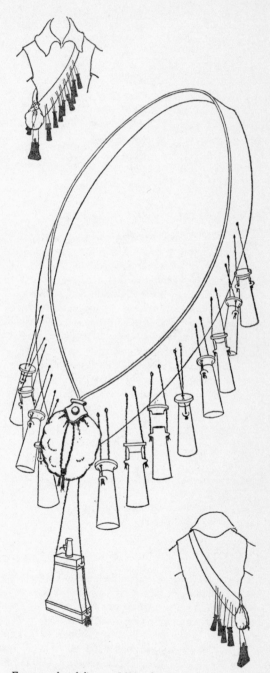

European bandolier, ca.1600, after De Gheyn

paper cartridge, caused the abandonment of the bandolier. Before the end of the seventeenth century, it had all but disappeared in western Europe and America.

In eastern Europe, Africa and Asia, however, the bandolier remained popular, and assumed new forms. Waist belts were used as well as shoulder belts. The cylinders were carried in separate pouches or compartments, as well as suspended on cords, and there were other local variations.

With the appearance of metal-cased cartridges in the nineteenth century, bandoliers in new forms gradually returned to favor throughout most of the world, for both military and civilian use, and they are still used today. Now they consist of a belt with loops for individual cartridges or with pouches to hold full magazine clips.   H.L.P.

Peterson, Harold L., *Arms and Armor in Colonial America, 1526–1783*, Harrisburg, Pa., 1956.

BAR PISTOL

Because of its thinness, this pistol is sometimes referred to as the book pistol. It could, if necessary, be concealed between the pages of an average-sized book. A solid, vertical, rectangular block holds four cartridges of .25 auto caliber, one above the other. The barrel is of the over-and-under type with two rifled bores. Cartridges are detonated by a single firing pin alternating between the two chambers. After firing the two upper cartridges, the rectangular block is released by pressure on a catch on the top of the gun, and revolved to place the unfired cartridges in position. Though they were patented in Belgium, England, Russia and North America, it is believed that most of the guns were produced in Germany during the period 1900–1910.   H.C.L.

Illustration: page 111.

Logan, Herschel C., *Hand Cannon to Automatic*, Huntingdon, W.Va., 1944.
Winant, Lewis, *Firearms Curiosa*, New York, 1955, 2nd edition 1961, and London, 1956.

BAYONET

A bayonet is an edged weapon designed to fasten to the forward end of a gun, thus converting it into a polearm as well as a firearm. The name derives from the city of Bayonne in southern France, long noted for its cutlery. Daggers from its workshops were called "bayonnettes" at least as early as the closing years of the sixteenth century, but it is not known when the practice of attaching them to gun muzzles was first introduced.

By 1640–47, however, ample references indicate that the technique was well known in the vicinity of its native city. Marshall de Puységur, a famous French soldier and a native of Bayonne, described these first bayonets as having straight double-edged blades a foot long with tapering wooden handles also a foot long. These handles could be inserted into the muzzle of a musket, and this has led such weapons to be called "plug bayonets" by modern students. A later French reference, of 1678, describes the blades as being a foot long and a "good inch" in width, but by this date the handle had shrunk to a more manageable eight or nine inches. Other versions appeared with knife blades of varying lengths, and even with triangular blades, useful only for stabbing. By this time, the handy weapon had spread widely throughout Europe. Some British regiments at Tangiers were equipped with it as early as 1663, and in France the regiments of fusiliers and grenadiers raised in 1671 were furnished with it. Interestingly, hunting guns also were sometimes equipped with bayonets, presumably to protect the hunter from an enraged animal once he had expended his single shot.

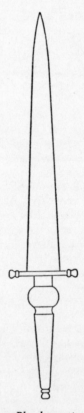

Plug bayonet

The plug bayonet had many drawbacks as a weapon and efforts were quickly made to improve it. Once it was inserted in the muzzle, no shot could be fired until it was removed. If it was pushed in too tightly, it was difficult to remove. If it were not pushed in tightly enough, it might fall out or be left in an enemy's body. About 1678, loose rings were attached to the hafts which could be looped around the gun barrel. These, too, had disadvantages, and their use never became widespread.

Real improvement came with the socket bayonet, a few years later. This boasted a sleeve which fitted around the barrel and locked in place with a slot and stud. The great

Socket bayonet

French military engineer, Vauban, devised such a bayonet in 1687, and, at his urging, it was adopted for the French infantry in 1688. Other nations soon followed France's example, and an improved version of the socket bayonet became standard for almost all European armies shortly after 1700. In its commonest form it consisted of a sleeve with a locking slot, an elbow bent out at right angles, and a straight blade, triangular in cross section. It remained the most common form of bayonet for some 150 years.

Even during the heyday of the socket bayonet's popularity there were many other forms in use to varying degrees. Retractable bayonets which slid in and out were fastened to the barrel or stock. Some versions of these are found which date at least as early as the mid-seventeenth century, and sliding-rod bayonets have been tried on numerous military arms since then. Hinged bayonets which could be folded back along the barrel also appeared. Such bayonets, activated by a spring so that they would snap forward into position when a catch was released, were highly popular for blunderbusses, and even pistols, during the second half of the eighteenth century; they ranged in length all the way from a ridiculous two inches to the normal musket size of sixteen inches. Almost all were triangular in section and good only for stabbing.

In an effort to make bayonets of more general use, many different blade shapes were devised. Flat single- and double-edged blades were tried, with the idea that they could be used as swords when not fastened on to the gun. Early examples of these sword bayonets usually had sockets for attachment, but since this made them awkward to hold in the hand, new fastening techniques were devised.

Usually they consisted of a loop at the base of the blade to go over the muzzle and a slot in the pommel with a spring catch to engage a stud farther down the barrel. Since sword bayonets were usually larger than simple socket types, they tended to make the gun muzzle heavy, and so were used primarily on the shorter firearms such as rifles and musketoons. Some of these blades were even equipped with saw teeth along the back, for use by engineer or pioneer troops, and some had full hand guards on their handles. Other experiments combined the bayonet with tools. The bolo bayonet was designed to serve as a tool or weapon in the hand as well as on the gun, and there were trowel bayonets and even pick bayonets for entrenching.

As long as most military firearms were single-shot weapons, the bayonet remained important. Soldiers needed it to fight at close quarters when there was no time to reload. When multi-shot guns became common, the bayonet was relegated to a supporting role, useful when all ammunition had been expended or when silence was desired. In the First World War and even as late as the Second World War and the Korean War, a few instances of bayonet

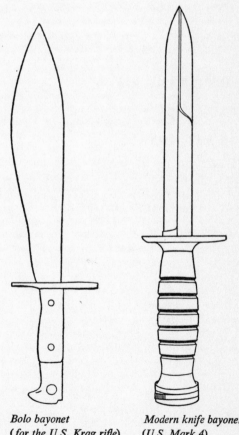

Bolo bayonet
(*for the U.S. Krag rifle*)

Modern knife bayonet
(*U.S. Mark 4*)

fighting were recorded, but by then the massed-bayonet attack was as archaic as the cavalry charge. The bayonet nevertheless remains useful, and has been retained, even for automatic rifles. Now, however, it has been shortened and modified so that it is primarily an all-purpose knife that can also be attached to a gun.   H.L.P.

Illustration: page 104.

Albaugh, William A., III, *Confederate Edged Weapons*, New York, 1960.

Alm, Josef, *Arméns Eldhandvapen Förr och Nu*, Stockholm, 1953.

Blackmore, Howard L., *British Military Firearms, 1650–1850*, London, 1961.

Foulkes, Charles, and Hopkinson, C. E., *Sword, Lance and Bayonet*, London, 1938.

Hicks, Major James Ernest, *United States Firearms, 1776–1956*, Beverley Hills, Cal., 1957 (revised edition of Hicks's *Notes on United States Ordnance*, Vol. 1, Mount Vernon, N.Y., 1940).

Margerand, J., *Armement et Équipement de l'Infanterie Française du XVIe au XXe Siècle*, Paris, 1945.

Peterson, Harold L., *American Knives*, New York, 1958.

Peterson, Harold L., *Arms and Armor in Colonial America, 1526–1783*, Harrisburg, Pa., 1956.

BENCH REST RIFLE

See: TARGET RIFLE.

BERDAN, HIRAM

Colonel Hiram Berdan, a mechanical engineer from New York, was well known in the United States as the organizer of a sharpshooter regiment during the American Civil War. He was also an inventor in the field of firearms.

His most lasting contributions included a method of rapid low-cost drawing of brass for cartridge cases, and his own metallic cartridge, which had a bump formed in the bottom of its primer pocket against which the primer was struck. It used a primer much like the old-fashioned percussion cap, with no internal anvil. This type of primer is still used in most parts of the world except the United States. The Berdan primer was the first generally successful and widely used primer in the United States. The primer pocket had a single small flash hole (later two or more) at one edge. Another type of primer, the Boxer, developed by Colonel E. M. Boxer of the British Ordnance, had a relatively large central flash hole, with its anvil incorporated in the primer itself. This later became popular in the United States, being easier to reload. A simple punch inserted into the mouth of the case entered the flash hole and knocked out the fired primer. The Berdan flash hole, off-center and small, was not adapted to this expedient and so lost favor in the United States.

Berdan resigned his commission in 1864 to devote his time to perfecting a system for converting the old large-caliber muzzle-loading rifles to breechloaders. His conversion used a hinged breech block. Several nations adopted his idea, including Spain and Russia. Spain ordered Berdan breech actions from the Remington Arms Company which were then incorporated into muzzle-loading rifles at a Spanish arsenal.

In 1869 Berdan patented a bolt-action breechloader, which was adopted by Russia. This rifle was ordered in considerable quantities from the Colt Patent Firearms Manufacturing Company; later it was made in Russia. Berdan died on March 31, 1893.   B.R.L.

See also: BOXER CARTRIDGE; CARTRIDGE; PRIMER.

BERTHIER RIFLE

A bolt-action, magazine-fed rifle developed by Berthier, a French official. Essentially the rifle is a combination of the French-developed Gras action, in modified form, with the Mannlicher vertical in-line magazine. It is therefore sometimes called Mannlicher-Berthier.

The bolt is of two-piece construction with dual locking lugs on the removable bolt head. The magazine of the original model (M1890) was fed with a three-round clip which is inserted in the action and functions as part of the magazine, falling out at the bottom when the last round is chambered. In 1916 a five-round magazine was adopted. All models are unusual in that they have no safety.

The Model 1890 carbine, which appeared in three slightly different versions – cavalry, cuirassier, and gendarmerie – was followed by the 1892 artillery and gendarmerie musketoons. Only the gendarmerie and artillery weapons used bayonets. The first true rifle to be extensively manufactured was the M1907/15, which had a barrel length of 30.71 inches compared to the 17.7-inch barrel of the carbines. Like the carbine, it had a turned-down bolt handle. In 1934, a quantity of M1907/15's were re-barreled with a shorter barrel chambered for the French 7.5 mm. M1929 cartridge and fitted with a five-round staggered box magazine; they are called M1907/15M34.

In 1916 a rifle and a carbine were introduced with a five-round magazine. They are basically the same as the earlier model Berthiers except for the magazine and the use of a horizontal bolt handle on the M1916 rifle.

All the Berthiers are chambered for the 8 mm. Lebel cartridge (M86), except the M1907/15M34. The muzzle velocity of this cartridge from the rifle is 2,380 feet per second.   J.E.S.

Illustration: page 207.

Hicks, Captain (later Major) James Ernest, assisted by André Jandot, *Notes on French Ordnance, 1717–1936*, Mount Vernon, N.Y., 1938.

Smith, Walter H. B. and Joseph E., *The Book of Rifles*, 3rd edition, Harrisburg, Pa., 1963.

BICYCLE RIFLE

Achieving its greatest popularity during the bicycling era of the "gay nineties," the bicycle rifle was, for the most part, a single-shot pistol equipped with either a wooden or metal detachable skeleton extension stock. This provided a convenient arm for carrying on a bicycle, for either hunting or target shooting. On occasion, the guns could be carried in a case strapped under the crossbar of the bicycle. The barrel length was usually ten to twenty inches, and calibers included .22, .25, .30 and .32, mostly rim-fire. For loading, some had side-swing barrels while others were equipped with tip-down barrels. Most popular of the American arms were the J. Stevens, Frank Wesson, and Quackenbush rifles.　　H.C.L.

BIRMINGHAM

From the early sixteenth century, Birmingham was noted for its smiths and cutlers, but it was not until the English Civil War that it began the manufacture of firearms. The new trade was firmly established in 1689, when five of the leading gunsmiths secured regular contracts from the Ordnance in London. Thus began family businesses which, in time, were to employ hundreds of outworkers producing by hand the various parts of a gun. During the eighteenth century the industry spread into the neighboring towns of Wednesbury, Solihull and Darlaston, and the district became the main source of supply for barrels and locks in Britain. Large warehouses were built by the main contractors for the storage of materials and assembly of arms; an Ordnance factory and proofhouse were built in Bagot Street in 1797, and by the end of the Napoleonic Wars the annual production of the district exceeded half a million arms. In 1813 the gunmakers constructed their own proofhouse in Banbury Street, authorised by Act of Parliament, and when Government orders declined began supplying large numbers of cheap guns to London and Liverpool merchants for the African and Indian trade. This export of guns reached its peak during the American Civil War, when nearly 10,000 people were reported employed in the trade. Increased competition from the Ordnance factory at Enfield forced the Birmingham gunmakers to use more and more machinery, and gradually the groups of small workshops were replaced by factories and the old

family firms were taken over by public companies. The largest of these was the Birmingham Small Arms Company, founded in 1861 and still in operation.　　H.L.B.

Harris, Clive (editor), *The History of the Birmingham Gun-Barrel Proof House*, Birmingham, 1946.

See also: PROOF MARKS.

BLACK POWDER

See: GUNPOWDER.

BLUING

An artificially induced oxidation of iron or steel by any one of many different chemical processes. The result varies in color from very light blue through purple-blue to blue-black. This process serves two functions: that of enhancing the appearance of the firearm, and that of offering a chemical barrier to future corrosion.

There are two general means of bluing recognized by gunsmiths: the hot blue, which involves equipment and skill, but which is recognized as the most durable; and the cold-blue technique. The latter is many times referred to as "patent blue" because it is available bottled ready for use and sold under various trade names. A third method which may or may not involve the use of chemicals is the heat blue, but this is suitable only for small parts and will not be considered here.

The bluing of firearms is probably not as ancient an art as its application to the decoration of armor, though it is encountered on guns made before 1550. Extensive use of blued military arms commences in the mid-nineteenth century.

The chemical mechanism by means of which a chemically induced blue is achieved has never been properly explained, but bluing can be accomplished by many chemical combinations, most of which contain nitrates in some form. Hot bluing is more difficult, but it is also the most desirable and is the type used by firearms manufacturers.

　　H.W.

Angier, R. H., *Firearms Blueing and Browning*, Onslow County, N.C., 1936.

Howe, James Virgil, *The Modern Gunsmith*, 2 vols, London and New York, 1934.

See also: DECORATION OF FIREARMS.

BLUNDERBUSS

A blunderbuss is a short firearm with an expanding bore, usually flaring out in a bell at the muzzle. The name is believed to be a corruption of the German *Dunder* (thunder) and *Buchse* (gun). It developed on the continent of Europe during the first half of the seventeenth century, spreading to England about mid-century, and from there to America.

The blunderbuss was a specialized weapon designed to scatter a quantity of shot in a wide pattern at relatively short range. A contemporary reference describes it as "very fit for doing great execution in a crowd, to make good a narrow passage, door of a house, stair-case; or in boarding a ship." It was thus the seventeenth- and eighteenth-century version of the modern riot gun, or, more closely, the antecedent of the shotgun carried by stagecoach guards of the last century and by many prison guards today.

The standard load was as many pistol balls or buckshot "as would chamber conveniently." A large one might take as many as twenty buckshot and a charge of 120 grains of black powder. The popular notion that blunderbusses were loaded with stones, broken glass, nails or bits of scrap iron is false. Such projectiles might have been used in an emergency, but they would have ruined the bore in short order. Lead balls provided a more uniform load and were more easily carried.

Another myth about the blunderbuss is that the size and shape of the bell determined the spread pattern of the bullets. This ballistic fallacy even fooled the early makers of the guns themselves. As a result, blunderbusses were made with huge bells for a wide spread in all directions, and oval or elliptical bells in an attempt to direct the bullets in an elongated pattern parallel to the ground, to avoid wasting the many shots that would fly over the enemies' heads if they followed a circular dispersion. Actually, balls can spread out at only a given rate. If the muzzle expands more rapidly in any direction, it ceases to have an effect upon the shot. Practical experience eventually indicated that those arms with a large basic caliber, a bore that expanded gradually throughout its entire length, and a short barrel, produced the widest spread of bullets, far exceeding those with huge bells. Thus the exaggerated flares of the early blunderbusses gave way after 1750 to shorter arms with almost cylindrical bores the flare being simulated on the outside by a thickening of the metal with decorative moldings at the muzzle.

Recent tests, held under the auspices of the National Rifle Association of America, have confirmed these theories about shot dispersal from blunderbusses. After firing several specimens with widely differing characteristics, it was demonstrated that they fired a fairly consistent shot pattern no matter what the size and shape of their muzzles. At 40 feet there would be a mean spread of 20–36 inches; at 60 feet, 40–50 inches. Furthermore, the test blunderbuss firing the widest spread had the largest bore diameter at the breech and the smallest muzzle diameter of the guns tested.

Even though it had little or no effect on the spread of the shot, a belled muzzle did have some real advantages. It had a wonderful psychological effect upon anyone at whom it was pointed, and it made the gun easier to load on a lurching stagecoach or a rocking ship.

The blunderbuss was primarily a gun of the flintlock period. A very few wheel lock specimens are known, and some late pieces were made with percussion locks after about 1825. The eighteenth century was the era of the blunderbuss, and it appeared in myriad forms, both in pistols and long guns. Brass-barreled specimens were especially popular, and many are found with triangular bayonets, which folded back along the barrel against spring pressure and were secured by a catch, ready to snap forward when the latch was released. Extra big versions were also manufactured, for use as swivel guns on ship gunwales and small boats. After 1800 the popularity of the blunderbuss in Europe and America declined rapidly, and by 1840 it had all but disappeared.

The center of blunderbuss production was western Europe, especially England. The density of population in this area, and the intense maritime activity, made it a highly desirable weapon. Less heavily populated areas in eastern Europe with little or no shipping found it of less use. Blunderbusses were imported into America during the late seventeenth century, but found little popularity at that time. It was not until the next century that increased urbanization and maritime commerce created a demand for them there. A few blunderbusses were made in America, including some military specimens during the early nineteenth century, but most were bought in England. Blunderbusses were also made in quantity in North Africa, the Near East and India. Normally these were small specimens, of little practical use, with huge bells and short butt stocks – almost caricatures of the true weapon. They have been produced there, largely for the tourist trade, until modern times.   H.L.P.

Illustrations: pages 40, 283.

Peterson, Harold L., *Arms and Armor in Colonial America, 1526–1783*, Harrisburg, Pa., 1956.
Peterson, Harold L., *The Treasury of the Gun*, New York, 1962 (*The Book of the Gun*, London, 1963).

BOLT ACTION

The breech mechanism known as bolt action was named from its resemblance to the common door-locking bolt. One of the earliest was that used in Von Dreyse's needle gun of the late 1830's. The bolt contains the firing pin, spring, and an extractor for withdrawing fired cartridges from the chamber. Lugs, an integral part of the bolt, hold it against the backward force of the powder explosion by transmitting the force to surfaces in the bolt housing or receiver.

There are many bolt types, designed for speedy, safe and dependable operation. Two main classifications are the straight-pull and the turning bolts. Of the former, the Swiss Schmidt-Rubin, Austrian Mannlicher and Canadian Ross are examples. Turning bolts can be placed in three general groups: (*a*) Mausers and Mauser types, (*b*) Mannlichers, and (*c*) other types. Among the last are such systems as the Krag-Jørgensen, Lebel, and Lee-Enfield. The Mauser has been the most extensively used.

The typical Mauser bolt has strong one-piece construction, with front locking lugs and an additional rear safety lug. Mausers are loaded by stripping cartridges from a charger or clip, pushing them down with the thumb. This clip, a thin metal strip with edges turned over, holds the cartridges by their grooves.

In a Mannlicher bolt, the locking lugs are a little further back on the separate bolt head, which does not rotate when the bolt is turned. A clip full of cartridges goes into the magazine, remaining until the last cartridge has been fired, then falling out below.

The Lee-Enfield bolt has its locking lugs at the rear. The Krag-Jørgensen has only one lug.   B.R.L.

Illustration: page 46.

Smith, Walter H. B. and Joseph E., *Small Arms of the World*, 6th edition, Harrisburg, Pa., 1960.
Textbook of Small Arms, H.M. Stationery Office, London, 1929.

See also: BREECHLOADERS; CHASSEPOT, ANTOINE ALPHONSE; DREYSE, JOHANN NIKOLAUS VON; GRAS RIFLE; KRAG RIFLE; LEBEL RIFLE; LEE RIFLE; MANNLICHER; MAUSER; MOSIN-NAGANT RIFLE; NEEDLE GUN; REPEATING ARMS; ROSS RIFLE.

BOOTLEG PISTOL

See: UNDERHAMMER GUN.

BORE

See: CALIBER.

BOURGEOYS, MARIN LE

Probably the inventor of the true flintlock. He was born *ca.*1550 at Lisieux, Normandy, into a family of locksmiths, crossbow-makers, armorers and clockmakers. He was ap-

parently trained as a painter, for the earliest references to him, commencing in 1583, relate to his employment on painting of various kinds. In 1598 he was appointed *valet de chambre* to Henri IV, a nominal position intended merely to free him from the control of the Paris guilds. Though he continued to paint, Le Bourgeoys had probably at this time already turned his attention to gunmaking. In 1606 he delivered to the king "a harquebus, a hunting-horn and a crossbow, all of his own design (*tout de sa façon*)", while an airgun designed by him is described and illustrated in Flurance's *Elements de l'artillerie* of 1607. In 1608, in a royal warrant granting him lodging in the Grand Gallery of the Louvre, he is described as "our painter and *valet de chambre*, worker in moving globes and other mechanical inventions." Despite his court appointment, he appears to have spent most of his life in Lisieux, where he was buried on September 3, 1634.

The earliest known true flintlock is on a magnificent gun, in the Hermitage, Leningrad, signed by Le Bourgeoys. This, together with the fact that he was noted as an inventor of mechanical devices at the time when he lived, provides the only evidence for regarding him as the inventor of the lock. The "harquebus . . . of his own design"

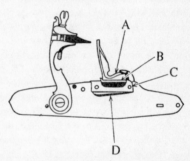

Flintlock by Marin le Bourgeoys, ca.1610, from the gun now in the Hermitage Museum, Leningrad

A. *Frizzen*
B. *Pan*
C. *Bridle for frizzen spring*
D. *Spring*

delivered to Henri IV in 1606 may have been a flintlock, but this cannot be proved. Even if Le Bourgeoys did not invent the lock, his fame as its first known maker and as an outstanding gunsmith remains assured.   C.B.

Illustration: page 39.

Huard, G., "Marin Bourgeoys, Peintre de Henri IV et de Louis XIII" in *Bulletin de la societé de l'histoire et de l'art Français*, Vol. 1926, Paris, 1927.

Lenk, Torsten, *Flintlåset, dess Uppkomst och Utveckling*, Stockholm, 1939.

Peterson, Harold L., *The Treasury of the Gun*, New York, 1962 (*The Book of the Gun*, London, 1963).

See also: FLINTLOCK.

BOUTET, NICOLAS-NOËL

The last of the great artist-gunmakers. Born in 1761, the son of Noël Boutet, *arquebusier des chevaux legers du Roi*, he married in 1788 Louise-Émilie Desaintes, the daughter of Louis XVI's gunmaker. Having succeeded to his father-in-law's office he worked for the king until the Revolution and then, in 1792, became technical director of the newly established state arms factory, the *Manufacture de Versailles*. This establishment was to be responsible mainly for supplying military weapons of all types, but it included a separate workshop for the production of fine-quality swords and firearms. These varied from the simple, but finely made, *fusils d'honneur*, given to outstanding members of the lower ranks of the services, to the elaborately decorated firearms and swords made for senior officers and government officials, and for presentation purposes.

In 1800 Boutet was granted an eighteen-year concession at Versailles under the terms of which he was not only to continue to make regulation arms but was also to train artists to carry on the great traditions of fine French gunmaking. Among these artists was his own son, Pierre-Nicolas, whom he took into partnership in 1804. It was during this period, which ended with the fall of Napoleon in 1815, that most of Boutet's finest work was produced, much of it ordered by the Emperor for his own use or for presentation to distinguished foreigners. Boutet's swords, though of fine workmanship, are of poor form; but his firearms, for technical excellence combined with splendid decoration, have never been surpassed.

In 1815 the *Manufacture de Versailles* was sacked by the Prussians, and most of its movable contents were sent to Berlin. It was never re-established, and Boutet set up in private business at 87 Rue de Richelieu, Paris, again taking his pre-Revolutionary title of *arquebusier ordinaire du Roi et des Princes*. Though the technical quality of his work remained as high as ever, he seems never again to have produced any very elaborately decorated arms. He died in Paris in 1833.   C.B.

Illustration: page 301 (plate 7).

Bottet, Maurice, *La Manufacture d'Armes de Versailles– Boutet directeur-artiste*, Paris, 1903.

Grancsay, Stephen V., "Napoleon's Gunmaker" in *The American Rifleman*, July 1948.

BOXER, EDWARD MOUNIER

Edward Mounier Boxer, born in 1823, was educated at Woolwich Academy and joined the Royal Artillery in 1839. Soon promoted to captain, he became interested in the practical problems of gunnery and, in 1849, invented a wooden time fuse for shells which was adopted by the British Army and was used successfully for many years. As a result of his experiments, Boxer was made Superintendent of the Royal Laboratory at Woolwich. Here he was responsible for many improvements to ammunition including a new shrapnel shell. His most important contribution was the small arms cartridge and primer which bore his name (see BOXER CARTRIDGE). His patenting of the cartridge and his financial connections with its manufacturers caused much adverse comment, and in 1869 he was forced to resign. He died in 1898 with the rank of major general.   H.L.B.

Boxer, Major General R. A., *Colonel Boxer and the War Office*, London, 1870.

Daw, George H., *The Central-Fire Cartridge before the Law Courts, the Government, and the Public: showing who introduced the system into England, who has improved it, who was benefited by it and who ought to be rewarded for it*, London, 1867.

See also: CARTRIDGE; PRIMER.

BOXER CARTRIDGE

The cartridge invented by Colonel Boxer was the first center-fire cartridge to be produced and used successfully on a large scale. It was designed for the Snider rifle, whose first cartridge with a papier-maché case had proved unsuccessful. The main point of the Boxer cartridge was its case, which was made of coiled sheet brass designed to expand on firing to give better obturation and to contract for easier extraction. The bullet used was of modified Minié design and the center-fire primer was based on the well-known Pottet pattern. Boxer patented his cartridge in June 1866, and it was officially approved for the Snider the following August. Further trials showed that the base was too weak; Boxer accordingly strengthened it with a heavy brass disc and also made a slight alteration to the primer. Both modifications were patented and were incorporated in the official Mark II cartridge.

The primer was the subject of a legal battle between the cartridge makers Eley Bros., who received large contracts for its manufacture, and the London gunmaker George Daw who claimed that it was based on Schneider's patent of 1861 which he had purchased. Daw's case received much sympathy and the *Standard* newspaper came out strongly in his favor, but in 1867 it was ruled that no infringement had taken place. The Boxer cartridge was made in several patterns, including one for the Adams revolver (approved 1868) and one filled with buckshot for the use of convict guards. When the Snider rifle was superseded by the Martini-Henry, the Boxer cartridge was adapted to the reduced caliber, but experience in the Egyptian campaign disclosed that under adverse conditions it was liable to jam. In 1885 it was replaced by a cartridge with a solid-drawn brass case. H.L.B.

Illustration: see PRIMER.

Daw, George H., *The Central-Fire Cartridge before the Law Courts, the Government, and the Public: showing who introduced the system into England, who has improved it, who has benefited by it and who ought to be rewarded for it,* London, 1867.

See also: BOXER, EDWARD MOUNIER; CARTRIDGE; PRIMER.

BOX LOCK

The term box lock has been applied to locks for muzzle-loading guns, usually percussion, in which the mechanism is contained within a metal box-like frame. The hammer, being within the side plate of this box, is less apt to become fouled in clothing or brush. Some locks which are more conventional in design, except for having the hammer within the confines of the stock, are also called box locks. An example of this sort is the United States Model 1843 pistol. B.R.L.

Illustrations: page 108.

See also: NOCK, HENRY.

BREECHLOADERS

The concept of a gun that could be loaded at the breech appeared very early in the history of firearms. The exact date is unknown, but breech-loading cannon are known to have been in use shortly after 1400, and they may well have been made much earlier, perhaps within a few years of the appearance of the first guns a century before. From the beginning, however, all designers of such weapons faced the problem of devising a breech opening that could be opened quickly and easily and yet would be strong, and tight enough to prevent any leakage of flame or gas from the explosion of the charge. The search for such a breech seal consumed the energies of countless designers for more than four centuries.

The early breech-loading cannon were made in two principal patterns. In the most common, the gun consisted of a simple tube with a separate chamber or breech piece. These chambers in turn were short tubes, closed at one end, and just large enough to contain a charge of powder. Usually they tapered or necked in a little at the mouth so that they could be inserted into the rear of the bore for a short distance to make a tight seal at the joint, and often they had handles so that they somewhat resembled a beer mug. Once they were set in position, they were locked there by a wedge or key. Breech-loading cannon of this type were made at least from the early fifteenth century until 1700. The other breech-loading system for early cannon comprised the screw breech, a short section including the rear of the bore, which was threaded and could be removed. It should be noted that only small cannon used this device for loading. Huge bombards such as the Dardanelles Gun at the Tower of London had threaded breeches also, but in these cases the removable portion was undoubtedly designed only for ease in transportation, permitting the great guns to be moved in sections. It would have been impractical to remove a breech weighing several hundred pounds merely to load the piece.

Breech-loading small arms appeared somewhat later than cannon. Once again, the date of the first is unknown, but by the early sixteenth century they were being made in some quantity. King Henry VIII of England owned a number of breech-loading long arms, and two are still preserved in the Tower of London. Both have hinged trap doors in the breech that may be opened to insert a small iron tube, remarkably similar to a modern cartridge in appearance, which held the charge. The original locks are missing from both guns, but they were undoubtedly wheel locks. One of these guns is dated 1537 and is especially important because it is the earliest definitely datable breech-loading small arm to have survived. Even more interesting, however, are a whole series of pistol shields which also belonged to Henry VIII. Each of these singular weapons bears a breech-loading matchlock pistol in its center. Once again a separate iron chamber is used to hold the charge, and the breech of the pistol is pivoted so that it may be raised for inserting the tube, then dropped back in place and locked with a latch. In 1544 an Italian gunsmith named Giovanbattista, from Ravenna, wrote to King Henry offering to make such weapons, and it is assumed that these pistol shields were produced shortly thereafter. If these arms were obtained with the idea of arming a special guard, as the number of surviving specimens would seem to indicate, they represent the earliest known attempt to issue breechloaders for a military or quasi-military purpose.

The late sixteenth century and the century that followed witnessed the appearance of many more attempts at producing successful breechloaders. Almost always these arms employed a screw breech or a separate chamber. Two or three reasonably successful breech-loading magazine repeaters were invented early in the seventeenth century (see REPEATING ARMS), but the single-shot weapons remained relatively stagnant, and it was not until after 1700 that any serious attempts were made to arm soldiers with such arms.

The system that produced the first real interest in military spheres was a variant of the screw breech. The idea of a threaded plug in the top, bottom or side of a barrel that could be removed for inserting a load had appeared early among the various screw-breech designs, but it had had serious drawbacks which had prevented it from achieving widespread acceptance. It was a slow and difficult process to screw such a plug back into place, especially if the shooter were excited. A plug could easily be dropped and lost, and powder fouling could make it stick so that it would be difficult or impossible to remove without a wrench. In 1704, however, a French engineer named Isaac de la Chaumette overcame most of these difficulties. In his design the plug passed all the way through the barrel, and the lower end was attached to the trigger guard which served as a handle and provided leverage for turning the plug if it became sticky. With this system it was no longer necessary to remove the plug entirely, for when it was lowered it left a hole in the top of the barrel through which a ball and a charge of powder could be dropped. When the plug was raised again, it closed this hole and sealed the breech. Here at last was a breechloader with a real military potential. Marshal Saxe recommended that the system be applied to both carbines and wall guns, and it is believed that at least one regiment of French dragoons was armed with La Chaumette's breechloaders in 1723.

The inventor, however, was no longer on the scene to capitalize on this recognition. As a Huguenot he had fled in 1721 to England, and it was there that the gun reached its highest development. First came the introduction of a quick thread which dropped the plug to the loading position with only one turn of the handle. La Chaumette may have developed this refinement himself or it may have been the work of a fellow refugee named Bidet who made the guns upon which it is first found. Then, in 1776, Patrick Ferguson perfected the system by modifying the plug to reduce fouling, thickening the bottom of the barrel so that the plug could be dropped completely below the bore for more thorough cleaning, developing a new adjustable rear sight and a system of four-groove rifling. One hundred of these rifles were made and issued to a special corps under Ferguson's command for service in America, thereby becoming England's first military breechloader and the finest arm to see service during the American War of Independence.

In the meantime, Giuseppe Crespi of Milan had invented a breechloader with a tip-up breech, and this new system soon attracted attention from the screw plug. For one thing, it was necessary to load plug-type breechloaders with loose powder and ball. In Crespi's system the rear portion of the barrel was pivoted so that it could be tipped up and loaded with a paper cartridge similar to those used in the standard muzzle-loaders. The Austrian Army experimented with this system from 1770 until 1779, but eventually abandoned it because it leaked gas. Great Britain tested a number of carbines made by Durs Egg on the same principle in 1788, experienced the same difficulty, and also abandoned it.

In America, John H. Hall, working without any knowledge of the European inventions, developed his own version of the tip-up breech which was both simpler and more efficient than the Crespi or the Egg. It still had a tendency to leak gas, but the United States adopted it as a standard arm for use by large numbers of troops in 1819. Previously, all issues of breechloaders had been to small units. This was the first time that one had been recognized as a major weapon.

Other designers in other nations also developed breechloaders with similar actions. In Norway Captain F. W. Scheel produced a tip-up breech reminiscent of both the Hall and the Crespi. August Hagström did the same in Sweden; and Nicolai Johan Löbnitz invented a pistol with a tip-up barrel which exposed a fixed chamber for loading. The really significant contribution to breech-loading design, however, passed almost unnoticed as a by-product of a gun with a break-open breech. Johannes Samuel Pauly invented such an arm while working in Paris in 1812. It also boasted an internal firing pin and was accompanied by a pistol with a tip-down barrel. The key feature, however, was a center-fire cartridge with a brass head and a wrapped paper body. The soft head of this cartridge was designed to expand and form a seal against the escape of flame and gases, and this is the theory on which almost all firearms operate today. Pauly's guns were fine arms and worked very well when fired by experts; but they were fragile, and this cost them success.

It remained for one of Pauly's workmen to develop a really popular breechloader. Johann Nikolaus von Dreyse, who had been a lockmaker for Pauly from 1809 until 1814, invented his famous needle gun between 1827 and 1829. The first models were muzzle-loaders and then, in 1837, he produced a breechloader and achieved lasting fame as the father of the modern bolt action. The nickname "needle gun" derived from the long slender firing pin which passed all the way through the charge of powder in the cartridge to detonate the primer nestled in the base of the bullet. It was the weak point of Dreyse's system, for the powder gases corroded the pin until it became fragile and broke easily. Antoine Alphonse Chassepot of France improved upon Dreyse's design in 1866 by employing a shorter firing pin which struck an inverted percussion cap in the head of the cartridge. Both arms were highly effective for their day, however, and saw widespread use in the wars which marked the unification of Germany. All modern bolt actions reflect portions of their design.

Meanwhile, in America, Christian Sharps approached the problem of the breech seal from an entirely different direction and produced in 1848 the first of the dropping-block actions. In Sharps's design a breechblock slid vertically in a mortise cut in the receiver. The trigger guard served as a lever, and when this was pulled down the block was lowered, exposing the rear of the chamber for the insertion of a cartridge. When the guard was returned to its normal position, the block was raised, sealing the aperture. The hammer had to be cocked separately, and when it fell, a pellet primer was fed automatically over the nipple. The Sharps action was strong and simple. It saw extensive use during the American Civil War and was rated the best breechloader in the service by the troops who used it. It was as good an arm as could be produced with the soft combustible cartridges of the period, and the system continued to be applied to later single-shot rifles firing self-sealing metallic cartridges, such as the Winchester, Stevens and Farquharson.

The American Civil War produced a host of other breechloading small arms firing combustible or separate-primed cartridges. A few were good, but most were undependable or downright dangerous. Not even a wartime economy could make successes of them. There were guns with sliding breechblocks, sliding barrels, dropping breechblocks, tilting breechblocks, rotating breechblocks, tilting barrels, top levers, and even one bolt-action with an underhammer.

The day of the self-contained metallic cartridge had dawned, however, and all of these arms were already obsolete. Pauly's idea of using the cartridge itself as a breech seal had finally been accepted. Even the older forms had performed so well in the Civil War, however, that the nations of the world took note; and the late 1860's marked the turning point in national armament as existing stores of muzzle-loaders were converted and new breechloaders were adopted. In the United States a trap-door breech hinged at the forward end and containing a firing pin was devised by Erskine S. Allin, Master Armorer of the Springfield Armory, and adopted in 1865. With minor improvements, it remained the standard long arm for the United States Army until the adoption of the Krag magazine repeater in 1892. In England a similar conversion designed by Jacob Snider of New York was also adopted in 1865. This time the trap-door was hinged on the side. It was a good arm, and with Colonel Boxer's improved center-fire cartridge of 1867 it shot even better than the muzzle-loading Enfield from which it was made.

Unlike the Americans, the British considered their conversion merely a stopgap until a brand new breechloader could be developed. In 1871 they adopted such an arm. Once again it had an American ancestry. In 1862 Henry O. Peabody of Boston had invented a breech system known as the falling block. In this action, the block was hinged at the back. Pulling down on a lever, usually the trigger guard, tilted this block downward and exposed the chamber at the foot of an inclined plane. Canada, France, Bavaria, Mexico, and Switzerland, among other nations, purchased a number of these arms. In Switzerland Friedrich von Martini improved upon the action and substituted an inside striker for the old exterior hammer. The British combined this action with a rifling system developed by Alexander Henry of Edinburgh and called in the Martini-Henry. Austria modified the action and called it the Werder, and there were Francotte-Martinis, Swinburns, Stahls, and others, all based on Peabody's falling breech.

One other widely used breech also developed from an invention which appeared during the American Civil War. This was the Remington rolling block, and in its day it was the most widely used breechloader of all. Leonard Geiger and Joseph Rider developed the system, bringing it to perfection late in 1865. It was as simple, strong, and foolproof as an action could be. The breech was opened by cocking the hammer and rolling the solid breechblock staight back with the thumb. A cartridge could then be inserted and the block rolled back up while a locking lever held the hammer cocked, then locked the breech closed. The force of the hammer when it struck added its weight to the breech strength, and in addition the pieces were so designed that the greater the internal pressure the tighter they interlocked. At the Imperial Exposition in Paris in 1867 the rolling block was selected as the finest firearm in the world, and dozens of nations hastened to purchase it in quantity for their armed forces. Among them were Denmark, Norway, Sweden, Spain, Egypt, Argentina, China, Austria, Italy, the United States and several South American countries. In all, more than a million rolling-block rifles and carbines were manufactured and sold.

There were other breech-loading systems of greater or lesser importance, but by 1870 all of the major types had been invented and perfected. The day of the muzzle-loader had passed. H.L.P.

Illustrations: pages 42–8, and endpapers.

Blackmore, Howard L., *British Military Firearms, 1650–1850*, London, 1961.

Plate 1

Wheel lock carbine, one of the finest made in the early period of the wheel lock. The barrel is damascened along its whole length with arabesques and geometrical patterns in gold and silver. The lock plate with chiseled dog is decorated *en suite*. The wheel cover is cast and pierced with figures of cupids in gilt bronze. The stock is overlaid with ebony engraved with gilt arabesques. In spite of such Italianate features as the gold damascened arabesques and the bronze wheel cover, the gun is probably of South German origin, *ca.*1540. From the collection of the Grand Duke of Baden.

Collection of W. Keith Neal.

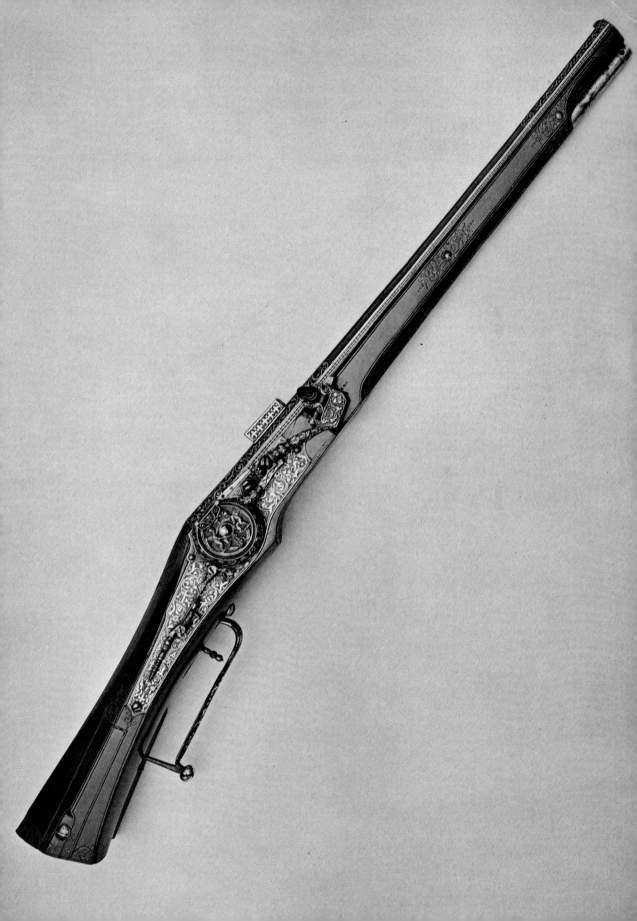

Fuller, Claud E., *The Breech-Loader in the Service*, Topeka, Kan., 1933.

George, John N., *English Guns and Rifles*, Plantersville, S.C., 1947.

Peterson, Harold L., *The Treasury of the Gun*, New York, 1962 (*The Book of the Gun*, London, 1963).

Smith, Walter H. B. and Joseph E., *Small Arms of the World*, 6th edition, Harrisburg, Pa., 1960.

Winant, Lewis, *Early Percussion Firearms*, New York, 1959, and London, 1961.

See also: ALLIN, ERSKINE S.; BALLARD, C. H.; BOLT ACTION; CHASSEPOT, ANTOINE ALPHONSE; DREYSE, JOHANN NIKOLAUS VON; FARQUHARSON RIFLE; FERGUSON, PATRICK; FERGUSON RIFLE; GRAS RIFLE; HALL, JOHN H.; HALL BREECH-LOADING ARMS; LEBEL RIFLE; LÖBNITZ, NICOLAI JOHAN; MARTINI-HENRY; NEEDLE GUN; PAULY, JOHANNES SAMUEL; SHARPS, CHRISTIAN; SHARPS RIFLES AND CARBINES; SNIDER RIFLE; TARGET RIFLE.

BROWN BESS

The affectionate name "Brown Bess," introduced in the last quarter of the eighteenth century, is now used to describe all types of British flintlock muskets made from 1720 to 1840. Basically, there are four models. The first pattern, a graceful weapon with a 46-inch barrel and distinctive brass furniture, came into production between 1710 and 1720. Not long afterwards the second model appeared, of similar build but with a 42-inch barrel. Designated the Long and Short Land muskets they weighed between ten and eleven pounds. In 1768 the short musket became the standard arm, the long model gradually disappearing. A shortage of guns at the outbreak of war with France led to the adoption in 1794 of the East India Company's cheap, easily made musket with a 39-inch barrel. Known as the India pattern, it was produced in large quantities up to 1815. The last model Brown Bess, a better made firearm named the New Land musket, was introduced gradually from 1802. All these muskets had a caliber of approximately .75 and carried a socket bayonet with a triangular 17-inch blade.   H.L.B.

Illustrations: page 40.

Blackmore, Howard L., *British Military Firearms, 1650–1850*, London, 1961.

BROWNING

Browning is a tight surface skin of induced rust or oxidation on the barrel, and occasionally on moving parts, of a firearm. Properly applied, it helps prevent further corrosion, is of use in concealment, and has been used for decorative purposes.

There are two types: the true or chemical method and the lacquer or paint. A barrel can be browned with relatively simple chemicals and equipment in the following manner.

The barrel is thoroughly polished by hand or mechanical means and then degreased, using solvents such as carbon tetrachloride, trichloroethylene or varsol. The barrel should not be handled with anything but wires or clean cloths. The barrel is now painted with one of the browning solutions and suspended in a warm and damp covered chamber made of wood or metal. After several hours a light rust will have formed which can be partially removed with a scratch brush or steel wool. Re-apply the browning solution and repeat scratching. Do this at least three or four times, plunging the barrel into boiling water for five or more minutes before scratching. This operation "sets" the rust. While it is still warm, coat the barrel with linseed oil and wipe off the excess. A typical browning solution is that of Mr J. V. Howe:

Mercuric chloride	3.45 gm.
Potassium chlorate	5.76 "
Potassium nitrate	4.60 "
Sodium nitrate	4.60 "
Nitric acid	5.75 "
Water to make	100 cc.

Lacquer browning is a "paint" applied to clean steel surfaces. It found limited usage during the nineteenth century, but is not as durable as true browning. Lacquered barrels can be detected by their somewhat purplish appearance, the absence of corrosion, and their susceptibility to solution in many organic solvents.   H.W.

Howe, James Virgil, *The Modern Gunsmith*, 2 vols, London and New York, 1934.

BROWNING, JOHN M.

John M. Browning was born on January 21, 1855, in Ogden, Utah, the son of a gunsmith. He patented a single-shot dropping-block action in 1879, which he sold to Winchester. In 1884 Browning secured patents on a lever-action rifle which he sold to Winchester, resulting in the 1886 Winchester rifle; the 1886 was the first lever-action rifle strong enough to use the high-power cartridges of its day. Browning also designed for Winchester the caliber .22 Model 90 pump-action rifle, the Model 1892, 1894 and 1895 lever-action rifles, Model 1887 lever-action shotgun, the 1897 pump-action shotguns, and other weapons. He designed the Remington Model 17 pump-action shotgun, the semi-automatic Model 24 .22 and the Model 8 semi-automatic high-powered rifle.

Browning became interested in automatic weapons in 1889, and his first design was a Winchester lever-action rifle modified to a self-loader by an improvised muzzle-mounted gas system. This was followed shortly by a gas-operated machine gun (see AUTOMATIC ARMS). Successful Browning automatic-weapon designs include the Model 1895 gas-operated machine gun, the Browning Automatic rifle M1918, the recoil operated Browning machine guns Model 1917 and Model 1919, and the caliber .50 recoil operated machine gun. Most of Browning's machine guns were produced by the Colt Patent Firearms Manufacturing Company.

He also did considerable design work on pistols, and the current United States .45 M1911A1 pistol is a Browning design, as are the .22 caliber Woodsman, and the .25, .32 and .380 Colt pistols. His first automatic pistol was patented in 1897 and was produced in 1900 by Fabrique Nationale (FN) at Herstal lez Liège, Belgium. FN also produced the .25 caliber automatic, the 1907, 1910, 1922 and Hi-Power pistols of Browning design, as well as most of his semi-automatic and automatic weapon designs and the Browning Automatic shotgun. Browning died on November 26, 1926, at Liège, while supervising the manufacture of his superposed (over-under) shotgun.

Browning's contribution to gun design is unexcelled. He designed successful lever-action, pump-action, bolt-action, gas-operated, recoil operated, and blowback operated weapons.   J.E.S.

Illustrations: pages 201–2, 204, 206.

Chinn, Colonel George M., *The Machine Gun*, 4 vols, Washington, D.C., 1951–55.

BRUNSWICK RIFLE

The British Brunswick rifle was designed by George Lovell, its official title being Lovell's Improved Brunswick rifle. First made in 1837, after a series of experiments with a rifle designed by Captain Berners, the Duke of Brunswick's field adjutant, it had a 30-inch barrel of caliber .704 with the two-grooved rifling developed by the Brunswick and Hanoverian armies, for use with a belted ball. The first models had Lovell's back-action lock, but all models after 1842 were fitted with his side-action lock. In 1840 two variations of the Brunswick were made; one with a socket bayonet for sergeants of Foot Guards, which was later converted to a cavalry arm, and a heavy model weighing nearly twelve pounds with a caliber of .796 for the navy. Both these rifles had 33-inch barrels. An improved bayonet fitting was introduced in 1847, but four

years later the Brunswick was superseded by the Minié. Nevertheless, some were made for the East India Government in 1864.   H.L.B.

Illustration: page 104.

Blackmore, Howard L., *British Military Firearms, 1650–1850*, London, 1961.

See also: LOVELL, GEORGE; RIFLES AND RIFLING.

BULLET

The term bullet is applied to any form of projectile designed to be fired from small arms. Though arrow-type projectiles were used in some of the first firearms, spherical or cylindro-conical bullets have been the usual forms. At first, round stones seem to have been fired. These were about as inefficient as the primitive gunpowder then available, and the combination was lethal only at very close range, mainly because it was impossible to hit a target at any distance. Soon the advantage of heavier metals became evident. Iron, bronze, brass, tin, lead, and even gold and silver, were tried. But as lead had the multiple advantages of great density, low melting point, and relatively plentiful supply, it was a natural choice for most purposes.

After a period of experimenting with many shapes, round balls were used almost exclusively. They were, in fact, potentially rather effective. Virtually the only trouble was a by-product of the residue of black powder which fouled the bore. This formed a thick abrasive coating in the bore which greatly impeded the ball in loading. To overcome this difficulty and permit rapid loading in military operations, muzzle-loading arms commonly had considerable windage. This meant that there was appreciable clearance allowed between the ball diameter and that of the bore. With this poor fit, instead of passing straight down the barrel when fired, the ball bounced from one side to the other, in a series of glancing blows. At the last such contact before leaving the muzzle, the ball acquired a spin toward that point of contact. This spin made the ball swerve to one side, much as does a curve ball thrown by a baseball pitcher. Since the last point of contact was a random affair, its location could not be predicted. Hence there was an inherent inaccuracy in smoothbore round-ball muzzle-loaders as they were commonly used. The maximum practical range at which one might expect to hit a man-sized object aimed at seems to have been 100–150 yards.

These difficulties could be overcome to a large extent by making the ball fit the bore tightly. This had been done from an early date for certain special weapons. Rifling helped still more, for the spin added stability to the ball's flight by equalizing the effect from any variations in density in the casting. Loading a tight-fitting ball was a slow and laborious process, however, even when a greased patch of cloth or leather was used to wrap the projectile. It was too slow for the military tacticians, who preferred the smoothbore musket for general infantry use. The rifle and its tight-fitting ball were considered appropriate only for special light infantry or skirmishers.

Towards the end of the eighteenth century, France began a series of elaborate experiments (probably the first research and development program) with the object of improving small arms performance. This work was carried over into the early 1800's, when extensive investigations were made by several French officers in order to permit rapid loading of rifle bullets. Elongated bullets were by then in use to some extent, though the round ball was still the most common type. The problem was to have a loose-fitting bullet that could be dropped quite freely down the barrel, but which would be expanded after reaching the powder charge, so as to fit the barrel when fired. Most of the attempts to accomplish this involved upsetting the bullet by beating on it with the ramrod after loading. Several methods were devised to avoid crushing the powder. These included a chamber of reduced cross section, so that the bullet was held by its rim; and a central post in the chamber, against which the bullet rested. The final solution was the system usually attributed to Claude-Étienne Minié, though others were earlier with the idea and still others perfected it. The base of the Minié bullet was hollow, with a conical plug fitted to it. Powder gas pressed against the plug, expanding the bullet skirt to fill the bore. Soon it was found that the plug was not necessary and that the gases would expand the skirts without it. By the early 1850's the elongated bullet with cylindrical center section and pointed nose was in use by most armies; it had one or more grease grooves around the cylindrical part, some with string tied in the groove. In sporting rifles in America a flat-based ball of nearly conical section called a Picket ball was popular.

Picket bullet

Lubrication, usually based on a mixture of beeswax and tallow, was either applied to the patch or placed in the bullet grooves. This was quite important, because of the powder fouling encountered after firing a few shots.

Many odd shapes of bullets have been tried, including triangular, square, hexagonal, and those cast with protruding studs or bosses to fit the grooves. Among the best known of these are the hexagonal bullet devised by Sir Joseph Whitworth, which had phenomenal accuracy; and the four-groove Jacob bullet, once popular in England for big-game rifles.

Most of the world's governments began to use smokeless powders in their rifle cartridges about 1890. Such cartridges developed much higher pressures and velocities than had been available with black powder, and the hot gases melted and cut away the sides of the bullet. This caused inaccurate flight, loss of velocity, and lead accumulation in the bore. To overcome this, a thin envelope or jacket had to be placed over the lead bullet. Steel was used extensively at first, but metals related to bronze have been favored in recent years. Some of these also caused metal fouling in the bore. However, the jacket material known as gilding metal, a copper-zinc alloy, has been found practically free from this trouble. Sometimes, to save expensive materials, this jacket is made of thin steel coated with gilding metal.

Though shooters who load their own ammunition still use the old method of casting bullets from molten lead, the commercial manufacturers all use heavy presses which extrude the bullet from a chunk of lead wire into a mold of proper shape. This is a faster method of production and produces a more uniform bullet. Jackets are made separately, then the lead core is dropped in, and the nose or the base closed, depending on the process used. The latter method is used for military bullets.

The form of the bullet has a great influence on its flight through the air. Much experimenting has been done to determine the optimum characteristics of a bullet. Most of the early jacketed bullets had round noses. Germany began using a sharp-pointed bullet with her Mauser Model 1898 rifle. This shape was copied by the United States in their caliber .30 Model 1906 cartridge, and it later became the shape generally used for military bullets. As powders were improved, higher velocities became practical, along with increased range.

The tapered-base bullet is commonly called a boat-tail bullet in the United States. The boat-tail design increases maximum range by providing reduced drag at velocities below the speed of sound. As most modern loads give substantially higher velocities at short ranges, the boat-tail bullet improves performance only at 600 yards or longer ranges, at which it reduces time of flight and sustains velocity better than the flat-base type.

Many special-purpose bullets have been tried, some of them becoming standard military items, others being found advantageous for sporting use. Among these several were adopted during the American Civil War. The Williams bullet had a separate base plug with a stem which entered a hole in the bullet base. Between base and plug was a thin, dished, zinc washer. On firing, the washer was flattened, increasing its diameter slightly. The washer then

Williams bullet

scraped the bore clean of fouling, which was a major problem with black powder. The idea was rejuvenated in recent years for revolver cartridges. Another Civil War bullet was the Shaler or sectional bullet. This took the place of the older buck and ball load used in the caliber .69 muskets, which had combined one round ball with three buckshot. When the caliber was reduced to .58 in 1855, this bore proved too small to handle three buckshot of effective size. Shaler's bullet had three short conical balls nested together, the point of one fitting into the hollow base of the one ahead of it. This idea has also been reborn recently, with the same idea of increasing the probability of a hit.

Explosive bullets have been made for over a century. Most of them involved a percussion cap in the nose, plus a bursting charge in a central cavity. Some simply had a hole drilled in the nose, filled by an ordinary rim-fire caliber .22 blank cartridge, base forward. Toward the end of the black powder era a special bullet known as "express" was popular for hunting. This type was relatively light and had a copper tube in the nose, which was hollow.

Express bullet

This gave better expansion on impact. This purpose was behind some military bullet designs introduced around 1900. The best known of these was the dum-dum bullet, named after the arsenal in British India where it was developed. International conventions ruled out this as well as explosive bullets for military use against personnel. Any unjacketed bullet (with exposed lead) has been considered banned by this agreement between nations. Practically every maker of commercial ammunition has developed his own special form of "soft-point," or expanding, bullet for use on game.

There are many special bullet types currently used in military weapons. These include such varieties as armor-piercing, tracer, incendiary, observing or spotting, and several combinations of these functions.

The armor-piercing bullet has a hardened steel or tungsten carbide core inside a lead envelope and the usual jacket. Its purpose is to penetrate hard targets such as parts of vehicles, light armor, etc., which would resist the regular ball-type cartridge with its pure lead filler.

Tracer bullets have a base cavity filled with a chemical mixture. This mixture contains a source of oxygen, and other materials which burn with a characteristic color. Some tracers use a combination which produces a brightly colored flame; red, green, or white being the colors most often used. Others leave a thin smoke trail behind. The main charge of the tracer composition is covered by an igniter charge, whose function is to transfer the flame from the burning powder gases to the tracer charge. Some tracers have another intermediate element, whose purpose is to provide a dim trace for the first 50–100 yards so that opponents cannot readily locate the shooter by watching the trace in reverse. The main use of the tracer is in machine guns, for which it is loaded in a ratio of 1 to 3–5 rounds of other types. This shows the gunner where his stream of fire is going and allows him to make the proper correction. Sometimes tracer is used by troop leaders to indicate an obscure target to others.

Incendiary bullets have a space in the nose filled with a mixture which is ignited by the heat of impact. Some use white phosphorus, but most modern types use powdered magnesium or similar metals. These are employed against inflammable targets, such as motor vehicles, aircraft, wood, cloth, buildings and the like.

Spotting or observing bullets are intended for target designation, giving a bright flash on striking. They may be no more than a special tracer type, or may have a small bursting charge with a percussion fuse. Some are intermediate between tracer and incendiary types.

Combinations are used extensively. These may be armor piercing-incendiary, armor piercing-tracer, incendiary-tracer, or combine all three functions. Others have a small charge of tear gas included in an armor-piercing bullet.

B.R.L.

Lewis, Colonel Berkeley R., *Small Arms and Ammunition in The United States Service, 1776–1865*, Washington, D.C., 1956.

Logan, Herschel C., *Cartridges*, Huntingdon, W.Va., 1948.

Peterson, Harold L., *The Treasury of the Gun*, New York, 1962 (*The Book of the Gun*, London, 1963).

Textbook of Small Arms, H.M. Stationery Office, London, 1929.

See also: BALLISTICS; BULLET MOLD; BURTON, JAMES HENRY; CARTRIDGE; MINIÉ BALL; SHOT.

BULLET MOLD

The bullet mold as a device for manufacturing bullets probably came into use about the time that lead began to be used for projectiles, sometime in the middle of the fourteenth century. It remained a major device for the manufacture of ammunition until machines were developed during the nineteenth century which swaged bullets faster and cheaper than they could be cast.

Little is known of the history and design of the first bullet molds. The earliest documentary references to them that have been discovered thus far occur in the accounts of the English Privy Wardrobe for the period 1373–75. These contain several entries of purchases such as "twelve iron ladles for casting lead pellets and ten brass molds for making them," but no further description which would indicate either size or design. Gang molds casting pilgrims' tokens have survived from this period, however, and it is logical to assume that bullet molds for small arms resembled them. Firearms themselves were scarce in these early years, and it was a period of experimentation with many types of projectiles which could not be cast in simple molds. Thus documentary references are scarce, and no actual specimens are known to exist.

After 1550 the bullet mold arrived on the scene in quantity, and the history becomes much clearer. Inventories of armories from this period indicate that it was the custom to provide a separate mold for each gun. Thus the armory of the Gonzaga family at Mantua, Italy, could list 140 bullet molds for musketoons and 1,750 bullet molds for arquebuses; and when Signor Vincenzo Bagno took out "115 arquebuses of the Spanish fashion" for his men, he also took 115 powder flasks and primers and 115 bullet molds.

Surviving molds of the sixteenth century indicate that they were normally gang molds, casting full-size balls for the gun, plus buckshot and swan shot of various sizes and sometimes other forms – teardrops, varieties of cones, and cylinders, to name a few. Both brass and iron molds were made. Usually they had long thin leaves with a hinge at one end and full metal handles at the other. Wooden grips do not seem to have been used. Sometimes the handles were pivoted so that they could fold back alongside the leaves and make a more compact unit for carrying. In molds casting a number of small balls at one time, the cavities were usually arranged within the leaves in two rows with pouring troughs on both top and bottom. Thus the molder could pour one row, let it stand for a moment, then turn his mold over and pour the other row. Because the leaves were so thin they broke easily and were subject to warping, which prevented a tight closure between the cavities.

With the seventeenth century, molds became simpler.

Gone were the myriad of projectile shapes sometimes found in sixteenth-century molds. The multi-leaved form also disappeared, and simple two-leaved molds became standard. The combination of cavities for full-size ball and various smaller sizes continued, but the mold leaves became thicker. They were still not thick enough, however, and seventeenth-century sites excavated in America have provided a number of broken fragments from molds of this type.

Most interesting of all for the seventeenth century is the appearance of the scissor-type mold. There is one in the Metropolitan Museum of Art which casts four balls and is equipped with a sprue cutter. Most of the scissor-type molds found in American colonial sites such as Jamestown, however, are simple affairs forged of iron with only one cavity, though also often with sprue cutters. A characteristic of these early types which sets them apart from the simple forms of the eighteenth and nineteenth centuries is the fact that the head has been forged around the cavity with thin walls on all sides. Apparently a hard metal core was used and the iron hammered around it, as contrasted with the solid forged block into which a cavity was cut with a cherry bit in the later types.

Another interesting scissor-type mold which apparently developed late in the seventeenth century was used for casting large balls for rampart guns or amusettes. These molds, with cavities 1–1½ inches in diameter, were often made with a cast brass head containing the single cavity, held in forged iron scissor handles. Usually the handles were designed for insertion into wooden grips.

The eighteenth century brought several interesting developments. The simpler iron scissor-type mold mentioned above became popular, especially for casting rifle bullets. The leaved mold casting both buckshot and ball remained popular, but the leaves became sturdier. The handles jutted out at a very characteristic angle and were proportionately short since they were universally designed for wooden grips. Both iron and brass were used, brass usually for the smaller molds such as would have been used by an individual owner, and iron for the large kinds which might cast up to twenty balls of .75 caliber. Some of the large gang molds were brass, however. In 1775, for instance, the Maryland Committee of Safety required "a pair of brass Molds for every Eighty Musquets to cast 12 Bullets on one Side, and on the other side, to cast Shot of such Size, as the Musket will chamber three of them . . ." In addition to the usual buck-and-ball combinations, another popular cavity arrangement offered four or even five balls of different calibers so that an individual owner might make balls for several guns with the one mold.

A final and seldom recognized development of the eighteenth century was the appearance in primitive form of the movable iron or steel sprue cutter containing the pouring trough and holes. In its final form this cutter is known to most students as it appears on Colt and other revolver molds and on most of the large nineteenth-century gang molds. In the early eighteenth century, however, it sometimes appeared on iron scissor-type molds which cast a number of balls. In these it was pivoted on the main pin and had a handle and locking device on its free end to help in making the cut. One such mold has been excavated by the National Park Service on the site of the English settlement at Fort Frederica, Georgia, and therefore dates from the 1740's.

The molds of the late eighteenth century and succeeding years are so well known that little comment is required. The scissor type in both brass and iron was made in a variety of forms with heads shaped as discs, cubes, cylinders, barrels and other designs. Gang molds became heavier and were better machined. The movable flat-plate sprue cutter became almost standard for leaved molds. Cylindro-conical projectiles, of course, became popular, including the hollow-based Minié type which required a movable plug at the bottom of the mold cavity.

One final kind of mold that should be mentioned comprises those made of stone. Such molds may, in fact, have been among the earliest types, though as yet there is no evidence of this. At any rate, they are known to have been popular during the seventeenth and eighteenth centuries and some, with cavities for cylindro-conical slugs, were used well after 1850. Soapstone, which is soft and easily cut, was the usual material. All known specimens were made in two rectangular pieces, usually with pins to hold them in the proper alignment when pouring. Some of these stone molds were undoubtedly used bare, but others were fastened in wooden frames to protect the hands.

The bullet mold was a necessity for the individual shooter as long as he prepared his own ammunition. For most, this lasted until the day of the metal-cased cartridge of the mid-nineteenth century. Even today, however, individual bullet molds are still being made. In fact, far better ones are available now than could be had during the years when men's lives regularly depended on the shot they produced. Today, however, they are the utensil of the hobbyist, the muzzle-loading enthusiast, and the handloader.   H.L.P.

Illustrations: pages 348–50.

See also: ACCESSORIES; BULLET.

BURTON, JAMES HENRY

James Henry Burton, missile designer and ordnance production expert, was born at Shenondale Springs, Virginia, on August 17, 1823. At the age of sixteen he entered a Baltimore machine shop to learn the trade and four years later obtained a job in the rifle works at the Harpers Ferry Armory. There his rise was rapid. The next year, 1845, he was appointed foreman, then Assistant Master Armorer, and finally Master Armorer, all within ten years.

It was while he was Assistant Master Armorer in 1849 that Burton perfected the American version of the Minié ball. Minié's original version had an iron cup in its base cavity which was driven forward by the force of the powder explosion to expand the bullet so that it would take the rifling. Burton's improvement changed the design so that this cup could be eliminated, thus making the projectile easier and cheaper to manufacture. The United States adopted Burton's projectile and introduced a series of arms designed to fire it in 1855.

That same year Burton terminated his association with the Harpers Ferry Armory and accepted an appointment as Chief Engineer of the Royal Small Arms Factory at Enfield, England. In 1860 he returned to America because of ill health, but when the Civil War broke out he accepted a commission as a lieutenant colonel of ordnance in the Confederate Army. In this position he expedited the production of arms, undertook a mission to Europe for the Confederate State Department, and designed a projectile for rifled cannon which was manufactured in the South. Meantime his version of the Minié ball had become the principal small arms projectile of the war.

After the war Burton accepted a position in England with a firm manufacturing machinery for a new Russian small-arms plant. He planned to go to Russia to assume technical direction of the factory when completed, but poor health again led him to return to Virginia in 1873. He died at Winchester, Virginia, on October 18, 1894. H.L.P.

See also: MINIÉ BALL.

CALIBER

The "caliber" of a firearm is the diameter of the bore; in a rifled gun it is measured between the lands, which are the ridges between the grooves in the barrel. In the United States, caliber is usually expressed in hundredths of an inch (.22, .30, etc.). In England it is usually expressed in thousandths of an inch (.270, .465, etc.). Most other countries use the metric system, expressing caliber in millimeters. The United States and Great Britain now use the metric system officially for calibers of military weapons, in connection with NATO standardization.

There is sometimes confusion about the term caliber as

used by the United States Navy. In such use, the caliber is still the bore diameter, but this unit is then used to measure barrel length, then referred to as so many calibers long. Thus a 5-inch, 50 caliber gun is one which has a 5-inch bore and a barrel 250 inches long, or 20 feet, 10 inches.

An older method stated firearm caliber in terms of the size of round lead ball which would fit. The size of the ball was expressed as the number of them contained in one pound. Thus a one ounce round ball would fit a 16-bore gun. Many of the older molds for casting round balls were marked with the fraction of a pound represented by one bullet. Sizes 54, 70, 90, and 120 were popular.

As shotguns varied in degree of choke as well as in the thickness of paper or brass cartridge cases, there used to be considerable variation between makers in the actual measurements of bores that were nominally the same. There is now in effect an international agreement among gunmakers which standardizes shotgun bore sizes or gauges:

Gauge	Bore diameter (inches)	Gauge	Bore diameter (inches)
1	1.669	19	.626
2	1.325	20	.615
3	1.157	21	.605
4	1.052	22	.596
5	.976	23	.587
6	.919	24	.579
7	.873	25	.571
8	.835	26	.563
9	.802	27	.556
10	.775	28	.550
11	.751	29	.543
12	.729	30	.537
13	.700	31	.531
14	.693	32	.526
15	.677	33	.520
16	.662	34	.515
17	.650	35	.510
18	.637	36	.506

B.R.L.

CALIVER

An English form of the French word *calibre*, first recorded in an inventory of 1568 referring to "Kalyvers, handgonnes, flaskes, etc." It is said to derive from the phrase *Harquebuse de calibre de Monsieur le Prince*, which indicated a weapon of standard bore as was ordered for use by the French Catholic Army before the battle of Montcontour in 1569. In 1590, the caliver was described by Sir John Smythe as "only a harquebuse; saving that it is of greater circuite or bullet than the other is of." In England,

however, by 1601, the caliver used by the army was the smallest of the three weapons fired from the shoulder; the musket and the bastard musket were heavier, longer, and of bigger bore.

The standard caliver of the early seventeenth century had a 3-foot barrel of 10 or 11 bore getting twenty or thirty shots from a pound of powder. It had either matchlock or snaphance ignition and was specifically the weapon of the smaller men in any regiment.   w.r.

Illustration: page 101.

CANE GUN

A cane, or walking stick, is by itself a fearsome weapon in the hands of a single-stick expert. A cane that is also a gun is potentially deadly, even in inexpert hands.

Some cane guns are true firearms and some are air guns. A few may actually be made of cane, but more are made of metal. When a cane is also a gun, the fact is often well hidden.

One interesting cane gun fired a bullet propelled by gunpowder, but had its striker mouth-blown by the shooter much as a dart is blown through a blowpipe by a primitive hunter. A cartridge was loaded in the chamber of the barrel, which ran from about the center of the perfectly straight cane to the ground end. A hollow tube containing a floating dart went back to the handle from the cartridge head. The handle was fitted with a screw-off cap. Remove the cap, raise the muzzle to let the dart slide back, and blow. The point of the dart detonated the primer in the special 7 mm. center-fire cartridge. This cane, when carried with the usual muzzle plug or cover, and with its silver cap in place on the handle, in no way appeared to be a firearm.

Cane guns were fairly common through the nineteenth century, when they were used chiefly for self-defense, although they then had some popularity with poachers as well.

Many of the cane guns of the late 1800's were not straight from end to end, as was the one described above. A popular model made by Remington for .22 and .32 rim-fires was offered with a curved handle. This was advertised for "Protection against Dogs and Highwaymen." (Earlier, Remington manufactured percussion-cap models.) A cartridge was inserted in the barrel chamber after the handle was pulled back "until a flat spring jumped up and prevented forward motion" of the handle. The action was enclosed in the handle, and the gun was cocked when the handle was drawn back. The spring catch, or stop, served as a rear sight. It and the almost hidden button trigger were all that served to reveal that the cane was a firearm.

Stress was often laid on a cane gun's value to taxidermists and ornithologists. The Remington advertisement stated: "Just the Thing for Taxidermists."

Cane guns made in sections frequently had one part a shoulder stock, which could be concealed under a coat and screwed to the barrel section at an appropriate moment. Such guns – even in flintlock – were used by poachers, especially where poaching had long been a livelihood for many.

Some cane firearms did not have barrels; they were hollow for only a short way at the handle end. When the curved handle was pulled off, a pistol, or perhaps a pepperbox, was presented.

Of the cane guns now found, some will be signed, but many will bear no maker's name. One of the early nineteenth-century makers whose signed cane guns were far-famed for more than a generation was John Day, of Barnstaple, Devon. Day was granted British Patent No. 4,861 in 1823 for the invention of his percussion-cap cane gun.

Cane guns discharging projectiles propelled by gas were in use early in the nineteenth century, and they continued in use at least to the end of the First World War. If the gas were other than air (if it were carbon dioxide, for instance), it was supplied in sturdy cylinders (see GAS GUN). If the gas were air, it was hand-pumped into the cane gun's air reservoir. Some experimental cane guns had the pump integral with the cane, but the commercially successful ones employed a separate pump (see AIR GUN). The spring-air-gun construction is unsuitable for canes, and therefore the pneumatic is the only type to be found – except, again, for an occasional experimental and unsuccessful model.

The air cane functions as does almost any other form of pneumatic gun. Pressure on a trigger, which cocks by turning a key, opens a valve and releases a burst of air from the air reservoir to send the projectile on its way. As with the great majority of pneumatics, the air reservoir is emptied only by repeatedly opening the valve. As many as twenty-five or thirty pulls on the trigger may be required to reduce the weapon to ineffectiveness.

A pneumatic air gun is a far more powerful weapon than a spring-air gun, and the bullets of the most powerful air canes give as great penetration and have as great shock effect as the bullets fired from any air guns used by infantrymen in warfare. The first shot from an air cane – with pressure fully built up, by hard work with a hand pump – may well deliver a muzzle velocity and penetration only a little below that which a .22 short rifle gives. Velocity falls only slightly at the second shot, but drops sharply after a few more shots.

Air canes came in the same shapes as firearm canes – with straight or bent handles – and they were bought with the same uses in mind, self-protection, poaching, small-game hunting.

Somewhat surprising is the fact that there was little disagreement among manufacturers as to the set of screw threads in the joint between the barrel and the reservoir sections. As a result, the reservoir section of one make would usually screw on to the barrel section of a different make.

When not in use as a weapon, the air cane gun was carried with its muzzle capped or with a tampion inserted, as was a gunpowder cane gun. In the case of the muzzle-loaded air cane, the tampion was a full-length ramrod kept in the barrel bore, rather than in thimbles.

The law regarding air canes, and air guns in general, varies widely in different countries. The air cane may be outlawed in one country or state – perhaps because it is a silent and deadly weapon, perhaps because it is a concealed weapon – or it may not even be subject to the restrictions placed on firearms (as it is not a true firearm).   L.W.

Illustrations: page 275.

Smith, Walter H. B., *Gas, Air and Spring Guns of the World*, Harrisburg, Pa., 1957.

Wesley, L., *Air-Guns and Air-Pistols*, New York and London, 1955.

Winant, Lewis, *Firearms Curiosa*, New York, 1955, 2nd edition 1961, and London, 1956.

Wolff, Eldon G., *Air Guns* (Milwaukee Public Museum Publications in History, No. 1), Milwaukee, 1958.

CAPPER

A magazine that holds a number of percussion caps and provides a quick and simple method of fitting each to the firearm nipple in turn. In an advertisement for his tape primer, Maynard wrote that "the act of priming the Cap gun is the most difficult the soldier has to perform in battle." The difficulty, which originated from the small size of the cap, became almost an impossibility when the soldier's hands were gloved, stiff with cold, or sweating from heat or excitement. The same reasons as were used to "puff" Maynard's primer led to the development of cappers in the second quarter of the nineteenth century.

Colonel Peter Hawker maintained that cap chargers were a French invention. He stated a preference for round cappers rather than the long type, which he found less pleasant to use and less efficient when loading a double gun, on which the advantage of using a capper was most pronounced. The favored "round chargers" are frequently shaped rather like a comma. At the tail is an opening with a gate to which the caps are fed one at a time by a spiral spring. While still within the gate the cap is engaged over the nipple and remains in position when the charger is pulled away either vertically, or, in the better sort, horizontally. At the top is a loop to hang it by a cord from a jacket button or the shot belt, a practice Hawker deplored as a "great annoyance." Round cappers of this type were recessed into the bases or sides of powder flasks by a number of makers, including G. and J. W. Hawksley.

English brass capper, the top plate removed to show the feed lever and the hook to keep the spiral spring under tension when loading

Colt capper of brass, made at Paterson, New Jersey, ca.1840

of Sheffield, and were even incorporated into gunlocks by the Frenchmen Lancry and Charoy. The best chargers, said by Hawker to have been invented by an Englishman, Captain Ward, were fitted with a dial to count the number of caps remaining. Another interesting French design of *ca.*1850 had a nipple primer fitted into the top of the capper.

The long capper, so disliked by Hawker, was a rectangular tube fitted with a manually operated feed lever to push the caps to the gate, or else with a spring feed. E. D.

Seely's United States patent for a musket capper, dated October 29, 1861, is of this type with two parallel tubes for caps.

A simpler, cheaper system was patented by Antoine Wollowicz in London on February 5, 1853. Rubber or leather strips were pierced with a series of small holes into which the caps could be pushed. The strip was easier to handle than the individual caps and could be used exactly as the metal tubular dispensers such as Seely's. An improvement over Wollowicz's design was made from a leather disc with holes and keyhole slots round the periphery to grip the caps. Verniaud and Spencer's United States patent of 1872 was similar except that it employed steel and rubber discs.   W.R.

Riling, Ray, *The Powder Flask Book*, New Hope, Penn., 1953.

CARABINE À TIGE

A muzzle-loading rifle invented by the French Colonel, later General, Louis Étienne de Thouvenin (1791–1882). A steel pillar, the *tige*, projected forward from the breech plug in the axis of the bore. The powder lay around the pillar against which the spherical bullet was driven with a heavy rammer to spread it into the rifling. Accumulated powder-fouling, the distortion to the ball, or a bent or fractured pillar caused inaccuracies which led to Delvigne's suggesting a conical bullet as a more suitable projectile (see RIFLES AND RIFLING). The rifle was also noisy to load and difficult to unload.

There is doubt about its actual date of invention, but Thouvenin's system did not receive official approval until 1841–42. Despite its faults, the rifle was introduced into the French service as the *Carabine modèle 1846*.

W.R.

Margerand, J., *Armement et Équipement de l'Infanterie Française du XVIe au XXe Siècle*, Paris, 1945.
Mordecai, Alfred, *Military Commission to Europe in 1855 and 1856; report of Major Alfred Mordecai of the Ordnance Department* (Senate Executive Document No. 60), Washington, D.C., 1860.
Peterson, Harold L., *The Treasury of the Gun*, New York, 1962 (*The Book of the Gun*, London, 1963).

See also: PILLAR BREECH.

CARBINE

A firearm similar to, but shorter and lighter than, a musket; the weapon of cavalry and lightly armed special troops. By 1559, Henry II of France employed light cavalry called *carabins*, armed with a pistol and a carbine described as three and a half feet long. The word never had the specific meaning that some writers have given it. A French inventory of 1620, for instance, described sixteen carbines, some with smoothbore barrels, some rifled, one at least with a flintlock and one with a wheel lock. During the eighteenth and nineteenth centuries, however, the term normally designated a weapon for cavalry, and therefore usually equipped with a sliding ring and bar for attachment to a shoulder sling. By 1630, its dimensions were standardized in England as 45 inches overall with a 30-inch barrel bored to take a ball of 24 to the pound "rowleing in." In the eighteenth century and subsequently, carbines were often carried by officers, artillerymen, light infantry and sappers, as well as by cavalry for which a full-bore musket and its ammunition were too heavy and clumsy. Today, "carbine" generally refers to a shortened version of a military rifle.   w.r.

CARCANO RIFLE

This rifle, which contains elements of several designs, was developed by Colonel Paraviccini and M. Carcano, the chief inspector of the Italian government arms plant at Turin. It has a modified Mauser bolt action and a Mannlicher-type in-line magazine fed with a six-round clip. The rifling is unusual in that it has a progressive twist commencing at the breech end with one turn in 19.3 inches and ending at the muzzle with one turn in 8.6 inches. The rifle, which is commonly called the Mannlicher Carcano, was adopted by Italy in 1891. It is chambered for the 6.5 × 52 mm. rimless M91/95 cartridge, which has a muzzle velocity of 2,395 feet per second with a 163-grain bullet.

The Carcano has a one-piece bolt with forwardlocking lugs like the Mauser. However, the bolt-handle position forward of the receiver bridge, and the safety, which is pushed forward and rotated to engage, are unlike the Mauser. The M1891 rifle has a 30.7-inch barrel, is 50.8 inches long and weighs 8.6 lb. It has a horizontal bolt handle and a one-piece stock in which a full-length cleaning rod is mounted.

Two carbine versions appeared about the same time as the rifle. The M1891 carbine has a bayonet which folds under the stock, and has a half-length stock; the M1891TS has a full-length stock and a bayonet lug. Both carbines have turned-down bolt handles and 17.7 inch barrels.

In 1938, Carcano rifles chambered for the 7.35 mm. cartridge were adopted by Italy; owing to the Second World War, however, the Italians did not completely change over to this caliber. Other models of the Carcano are carbine 91/24, carbine 38 and rifle 41.   j.e.s.

Illustration: page 182.

Smith, Walter H. B. and Joseph E., *The Book of Rifles*, 3rd edition, Harrisburg, Pa., 1963.

Smith, Walter H. B. and Joseph E., *Small Arms of the World*, 6th edition, Harrisburg, Pa., 1960.

CARTRIDGE

The term cartridge has been used to designate any disposable container for a single load for a firearm. In the beginning only a charge of powder was contained in a cartridge of wrapped paper, which was bitten or torn open by the soldier as he poured the powder down the barrel. The ball was loaded separately, and ignition was separate. By the end of the sixteenth century, however, the ball was being attached by a flange or a sprue in some instances and within a few years it had become the practice to wrap the ball inside the paper with the powder. Early in the eighteenth century this practice was standardized by most of the major European powers, and the older methods of carrying loose ammunition were completely superseded except for special weapons such as the rifle and some breechloaders which could not use packaged ammunition efficiently.

Still, the ignition remained separate – the spark from a wheel lock or one of the flint arms or the flash from a percussion compound through the nipple or touchhole. Cartridges were thus made of combustible materials such as paper or collodian or goldbeater's skin, or they might be of metal foil or other soft substances which could be cut or broken in the process of loading so that the powder would be exposed to the separate spark. Still others were cased in more durable materials such as metal or

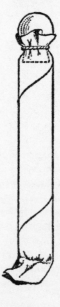

Sixteenth-century cartridge

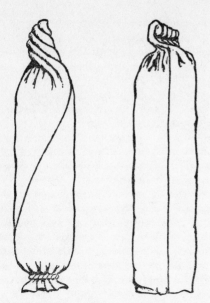

British (left) and French cartridges, ca.1750

hard rubber with holes for the entrance of the vital flame. Cartridges of this sort have been called "separate primed" by students, and they continued in use throughout the era of the American Civil War.

In the meantime, however, steps were being taken to produce the cartridge in the modern sense with primer, propellent charge and projectile all in one case, usually of metal, which conveniently seals the breech gas-tight as it discharges. It was a long, slow process, with many inventors working independently with slightly differing approaches, all attempting to use the new detonating compounds of the early nineteenth century. Because contemporary efforts were so widespread and varied, many conflicting statements and claims have been made. The statements which follow are matters of official record, but even as such do not always establish the real origin of an idea. The patentee may have pirated or purchased the idea from the true inventor, or acted as an agent.

Before percussion ignition, there were metallic cases to hold powder and ball, which were loaded into the gun and fired, using external ignition. But these should be classed as auxiliary breeches, forming a part of the gun. While paper cartridges were acceptable for muzzle-loaders, they were easily broken, absorbed moisture readily, and, most important, did not seal the breech joint well enough for breechloaders. The metallic cartridge inventors of the early nineteenth century sought a good breech seal more than a complete cartridge system. But in time all the essential elements were combined successfully.

In 1812, the versatile Swiss inventor Johannes Samuel

Pauly obtained a patent covering a center-fire obturating cartridge for a breech-loading gun. Pauly's invention made the first practical use of percussion compounds to ignite a complete cartridge. His cartridge case was heavy brass, forming its gas seal by its stopper-like head, which had at the center either a pellet of exposed fulminate or a small nipple and cap. The round ball was inserted into a counterbored case mouth. Pauly's shotgun cartridge was really only the head of the case just described. The body was made of a rolled tube of paper having a thick perforated wad glued into one end. The head had a protruding screw with a central flash hole, on to which the body wad was twisted. The powder and shot charges were then placed in the tube, a top wad holding them in place.

The next major step came from Galy-Cazalat, who had a French patent in 1826 covering a complete cartridge in the modern sense. It consisted of a parchment case containing an inside center-fire primer in its base. The case material was unsatisfactory, leaking gas somewhat. It did work, however, and some military arms were made on that system in France. The idea of a complete expendable cartridge has been revived in recent years.

In 1829 Clement Pottet patented a cartridge having a removable base with a pocket for fulminate, or as an alternative, a cap on a base nipple. When combined with his 1855 improvement, this invention became the modern shotgun shell.

In 1831 Augustus Demondion of London patented a breechloader which used a detonating tube as part of its cartridge. It stuck out at the rear, where it was struck by an unconventional hammer-mainspring combination. This eventually failed for lack of a perfect gas seal. Paper was just not good enough.

Another 1831 patent was J. A. Robert's, for a case with priming extending across its flat head. By omitting the composition in the center, this became the familiar rim-fire cartridge.

In 1835 Lefaucheux introduced a new breechloader and its special reloadable cartridge, which made a double-barrel breechloading shotgun practical for the first time. His cartridge had a paper case with brass cup-like head. A percussion cap laid inside against the lower part of the head (when chambered) was struck by a pin entering the head from the opposite side, where it was hit by the fall-

Pin-fire cartridge

ing hammer. There was no internal reinforcing in this cartridge, which therefore sometimes failed at the pin hole from a heavy charge. A fine wire passing through two holes in the head was all that held the cap and pin in place.

The pin-fire cartridge was brought to its modern form by Houiller in 1846. He added internal reinforcement in the form of a heavy perforated wad which held the primer and pin in place.

In 1838 Johann Nikolaus Von Dreyse perfected his needle gun, the first breech-loading military rifle using a complete cartridge. This cartridge has a bullet of less than bore diameter, held in a paper carrier, or sabot, which engages the rifling. The sabot's base has a cavity containing fulminate, which is fired by a long slim firing pin (the needle) passing through the powder charge. Insufficient primer support caused misfires in many of the early cartridges. In 1848 Prussia adopted the needle gun and used it with great success in several subsequent wars. Italy, Norway, Russia, and Sweden also tried needle guns.

John Hanson and William Golden obtained a British patent in 1841, covering a bullet with fulminate in its base cavity. The drawings also show a small case attached to the ball, with priming composition alone or with both priming and powder.

Flobert patented essentially the same thing in France in 1849, using this cartridge in his simple, well-known breech action. Really, this simply used a small round ball stuck into a percussion cap. The priming was enough to send the ball a short distance, sufficient for target practice.

The United States patent taken out by Walter Hunt in 1848 covered a hollow-base ball filled with powder and sealed by a perforated base wad. It was fired by external priming. His idea was patented a year earlier in England by his agent, Stephen Taylor.

Two new shotgun actions were developed in England early in the 1850's. That of Joseph Needham in 1852 was a needle-fire type. The cartridge was a paper tube closed at its base by a zinc-reinforced wad. The firing pin went through a small hole in the base and fired the cap inside. These cartridges had the disadvantage that they could not be reloaded, and the action leaked enough gas to make trouble after a while. Charles W. Lancaster's gun of 1854, on the other hand, had a gas-tight drawn copper case – the first large one successfully drawn. It had inside center-fire priming, fired through the thin center of the base. This one could not be reloaded either, hence was expensive to shoot.

Daw's English patent for a shotgun shell was really a minor improvement on the older Pottet type. It differed only in the shape of the tiny anvil inside the primer. However, Daw controlled the British shotgun shell field for some time on the basis of this patent.

Smith and Wesson received an American patent in 1854 for a cartridge intended for use in their Volcanic pistols. This was a copper case having a center-fire primer held in an internal metal disc. It never worked well, and they finally used a different cartridge, patented in 1856, with a hollow ball holding powder and primer in its base.

In 1860 Smith and Wesson patented a rim-fire cartridge similar to those made today. It differed from the Flobert version in having a definite rim, instead of just tapering under the head. Though it was not patented till 1860, they had used this cartridge in the small revolvers they began to make in 1857–58.

G. W. Morse's 1856–58 patents covered the major features of the center-fire cartridge as now made. He showed a rubber disc to close the base, another with solid base and rubber around the cap, and a final form using only the cap for obturation. Oddly enough, though he favored the last type, most of the cartridges he made were the first type, with rubber base. Morse said this was because the government required him to use musket caps, the flanges of which prevented him from using the better construction.

Though metallic cartridges were the main trend of development, many other materials were tried and used extensively. The period 1850–65 was one of specially rapid and varied development. The American Civil War gave a great impetus to inventors of arms as well as of ammunition. New ideas for breechloaders often called for new and special cartridges to go with them. Many involved external ignition, the cartridge having a small hole in its base to pass the flame of a regular or Maynard-type percussion cap. Such cartridges were made of plain or nitrated paper, foil, linen, silk, and other fibers. Others were made by encasing a pressed powder charge in membrane from pig gut, collodian, or varnished fabric. These last mentioned were often encased in a paper tube for protection. A little cloth tear strip was provided to help remove the case when ready to use the cartridge.

Following Professor Schönbein's discovery of guncotton in 1846, that product was tested as a propellant for small arms ammunition. Though it could be made to work very nicely under proper conditions, its tendency to detonate with pressures much over normal made it unsafe to use. In tests at the Washington Arsenal, half the usual charge gave normal velocity with little or no fouling. A double charge burst the barrel, however. Further development was required before smokeless powders could be used.

By 1866 good rim-fire and center-fire cartridges were being turned out by the million in Europe and the United States. Further development had to await the perfection of deep-drawing techniques before longer cases could be produced. During the American Civil War some large rim-fire cartridges were made in great quantities. This type was perfected in the United States and described in 1867, in a report on the Paris Exposition of that year, as the "American" cartridge. Sizes as large as one-inch Gatling had been made by 1865. The great failing of the rim-fire type was that it could not be reloaded. This was an important consideration among the military, so when an acceptable reloadable center-fire type became available, the rim-fire disappeared from military use.

In the late 1860's two different types of cartridge case were developed. That produced in 1866–69 by United States arsenals was inside-primed, either with the Martin bar anvil, or Colonel S. V. Benét's cup system. Frankford Arsenal had also experimented with outside-primed cases, one with a brassfoil, spirally-wound body and an iron or brass head being patented in 1863 by Colonel Silas Crispin. Its head had a reinforced primer pocket, fairly similar to the modern shotgun shell. In 1866 Colonel Hiram Berdan patented a reloadable center-fire cartridge, which used a relatively wide cap, and incorporated its anvil in the metal forming the primer pocket. About the same time, Colonel Edward M. Boxer, Superintendent of the Royal Laboratory at Woolwich, developed a different system, using a separate small anvil as part of the primer. Oddly enough, the British Boxer primer is now the only kind made in the United States, while the American Berdan type is almost exclusively used in Europe. The prevalence of reloading in the United States influenced this situation, as the Berdan primer is not as easily removed from a fired case.

The first center-fire cartridges were made about the same as the rim-fires. That is, their case was punched up from a brass or copper cup, then the head end formed and folded to make the rim. This was suitable for the first, rather weak, rim-fires, but as cases became longer to obtain higher velocities with the smaller-caliber bullets then introduced, the pressures became too great for this kind of construction. Much experimenting was done, notably at the Frankford Arsenal, to reinforce the head area so as to eliminate failures at the rim. Eventually a solid head was devised in which the rim was of continuous metal and the primer completely enclosed in the head, instead of being in a balloon-like pocket folded in. This got rid of most of the failures in the primer and head areas. One of the first commercial cartridges made in this manner was for the caliber .50–115 Bullard rifle.

The development of the West in America in the decades following the Civil War provided a further incentive to arms and ammunition makers. Many powerful black-powder cartridges were available for Wesson, Sharps, Ballard, and Remington rifles. Later, Winchester introduced a single-shot rifle which became very popular. Many cartridges for these rifles were available with paper patches on their bullets, for long-range hunting and for competitive shooting. During the same period British activities in Africa and India opened a great market for big game hunting rifles and ammunition; many of the cartridges were for double rifles, never popular in America. The double-barreled rifle of large caliber tended to channel cartridge development into straight-type cases, as the chambers of such rifles could not be much greater than bore diameter. At the same time, the trend in America was to the bottle-necked case type.

The first of the modern rimless cartridges, in which the extractor engages a groove cut into the head instead of acting on a projecting rim, was adopted in 1888 by Germany for the 8 mm. rifle then standardized. Such rims had been patented in England in 1866 and in the United States in 1872, but had never before been used extensively. Of course, almost every conceivable shape had been tried. Some cartridges were made with no rim or groove at all – such as the initial series for the Bergmann pistols. Another short-lived type, introduced by Burton, had its head beveled off, without any rim or groove.

The old form of paper-wrapped small arms ammunition remained the main military type till about 1865. During the Civil War, the United States had tried many new breech-loading carbines, using special cartridges, with great success. All governments were convinced that the future lay in that direction, so they all began to convert to breechloaders, using at first the older large-caliber rifles on hand, before changing to entirely new models. Most of these first conversions used cartridges with calibers between .58 and .70. A few were rim-fires, but these were short-lived and in a year or two were displaced by new center-fire types. Initially they were unable to draw cases of copper or brass over an inch long. When this technical limitation was overcome, longer cases with correspondingly greater powder charges were possible. This led, in turn, to smaller calibers, as the muzzle energies could be kept at the desired level with lighter bullets and greater velocity.

This pattern of change, first altering muzzle-loaders to breechloaders, using the old calibers, then through a series of reductions, was the common one. The Germans made an abrupt change from the old needle gun, first to 11mm., then to 8mm. (later called 7.92mm.), which was retained throughout the Second World War. France first altered some old rifles by a Snider breech system, popularly called Tabbatière. In most countries the evolution was similar – first something between .50 and .60 calibers, then something in the .43–.45 range, then down to about .30. In the 1890's there was quite a flurry of interest in very small calibers, some as small as 5 mm. being tried by a few governments. The United States Navy adopted briefly a 6mm. rifle, while others went to 6.5mm.

Smokeless powder was the source of the last great advance in ammunition. The first cartridge using it in America was that for the Model 1892 Krag-Jørgensen rifle. Early types of this powder gave short barrel life, and at the same time combined with the material of the bullet jacket to form serious metal fouling in the bores. Adding

British .303 cartridge, a typical modern centerfire cartridge

tin to the powder helped to reduce fouling, but it was not really eliminated till the 1920's when gilding metal was generally adopted as jacket material.   B.R.L.

Illustration: page 45.

Daw, George H., *The Central-Fire Cartridge before the Law Courts, the Government, and the Public; showing who introduced the system into England, who has improved it, who has benefited by it and who ought to be rewarded for it*, London, 1867.

Lewis, Colonel Berkeley R., *Small Arms and Ammunition in the United States Service, 1776–1865*, Washington, D.C., 1956.

Logan, Herschel C., *Cartridges*, Huntingdon, W.Va., 1948.

White, Henry P., and Munhall, Burton D., *Cartridge Identification*, 2 vols, Washington, D.C., 1948–50.

See also: BERDAN, HIRAM; BULLET; BURTON, JAMES HENRY; LEFAUCHEUX; PAULY, JOHANNES SAMUEL; POTTET, CLEMENT; PRIMER.

CARTRIDGE BOX

This rather loose designation for military accoutrements designed for carrying cartridges on the body of the soldier must include both the cartridge pocket and the pouch, as these terms are found to be influenced as much by language and official designation as by their shape. Regardless of varied style, they all have the feature of being suspended from the shoulder or waist, by belting or harness.

The development of the cartridge box naturally follows that of weapons and ammunition. Details of early cartridge use are obscure. It is unlikely that paper cartridges were popular before the advent of the wheel lock early in the sixteenth century, for lighted matches would present a threat of accidental ignition to paper-wrapped charges. In the mid-sixteenth century, cartridges were carried in a patron, a small metallic box containing a block with about five drilled holes.

As the early soldier was not generally armed with so expensive and delicate a weapon as the wheel lock, it is with the development of flint arms that the cartridge, and its box, became tactically important. Gustavus Adolphus of Sweden is popularly credited with introducing the widespread use of cartridges by infantry. A description of a mid-seventeenth-century Swedish box suggests that they were flat leather bags with three or four compartments.

A late-seventeenth-century French accoutrement illustrated in St-Rémy's *Mémoires d'Artillerie* suggests that this flat shape was still in prevalent military use, but rather than cartridges, seven or eight metal chargers were carried by French troops until the adoption of the paper cartridge about 1704. This bag was suspended from the shoulder together with a powder flask and bayonet. As late as 1800, the British Royal Regiment of Artillery used a flat pouch suspended from the shoulder with a wooden block bored for nine cartridges.

The first use of drilled wooden blocks is obscure. An early specimen exists bearing the cipher of George II of England, placing it between 1727 and 1760. It consists merely of a wooden block with fourteen bored holes, and a leather cover and waist-belt loops. This assembly was often slung from the left shoulder during the Seven Years War. The French are known to have used wooden blocks in leather pouches about 1754.

The usual regulation military method for suspension of the cartridge box during the eighteenth and early nineteenth centuries was by a sling from the left shoulder, the box resting on the right hip. Horse troops, light infantry and militia were often equipped with boxes on the waist belt having nine to twenty holes in their blocks; some of plain wooden blocks with covers, others with their blocks completely covered in leather, and a variety having "twelve tin pipes" are known to have existed in 1778.

Generally, the military cartridge box had, by the period of the American Revolution, 1775–83, progressed to a closer fit around a large wooden block with from twenty-four to thirty holes of about three-quarters of an inch in diameter. The principal military powers often had metallic insignia applied to the protective flaps.

Scarcity of leather during the Revolution forced the Americans into such expedients as the use of linen for slings, and the fabrication, in 1777–8, of tin canisters, slung from the shoulder. These were found efficient, being smaller than the conventional box, yet providing portage for 36 cartridges, laid horizontally in fours. They also gave fine protection from rain and accidental ignition, because of their close-fitting tops.

Along with the use of wooden blocks, which continued far into the nineteenth century, tin began often to be used beneath the block to fashion a reservoir compartment for ammunition, and eventually for replacing the block entirely by clustering tin pipes. In this period large boxes were also worn on the front of the waist belt, but, owing to their considerable weight, they were usually supported from the shoulder by one or two straps.

By 1850, tin inserts of various patterns fitted in sturdy, well-made leather boxes typified most box construction. These were designed for forty to fifty rounds of ammunition, and were still suspended from the left shoulder for line infantry and from the waist belt for light infantry. Cavalry carbine boxes were often suspended from the carbine slings themselves, as had, in many cases, been done earlier.

The mid-nineteenth century brought rapid improvements in firearms. The cartridge boxes of many nations retained the drilled block, tin pipes and open pouch, now fleece lined, for accommodating the newly developed metallic cartridges for single-shot weapons. Leather and web loops were also frequently used. The Blakeslee box, *ca.*1864–5, for quick-loading the Spencer repeaters, is worthy of special mention as a prototype of special pockets and pouches for magazines of a later era, since it held six or more tubes, each carrying seven rounds for the magazine in the butt of the arm.

Two major changes came in this period. Packing of ammunition in compartmented cardboard containers led to the abandonment of box liners of any type, and dissat-

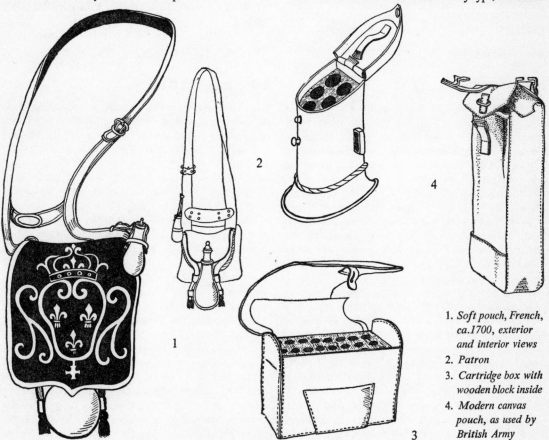

1. *Soft pouch, French, ca.1700, exterior and interior views*
2. *Patron*
3. *Cartridge box with wooden block inside*
4. *Modern canvas pouch, as used by British Army*

isfaction with the heavy single box resulted in serious efforts to distribute the weight of ammunition about the body and counter the weight of the pack. In America the web cartridge belt was preferred, and the cartridge box became reduced in size and restricted to ceremonial use; but most nations, until well into the twentieth century, used leather boxes, clip pouches or pockets suspended from shoulder harness in pairs or more. Canvas and woven web equipments designed for cartridges in clips were favored in the British and American services during this later period, and with the adoption of many quick-firing weapons have recently become simply large pouches for box magazines. These are usually harnessed to the body high and to the front.   R.L.M.

Lewis, Colonel Berkeley R., *Small Arms and Ammunition in the United States Service, 1776–1865*, Washington, D.C., 1956.

Margerand, J., *Armement et Équipement de l'Infanterie Française du XVIe au XXe Siècle*, Paris, 1945.

Peterson, Harold L., *Arms and Armor in Colonial America, 1526–1783*, Harrisburg, Pa., 1956.

CASES

See: ACCESSORIES.

CHAMBERS SYSTEM

The idea of loading several charges into one gun barrel so that they could be fired one after the other can be traced back to the sixteenth century. The easiest method was to use balls with holes drilled through them and filled with gunpowder. A number of them could be inserted in a barrel, separated by charges of gunpowder, so that when the front charge was ignited the flame fed back into the charge behind and the remaining charges went off one after the other in the fashion of a roman candle fire-work. The great disadvantage of the system was the lack of control over the firing once it had commenced. Never-theless, it was continually re-invented and tested until the breechloader became supreme.

One of the many "inventors" was Joseph G. Chambers of Pennsylvania, who took out a patent in 1813 for a system of "repeating gunnery" which was, once again, simply the old "roman candle" method. The United States Navy and the Commonwealth of Pennsylvania ordered muskets, rifles, pistols and swivel guns of the Chambers type, and they were used against the British forces on the Great Lakes in 1814 during the War of 1812. The muskets were loaded with eleven balls and the pistols with five or six. The swivels had seven barrels each con-taining thirty-two balls. The small arms were fired by

conventional flintlocks; the swivels were ignited by a match at the muzzle.

The Chambers gun had the advantage of being fitted with two locks. The front lock set off the multiple charges but the last charge at the breech was isolated by a solid ball and could be fired independently by a lock in the normal position. This meant that ordinary muskets could easily be converted and still be used as single-shots. The theory has been advanced that late versions of the Cham-bers system for small arms had sliding locks, but this is hotly disputed by other students.

One of the men engaged in making Chambers guns, John Bland, a black-and-white smith of Philadelphia, came to London in 1815 and persuaded the Ordnance to convert a Tower musket for trial. Although the Ordnance rejected the gun, it has been preserved at the Rotunda, Woolwich – the only known specimen of a Chambers musket. One of the swivel guns survives at Liège, Belgium.
                                                    H.L.B.

Illustrations: pages 183, 283.

Blackmore, Howard L., "Chambers Repeating Flintlock" in *The American Rifleman*, Sept. 1958.

See also: ESPIGNOLLE; REPEATING ARMS.

CHARLEVILLE

Charleville, on the banks of the Meuse, is one of the towns of the old province of Champagne, situated on the Bel-gian frontier. It was founded by Charles I, Duke of Nevers (1580–1637). This prince was the grandson of Frederick II, Duke of Mantua, and the son of Louis de Gonzaga, who had been brought up at the court of Henry II of France. Louis de Gonzaga had become Duke of Nevers in 1565 by his marriage to Henrietta of Clèves, heiress of the duchy. With the death of the last Gonzaga, the princip-ality of Charleville reverted finally to the French Crown and became, until the Revolution, a fief of the Condé family.

On one of his journeys, Louis XIV, inspecting his fort-resses in the northeast to check their condition, went to Charleville, and it was in this town that he signed the patent founding the Comédie Française, on August 18, 1680.

Attracted by the privileges granted by Duke Charles de Gonzaga, workers from Liège founded the first armories of the town. From the start, these men concentrated on producing work of high quality. Therefore Louvois, the Secretary of State for War, wrote to the town authorities of Charleville in 1667 ordering them to reserve for the king all arms produced in the principality. Louis XIV had

Plate 2

Wheel lock musket made in Munich by the court artists of the Duke of Bavaria. The barrel, lock and mounts are chiseled in low relief with figure subjects against a gold ground and further enriched with gold dots. On the barrel are three panels, each with a classical god under a balda-chino, separated by longitudinally fluted areas. Only the first of these panels is shown in the photograph. The lock plate is chiseled with a bear hunt. The stock of snakewood is inlaid with delicate compositions of scrollwork and foliage in white staghorn. The steel chiseling is the work of Daniel Sadeler; the stock is signed by Hieronymus Borstorffer. South German, *ca.*1620.

Wallace Collection, London.

just created the Royal Magazine of the Bastille, whose supply was the responsibility of a general contractor for the whole kingdom. To arm their companies, commanding officers had to apply solely to the royal magazines of the provinces, which were in turn supplied from the central magazine of the Bastille.

The persistence of an arms contractor of the town, Toussaint Fournier, combined with the support of Louvois, resulted in the establishment of a royal magazine at Charleville; this was to become a "Royal Manufactory" in 1688, and the first of the royal manufactories of France.

The term "Charleville" is often used by American collectors to designate the French infantry musket Model 1763, which was produced at Charleville as well as at other royal manufactories.   CL.B.

CHASSEPOT, ANTOINE ALPHONSE

Antoine Alphonse Chassepot was born at Mutzig in 1833 and died at Paris in 1905. He was the French inventor of the breech-loading rifle adopted by the French Army in 1866 and used by France throughout the Franco-Prussian War. The bolt-action Chassepot is called a needle gun, but it is unlike its forerunner, the bolt-action Dreyse rifle, in that the needle does not drive through, or even into, the powder charge before striking the fulminate, as in the Dreyse. The Chassepot needle merely pierces the base of the combustible cartridge sufficiently to enter the open end of an inverted percussion cap and detonate the cap's fulminate. (The ignited fulminate passes through holes in the top of the cap and fires the gunpowder.)

Chassepot took up his father's vocation, gunsmithing, and entered government service in 1858, attaining the rank of Principal in 1864 when attached to the national manufactory at Châttelerault. He designed his first breech-loading rifle in 1863. For his Model 1866 rifle he was decorated and became a Chevalier of the Legion of Honor.

Before the Chassepot rifle was used in combat, experiments showed that its bullets produced extraordinarily large exit wounds when fired into carcasses of animals, but reports by doctors who treated Garibaldians hit by Chassepot bullets in the sanguinary engagement at Mentana proved that wounds in living men were less frightful.

The Chassepot was quick to foul, with, in consequence, difficult reloading of its long, soft, self-consuming cartridge. It was complicated and lacked durability, and it was expensive. Still, because of the gun's breech construction, and also because of its cartridge's construction, the Chassepot had much better obturation than the Dreyse. With its bullet of smaller caliber, it had longer range and better accuracy, but its small bore was harder to keep clean. Its lighter weight made it easier to carry, but that light weight made its recoil objectionable. The question of which gun, the Dreyse or the Chassepot, was on the whole the better, is still a matter of debate.

Despite the faults evident both in the French Chassepot and the German Dreyse, those guns proved beyond doubt in the Franco-Prussian War that even imperfect breechloaders were much to be preferred to muzzle-loaders in a military campaign.

After the invention of the Dreyse in Germany but before the acceptance of the Chassepot in France, the Chatauvillard needle gun was patented in England, in 1849, and the Needham was produced in the early 1850's. The Needham's percussion cap primer was positioned much as was the Chassepot's – and so was the Chatauvillard's, except that the Chatauvillard's cap had its open end toward the bullet.

In 1874 the Chassepot was modified for use with metallic cartridges – and became the Gras rifle.   L.W.

Blanch, H. J., *A Century of Guns*, London, 1909.

Greener, William W., *The Gun and Its Development*, 9th edition, London, 1910.

Marks, Edward C. R., *The Evolution of Modern Small Arms and Ammunition*, London, 1898.

Ommundsen, H., and Robinson, Ernest H., *Rifles and Ammunition and Rifle Shooting*, London and New York, 1915.

Winant, Lewis, *Early Percussion Firearms*, New York, 1959, and London, 1961.

See also: BREECHLOADERS; CARTRIDGE; DREYSE, JOHANN NIKOLAUS VON; GRAS RIFLE; NEEDLE GUN.

CHOKE

See: BALLISTICS; FOWLING PIECE.

COLLIER REVOLVER

See: REVOLVER.

COLT, SAMUEL

History has already proved Samuel Colt to be one of the really significant contributors to the development of firearms. It would be difficult to name any one man in the field who was more versatile than Colt or who accomplished so many notable achievements in such a short span of time.

Born at Hartford, Connecticut, the son of Christopher and Sarah Caldwell Colt, on July 19, 1814, the boy early exhibited characteristics of promotional enterprise and inventiveness that were to see him become one of the industrial giants of his day. Throughout his early years he aspired to invent, to become a leader and become successful financially. He fulfilled each one of these aspirations.

Exactly how Colt hit upon the idea for his revolver is a matter for conjecture, but it probably stemmed from interest in earlier models of other inventors, giving him the stimulus to make improvements and bring forth his own design. The idea of a hand revolving cylinder gun was anything but new in Colt's time.

With the aid of some working drawings and pilot models produced by Anson Chase of Hartford, Colt applied for an English patent covering his invention, which was granted him on December 18, 1835.

Essentially, the patentable features consisted of the fact that upon bringing the hammer to full cock, the five-shot cylinder, revolving on an arbor fixed to the breech, was rotated simultaneously and locked in proper alignment to fire.

This patent and the subsequent American one issued on February 25, 1836, were much more encompassing than the description given here, and covered in detail the indexing and locking of the cylinder, the fact that the nipples of each percussion chamber were isolated, a description of the "lifter and ratchet" mechanism, etc.

Refined pilot models were produced by John Pearson and his workmen in Baltimore, and Colt was ready to capitalize on his idea.

Suffice it to say that these patents stood the test of time and were defended successfully until they expired in 1857. Thus it can be seen that Colt's success came neither through piracy nor fluke.

The Colt Patent Arms Manufacturing Company was chartered at Paterson, New Jersey, on March 5, 1836, only a few weeks after the United States patent had been issued, and had $230,000 capital pledged – a tremendous sum for those days, again proving Colt's versatility.

Now, Colt needed orders, and substantial ones at that. As in modern times, government contracts were a must, if the venture was to prosper.

Colt spread himself thinly, dividing his efforts between the production tooling of the factory, trying to keep the stockholders calm and attempting to interest the government in his invention.

The latter task was as great a problem then as it is today. Ordnance officials were chary of new ideas, particularly of weapons that might malfunction under conditions of hard usage in the field.

While his arms won awards for excellence in the period, governmental orders were not forthcoming, until a small order for fifty Paterson eight-shot rifles was issued in 1838 for use in the Seminole Indian War. Another small contract for five-shot Paterson revolvers was issued by the Texas Navy, but neither was enough to support the Paterson enterprise. The high price of Colt's firearms was curtailing civilian sales, despite herculean efforts by Colt, and the result was inevitable. Hounded by his stockholders and creditors, he liquidated the Paterson venture in late 1842 and early 1843.

However, the modest government and Texas orders, and trial presentation pieces placed with important personages, began to bear fruit.

In Florida, as in Texas, Indians used to charging in for the kill after a single army volley were decimated by the soldiers who had the advantage of the multi-shot fire power of Colt's guns. Here was something really new in weaponry.

Field commanders were high in their praise, and Captain Samuel H. Walker of the United States Dragoons, stationed in Texas, who had purchased Paterson revolvers, made significant design suggestions to Colt for a heavier, stronger revolver, more suited to military use.

Colt, undaunted by previous setbacks, and still owner of his patents, went to Hartford, and by assigning his contract, which was the result of initial government approval, enlisted the aid of Eli Whitney Jr. to produce in 1847 the renowned "Walker" model of his revolver.

Helped by the Mexican War and expansion towards the West, Colt was successful in obtaining further government contracts and establishing his own factory in Hartford in 1848.

From there, he followed the road to success and wealth that was terminated only by his untimely death, at the age of forty-eight, in 1862. Not only did he become the largest and most influential individual manufacturer of revolvers in the world, but he incorporated both modern machinery and mass-production methods in his factory.

Colt was an inventor, an engineer, a man who could consistently choose the right person for the right job, a super-salesman and merchandiser and a man with both courage and foresight. He had his faults, and lack of modesty was one of them. Nevertheless, historians will search far to find one man who did as much to shape the course of the development of firearms as did Samuel Colt.

J.S. DU M.

Rohan, Jack, *Yankee Arms Maker*, New York, 1935.

See also: COLT REVOLVER; REVOLVER.

COLT REVOLVER

Commencing with the first guns manufactured at Paterson, New Jersey, in 1836, Colt produced his single-action percussion revolvers in three general sizes: pocket, usually in caliber .31, but sometimes in .28; belt, normally in caliber .36; and holster in caliber .44 – the latter being designed primarily for military sales, while the former sizes were directed at the civilian market. A variety of barrel lengths were produced as standard, usually in the two smaller sizes of percussion pistols.

Models are listed in order of introduction. Dates and numbers are approximate. Paterson models were made in the New Jersey plant, Walker models in the Whitneyville, Connecticut, factory of Eli Whitney, Jr., and the remainder of the models first at the Pearl Street shop in Hartford, Connecticut, and after 1855 at the South Meadow factory in Hartford, still in existence today after rebuilding in 1864, or at the factory in London, England. Some collector designations for various models are listed in parenthesis. Oddities and non-standard items of small production are not listed, nor are long arms.

Paterson models: 1836–42; 2,000 produced in calibers .28, .31, .34 and .36.

Walker Model: 1847; 1,100 produced in caliber .44.

Old Model Army (*Dragoon*): 1847–62; 21,000 produced in caliber .44 (700 being made with English markings).

Old Model Pocket Pistol (1848 *Baby Dragoon; Wells Fargo*): 1847–49; 11,000 produced in caliber .31.

Old Model Pocket Pistol (1849 *Pocket Model*): 1849–75; 330,000 produced in caliber .31. The London factory (1853–59) produced 11,000.

Old Model Navy Pistol (*Navy Belt Model* 1851): 1850–72; 215,000 produced in caliber .36, with an additional 40,000 made in the London factory (1853–57).

New Model Pocket Pistol (*Root* 1855 *Sidehammer*): 1853–72; 40,000 produced in calibers .265 (.28) and .31.

New Model Army Pistol (1860 *Army Model*): 1860–72; 200,000 produced in caliber .44.

New Model Navy Pistol (1861 *Round Barrel Navy*): 1861–72; 38,000 produced in caliber .36.

New Model Police Pistol (1862 *Belt Model*): 1862–72; 25,000 produced in caliber .36.

New Model Pocket Pistol of Navy Caliber (1853 (*erroneous*) *Pocket*): 1863–72; 12,000 produced in caliber .36.

SINGLE-ACTION CARTRIDGE MODELS

Transitional models: Conversion to cartridge by Thuer's patent or by Richard's or Mason's patents of standard percussion models, primarily in belt and holster sizes and in .38 and .44 rim-fire calibers. Approximately 5,000 produced 1868–72.

Single-Action Army Model (*Peacemaker, Frontier*): 1873–1940; 360,000 produced, varying calibers and 3–16-inch barrel lengths. Production resumed 1955 and continuing.

Bisley Model (*Single-Action Target*): 1896–1912; 45,000 produced in various calibers.

DOUBLE-ACTION CARTRIDGE MODELS

Double-Action Lightning Model: 1877–1910; 40,000 produced in .32, .38, and .41 calibers.

Double-Action Army (*Frontier*) *Models of* 1878 *and* 1902: 1877–1905; 47,000 produced in various calibers.

In the period 1871–90, single-action, single-shot "Derringers," "Old Line" and "New Line" pocket and "Police" and "House" (including "Cloverleaf") model cartridge revolvers were produced in five basic calibers. The "Derringer" line was not discontinued until 1912. The era of the swing-out cylinder revolvers followed.   J.S. DU M.

Illustrations: pages 172–3, 320 (plate 8), and endpapers.

Haven, Charles T., and Belden, Frank A., *A History of the Colt Revolver*, New York, 1940.

Parsons, John E., *The Peacemaker and its rivals*, New York, 1950.

Serven, James E., *Colt Firearms, 1836–1960*, Santa Ana, Cal., 1954.

Wilson, J. Larry, and du Mont, John S., *Samuel Colt Presents*, Hartford, Conn., 1961.

See also: COLT, SAMUEL.

COMBINATION WEAPON

As here arbitrarily used, the term refers to a combination of a firearm either with a different weapon or with some implement, tool, or utensil. Excluded are combinations of two weapons neither of which is a firearm (as a bow with a spear). Most frequently the combination is of a gun with a cutting or piercing weapon. Sometimes the firearm is the primary weapon – as is the case when a dagger is affixed to a pistol or revolver – but in many cases the firearm is secondary.

Combination weapons came into wide use in the early days of firearms, when they were often combined with such weapons as battle-axes, maces, halberds. Some of these old weapons were reasonable enough – a gun with a shield for defense, or a sword for offense; others were incongruous – a gun with a table fork, or with a plow.

A buckler-and-gun combination was manufactured for King Henry VIII in the mid-sixteenth century. The curved shield is of wood faced with steel plates. The gun barrel protruding from the front of the shield chambered a steel cartridge loaded with powder and ball. Discharge was effected by igniting the gunpowder with a slow-burning match.

Clubs were weapons of the first human beings, and one of the earliest combination weapons embodying a firearm was a mace, or spiked club, with gun barrels through part of its length. Only the wealthy could afford mace-firearm combinations, some of which were very elaborate. Of such weapons that survive, examples of the "holy water sprinkler" are probably the most interesting. An item in the 1547 inventory of weapons in the Tower of London is: "Holly water sprincles wt thre gonnes in the Topp." "Holy water sprinkler" was a name applied to any mace with a liberally spiked business end. The weapon has no resemblance to a churchman's holywater sprinkler, or aspergillum. Skelton, in Meyrick's *Ancient Armour*, says "To sprinkle holy water was the cant phrase for fetching blood."

One of these weapons, with four 9-inch barrels, has a stock of wood with fanciful bone inlays and is of the hand cannon type. Other elaborately inlaid holy water sprinklers with three or more barrels are in museums. Mostly these multishot weapons are equipped with matchlocks or wheel locks, have several spikes around, and have a spear point at the muzzle end.

If any of these wood-stocked museum pieces had battered a head it might itself have shattered, but a steel mace-gun would crush a skull without itself breaking. The all-metal combinations were usually finely engraved, with wheel lock ignition.

A combination of a pistol with a sword was normally a combat weapon, but combinations of pistols with edged weapons – and sometimes with other weapons – were produced for use in the hunt, in killing or dressing game.

Guns were deemed unchivalrous by the knights, and swords fitted with guns to be fired at animals were sometimes condemned as unsportsmanlike by hunters.

Much prized are wheel locks combined with edged weapons having calendar blades. A calendar blade is one etched with a perpetual ecclesiastical calendar, where one column has the days of the month, the next column has the days of the week, represented by the first seven letters of the alphabet, and a final column has the name of a saint to whom to appeal on each day.

There exist a few examples of rare gun-and-crossbow combinations (see WHEEL LOCK). One has an arquebus for large game combined with a prodd, or bullet-throwing crossbow, for small game.

A combination weapon consisting of a pistol and a sword usually has the pistol quite inseparable from the sword, with the bullet taking a path along the sword's blade. One combination of sword and gun, however, was made to resemble a curved-handle umbrella. The curved handle was a pistol that could be pulled free, as a holstered pistol might be drawn, to be fired in any direction. The pseudo-umbrella was a brass scabbard covered with velvet, concealing a sword.

Still another type of sword gun was developed in Burma, with the barrel and the sword one long, nearly straight, piece of steel, the point of the blade at one end and the gun muzzle at the other. The basic weapon is the sword, which may be used two-handed, with the gun barrel its grip when the sword is out of its scabbard. When the sword is in its scabbard, the piece becomes a gun with a short barrel and an unusually long butt. No fastenings are required to hold the assembled weapon, and either assembly or disassembly takes but a moment.

Of combination weapons produced after the gun became accepted as a trustworthy primary weapon – and doubts on that score persisted even into the nineteenth century – one highly esteemed by collectors is the Elgin pistol, an American percussion pistol with a heavy cutlass, or Bowie-type, blade fastened under the barrel, patented by George Elgin in 1837, and actually issued to American sailors as an official weapon for one exploring expedition.

A little later, with the coming of metallic cartridges, revolvers were now and then supplied with blades, and swords with revolvers.

In Bordeaux in 1917, a collector came across the most fantastic arsenal of combination weapons ever designed to be carried by one man. There was a cuirass mounting nineteen cartridge pistols that could be fired in batteries of four and five, a revolver with a huge blade of the type made famous by James Bowie, and a pair of stirrups each with two pistols that could be fired by pulling straps.

A firearm much sought by collectors of freaks and oddities is the combination of revolver, dagger, and brass knuckles known as the Dolne apache pistol. This triple-threat weapon made by Dolne was supposedly a prime favorite of the Paris underworld.

Another French, and scarcer, type of this weapon is the Delhaxie. On the Dolne, the blade, the "knucks" and the trigger will all fold, but only the blade will fold on the Delhaxie. When the Dolne is held in shooting position with its blade extended for thrusting, its handle is not then ready for use as a striking weapon; but when the Delhaxie is in shooting position, its handle is being clutched for pounding, and its opened blade is pointed downward ready for use as a dagger.

The "My Friend" pistol is a knuckle-duster combined with a cartridge pepperbox having an unconventional grip, or, less commonly, with a short-barreled revolver. The all-metal (sometimes brass, sometimes steel) "My Friend" was patented in 1865 in America by James Reid, of Catskill, New York. It was chambered for .22, .32, and .41 rim-fire cartridges, and was made in both five-shot and seven-shot models. The cylinder of the common pepperbox type must be removed for reloading, and it is necessary to withdraw a center pin (which unscrews in a clockwise direction) to get the cylinder out. The patent drawing shows how the Reid invention should be gripped to make it an effective punching weapon: it should be clutched in the fist with the little finger passed through the "ring or bow." It seems that someone – legend points to a prison warden – suggested to Reid that the addition of a barrel would result in a better grip for striking a blow. The improved footpad's companion was known as "Reid's New Model My Friend."

Another, much earlier, all-metal pistol that was intentionally designed to be suitable for use as a striking weapon was made by the famous gunmaking firm of Rigby, of Dublin. It had percussion cap ignition and was made in three-barrel, four-barrel, and six-barrel versions. Shots were fired successively, with manual turning of a plate necessary between shots, to line up the hammer with the capped nipples one after another.

Well into the twentieth century, penknife pistols, and clasp-knife pistols and revolvers were widely popular. Best known of the pocketknife pistols, both in Europe and America, are the Unwin & Rodgers and the James Rodgers, made in Sheffield. Rodgers pistols were first percussion cap and muzzle-loaders; later they were rim-fire cartridge breechloaders. The muzzle-loader was regularly supplied with two small accessories, a ramrod and a bullet mold, held in slots in the handle. Knife pistols as made by either Rodgers firm were usually one-barrel with two knife blades in the handle, but a few were two-barrel with four blades in the handle.

Some knife pistols had pistol grips, but most had the customary pocketknife hafts of horn, bone, pearl, ivory and the like. Often the blade (or blades – the number would range from one to four) could be locked open or closed. A few were special-purpose, or multiple-use, inventions. One had built-in shotgun shell extractors; another, for horsemen, contained a hook to clean a horse's hoofs; another, for sailors, a marlinspike.

We may call a truncheon a weapon. A considerable number of metal truncheons that embodied a percussion-cap pistol were manufactured in England. The inventor was the same John Day who was given a patent for a cane gun in 1823. Day's truncheon gun used the same firing mechanism as his cane gun, but it did not have a similar success.

There is no end to the concoctions invented to combine firearms with implements, tools and utensils. Guns were combined with whips, pipes, belt buckles, bicycle handle bars, keys, umbrellas, purses (a purse-pistol is described in Sir Walter Scott's *Rob Roy*), torches, plows, watches, helmets, fishhooks, cameras, wrenches, knives, forks and spoons. Some of the patented inventions never passed the drawing-board stage, but others, notably cane guns, pen pistols, and knife pistols, had large sales.

One creation that did not succeed was the combination of helmet and blowback automatic patented in the United States by Albert B. Pratt during the First World War. This was, supposedly, aimed by turning the head and fired by blowing through a tube to inflate a bulb which acted as a trigger.

One that was manufactured and issued to a few Nazis during the Second World War was a combination of a four-shot battery with a belt buckle. The belt buckle could be opened and four shots fired in unison before a surprised victim knew what was happening.

There exists also a beautiful set of three pieces of silver cutlery – a knife, a fork, and a spoon – each combined with a flint pistol.   L.W.

Illustrations: pages 36–7, 42, 170, 337, 341–3.

Greener, William W., *The Gun and Its Development*, 9th edition, London, 1910.

Logan, Herschel C., *Hand Cannon to Automatic*, Huntingdon, W.Va., 1944.

Stone, George Cameron, *A Glossary of the Construction, Decoration and Use of Arms and Armor in All Countries and in All Times together with some Closely Related Subjects*, Portland, Me., 1934.

Winant, Lewis, *Firearms Curiosa*, New York, 1955, 2nd edition 1961, and London, 1956.

See also: ALARM GUN; CANE GUN; TRAP GUN/ TRIP GUN.

COMINAZZO

The Cominazzi were a famous family of barrelmakers originating at Gardone in the Val Trompia, a little to the north of Brescia. Many generations are concerned, and the family tree, so far as it is known, is one of great complexity. The founder of the family appears to have been a certain Lazaro, working in Gardone in the second half of the sixteenth century. His son, Angelo Lazarino Cominazzo, was the first member to achieve fame and the first to sign his productions with the name Lazarino Cominazzo. He was described by a contemporary as "one of the greatest masters there has ever been." He was born in 1563 and was still active in 1646, the year in which John Evelyn, the diarist, purchased from him "my fine carbine which cost me nine pistoles." By this date he seems to have been established in Brescia itself.

Angelo Lazarino had a son, Lazaro, who signed his work in like manner to his father. He was, however, short-lived, dying in 1639, but his place in his father's workshop was filled by four cousins, the sons of his father's brother Fortunato Cominazzo. These four were named Lazaro, Giacomo, Lorenzo and Carlo. The eldest, Lazaro, signed

gunmakers in England, France, and other countries. The family paid the price of fame by having their signatures placed on many barrels which had never left their work-shops, and it is probable that more falsely inscribed Cominazzo barrels exist than genuine examples.

The Cominazzi appear to have been exclusively barrel-

The Cominazzi of Brescia

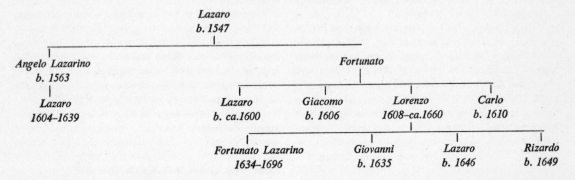

his work Larazino Cominazzo in the same manner as his uncle and cousin.

Lorenzo, the third of the brothers, had four sons of whom the eldest, Fortunato Lazarino (born 1634), continued the family custom by inscribing his name in the same form, and it is this member of the family to whom may be ascribed the majority of the later Cominazzo barrels. He was killed by a gunshot in 1696 as a result of becoming involved in an insurrection against the Venetian authorities. One of his brothers, Lazaro, was well known, and distinguished his barrels from Fortunato's by signing them Lazaro Lazarino. Many firearms with barrels bearing his name survive.

Members of the Cominazzo family continued as crafts-men in the gun trade throughout the eighteenth century; the last, Marco Cominazzo, published a family history in 1843. The later members, however, never attained the reputation of their seventeenth-century forebears.

The barrels made by the Cominazzi follow the general form of barrels produced by other makers in Brescia and its neighborhood in the seventeenth century, all tending to be of small bore and slender, graceful proportions. The breech section is almost invariably octagonal, with the portion towards the muzzle circular in section or occasion-ally polygonal or shaped to a slight central ridge. Some of the finest of the Cominazzo barrels, notably those made by Angelo Larazino, have the octagonal breech section decorated with longitudinal ridges while the forward por-tion is spirally fluted.

The production of the Cominazzo workshops was quite large, and barrels were sent abroad to be stocked by

makers, at least until the end of the seventeenth century; weapons may occasionally be found bearing the famous name on the lock, but these are invariably attempts to mislead by a non-Italian gunmaker. A.N.K.

Gaibi, Agostino, "Biografiske undersøgelser om familien Cominazzi" in *Vaabenhistoriske Aarbøger*, Vol. 11, 1962.

COMMITTEE OF SAFETY MUSKET

Using the term in its strict sense, a committee of safety musket is one of a small number of arms made by an American gunsmith directly under contract to one of the various committees or councils of safety during the early years of the American Revolution and following their specifications. These muskets were few in number and made for only a short period. The first committee contracts were let in the spring of 1775, after the battles of Concord and Lexington had already taken place. Then, as soon as new state constitutions had been written and formal governments established, the committees and coun-cils of safety were disbanded and their functions taken over by other bodies.

During the short period of their lives, however, the committees did establish specifications for the guns to be made for them. Contracts and copies of these specifica-tions still exist for almost every colony, and they are remarkably unanimous in following the design recom-mended by the Continental Congress in July 1775, even though some of the individual contracts had preceded that recommendation by three months. The muskets were to be patterned after the most recent British arm with which the Americans were familiar. This was the so-called second model of the Brown Bess with a 42-inch barrel and a caliber of .75. Mountings were to be brass, but sometimes iron was permitted. Walnut was preferred for stocks, but maple also was allowed in many instances. The use of single-bridle instead of double-bridle locks was also permitted as an expedient, but in all other details the British arms were to be copied as closely as possible.

Many arms were made in America during the Revolutionary War which had no connection with any of the committees or councils of safety. A number of these, after 1777, copied French patterns. Still other guns were assembled from miscellaneous foreign and American parts. There has been a tendency in some circles to lump all arms made or assembled in America during the War under the term Committee of Safety. This is an inaccurate use of the term, however, and leads to considerable confusion.   H.L.P.

Peterson, Harold L., *Arms and Armor in Colonial America*, 1526–1783, Harrisburg, Pa., 1956.

CONFEDERATE FIREARMS

Individually and collectively, the southern states that formed the Confederate States of America were ill-equipped to wage war. They were geared to an agricultural complex that did not include the making of firearms, and only one State had had continuous experience of doing so – Virginia. Shortly after the War of Independence Virginia saw the need of maintaining and equipping her own militia. In 1802 a large armory was erected in Richmond, the Virginia Manufactory, and here for the next twenty years very large quantities of arms and accoutrements were made.

With the darkening of war clouds in 1860 the old armory was completely refurbished, and the flintlock muskets, rifles and pistols that had been made there before 1822 were converted to percussion.

With actual secession, practically every Federal arsenal within the South was seized and claimed by that state within whose boundaries it lay. While such establishments proved valuable later on, the amount of arms so taken was comparatively small. The United States arsenal at Harpers Ferry, Virginia, was another matter. Its seizure by state troops on the eve of Virginia's secession was of incalculable value, for despite its attempted burning by the Federals, many thousands of arms and parts were taken, along with the very fine machinery for making rifles and muskets (Model 1855). As the arsenal's location rendered it extremely vulnerable, its contents were

removed. All the musket machinery was set up in the old Virginia Manufactory in Richmond, while the rifle machinery was installed in the old United States armory at Fayetteville, North Carolina. Both establishments began operating soon and were, without question, the largest small-arms plants in the Confederacy. Both continued operations until the end of the war, their products all being marked with their location and date of manufacture.

Thus the Harpers Ferry machinery became the heart, while Virginia acted as the body of Confederate ordnance. Richmond was also the location of S. C. Robinson, manufacturer of imitation Sharps carbines. Some 1,500 bearing his name were made before he sold out to the government, which continued manufacture of this type of arms until 1864, when the factory was removed to Tallasee, Alabama. Here, some five hundred muzzle-loading carbines were made, very similar to the Enfield cavalry carbines, but these were captured by the Federals before their issue. Norfolk was the location of Thomas Cofer, who made some seventy-five brass-framed imitation-Whitney revolvers, but with sheath triggers. As originally conceived, the cylinders were halved for a special metallic cartridge. The difficulty in such manufacture was realised, and after the first thirteen, the remainder of the revolvers were of conventional percussion pattern. J. B. Barrett of Wytheville assembled guns from parts saved at Harpers Ferry and from the barrels of the Hall rifles, but in so doing converted them from breech to muzzle-loaders. Similar conversions were made at Danville where Keen Walker & Company produced the Read brass-framed carbines vaguely resembling the Perry or Maynard. J. D. Bennett, C. Bilbers and G. H. Hall, all of Pittsylvania Courthouse, each received contracts to alter and to make muskets.

In North Carolina there was, in addition to Fayetteville, a government armory at Asheville, where a small number of Enfield-type rifles and carbines were produced. Here also was M.A. Baker, who made sharpshooter's rifles, altered flintlocks and made guns from Harpers Ferry parts. Lamb & Brother, and Mendenhall, Jones & Gardner of Jamestown were awarded state contracts for 10,000 Mississippi rifles – neither was fulfilled. At Greensboro, J. F. Garrett made a few brass-framed single-shot pistols from old United States Model 1842 barrels, and later manufactured the Tarpley carbines in even more limited quantity.

South Carolina had some slight previous experience in arms making. In 1852, feeling the need to increase arms within the state, a contract was awarded to William Glaze, the private owner of the Palmetto Armory, Columbia, for 6,000 muskets, 1,000 rifles and 2,000 pistols. Oddly enough, during the war the Palmetto Armory did not engage in arms making. However, there was a Confederate armory in Columbia to which the machinery from Asheville, North Carolina, was removed; it was in the process of making carbines and rifles when the war ended. In Greenville, George Morse established the State Rifle Works after his removal from Nashville, Tennessee, and there made the only metallic cartridge carbines used in the South. A thousand were made for the state, but were used mainly within its confines by the militia, prison guards and the Home Guards. The lack of brass with which to make the cartridges rendered them impractical for armies in the field. Morse also made limited quantities of muskets with inside locks.

Next to Virginia, Georgia was the largest in production of arms. The Confederate armory at Macon was the site to which the Spiller & Burr revolver factory was taken, from Atlanta, after its purchase by the government. The total production was 1,300 brass-framed copies of the caliber .36 Whitney. Also in Macon was D. C. Hodgkins, who altered flintlocks and produced a few cavalry carbines. Griswold & Gunnison produced some 3,600 brass-framed imitation Colts at Griswoldville. The private armory of Cook & Brother was located at Athens, having first operated at New Orleans, Louisiana. Here, all types of rifles and carbines, 8,000 altogether, were made, being particularly attractive because their stamping includes a Confederate flag, the name of the firm, and the date and place of manufacture. The State Penitentiary at Milledgeville was converted into an armory and made a number of rifles bearing the name "Georgia Armory." A musket factory was located at Tilton, but production was very limited. At Columbus, rifles and carbines were made by J. P. Murray and Greenwood & Gray. Here also operated L. Haiman & Brother who produced a few imitation Colts under the name of The Columbus Firearms Manufacturing Company. Greensboro was the final location of Leech & Rigdon's revolver plant which first began operations in Memphis, Tennessee. These are caliber .36 imitation Colts stamped with the firm's name and "C. S. A." The partners produced 1,500 before separating in January 1864. Leech continued small operations in Greensboro, and his partner went to Augusta, making an additional 1,000 revolvers under the name of Rigdon-Ansley. Also in Augusta was the Confederate Machine Works, where an undetermined number of fine imitation Colts were made with long octagonal barrels and most with twelve cylinder stops.

In Tennessee, records cite manufacture of rifles in Nashville, but by whom, or in what quantity, is not known. The same applies to Gallatin. Schneider & Glassick, Memphis, produced fourteen revolvers (imitation Colts). At Pulaski a few rifles were made, of hybrid nature, combining features of both sporting and military pieces.

Alabama had various arms-making activities, such as the Alabama Arms Manufacturing Company, Montgomery, officially reported to have made excellent Enfield rifles, and Winter's Iron Works. C. Kreutner and G. Todd, also of Montgomery, made rifles under State contract. At Talladega, a small-arms plant was destroyed by Federal raiders in August 1864. It had been owned either by D. Wallis or by L. G. Sturdivant, both of whom were under contract with the state. Dickson, Nelson & Company also made Mississippi rifles for the state, but their production was small, owing to their frequent re-locations to keep one step ahead of the enemy. At the Montgomery Arsenal a number of flintlock arms were converted to percussion. Selma was a center of ordnance activity: it is said that rifles and pistols were produced there. Davis & Bozeman, Coosa County, were paid for 900 Mississippi rifles by the state. A. C. Suter was also under contract with Alabama for rifles.

In Mississippi the State Arsenal was located at Panola, later removed to Brandon, and still later removed to Meridian. There is reason to believe that it produced a few guns.

At Arkadelphia and Little Rock, Arkansas, a few very poor-grade rifles were made, early in the war, before all this state's ordnance activities were removed to the Confederate Armory at Tyler, Texas (previously a private enterprise of J. S. Short). Here the manufacture of Enfield rifles was continued, the lockplates bearing the place of manufacture. Also in Texas were Tucker & Sherrod, Lancaster, who secured a state contract for revolvers, which, however, was cancelled before the completion of more than a few. Dance Brothers, Columbia, had a state contract for revolvers and also made rifles, though few were forthcoming. Whitescarver, Campbell & Co., Rusk, and Billings & Hassell, Plentitude, received state contracts for 900 and 1,200 rifles respectively. N. O. Tanner, Bastrop, also made a small number of rifles.

Despite the remarkable efficiency of Confederate ordnance under the able command of General Josiah Gorgas, the South was always faced with a shortage of arms and of material with which to make them. In the early part of the war this resulted in arming some volunteers with pikes, since sufficient guns were not available. In the latter part of the war it meant substitution of twisted iron for steel, brass for iron, and lead – or even wood – for brass. The quality of such arms left much to be desired, but Union casualty lists are a mute testimony to their effectiveness.

Owing to this perpetual shortage of arms, the likelihood that most Confederate weapons saw active duty is great. This may account in part for their present popularity. The possession of one virtually assures its owner of handling a gun actually fired in anger and in the heat of battle – a characteristic which extends to few other firearms.   W.A.A.

Illustrations: pages 212–13.

Albaugh, William A., III, *The Confederate Brass-framed Colt and Whitney*, Washington, 1955.

Albaugh, William A., III, *Confederate Edged Weapons*, New York. 1960.

Albaugh, William A., III, *Tyler, Texas, C.S.A.*, Harrisburg, Pa., 1958.

Albaugh, William A., III, Benet, Hugh, Jr., and Simmons, Edward N., *Confederate Handguns*, Philadelphia, 1963.

Albaugh, William A., III, and Simmons, Edward N., *Confederate Arms*, Harrisburg, Pa., 1957.

Albaugh, William A., III, and Steuart, Richard D., *The Original Confederate Colt*, New York, 1953.

Fuller, Claud E., and Steuart, Richard D., *Firearms of the Confederacy*, Huntingdon, W.Va., 1944.

See also: LEMAT REVOLVER.

COOKSON

See: LORENZONI REPEATING SYSTEM; REPEATING ARMS.

CREEDMOOR RIFLE

See: TARGET RIFLE.

D

DAG

An archaic word of unknown derivation meaning a pistol. The word was in common use in England and Scotland in the sixteenth and seventeenth centuries and many "dagges" are listed among the possessions of King Henry VIII. The word was soon displaced in England by the fashionable "pistol" but continued in common use in Scotland until the eighteenth century.   W.R.

DAMASCUS BARREL

The term Damascus barrel derives from a welding technique designed to give strength and decorative structure to a gun barrel. It was apparently developed in the Near East in the sixteenth century. From there it spread south and east at least as far as India, where fine Damascus barrels were being made by 1650, and north and west to Europe, where the first detailed description of the process appeared in 1773.

A Damascus barrel is easily recognizable by the intricate patterns visible on its surface. These occur at acute angles to the length of the bore and are the result of the method of manufacture which varied somewhat among gunsmiths of different countries, but essentially they followed the same process. Piles of steel and iron rods or strips in varying numbers were stacked alternately, heated, and forged together. The resulting bars were then run through a rolling mill and the mass again heated and then twisted in a lathe-like device. Two or more of these end-products were then heated, welded together and rolled into a rod and finally flattened into a strip. This strip was in turn heated red-hot and twisted in a spiral around an iron mandrel, all the time being hammered and welded. The rough barrel thus formed was then filed smooth, bored out, and etched with acid to bring out the design.

The Damascus barrel achieved four things. It made for a lighter barrel than was possible at the time with conventional barrel-making techniques; it combined the toughness of wrought iron with the hardness of steel; it provided almost limitless artistic opportunities for the barrel-maker in the complexity of his welding patterns; and it made possible the manufacture of cheaper shotguns during the nineteenth century by utilizing barrels with thinner walls.

Damascus barrels also had their weaknesses. Well made barrels stood up very well under the relatively low pressures obtained by black powder, but if excessive pressures were generated or if the welding had been faulty, they were apt to "unwind" along their weld lines.   H.W.

Illustration: page 211.

Greener, William W., *The Gun*, London, 1835.

Knight, Edward H., *Knight's American Mechanical Dictionary*, Vol. 1, New York, 1874.

Smith, Cyril S., *A History of Metallography*, Chicago and London, 1960.

Tomlinson, Charles, *Cyclopedia of Useful Arts and Manufactures*, Vol. 1, London and New York, 1854.

DECORATION OF FIREARMS

Almost from the beginning, firearms designed for personal use have been embellished to increase their attractiveness so that they might serve as an ornament to the dress of their owner and an evidence of his taste and affluence. The techniques used and the style of ornamentation have varied according to the period and area of origin, so that, in the absence of a maker's signature, the decoration of an arm often provides the best evidence for assigning it a date and a place of manufacture. For the most part, the designs used to decorate European firearms have been drawn from printed pattern books and plates. Exceptions are found in arms made by certain local schools of gunsmiths which were able to draw upon an indigenous style of ornament, such as the Scottish gunmakers who continued to employ Celtic ornament until late in the eighteenth century, the schools of Brescia and Naples in Italy with their traditional designs in pierced and chiseled iron, and the stock inlays of some of the Baltic provinces. In Asia, traditional decoration was almost always the rule, and conventional designs were used over long periods with differences only in workmanship and spirit. In America, local styles predominated, notably in the carving and inlays by which the native Kentucky rifle can be assigned to a specific small area or even an individual maker. It was not until the nineteenth century was well advanced that printed sheets came to be used as guides in the United States, and then only for patterns to be engraved as extra embellishments on mass-produced weapons.

The study of the printed pattern books and plates is an interesting and rewarding one for any student of European firearms. Excellent collections of them may be found in several museums, among them the Victoria & Albert Museum in London, the Oesterreichisches Museum in Vienna, and the Metropolitan Museum of Art in New York. The study of techniques and workmanship in ornamentation is necessary for even the most basic understanding of any field of firearms history. A brief survey of the principal techniques and their application in various eras and areas, with special reference to the western world, is presented below.

Bluing

The blued surface, which has been the usual finish given to gun barrels since earliest times, has a dual purpose: firstly, to reduce reflection of light which might prejudice the accuracy of the firer's aim; secondly, to provide some resistance to corrosion by rust. It must soon have been recognised that this finish, which was achieved as a natural consequence of hardening and quenching iron, had definite decorative possibilities. It provided an attractive ground for gold or silver damascening and has been used for that purpose from the sixteenth century until modern times. Bluing was formerly carried out by heating; chemical bluing is a more modern process.

Carving

The main decorative treatments for gunstocks were either inlaying or carving. For practical reasons, carving on gun or pistol stocks had to be carried out in low relief. The main exceptions were the ivory or ebony heads carved in the round that formed the pommels of Dutch, especially Maastricht, pistols of the second half of the seventeenth century, and the animal heads carved in high relief under the butt and just behind the trigger guard of French or French-style fowling pieces of the early decades of the nineteenth century, which practice seems to have been introduced by the famous Napoleonic gunmaker Nicolas Boutet.

Carved decoration has not been consistently fashionable on gunstocks. Apart from a very few Flemish wheel lock firearms with stocks veneered with panels of carved ivory, it was unusual in the sixteenth century. Towards the middle of the seventeenth century carved decoration was developed as an alternative to the inlaid ornament characteristic of German wheel lock stocks. Two important workshops were established, each of which turned out considerable numbers of finely carved stocks: the Maucher workshop at Schwäbisch Gmund and that of the anonymous *Meister der Tierkopfranken* (Master of the animal-headed scrolls) in Salzburg. Of the two Mauchers, father and son, the latter, Michael Maucher, was the more important, in particular because he developed a new style of gunstock set with panels of carved ivory, usually of a quality more suited to the cabinet of curiosities than the gun-room. The Salzburg master worked in walnut, covering almost the whole area of his stocks with fine scrolling foliage inhabited by figures of hunters and animals of the chase.

During the second half of the seventeenth century it became usual to apply some slight carved decoration to flintlock gun and pistol stocks. This consisted of a simple scroll behind the rear ramrod pipe and a formalized leaf behind the barrel tang. Towards the end of the century these details received increasingly elaborate treatment, the scrolls on the fore-stock being intertwined with serpents. The German rifle with shoulder stock (*Müller Büchse*) often had the patch-box cover carved with a single figure, while the standard south German or Austrian wheel lock rifle of the early eighteenth century had the stock profusely carved with abstract scrollwork derived from the engraved designs of the Prague engraver, Johann Smischek. In America, these scrolls were perpetuated on the stocks of Kentucky rifles.

During the eighteenth century low-relief carving became more profuse, especially in the rococo period when all the mounts were outlined with asymmetrical scrolls.

The finest carving ever executed on gunstocks was done in the workshop of Nicolas Boutet. The precision and delicacy with which the Empire ornament was carved on his gun and pistol stocks is beyond compare. During the nineteenth century, carved ornament ceased to be of importance, with the exception of pieces made specially for exhibition or for presentation.

Casting (Bronze)

Ornament in cast and gilded bronze or brass was used by various schools of gunmaking from the sixteenth century onwards. In the late sixteenth and early seventeenth centuries the Saxon gunmakers decorated wheel lock plates and also stocks with bronze plaques cast in the form of cherubs' heads, human figures or geometrical ornament. One of the most determined users of gilt bronze was the Zürich goldsmith-gunmaker, Felix Werder, who not only provided his stocks with gilt bronze furniture but made his barrels and lock plates of the same material. In the first half of the eighteenth century, gilt bronze mounts were adopted generally in the Low Countries, where they were probably supplied by the bronzefounders of Liège, and in Austria, Bavaria and Bohemia. The most prolific users of bronze furniture were the gunmakers of the Bohemian town of Carlsbad, which enjoyed a period of florescence during the first half of the eighteenth century. The material was not much used after the mid-eighteenth century.

Casting (Silver)

Cast and chased silver mounts were used earlier, but it was not until the last quarter of the seventeenth century that they became usual. From that period they became the normal alternative in western Europe to mounts of chiseled steel. Though the precious metal was more expensive than steel, the work of casting and chasing silver was far less time-consuming than the arduous one of forging, chiseling and finishing steel. Most good-quality English eighteenth-century firearms have cast silver mounts. After rough casting, these mounts were engraved or chiseled. Silver mounts were also used in France, Italy, Spain, the Low Countries, etc. The most effective and handsome cast work is found on the mask butt cap and the side plate. The provision of silver gun furniture was the work of specialist silversmiths, but their names are rarely known. Silver continued in use into the nineteenth century, when it was generally replaced by blued steel.

Chiseling

This term is used for carving in metals such as silver, bronze or iron. The two former metals were first cast and the detail was then sharpened and the traces of the casting sand removed with fine chisels and punches. Iron had to be wrought, as cast iron was too brittle to be worked with hammer and chisel. In the sixteenth century barrels were chiseled in high relief, sometimes being treated as a Corinthian or Ionic pillar with the muzzle rendered as the capital. Later the ornament was, doubtless for practical reasons, executed in lower relief. The most outstanding German masters of this technique were the brothers Emanuel and Daniel Sadeler, and Caspar Spät, who were employed in succession as chiselers and gilders at the Bavarian court in Munich. No less gifted were the iron-chiselers of Brescia where an individual style was developed which derived from folk art and owed little to classical antiquity. The Brescian school lasted on into the eighteenth century, but their work was eclipsed by that of artists in other Italian towns, such as Acqua Fresca of Bargi, near Bologna, and Michele Lorenzoni of Florence.

During the second half of the seventeenth century, the Parisian masters became predominant. During the first half of the eighteenth century, many of the finest firearms had mounts of iron chiseled with scrollwork or busts against a gilded pointillé (sometimes known from its appearance as "fishroe") ground. This work was done widely in Europe, but demand died away during the last quarter of the century. Very fine chiseling was still applied to the locks of percussion-cap guns and pistols in Spain up to the mid-nineteenth century. In particular, the family of Zuloaga of Madrid produced remarkable presentation arms elaborately enriched with chiseled ornament, derived from earlier styles.

Damascening

This term describes the decoration of a base metal, usually iron, with applied gold or silver wire or foil. Two methods must be distinguished: false damascene and true damascene. In the former, which was that normally employed, a large number of minute ridges were raised on the iron surface by means of a file; gold or silver wire was then hammered on according to the desired pattern and the edges trimmed to shape. In the latter system, channels were cut into the base metal corresponding to the pattern and precious metal was hammered into them. The surface was then polished smooth.

In the sixteenth century false damascene was much used on the barrels, lock plates and mounts of both matchlock and wheel lock arms. Particularly fine work was done in England in the late sixteenth and early seventeenth centuries, perhaps by immigrant masters. The Paris gunmakers of the reign of Louis XIV made lavish use of damascened ornament, as they did of every other process of ornamentation. In the eighteenth century, gunmakers in Austria, Bohemia and Spain used the true damascene technique to sign their barrels in gold letters. Towards the end of the century, it was used for signatures in England by masters such as Durs and Joseph Egg, Ezekiel Baker and the Manton brothers.

Embossing

This process of beating a design or pattern with punches into metal can be applied only to fairly thin sheets, so the possibilities of its application to firearms were limited.

It was mainly used for firearms with all-metal stocks, such as those made for the arsenal of Duke Heinrich Julius of Brunswick (1564–1613). These were made of either brass or iron, but three very fine Saxon wheel lock pistols (Kunsthistorisches Museum, Vienna), with barrels dated 1555, have stocks built up of silver sheet embossed with hunting subjects. Italian eighteenth century fowling pieces of "Roman" type sometimes have parts of the barrel sheathed in embossed silver, but in later periods embossing was confined to oriental and Near-Eastern firearms. Embossed ornament might be applied either with a repeating stamp or with punches of various shapes and sizes.

Enameling

Enameled decoration is rare on firearms, perhaps because it was usually carried out on precious metals, preferably gold, and arms decorated in so sumptuous a way have been broken up to recover the value of the metal. The most famous enameled gun is the wheel lock rifle of the Emperor Rudolph II, which was made by Daniel Sadeler and enameled by David Altenstetter (Kunsthistorisches Museum, Vienna). The whole of the stock is covered with plaques of silver enriched with translucent enamel. A pair of wheel lock pistols in the Rosenborg Collection at Copenhagen, now much altered and converted to flint action, have mounts of enameled gold, as does a wheel lock rifle made by Michael Gull at Vienna (Kunsthistorisches Museum).

Encrusting

This process is similar to true damascening, but differs in that the precious metal stands out in relief instead of being polished flush with the metal of the ground. In this process channels or crevices were cut in the base metal (usually iron or brass) surface to be decorated. These were then under-cut and the gold or silver hammered on top so that, expanding into the under-cut areas, it was keyed to the ground. The projecting lumps of precious metal were then carved to the required design. This form of decoration was not widely applied to firearms, as such projections were inconvenient. It is found on seventeenth-century gun and pistol barrels, particularly on those of French or Flemish origin. In the mid-seventeenth century it was employed by a Salzburg master who decorated the wheel lock guns stocked by the *Meister der Tierkopf-ranken*. In the eighteenth century it is not unusual to find just one figure, either of silver or gold, encrusted in a gun barrel, usually over the breech. It was most extensively practised by the decorators working in the Russian imperial factory at Tula. It was not often applied to lock plates, as these had to be softened before the crevices into which the metal was hammered could be cut.

Engraving

Engraved decoration has been applied to most parts of the firearm at one time or another – to the staghorn, bone, mother-of-pearl or silver inlay in the stock, to the steel, brass or silver mounts, to the lock plate and the barrel. Engraved ornament is still applied to the action of the modern sporting gun, and is the only form of embellishment that has persisted throughout the history of the firearm.

The great period of engraved staghorn was the hundred years from the mid-sixteenth to the mid-seventeenth centuries. The elaborate inlay was engraved either by the gunstocker or, if a work of exceptional quality was required, by a professional engraver to whom the piece was sent for decoration. During the second half of the sixteenth century, inlay with engraved horn was the standard method of decorating the stocks of matchlock, wheel lock and snaphance guns in most European countries. It persisted in Germany throughout the seventeenth century and even into the eighteenth century, but elsewhere it had long before been given up. The engraver often signed his work, but as a rule only with a monogram, so that the names of the artists are not known. Johann Sadeler, who belonged to the same family as the iron chiselers Emanuel and Daniel Sadeler of Munich, first learnt his trade as an engraver by decorating gunstocks. Adam Vischer of Munich engraved the inlay on some of the finest of the Munich-school firearms.

Some of the seventeenth-century tschinkes have engraved brass plaques inset in their stocks, but the finer seventeenth-century guns have inlaid and engraved silver panels. Such work first appears in profusion on a wheel lock rifle made in 1628 by Hans Schmidt of Ferlach for the Archduke Leopold V of Styria (Kunsthistorisches Museum, Vienna), but was more usual in the last quarter of the seventeenth century, when it became a normal feature of any good quality flintlock firearm. Signatures are, once again, more than rare, but a double-barreled turn-over fowling piece at Stockholm (Livrustkammaren) bears the name of the artist, Jean Bérain, engraved on the silver inlay work.

Engraving is better suited for the decoration of softer metals, such as silver or copper, rather than iron or steel, but wheel lock plates were nevertheless often decorated this way – sometimes in a mixed technique of etching and engraving. The lock plates of flintlocks were decorated with engraving from the earliest invention of the system at the beginning of the seventeenth century until the nineteenth century. The most elaborate work is found on French and Italian locks of the second half of the seventeenth century. It was necessary to harden the lock plate after the engraving had been done.

Good quality arms, both pistols and long arms, had

their furniture engraved, those intended for warfare with trophies of arms or battle scenes drawn from Roman or contemporary history, those intended for the chase with hunting subjects. In the course of the nineteenth century, blued steel mounts did not provide as effective a background for engraved ornament, and the latter became more standardized, consisting of an arrangement of tight scrolls on the trigger guard and action.

Etching

Etched ornament is first found on sword blades in the thirteenth century and on armor in the fifteenth century; it was also one of the first techniques of decoration to be used on firearms. During the sixteenth century it was particularly favored in Germany, where it was applied not only to iron and steel but also to copper, brass and silver, all of which metals were used by the gunmaker. In the gunmakers' workshops it was, however, mainly restricted to the decoration of iron and steel. Etched decoration is found on the earliest wheel lock pistols, including those made for the Emperor Charles V dating from the 1530's. A three-barreled, dart-firing, wheel lock pistol of Charles V in the Turin Armory is etched and gilded all over. This pistol has a stock entirely of steel, and all steel pistols of the sixteenth century were usually decorated in this way. The patterns used followed those employed by the armorers, hunting subjects and panels of Mauresque ornament being preferred. Those parts that were etched were either gilded or else the ground was darkened so that the design stood out white on black. On some of the Saxon wheel lock pistols etched and gilded panels alternated with those in black and white, producing a most striking effect.

Etched decoration is found on French wheel lock firearms, including those rare examples with all-steel stocks, and there is no reason to doubt that it was applied to English ones also. Although innumerable Italian armors were decorated with etched ornament, Italian gunmakers rarely used the technique for firearms. During the seventeenth century, French gunmakers used a combination of etching and gilding in a manner that was probably first introduced by the French court gunmaker, Marin le Bourgeoys. The ground was first etched away, and the surface of the design, which stood out in slight relief, was hatched to provide a key for the gold foil that was then hammered on. This process was used in France until the early eighteenth century, and was also used in England in the second half of the seventeenth century by masters such as Harman Barne and Truelock. The thin silver mounts on some Dutch and French pistols of the second quarter of the seventeenth century were etched, as the precious metal was too thin for engraving.

The advantage of etching was that the acid would bite into the hardened steel of the lock plate and it was not necessary to subject an etched plate to a hardening process afterwards.

Gilding

This has always been one of the most important methods of decorating firearms. We find gilding applied to iron, silver, brass or bronze; in each case the same technique was employed, namely that gold powder was mixed with mercury in an amalgam and applied to the metal surface to be gilt. The metal was then heated to a sufficiently high temperature to drive off the mercury in the form of vapor. The gold was left on the surface as a deposit and was burnished. Iron could also be gilded by hatching, but this method is dealt with under *Damascening*.

There is no period before the mid-nineteenth century in which gilding was not used in profusion for the decoration of fine quality firearms. It had the advantage of resisting oxidization better than any other surface treatment, quite apart from the fact that gold has always been regarded as the most precious and decorative of all metals. With some exceptions the gold was quite thin, and time has often worn it thinner still, so there are few firearms extant on which the gilding can be seen in its pristine state.

An effective use was in combination with bluing. Blued and gilt barrels were usual from the introduction of the wheel lock pistol in the early sixteenth century until the nineteenth century. The barrels of the rifles known as tschinkes were usually decorated with alternate areas of bluing and gilding. Completely gilt barrels are found in the sixteenth and seventeenth centuries, especially on arms made by the Zürich gunmaker, Felix Werder. Thereafter it was realised that the bright effect of a barrel gilt all over had practical disadvantages.

Silver mounts on French firearms were often gilded in the late seventeenth and eighteenth centuries, as were the brass or bronze mounts of firearms made in the Low Countries, Austria and Bohemia, especially Carlsbad.

A group of south German pistol stocks, probably made at Augsburg, which were veneered with ebony, were further decorated with incised foliage which was then picked out with gilding – in this case with gold leaf; one of the rare examples of the application of gilding with leaf to gunstocks.

Inlaying

Here only inlay into a wood base is considered. (For inlay of one metal into another, see under *Encrusting* and *Damascening*.)

The shapes available for decoration on a gun or pistol stock lend themselves most readily to inlaid ornament, and, until the firearm became a largely utilitarian implement, practically all the finest were furnished with inlaid stocks. The list of materials with which gunstocks were inlaid includes the metals, gold, silver, copper, brass, pewter, and iron, in the form of either plaques or wire, and, among other materials, ivory, staghorn, mother-of-pearl and ebony.

During the sixteenth century staghorn was the most popular material; this was cut, pierced and engraved in every imaginable form to represent hunting subjects, classical or grotesque figures, or a continuous pattern of closely set scrolls. To give variety, some of the horn was stained green. The Germans were the pre-eminent masters of the technique, but it was practised widely in Europe; in England, even military matchlock muskets received roughly engraved horn and mother-of-pearl inlay. While other countries preferred these latter materials, in Italy, especially in the region around Brescia, inlay of panels of pierced steel was used. During the seventeenth century this developed into lacework of miraculous fineness that is rightly recognised as one of the greatest artistic achievements in the history of gunmaking.

The German cheek stock was more suited to the display of fine inlaid work than the French shoulder stock, and it follows that the finest work of the first half of the seventeenth century was German. Some of the leading German masters are known by name: Hieronymus Borstorffer of Munich, Elias Becker of Augsburg, and the Alsatian master, J. C. Tornier of Massevaux. Sixteenth-century gunstocks were inlaid with thin strands of horn as well as with plaques. It was perhaps from the former that the idea arose of using metal wire. Spirals of brass wire are already found on late-sixteenth-century French firearms; subsequently silver and even gold wire was used.

While the second great school of inlay work was that around Brescia in the mid-seventeenth century, the third was that of the Parisian masters of the last decades of the century. Here both engraved plaques and inlaid wire were used in profusion. The style was by no means a French invention, for it had been anticipated half a century before by Hans Schmidt of Ferlach in Carinthia.

In the eighteenth century the use of silver-wire inlay was no longer confined to luxury arms, but was applied, especially in England, to all kinds of pocket pistols. By far the most imposing examples of inlaid wire work are found on the presentation pistols made by the royal gunmaker La Roche for the French court during the middle decades of the eighteenth century. The stocks of these pistols are inlaid with gold plaques and gold wire in the liveliest rococo designs. In England, one even finds wire inlay in the prevalent *chinoiserie* taste.

The sober and intensely practical English style of the late eighteenth century put an end for a while in most countries to such decorative tricks, but fine inlaid work was revived during the Napoleonic period in Boutet's workshop. Inlay of a decadent nature is still found in the stocks of some of the turn-off pocket pistols with percussion locks of the second quarter of the nineteenth century.

Veneering

Gunstocks were sometimes veneered with other woods, such as ebony or palisander, or with some rare or precious material, such as ivory, tortoiseshell, staghorn or mother-of-pearl. The foundation wood of the stock would be of beech or walnut. Veneered stocks were always exceptional and are normally found only on guns or pistols of high quality, such as those made by Hieronymus Borstorffer of Munich for the Bavarian court. It was necessary to use veneers of ebony and other rare woods, owing to the difficulty of finding pieces large enough to form a solid gunstock. In the late seventeenth and early eighteenth centuries, German wheel lock gunstocks were veneered with highly figured walnut; in this case the veneering was necessary because figured wood was short in the grain and therefore too fragile for use in the solid. In the sixteenth century the German city of Augsburg specialized in the use of ebony, and in the following century most of the tortoiseshell veneered stocks seem to have been made there. Examples were, however, also made in Italy, and a spectacular tortoiseshell veneered stock, enriched with gold inlay and hardstone cameos and made for the Emperor Charles VI (Kunsthistorisches Museum, Vienna), is probably of Neapolitan make. J.F.H.

Illustrations: pages 38–9, 42, 45, 65 (plate 1), 84 (plate 2), 102–3, 107, 133 (plate 3), 152 (plate 4), 172–3, 233 (plate 5), 252 (plate 6), 270, 272–3, 301 (plate 7), 320 (plate 8), and endpapers.

Grancsay, S. V., *Master French Gunsmiths' Designs*, New York, 1950.

Hayward, J. F., *The Art of the Gunmaker*, 2 vols, London and New York, 1962–64.

Hayward, J. F., *European Firearms*, London, 1957.

Lenk, Torsten, *Flintlåset, dess Uppkomst och Utveckling*, Stockholm, 1939.

Picquot, Thomas, *Livre de diverses ordonnances*, Stockholm, 1950 (reprint of 1638 edition).

Stöcklein, H., *Meister des Eisenschnittes*, Esslingen, 1922.

See also: DAMASCUS BARREL; FAKES AND FORGERIES.

DERINGER, HENRY

Henry Deringer, 1786–1868, whose name defines a type of pistol, was born in Easton, Pennsylvania, the son of a gunsmith of the same name who came to America from Germany before the Revolution. After an apprenticeship in Richmond the son moved to Philadelphia, where he lived and made arms from 1806 onwards. His manufactory supplied over 20,000 rifles and pistols on contract to the United States government, many of them flintlock hunting rifles for the Indian tribes removed beyond the Mississippi river. Deringer also made excellent rifles and dueling pistols for the civilian market. His fame rests, however, on his distinctive small percussion pistol with a "bird's-head" grip, which became exceedingly popular as a pocket arm in the South and West, particularly during the vigilante days of the California gold rush. This compact single-shot pistol of large bore became known as the deringer. Though the inventor lived to see his design copied extensively by others and his name used as a common noun, he sustained his trademark "Deringer, Philadela." in a famous lawsuit.   J.E.P.

Parsons, John E., *Henry Deringer's Pocket Pistol*, New York, 1952.

See also: DERINGER PISTOL.

DERINGER PISTOL

The deringer, as designed by its originator, Henry Deringer, the Philadelphia gunsmith (1786–1868), was a compact single-shot pistol of large bore with a short barrel. Its distinctive feature was the bird's-head handle of its walnut stock, which was fitted with a back-action percussion lock supporting an outside hammer. German-silver mountings let into the wood included a trigger guard and floor plate, side plate, escutcheon, butt plate, wedge plate and stock tip. Two bolts, one vertical connecting the barrel tang and trigger plate, the other horizontal between the lock and side plate, held the action together, while a wedge or key secured the barrel to the fore-stock. A round barrel flattened on top, of wrought iron, was rifled with seven grooves turning clock-wise; it was finished brown with copper-colored streaks simulating a Damascus twist. The iron hammer, lock and bolts were blued.

Deringer made this style of pistol in a great variety of sizes and calibers; barrel lengths from twenty-seven thirty-seconds of an inch, measured exclusive of the breech plug, to four inches and over, are known, with intervals as little as an eighth of an inch, and calibers all the way from .33 to .51. Over-all, the pistols measured from $3\frac{3}{4}$ inches to 9 inches, those more than $6\frac{3}{4}$ inches long usually having ramrods. The arm was generally sold in pairs, but cased specimens, fitted with loading tools, are scarce. Assisted by a few workmen, Deringer turned out from his manufactory in Philadelphia less than a thousand pairs a year, their retail price being about $25. Each arm bore on its lock and breech the maker's trademark "Deringer, Philadela.", and for a proof mark many carried the letter "P" inside a sunburst on the left of the breech plug. This was sometimes inlaid with gold or silver bands. A few fine pistols had gold-plated mounts, but foliate engraving was standard.

Introduced in the 1830's, the percussion deringer gained great popularity in the South and West during the decade of the California gold rush. Primarily a short-range weapon of self-defense, it could be carried inconspicuously in any pocket. The names of agents who sold it were occasionally stamped on the barrel flat, in styles such as MAND FOR HYDE & GOODRICH AGENTS N.O. or C. CURRY SAN FRANCO CALA AGENT. But as the genuine article was in limited supply, the design was widely copied, not only by gunsmiths who put their own names on the product, but by others less scrupulous. In New York, Daniel O'Connell had the temerity to advertise himself as "Imitation Deringer Pistol Manufacturer." In Philadelphia, a group of Henry Deringer's own workmen left him to set up the firm of Slotter & Co. For several years they copied both his design and his trade-mark, marketing their imitations in California through Adolphus J. Plate, a dealer who had once handled the genuine product.

When Henry Deringer brought suit against Plate for infringement of trade-mark, Slotter & Co. took into the firm a tailor called John Deringer, at the same time changing the marking of their arms to "J. Deringer, Philadela." But this stratagem did not survive the granting of an injunction and damages against Plate in the Supreme Court of California. Thenceforth Slotter deringers were marked "Slotter & Co. Phila.", and some stamped on the barrel, "Made for A. J. Plate, San Francisco." Their pistols had barrels of steel and were at least as well made as Deringer's but did not command so high a price. Other copyists stamped their products "J. E. Evans, Philada.", "A. Wurfflein, Phila.", "Krider, Phila." and "Tryon, Philada." While imitation was not limited to that city, its name became so associated with the design as to give rise to the descriptive phrase "Philadelphia deringer."

The word deringer itself, often rendered "derringer" through derivation from a mis-spelling of the originator's name, evolved into a common noun soon after the Civil War. The little arm had figured in a series of sensational homicides, the most publicized being the assassination of Abraham Lincoln by John Wilkes Booth in 1865. After firing the single fatal shot, Booth dropped the pistol in the Presidential box at Ford's Theater where it was picked up, and it was described by name at the trial of the conspirators. Through repeated mention in the press, and also in literature, where the arm was a favorite of Bret

Musketeer, reproduced from *Maniement d'Armes*,
by Jacob de Gheyn, 1608.

Caliverman, reproduced from *Maniement d'Armes*,
by Jacob de Gheyn, 1608.

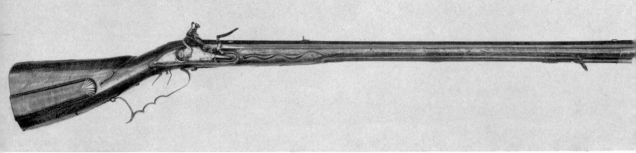

Jaeger rifle made by Michael Wagner, Cronad. Dated 1703, but similar
in design to those made as early as 1675, and typical of early jaeger rifles.
Collection of Bluford W. Muir.

Jaeger rifle made by Ioh Andre Kuchenreiter, *ca.*1775; except for the
trigger guard, typical of those made in the late eighteenth century.
Collection of Bluford W. Muir.

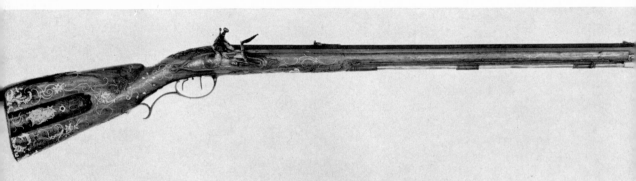

Extremely fine jaeger rifle made by I. G. Horneffer, 1730–40; the lock
chiseled with rococo scrolls, the stock carved and inlaid with floral designs
and figure subjects of engraved horn. The modern-looking trigger guard
is actually found on rifles made as early as 1710, and is the type
usually seen on jaegers made during the last half of the eighteenth century.
Collection of Bluford W. Muir.

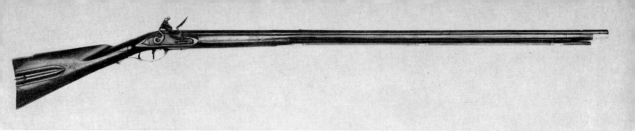

Early Kentucky rifle with sliding wooden patch box cover.
Collection of Joe Kindig, Jr.

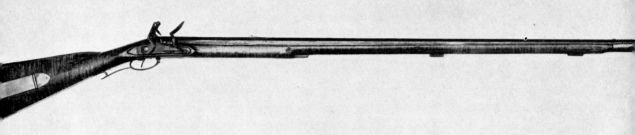

Pre-Revolutionary Kentucky rifle.
Collection of Joe Kindig, Jr.

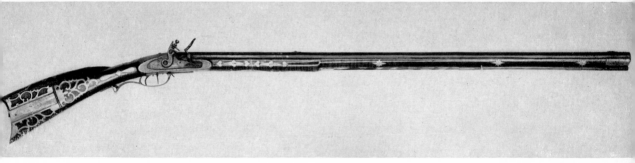

Kentucky rifle with brass and silver inlays, *ca.*1815–20.
Collection of Joseph E. Aiken.

Late Kentucky rifle with angular butt and percussion lock,
the stock inlaid with engraved brass tracery.
Collection of Joseph E. Aiken.

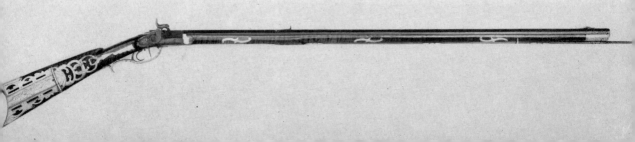

Baker rifle, *ca.*1800.
Armouries, Tower of London.

Brunswick rifle.
Armouries, Tower of London.

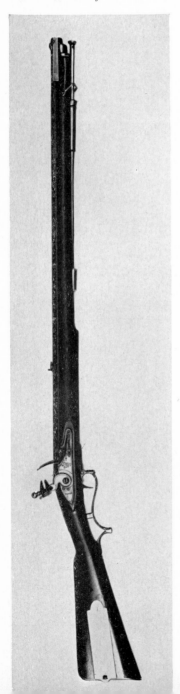

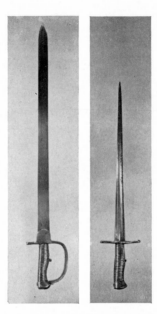

Standard sword bayonet for
the Baker rifle (LEFT)
and the hand bayonet
introduced in 1823.
Armouries, Tower of London.

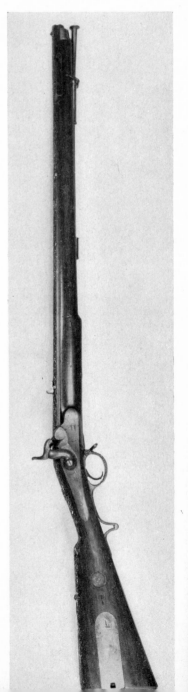

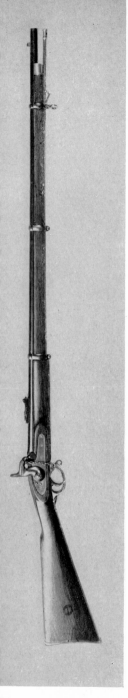

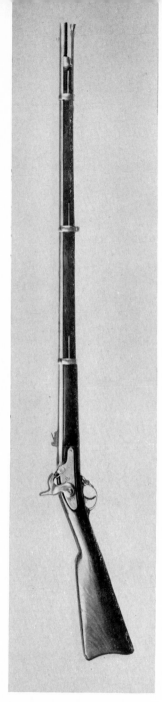

British Enfield rifle musket,
Pattern 1853.
Smithsonian Institution.

U.S. Springfield rifle musket,
Model 1863.
Smithsonian Institution.

Whitworth military rifle, an
experimental model of *ca.*1862.
Armouries, Tower of London.

Japanese Arisaka rifle, 6.5 mm. Type 38.

Krag-Jørgensen rifle, U.S. Model 1892.
Smithsonian Institution.

Plains rifle made by S. Hawken, St. Louis, Missouri.
Colorado State Museum, Denver.
Photo: M. Mazzulla.

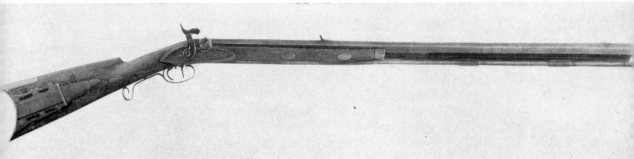

Winchester Schuetzen target rifle.
Smithsonian Institution.

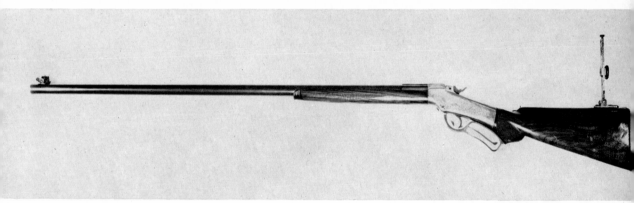

Creedmore rifle.
Milwaukee Public Museum.

Brescian flintlock pistol, signed **PIETRO FIORINTIN** on the lock
and **PIETRO PALINO** on the barrel; the lock plate, stock, and mounts
engraved and chiseled with floral ornament; late seventeenth century.
Walters Art Gallery, Baltimore.

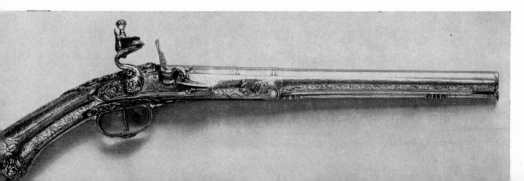

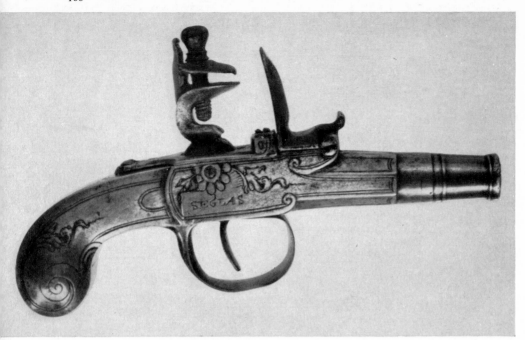

Single-barreled flint box lock pistol, with bulging butt; signed SEGLAS, LONDON; no proof marks. Made in Liège, third quarter of the eighteenth century. *Collection of Paul J. Wolf.*

Single-barreled flint box lock pistol with flat butt pierced for use as a barrel wrench. Signed LAMBERT DIT BIRON, a well-known Liège gunsmith of the late eighteenth century. *Collection of Paul J. Wolf.*

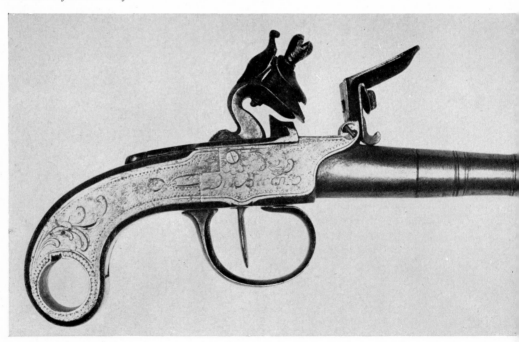

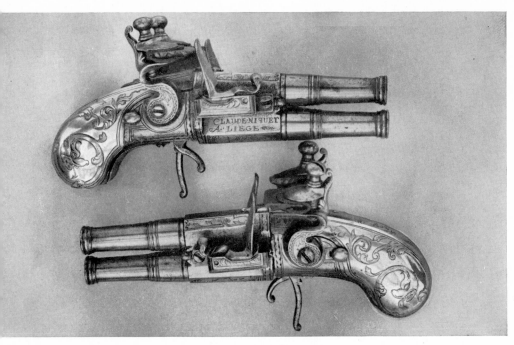

Pair of silver-stocked, engraved, superposed, double flint pistols, with side locks;
signed CLAUDE NIQUET A LIÈGE. *Collection of W. Keith Neal.*

Double-barreled, superposed, tap-action flint pistol, signed ASPINALL, LONDON
with London proof marks. English, *ca.*1790. *Collection of Paul J. Wolf.*

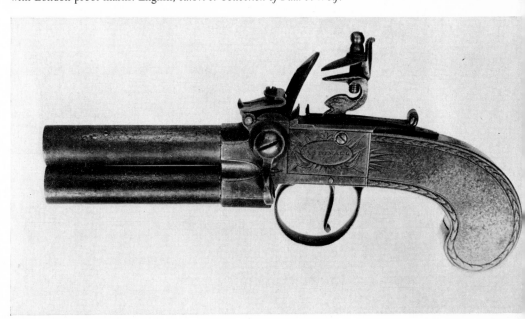

Deringer percussion pistol.
Smithsonian Institution.

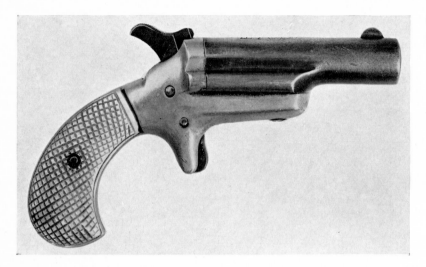

Colt deringer pistol.
Smithsonian Institution.

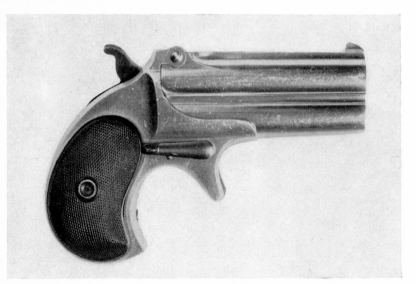

Remington double deringer pisto
Smithsonian Institution.

Bar pistol.
Collection of Lewis Winant.

Case of percussion dueling pistols made by James Purdey,
London, *ca.*1845, with alternative rifled and smoothbore barrels.
Armouries, Tower of London.

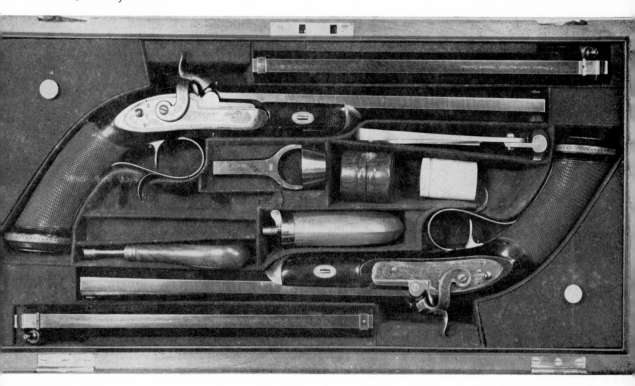

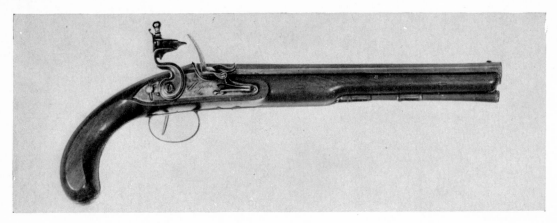

Flintlock dueling pistol made by Robert Wogdon, London, 1785.
Armouries, Tower of London.

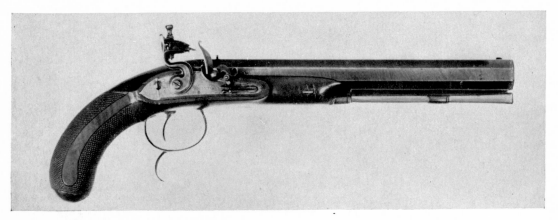

Flintlock dueling pistol made by John Manton, London, 1805–10.
Armouries, Tower of London.

Flintlock dueling pistol made by Simeon North, Middletown, Conn., *ca.*1815.
Armouries, Tower of London.

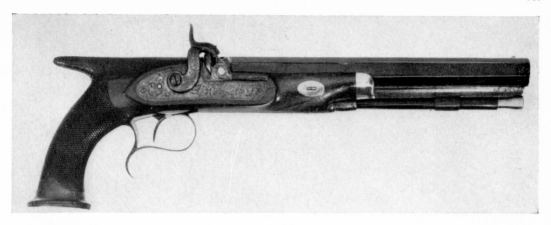

Percussion dueling pistol with saw-handled butt made by J. Blake & Co., London, 1825.
Collection of A. N. Kennard.

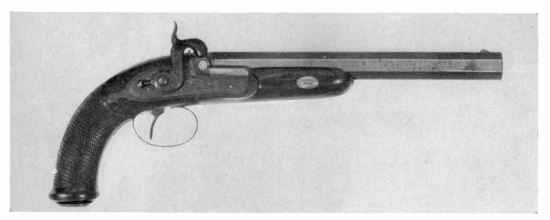

Percussion dueling pistol made by John Manton & Son, 1825.
Armouries, Tower of London.

Percussion dueling pistol made by Gastinne Renette, Paris, dated 1839.
Collection of A. N. Kennard.

Liberator pistol.
*National Rifle Association
of America Museum.*

Gaulois squeezer pistol.

Webber palm pistol.
Collection of Robert Abels.

Chicago palm pistol.

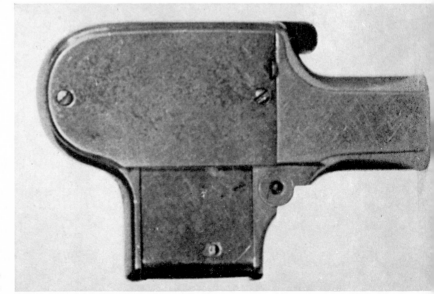

Shatuck Unique palm pistol,
caliber .32.

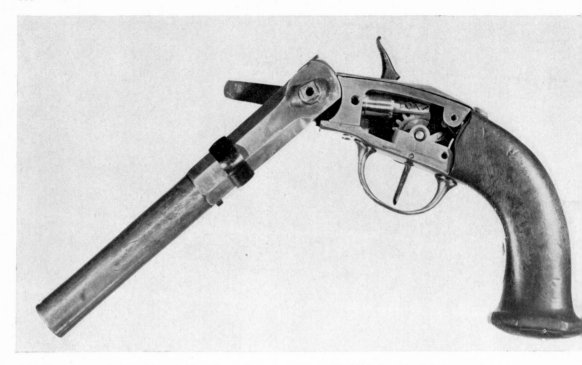

A Pauly compressed-air ignition pistol made on the system patented in 1814, the side plate removed. *Collection of A. N. Kennard.*

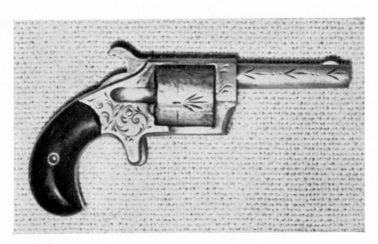

"Ranger No. 2" revolver, caliber .32, made by E. L. Dickinson, Springfield, Mass. *Collection of Donald B. Webster, Jr.*

Harte, the rhythmic name of its inventor took on a generic meaning. This result was furthered by the development of cartridge types, which were freely advertised as deringers, particularly by the Colt and Remington companies.

The first breech-loading deringer in .41 caliber rimfire was patented in 1861 by Daniel Moore. It utilized an all-metal frame and a barrel rotating downwards on an under-pivot that secured it to the frame. The design was marketed by the National Arms Company and later sold to Colt's who issued it and a wooden-handled variant as "No. 1" and "No. 2." Colt's also introduced a No. 3 model patented in 1870 by F. Alexander Thuer; this style had a side-swinging barrel equipped with an ejector. The "bird's-head" grip of the percussion deringer was faithfully copied. An advertisement in the *Illustrated London News* of 1871 stated that "Colt's new Breech-Loading, Large-Bore Deringer Pistol can be carried in the waistcoat pocket. Shoots accurately and with great force. Price 30s. or £3 the pair." The Colt No. 3 was very popular in England, over 10,000 being sold there in a decade. It remained in production at Hartford until 1912, and the design has recently been revived by Colt's in .22 rim-fire for the collector's market.

By 1872 seven distinct types of action for breechloading deringers had been patented and manufactured in the United States. The four-barreled Sharps (1859) and the Williamson (1866) exemplified the system of sliding the barrel forward from a fixed breech. After the Moore came the design of a fixed barrel and rolling breechblock by Remington. In quick succession followed the tip-down barrel (Starr, Ballard), the side-swinging barrel (Allen, Southerner, Marlin, Colt No. 3) and the rotating double barrel, sometimes sliding forward also (American Arms, Frank Wesson). Many of these were caliber .41 with the characteristic "bird's-head" handle. The seventh system, longest to survive, was the Remington double deringer with superimposed barrels hinged to the top of a fixed breechblock and tipping up to load. It was undoubtedly the most favored, continuing in production in caliber .41 rim-fire until 1935. This design has also been recently revived, but not by the original maker.

In the mid-nineteenth-century day of the deringer, its popularity was attributable to a widespread desire for an inconspicuous but powerful firearm for personal protection. From the southern states its vogue spread to California where the sporting gentry, gamblers, politicians, editors and miners made it a favorite. There a pistol shot was heard more often than the voice of the turtle, and one quarrelsome man could compel a dozen others to equip themselves in self-defense. As a secondary or "hide-out" gun, the cartridge sequel throve from the 1870's onward, until the small automatic eventually drove it out of use. But a colorful past has brought about a

revival today, and Henry Deringer remains the only American gunsmith whose name is a common noun in the English language.   J.E.P.

Illustrations: page 110, and endpapers.

Karr, Charles Lee, Jr., and Karr, Caroll Robbins, *Remington Handguns*, 3rd edition, Harrisburg, Pa., 1956.

Parsons, John E., *Henry Deringer's Pocket Pistol*, New York, 1952.

Serven, James E., *Colt Firearms, 1836–1960*, Santa Ana, Cal., 1954.

See also: DERINGER, HENRY.

DETONATOR

See: FORSYTH, ALEXANDER JOHN; PAULY, JOHANNES SAMUEL; PERCUSSION SYSTEM.

DOG LOCK

Dog lock is the modern term applied to any lock which incorporates a dog catch that hooks into the rear of the cock to act as a primary or secondary safety device. Since this feature is found as a variation on most types of lock developed over a period of 250 years, it should be qualified, when used, with a further description of the ignition.

Before the snaphance, with its two-piece frizzen and pan cover – which was, in effect, a means of preventing accidental discharge – could be superseded by the flintlock with its one-piece frizzen and pan cover, some form of safety device had to be incorporated into the lock mechanism. The simplest method was to attach a dog catch to the lock plate, which would hold the cock in place until manually released.

The dog catch, when applied to a gun, was generally intended to serve the same purpose as the half cock notch, but guns with both a half cock notch and a dog catch are frequently found. This may be an indication that there was a lack of confidence in the early half cock position on the part of the customer, or it may indicate that the gunmaker was aware of the deficiencies in the quality of his steel. Whatever the reason, it means that today one might find eight different types of dog lock.

Type 1

The snaphance had an effective safety device in that the frizzen could be moved out of reach of the cock while still remaining primed and ready to fire. But if the cock slipped out of full bent position, the movement of the tumbler would bear on the arm which slid the pan cover off the pan. This would invariably cause the loss of the priming powder and put the gun out of operation until reprimed. For this reason, a dog catch is occasionally found on firearms with snaphance ignition.

Type 2

The two-piece laterally acting sear of the wheel lock and snaphance was carried over to other early flint arms. The sear bar was made with a horizontal block working through the lock plate and acting on the tail of the cock. There were no notches on the tumbler. Externally there was usually a buffer fastened to the plate in front of the cock to prevent it from moving further than was necessary to produce the spark. This lock was introduced in the

Dog lock, type 3, exterior and interior views

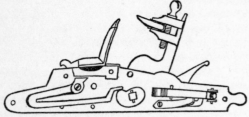

Dog lock, type 2, exterior and interior views

early years of the seventeenth century. In a later European variation of this lock, the sear engaged a depression cut into the reverse side of the cock. If any form could be considered a "true" dog lock, it would be Type 2 or Type 6 (below), for on these the dog provides the only form of safety. In other types, the catch is a supplement to the safety device on the tumbler.

Type 3

Early in the seventeenth century, a development now known as the English lock began to add safety features to the tumbler. It had a one-piece laterally acting sear working through the plate on the tail of the cock for full bent, and an extension on the sear bar which bore against a ramp or wedge on the tumbler.

Type 4

This is a variant of Type 3, with a half cock notch on the tumbler but retaining the laterally acting sear working through the plate on the tail of the cock. Another lock which fits into this category has the sear working through the lock plate and catching in a notch cut into the back of the cock.

Dog lock, variant of type 4, exterior and interior views

Type 5

This, the last of the flint arms to use a laterally acting one-piece sear, had a half and full cock position on the tumbler. The half cock was held by a heavy hook on the sear bar which slipped over a lug on the tumbler. As the cock was drawn back to full bent position, the sear nose moved into position at the top of a ramp cut into the tumbler. Judging from the number of existing examples of this lock, it must have become extremely popular from *ca.*1640, when it was introduced, until its demise about 1660.

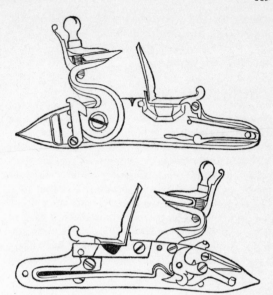

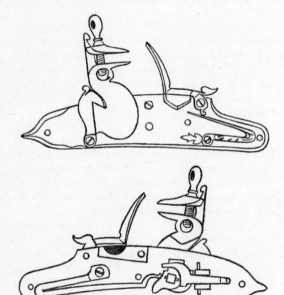

Dog lock, type 6, exterior and interior views

Type 8

A dog catch is occasionally found on percussion arms. Although it had disappeared from most of Europe by the middle of the eighteenth century, it was retained by the military in some countries until about 1850, and in those areas was occasionally used on privately owned weapons.

Dog lock, type 5, exterior and interior views

Type 6

Before the end of the seventeenth century, the French flintlock with a vertically acting sear had displaced all others. It had taken about fifty years to accomplish this task, but the merits of the design are attested by the fact that it continued in use for the remainder of the flint era and all through the percussion era. The earliest dog locks with this mechanism had a vertically acting sear working on a tumbler with a full cock notch only.

Type 7

This is the same as Type 6 except that the dog catch is supplemented by a half cock notch on the tumbler. It will be found both with and without a bridle over the tumbler.

Dog lock, type 8, exterior view

The dog lock was manufactured from the beginning of the seventeenth century until the middle of the nineteenth century, but most of its variations appeared in the major period of production between 1620 and 1670. It is impossible to place them in chronological order without considering geographical differences.   S.J.G.

George, John N., *English Pistols and Revolvers*, Onslow County, N.C., 1938.

Peterson, Harold L., *Arms and Armor in Colonial America, 1526–1783*, Harrisburg, Pa., 1956.

See also: ENGLISH LOCK.

DOUBLE-ACTION

Double-action is a descriptive term applied to guns, usually pistols or revolvers, in which the action of the trigger first cocks the piece and then releases the hammer to fire it. There were a few early attempts to produce practical double-action locks, but general introduction of the type is usually dated from Ethan Allen's patent of 1837. The double-action lock was faster than the single-action, but the heavier trigger pull required to cock the hammer made accurate shooting difficult. European nations generally adopted the double-action revolver for military purposes quickly. Americans were much slower to accept it for either civilian or military use.　　　　H.L.P.

See also: ALLEN, ETHAN; REVOLVER; SINGLE-ACTION.

DREYSE, JOHANN NIKOLAUS VON

Johann Nikolaus Von Dreyse was born in Soemmerda, Prussia, on November 20, 1787, and died there on December 9, 1867. He invented what Edward Crabbe in *The American Rifleman*, February 1941, called "The great granddaddy of all bolt-action rifles ... the magic wand with which the various Germanic states were united to form Germany under the Hohenzollern dynasty."

Dreyse devoted more than fifty years to gunsmithing. As early as 1809 he was working with the famous Pauly in Paris; as late as 1860 he invented an explosive bullet – banned for military use in 1868 by the conference of nations at St. Petersburg.

About the time of Waterloo Dreyse was back in Prussia, experimenting with improvements in percussion ignition. Although he had worked with Pauly when Pauly brought out the world's first breechloader to use a self-contained cartridge, Dreyse's own first guns were muzzle-loaders. Dreyse, with a partner named Collenbusch, was one of the early manufacturers of percussion caps. The two men worked on an entirely new method of using percussion ignition in a muzzle-loader. They put a fulminate primer at the base of the bullet, where it was detonated by the blunt point of a long needle driven completely through the powder charge. The fulminate being in a cavity in a spherical bullet, it was necessary to prevent the ball's turning when rammed on top of the loose powder that had been poured down the barrel. This was effected by holding the bullet in a hollow cardboard cylinder.

Muzzle-loaders signed "Dreyse & Collenbusch" exist in collections, but the later breechloaders, adopted by Prussia for its armed forces, were probably the responsibility of Dreyse alone.

The Dreyse muzzle-loading needle guns date back to 1828; the military breechloaders to 1841. Soon after 1841, the Dreyse breechloader was tested by the Prussian military, but the gun was not officially adopted until 1848. It was a great advance; it fired a breech-loading, non-metallic, but unified cartridge that held the projectile, propellant and primer – and it was bolt-action. The superiority of the bolt action was not fully grasped, however, until the modern bolt-action repeaters were developed.

When Prussia adopted the Dreyse, a royal pronouncement referred to the invention as "a special dispensation of Providence for the strengthening of our National resources," and piously hoped "that the system may be kept secret until the great part it is destined to play in history may couple it with the glory of Prussian arms and the extension of Empire."

Never was a secret better kept. Even after the gun had seen action, at Baden, completely absurd reports of its construction were circulated. Although the advantage of spiral rifling was then well understood, and although the Dreyse rifling – four-groove, so deep that the bore seemed square – was spiraled for one turn in forty-two inches, the *London Athenaeum* (September 1850) printed this: "The barrel is slightly rifled, but the grooves are perfectly straight, and not spiral, as is the case in our guns. By this means, much of the force of the powder, which is usually expended in giving the ball a rotary motion, is saved, and the ball is consequently thrown to a much greater distance. Indeed, it is said that with half the charge used in a percussion musket, it will carry the ball to the mark at a distance of 900 yards."

After Prussia's spectacular successes in her short war with Denmark in 1864 and in the Seven Weeks War with Austria in 1866, all Europe was agog and aquiver. The *Chambers Journal* (August 18, 1866) declared that the fame of the Dreyse was "ringing throughout the world" and that there was "one universal cry from every civilized nation for the arming of their troops in like manner."

Of the Dreyse's faults, two were grave. First, the gun too often became inoperative as a result of the needle's breaking. The needle was in the gunpowder at the instant of discharge, and it was unable to withstand a long continuation of exposures to the intense heat. Second, the obturating qualities were so poor that many men long trained to make every shot count became so afraid of the flareback when the gun was aimed and fired from the shoulder that they resorted to shooting from the hip.

In the frantic haste of all nations to obtain a breechloader as good as the Dreyse, France had her troops equipped with a similar bolt-action rifle when the Franco-Prussian War broke out.

Many double-barreled needle-fire shotguns, and a few – now quite scarce – needle-fire revolvers were signed Dreyse. These non-military pieces were developed by Franz Dreyse, son of Johann Nikolaus, whose renown rests on his rifle, the first bolt-action military breech-loader.   L.W.

Illustration: page 46.

Blanch, H. J., *A Century of Guns*, London, 1909.

Deane, John, *Deane's Manual of the History and Science of Firearms*, London, 1858, and Huntingdon, W.Va., 1946.

Greener, William W., *The Gun and Its Development*, 9th edition, London, 1910.

Marks, Edward C. R., *The Evolution of Modern Small Arms and Ammunition*, London, 1898.

Ommundsen, H., and Robinson, Ernest H., *Rifles and Ammunition and Rifle Shooting*, London and New York, 1915.

Winant, Lewis, *Early Percussion Firearms*, New York, 1959, and London, 1961.

See also: BOLT ACTION; BREECHLOADERS; CARTRIDGE; CHASSEPOT, ANTOINE ALPHONSE; NEEDLE GUN; PAULY, JOHANNES SAMUEL; PERCUSSION SYSTEM.

DUCK'S FOOT PISTOL

See: VOLLEY GUN.

DUELING PISTOL

Pistols specially designed for dueling were evolved between 1770 and 1780, their appearance coinciding with, and being at least in part due to, the decline in the fashion of wearing a sword with everyday dress. The earliest specimens are English. The barrels, averaging 9–10 inches in length, have a bore that rarely exceeds .57 of an inch, or 24 bore. Apart from their small bore, they follow normal practice for long-barreled pistols of the period in being stocked to the muzzle, while the butt caps are either small and flush-fitting or entirely absent. Mounts are occasionally of silver but more often of plain, blued steel, since anything bright which might guide the eye of the opponent was to be avoided. Back sights are always fitted. Pistols of this type were produced by most of the better British gunmakers, Robert Wogdon, of the Haymarket, London, being especially famous for his dueling weapons.

By 1800 the English dueling pistol had become more specialized. Barrels were now invariably octagonal while previously they had occasionally been round with a sighting flat, and they were made much heavier, though still of the same bore. The stocks have short fore-ends finished with a horn cap, the barrels having a rib on the under side to carry the ramrod. Hair triggers, rare previously, now become common. While rifling is occasionally found, this was never usual, and when it occurs the grooves are very shallow. Rifling in dueling pistols was, in fact, considered somewhat unsporting, and was generally frowned upon. About 1805 the spur trigger guard appeared, this being a guard with a curved extension for the middle finger, intended to give a more rigid grip and to make the pistol as far as possible an extension of the user's arm. The same idea lay behind the so-called saw-handled butt which became fashionable about 1810. These butts extend back over the top of the firer's hand, and, combined with a spur trigger guard, give a grip of great rigidity. Pistols with saw-handled butts are a peculiarly British feature and continued in fashion into the percussion period. In England the general build of dueling pistols altered little on the adoption of percussion ignition. Weapons made after 1835 are apt not to have hair triggers, while also after this date the pistols are frequently not fitted with ramrods, loading being effected with a separate loading rod kept in the case. Dueling pistols were invariably cased, from their first appearance in the eighteenth century, though in this they did not differ from good quality pistols in general.

Apart from the usual accessories, a tubular brass powder measure was often included, which screwed on to the loading rod or in some cases on to the ramrod of one of the pistols, and was used to seat the powder charge neatly in the chamber. In some pistol cases – and invariably when the pistols were rifled – a detachable mallet head was included which screwed on to the loading rod, thus forming a mallet for driving home the patched ball.

The production of dueling pistols ceased in England after 1840. The number of duels fought had declined for some years previously, though duels between officers in the army were still frequent. However, an amendment to the Articles of War in 1844 finally put an end to it, the last recorded duel being that between Lieutenant Monro and Colonel Fawcett in 1843 in which the latter was killed.

The only other country which can be said to have produced dueling pistols with national characteristics is France. In that country, dueling with swords was a common practice until society was disrupted by the Revolution, and it was not until the re-establishment of an ordered way of life under the Consulate and Empire that dueling once more became common. When it did so, pistols were frequently used, and suitable weapons began to be produced. The French dueling pistols of the period

1800–1815 are invariably stocked to the muzzle, while the butt has a sharp downward curve. Barrels are octagonal and usually rifled, the rifling generally of fine, multigroove type, while the bore is usually a little larger than with English pistols. Spur trigger guards are rare, and hair triggers are also the exception rather than the rule. On late flintlock examples, no ramrods were fitted, while at the same time the spur trigger guard was introduced, possibly due to English influence.

In the percussion era, the French dueling pistol had by 1835 acquired the form which it was to keep for the rest of its existence. The barrels were octagonal, or sometimes octagonal at breech and muzzle and sixteen-sided for a length in between, the rifling usually being of more normal type with wider lands and grooves, while the bore was reduced to about .5. Fore-ends were always short, the butts not as sharply curved as formerly and usually fluted both for decorative effect and to give a good grip, checkering never being as popular on the Continent as it was in England. Spur trigger guards were usual. Since ramrods were not fitted after 1820, French dueling-pistol cases almost always contain a brass or steel loading rod together with a mallet for driving the ball down the rifled barrel. In France, dueling has continued to be regarded more leniently than in England, and pistol duels, though usually bloodless, are sometimes fought today.

In Germany and those countries under German cultural influence, the sword duel was always more usual than the combat with pistols, and the production of dueling pistols was small. In the second half of the eighteenth century a number of rifled pistols fitted with hair triggers were made, notably by members of the Kuchenreuter family of Regensburg, but these, although suitable for dueling, were also intended as holster pistols. In the percussion era, German dueling pistols show strong French characteristics.

Dueling pistols were made in America, though in small numbers as far as the flintlock period is concerned. Men of means who wished to acquire a pair preferred to import them from England. An exception are the fine pistols of English dueling type made in the workshops of Simeon North at Middletown, Connecticut, between 1815 and 1820. The production, however, was limited. In the percussion period greater numbers of dueling pistols were produced, fine examples surviving by such makers as Henry Cooper of New York and Constable of Philadelphia. Most show strong English characteristics.

Dueling pistols are accurate at the distance at which they were designed to be used, which was normally between ten and fifteen paces. They were loaded with a small powder charge, rarely greater than three eighths of a dram, since heavier charges tended to throw the muzzle upwards.   A.N.K.

Illustrations: pages 111–13, 301 (plate 7), and endpapers.

George, John N., *English Pistols and Revolvers*, Onslow County, N.C., 1938.
Peterson, Harold L., *The Treasury of the Gun*, New York, 1962 (*The Book of the Gun*, London, 1963).

ENFIELD

The Royal Small Arms Factory at Enfield Lock, Middlesex, though first established in 1804, was not put on a serious footing until 1854. For the first fifty years of its existence it was mainly concerned with the assembling of arms from parts received under contract from private manufacturers. The only real exception was the production of barrels and special arms requiring that high standard of workmanship for which the factory has always been renowned.

By early 1854, the complete failure of the traditional contractors to deliver the arms urgently required in the face of the threat of war with Russia induced the government to press for the establishment of a mechanized state arms manufactory. After much bitter debate, a Select Committee, undoubtedly influenced by evidence from America of the possibilities of economic use of machinery in the production of high-grade arms, recommended the experimental mechanization of the existing factory at Enfield. A considerable quantity of machinery, and technicians to oversee its installation, were procured in the United States. In all, £315,000 was spent on land, buildings, machinery, etc., for the newly reorganized establishment. With W. M. Dixon as the first Superintendent, and J. H. Burton, formerly of Harpers Ferry, as Manager, the new machinery was first brought into use for the manufacture of the Pattern 1853 rifled musket, the arm otherwise known as the Enfield rifle.

Though the use of machinery saved a great deal in labor costs (for example, in 1858 only one fifth of the 1,250 workmen employed in the manufactory were skilled), the demand for military arms was bound to fluctuate and, at times, there was scarcely enough work to keep the factory running. By 1900, however, the factory had, at one time or another, manufactured at least thirty different types of arms and given its name to the system of rifling used in the Martini-Enfield and Lee-Enfield rifles. Indeed Enfield, which to this day remains the center of the official manufacture of arms in Great Britain, has for more than a century played an indispensable part in the detailed development of British military small arms.

     C.H.R.

Illustration: page 105.

Blackmore, Howard L., *British Military Firearms, 1650–1850*, London, 1961.

Cottesloe, Lord, and Roberts, G. H., "Royal Small Arms Factory, Enfield" in *Journal of the Society of Army Historical Research*, Vol. 20.

Reynolds, E. G. B., *The Lee-Enfield Rifle*, London, 1960.

See also: BURTON, JAMES HENRY.

ENGLISH LOCK

At some time during the first two or three decades of the seventeenth century, a lock was introduced in England which incorporated some of the features of the earlier snaphance with those of the flintlock. The flintlock's frizzen and pan cover of one-piece construction was adopted, but the main characteristic of the English lock was the incorporation of a safety device into the sear mechanism.

That portion of the earlier firing mechanism consisting of the laterally acting sear working through the lock plate on the tail of the cock was retained. Along the lower edge of the tumbler was added a wedge-shaped projection, the point of which engaged in the notch of the sear bar when at half cock. An alteration was made to the sear bar by adding an arm into which was cut a notch to engage with the altered tumbler. This in effect gave the sear two noses – one which engaged the tail of the cock at full bent, the other acting on the tumbler at half cock.

When the cock was drawn to the half cock position, the sear nose slid down the wedge and the knife edge jumped

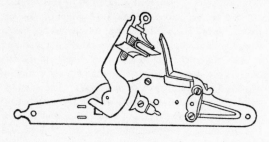

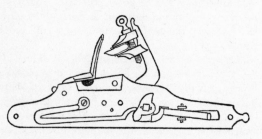

English lock, exterior and interior views

into the notch in the sear bar. As the sear moved horizontally, it was impossible to disengage the sear nose from the half cock wedge on the tumbler, except by drawing the cock to full bent position.

When the gun was fired, the sear moved far enough to become disengaged from the tail of the cock, allowing it to fall; at the same time, the nose of the sear bar slid up the longer side of the wedge.

The English lock had a life span of about twenty years and was used extensively on arms made for the military. Judging from the large numbers that have been found on Indian sites in the northeastern United States, it was also used on the early trade guns. 　　　S.J.G.

Blackmore, Howard L., *British Military Firearms, 1650–1850*, London, 1961.

George, John N., *English Pistols and Revolvers*, Onslow County, N.C., 1938.

Glendenning, Ian, *British Pistols and Guns, 1640–1840*, London, 1951.

Lenk, Torsten, *Flintlåset, dess Uppkomst och Utveckling*, Stockholm, 1939.

Mayer, Joseph R., *Flintlocks of the Iroquois, 1620–1687* (Research Records of the Rochester Museum of Arts and Science, No. 6), Rochester, N.Y., 1943.

Peterson, Harold L., *Arms and Armor in Colonial America, 1526–1783*, Harrisburg, Pa., 1956.

See also: DOG LOCK.

EPROUVETTE

See: POWDER TESTER.

ESCOPETTE/SCUPPET

From the Spanish *escopeta*, first recorded in Spain in 1517, having derived from the fifteenth-century Italian *schioppetto* and *scoppietta*. The Spanish word implied a gun of smaller than usual size.

A "scuppet" is referred to, in a text of 1611, as an alternative arm to the pistol usually carried by targeteers in Virginia. In this context a carbine is intended, presumably one fitted with a wheel lock. The word passed out of use in Europe but survived in America, particularly in areas close to the Spanish-speaking parts. By the early nineteenth century a carbine was almost exclusively meant when the word escopette was used, as it was most commonly in Mexico and the adjacent areas of the United States. A reference of 1805 describes fifty dragoons and fifty mounted militiamen as being armed with "lances, escopates and pistols." In 1854 one reads of a man being beaten with the butt of a Mexican's *escopetto*. 　　　W.R.

ESPIGNOLLE

An espignolle is a muzzle-loading repeating gun of small caliber, employing super-posed loads.

The barrel was loaded alternately with charges of powder and bullets. Each bullet had a longitudinal channel filled with powder to transmit the fire backwards after the foremost charge had been ignited, in roman-candle fashion. Once the first shot had been fired, it was impossible to stop firing until the bore was empty.

The roman-candle principle of the espignolle was transferred to firearms at an early date. A reference of 1580 seems to indicate that it was already being applied at that time. Giambaptista della Porta (1536–1605) described a variant of the system in his *Magiae Naturalis*, and there were numerous inventors, re-inventors and improvers during the succeeding centuries. Among them were Joseph Chambers of the United States, whose guns saw service during the War of 1812, and Captain A. A. F. Schumacher of Denmark, who began his work with the espignolle before 1816.

Schumacher's espignolles saw wider service than any of the others. They were multibarreled weapons, loaded with changeable pipe magazines, each filled with 16–32 charges, and the priming was ignited from the muzzle. Both the Danish Army and Navy adopted the weapon, and it continued in use until about 1870.   E.E.

Illustrations: pages 183–4, 283.

Blackmore, Howard L., "Chambers Repeating Flintlock" in *The American Rifleman*, Washington, D.C., Sept. 1958.

Eriksen, Egon, *Dänische Orgelespingolen* [Danish organ-espignolles] *1848–1877*, German translation of Danish edition, Copenhagen, 1945.

Peterson, Harold L., *The Treasury of the Gun*, New York, 1962 (*The Book of the Gun*, London, 1963).

See also: CHAMBERS SYSTEM; REPEATING ARMS.

F

FAKES AND FORGERIES

It is not now and probably never will be possible to give a coherent and adequately documented account of the history of faking firearms. For obvious reasons the faker wishes to remain anonymous and, though he may abuse another master's signature, he never uses his own. A few names have been rescued from their well-merited obscurity, but these are rare exceptions. The faker is guided by fashion in collecting, and at any one time he produces only the type of article that is most in demand. The history of faking firearms begins in the last quarter of the nineteenth century, some fifty years after the production of spurious swords and armor had commenced.

There may have been lesser lights who went before, but the first great name in firearms faking was the Paris dealer, Frédéric Spitzer (1815–90). Born in Vienna, he established himself in Paris in 1852 where he soon obtained a commanding position in the art market. He numbered among his clients the Rothschilds and the immensely rich Sir Richard Wallace, whose collection survives as the Wallace Collection in London.

Spitzer was convinced and managed to convince his customers that a firearm must be decorated all over to be worthy of attention. He maintained a workshop for adding decoration to authentic pieces, and – even worse – for making elaborately decorated arms by taking elements from different firearms and assembling them in different combinations. The purpose of this was to provide a richly inlaid stock with a barrel and lock of comparable elaboration of ornament. The sixteenth-century gunmaker, even when producing an enriched gun, did not ignore practical considerations. The barrel was not as a rule given much ornament, and if it was decorated, this was done in low relief. A wheel lock arquebus in the Wallace Collection has a combat scene chiseled so deeply into the metal just over the breech in the nineteenth century that it seriously weakens it. This would never have been done by a sixteenth-century gunmaker.

Spitzer must have had some highly skilled steel chiselers in his workshops; often their work shows no stylistic fault, but can be recognised on functional grounds. The sixteenth-century wheel lock plate was usually finished flat; if damascened in precious metal, the metal was not encrusted in relief but hatched on so that it was level with the surface. This was not appreciated by the Spitzer workshop and one finds lock plates with encrusted ornament in high relief. The nineteenth-century faker was also sometimes a little uncertain as to the date of a wheel lock, and one may find ornament of seventeenth-century style applied to a sixteenth-century gun or pistol. The reverse need not necessarily give rise to suspicion, as many of the seventeenth-century gun-decorators continued to use earlier pattern-books.

Judging by the Spitzer pieces which are to be found in the Wallace Collection, the British Museum (Waddesdon Bequest) and the Waddesdon Collection (near Aylesbury, Bucks, England), one of Spitzer's favorite practices was to change the barrel on a firearm. This can always be recognised in the case of an inlaid stock as it was almost inevitably necessary either to lengthen or to shorten the stock in order to accommodate the different barrel. If the former was done, an additional portion had to be added to the decoration, if the latter, the ornament had to be cut off short, and in either case the fore-end decoration shows signs of having been tampered with. A great deal of knowledge is called for in recognising this type of fake, as many pieces were re-stocked or re-barreled during their working life and these may show similar contrasts or even contradictions of style in their make-up. Spitzer confined his attention to the very rich pieces, and the plainer ones that show discrepancies of style or period in their elements are not likely to be his work.

He seems to have been proud of the productions of his workshop, for he had several of these altered pieces in his own collection, which was sold by auction in Paris in 1895. As with many other dealers, the distinction between his stock and his private collection was probably fairly fluid.

Possibly a production of the Spitzer workshop, perhaps made elsewhere, was a series of firearms with barrels, locks and mounts chiseled in the Sadeler manner with the detail in blue against a gold ground. When seen on their own these pieces are not unimpressive, but set one against a genuine sixteenth- or seventeenth-century Sadeler arm and the coarseness of their finish and poverty of their invention are clearly evident. Two examples from this workshop, now in the Victoria and Albert Museum, were plain military arms before they were elaborately chiseled. One was originally a wheel lock carbine of the type carried by the bodyguard of the Prince-Bishops of Salzburg, the other a Saxon wheel lock holster pistol. In each case the very simple horn inlay in the stock contrasts oddly with the costly ornament on the metal parts.

The collectors of the late nineteenth century who formed Spitzer's clientèle were not specifically interested in firearms. They were collectors of works of art, and only those firearms that were chiseled, damascened, etc., rated as such. This was the great era for all-over embellishment of firearms. Thereafter interest in firearms seen purely as works of art waned, and this activity slackened off.

An alternative to adding embellishment to a firearm was to add some inscription that would give to the piece a spurious historical value. This has been done from the earliest times of collecting, and it still continues. One English faker had the idea of adding to authentic English naval pistols of the Trafalgar period the name of a well-known ship, such as the "Victory." This was engraved on the pommel, but, although such an addition should be fool-proof, the faker made two mistakes – he used the wrong type of lettering, and he filled the lines of the engraved letters with black paint, which when lifted showed the raw metal underneath. Such additions are not always made with intent to deceive; sometimes a true family tradition has been recorded by engraving an inscription at a later date. In this case also the inscription is usually in the wrong style for the alleged date of the piece.

Some of the earlier firearms collectors were very easily taken in; during the early years of the present century, there was a faker, probably of German nationality, who made up wheel lock pistols in which the lock was the only authentic part. He supplied the barrels, furniture and stocks, using as his model Saxon wheel lock holster pistols of the early seventeenth century. He made the stocks with either ball-butts or pear-shaped butts and inlaid them all-over with roughly engraved horn and mother-of-pearl. In order to save trouble he did not bother to cut the stocks to accommodate the spring and sear mechanism, but simply removed the latter from the lock plate. To recognise the deception, therefore, it sufficed to remove the lock and examine the inside of the lock plate. This faker could evidently rely upon his customers' failing to take even this elementary precaution. Wheel lock pistols of this type must have been manufactured in quantity, for many survive; they can often be recognised in early twentieth-century auction sale catalogue illustrations.

One of the most skilled fakers of all time was a Dresden locksmith named Konrad who was born in 1879 and died in 1938. He is exceptional in that a great deal is known of his life and work. He formed a close relationship with the Berlin firm of the Kahlert Brothers, who enjoyed the title of *Kaiserliche und Grossherzogliche Hofantiquare* (Antique Dealers to the Imperial and Grand-ducal Court). The great majority of his fakes were swords, mostly based on examples preserved in the Historisches Museum at Dresden. There is, however, some evidence that he also turned out spurious firearms, though none have as yet been recognised. Many of his pieces were made for sale to the American millionaire, William Randolph Hearst, and, as the latter disliked buying from dealers, whom he suspected of overcharging him, Konrad's productions were usually put into the sale-rooms where they were purchased by Hearst's agent.

The embellishment of firearms practised by the Spitzer workshop had mostly been confined to matchlocks and wheel locks, but in the 1930's the flintlock began to fetch a high enough price to be worthy of the faker's attention. A London faker working at this period specialised in the addition of spurious signatures to authentic firearms. His work was, however, unconvincing, as he put the names of prominent London makers, such as Harman Barne, on pieces of quite inferior quality. He particularly favored signatures with the town name in its Latin form (Londini) engraved in a rather shaky script instead of the calligraphic flourishes of the genuine late-seventeenth-century style.

A form of faking that made its appearance at that time

was the reconversion to flint of fine flintlock arms that had been converted to percussion in their working life. This is not difficult to do in the case of plain military arms, but extremely difficult on more elaborately decorated ones, as it is necessary to find or to make both cock and steel to match the decoration on the rest of the lock-face. Original parts were not to be found and few fakers possessed the skill to match the replacements to the original. Reconversions of American Kentucky rifles from percussion back to flint are, however, normally accepted by American collectors as legitimate repairs; early Kentucky rifles in original condition are extremely rare. The same is true of other early colonial arms.

The most recent forgeries, dating from after the Second World War, are intended specifically for the American market. A popular practice is to improve a Colt revolver in one or other of the following ways: (*a*) by adding ornament or a presentation inscription, thus turning an ordinary example into a special one; (*b*) by deleting the original serial number or part of it and substituting an early number, implying that the pistol is one of the first made; (*c*) by adding some exceptional mechanical feature, thus making the pistol a unique model. Especially valuable models, such as the Paterson and the Walker, are sometimes made up completely and "antiqued" so that they appear to be genuine. The most easily recognised fakes are those with added damascening or gold inlay; the faker usually fails to copy exactly the nineteenth-century manner of engraving.

Another form of faking that has appeared in recent years is the production of spurious early nineteenth-century American dueling or traveling pistols. These are extremely rare in the United States, but surviving examples show that there was hardly any difference between the American and the English pistol of this period apart from the signature. Many of the American pistols were, in fact, made by craftsmen who had but recently emigrated from England. The only essential differences, therefore, between an English and an American pair of flintlock dueling pistols lie in the signature and proof marks and, of course, in their present-day value. Two or three minor alterations only were required in order to convert an English into an American dueler. In the first place, two inscriptions had to be filed out: the name on the lock plate and the name again or the town of origin along the top flat of the barrel. The London proof marks had also to be removed from the under-side of the barrel, where they were concealed by the stock. In the place of the original signature an American name – often Simeon North of Middletown, Connecticut – was engraved on an inlaid gold plaque or scroll. A considerable amount of metal had to be filed away from both lock plate and barrel and the inlaid gold scroll helped to conceal this fact. Some-

times, however, the barrel (octagonal in the case of a dueling pistol) was somewhat deformed after the filing, and if the faker did not file up each flat equally, the deception can easily be recognised. To add conviction to the idea of an American origin, an American eagle was engraved on the metal of the butt-cap or inlaid in silver in the butt. A mistake sometimes made by this faker was to inlay the maker's name in gold on what was evidently a second-quality pistol. Gold was reserved for first quality arms in the early nineteenth century.

Other common forms of faking for the American market include the production of Confederate revolvers. Sometimes these are made completely new, sometimes genuine parts are utilized along with new ones, and sometimes portions of more common Colt and Remington revolvers are altered and combined with new frames.

There are also simpler operations which convert relatively common arms into more desirable ones. Model 1842 military pistols made by Aston or Johnson have had their inscriptions removed and replaced by the marks of the Palmetto Armory, which more than trebles their sales value. Aside from detecting signs of the reworking of inscribed areas, the specialist can also note two or three minor variations between the new stamp and the original which immediately enable him to detect the forgery.

An even simpler alteration is the addition of brass-headed tacks and rawhide wrappings to a firearm of the mid-nineteenth century. This enables such a gun in fair to poor condition to be passed off as having had Indian use, and an almost worthless piece takes on considerable value.

The possible variations and types of faking and forgery are almost endless. The connoisseur must have an extensive knowledge of styles, techniques and materials if he is to avoid the traps set for the unwary. Amateurs are well advised to seek competent advice, to do business with reputable firms, and to obtain a bill of sale for each piece that they purchase stating what it is and what alterations, if any, have been made to it. American courts have held that any dealer selling a firearm has represented himself as an expert, and he can be tried for selling a fake. In England, an intending litigant would be likely to experience some difficulty in proving that an object purchased was not genuine.   J.F.H.

Illustrations: pages 351–2.

FALSE MUZZLE

A false muzzle is an accessory to a muzzle-loading target rifle which is installed each time before loading and removed before the piece is fired. It facilitates loading and greatly lessens the wear on the actual firing muzzle, thus prolonging the target qualities of the barrel. It was patented by Alvan Clark, on April 24, 1840, in the United States, Patent No. 1,565.

A false muzzle is fashioned in the following manner. The rifle barrel is made several inches longer than its intended shooting length. Four $\frac{1}{4}$-inch pin holes, irregularly spaced, are bored midway between the barrel's inside and

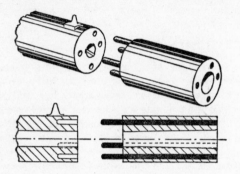

Clark's loading muzzle

outside diameters and parallel to the bore about four inches deep. A segment of the barrel about three inches long is then removed and the new muzzle and the false-muzzle segments are faced off on a lathe to a true fit at right angles to the bore. Hardened steel pins are then permanently fixed into the pin holes of the false muzzle, protruding so that they may fit into the corresponding holes left in the muzzle of the barrel. A simple clamp is then affixed to the false muzzle which hooks on to short pins fixed to the outside of the barrel at right angles to the bore. In the loading position, the pins of the false muzzle fit into the four holes of the barrel and, being irregularly spaced, can fit only in one intended position.

The barrel and the false muzzle having been rifled as one, the rifling of the barrel and of the false muzzle exactly coincide. The loading face of the false muzzle is chamfered, but as so enlarged does not extend to the shooting muzzle and thus permits easy entry of the bullet by finger pressure. In loading, a short starter ramrod is fixed over the false muzzle and struck a sharp blow with the palm which shapes the bullet to the rifling and forces it about four inches into the barrel, or past the choke of the bore. The bullet is then seated on the powder at the breech, with the loading ramrod. The false muzzle is removed before the piece is fired, and to ensure its removal a knob or plate is fixed to the false muzzle, obliterating the target picture in the sights, thus reminding the shooter to remove it.

The actual shooting muzzle is not chamfered, or crowned, the false muzzle substituting for the usual crowning of the muzzle. Great care is taken that neither the face of the barrel nor the false muzzle are dented or damaged and no foreign matter is permitted to remain on the mated faces, thus insuring a proper tight fit.

Round balls, lubricated with saliva, are patched with cloth, while the elongated bullets or slugs are patched with pure linen paper soaked in sperm oil. The false muzzle permits the loading of a tightly fitting bullet without damage to its patch, thus promoting accuracy. The false muzzle takes the usual wear encountered at the shooting muzzle in the cleaning and loading processes, thereby promoting prolonged barrel life for target shooting purposes.

The newly made muzzle-loading target rifles seen at today's shoots are equipped, except in few instances, with the false muzzle, thus indicating the modern shooter's acceptance of that accessory.　L.J.

Roberts, Ned H., *The Muzzle-Loading Cap Lock Rifle*, 3rd edition, Harrisburg, Pa., 1947.

FARQUHARSON RIFLE

The Farquharson breech action was, in principle, the invention of John Farquharson of Blairgowrie. In so far as it was one of the general class of dropping-block actions, its design was not new. Christian Sharps's system, from which it was obviously derived, was first patented in England in 1852. Moreover, Auguste Bellford, a patent agent, registered another very similar mechanism two years later. Farquharson's action, however, improved upon these earlier designs in that, when the operating lever was forced downwards to open the breech, a link pivoted in front of the operating lever moved backwards to cock the internal hammer. By means of a slot in the breech-opening link, striker removal was accomplished

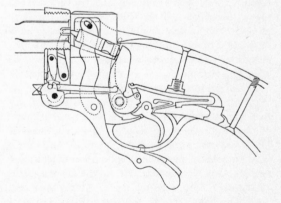

Cross section of the action of the Farquharson rifle

before the block itself moved. As only two screws were used in the entire action, everything else being pinned in position, the whole internal mechanism could be stripped for cleaning without a single tool.

Farquharson did not himself exploit his invention, but sold his registered design to George Gibbs of Bristol. It was the ideal action for use in conjunction with W. E. Metford's system of rifling. The first Gibbs-Farquharson-Metford was issued as a military breechloader in 1874, and quickly proved itself probably the finest target rifle on either side of the Atlantic. To the epoch-making Metford barrel and bullet was added, in the Farquharson action, a mechanism at once so efficient, so simple, so strong, and possessed of such excellent powers of ejection, that even today it is a highly prized acquisition for both target and sporting purposes.   C.H.R.

"Stonehenge" [John Henry Walsh], *The Modern Sportsman's Gun and Rifle*, 2 vols, London, 1882 and 1884.

FERGUSON, PATRICK

Patrick Ferguson was born in 1744, the second son of an Aberdeenshire laird, James Ferguson of Pitfour. Joining the Royal North British Dragoons at the age of fourteen as a cornet, he saw action in Germany. After a period of ill-health, he obtained a captaincy in the 70th Regiment at Tobago in 1768, but campaigns in the West Indies brought more illness and he returned home in 1774. It was then that he designed his famous breech-loading rifle. With great skill he demonstrated it before the King at Windsor and before a committee of officers at Woolwich. On the latter's recommendation, one hundred of the rifles with bayonets were ordered for trial. Having supervised their manufacture at Birmingham, Ferguson trained a detachment of men in their use and embarked for America in 1777. Here the riflemen distinguished themselves in the Battle of Brandywine, but Ferguson was severely wounded and his small corps was forced to disband. With his right arm useless, Ferguson learned to write and fight with his left. In 1778 he resumed his military career and led successful attacks on the rebel-held Little Egg Harbour and Stony Point. He was given the command of a small corps of loyalists called the American Volunteers and after leading them in a series of daring raids was promoted major. In 1780, with the acting rank of lieutenant colonel, he became Inspector General of Militia in Georgia and the Carolinas. While at the head of a battalion of this militia he was surrounded by a superior force of rifle-men. He fought his last battle – October 7, 1780 – on the top of King's Mountain, South Carolina, where he and many of his men were killed after a long and bloody battle.   H.L.B.

Blackmore, Howard L., *British Military Firearms, 1650–1850*, London, 1961.

Ferguson, James, *Two Scottish Soldiers*, Aberdeen, 1888.

Peterson, Harold L., *Arms and Armor in Colonial America, 1526–1783*, Harrisburg, Pa., 1956.

Peterson, Harold L., *The Treasury of the Gun*, New York 1962 (*The Book of the Gun*, London, 1963).

See also: FERGUSON RIFLE.

FERGUSON RIFLE

The action of this rifle, the first English military breech-loader, was a modification of one patented by Isaac de la Chaumette, a Huguenot refugee in London in 1721. It consisted of a plug with a quick thread screwed vertically through the breech end of the barrel, the base being joined to the front of the trigger guard. One turn of the guard was sufficient to lower the plug so that the bullet and powder charge could be poured into an aperture on top of the barrel. In use, the plug was liable to jam because of fouling, and Ferguson's idea, patented in 1776, was to cut channels in the plug which kept it free. One hundred of these rifles were made for the British Army in 1776; others, varying in the barrel length, size of bore and number of grooves, were made for the East India Company, for volunteer regiments and for sporting purposes. The only known specimen of the government model is in the Morristown National Historical Park Museum, in the United States, and this has a 34-inch barrel of caliber .68 rifled with eight grooves.   H.L.B.

Illustrations: page 43, and endpapers.

Blackmore, Howard L., *British Military Firearms, 1650–1850*, London, 1961.

Peterson, Harold L., *Arms and Armor in Colonial America, 1526–1783*, Harrisburg, Pa., 1956.

Peterson, Harold L., *The Treasury of the Gun*, New York, 1962 (*The Book of the Gun*, London, 1963).

See also: BREECHLOADERS; FERGUSON, PATRICK; RIFLES AND RIFLING.

FIRELOCK

An archaic term which has meant, when used by different writers at different times, a wheel lock, snaphance lock, flintlock, percussion lock or a weapon fitted with any of these. It meant originally any gunlock in which sparks were produced to ignite the priming. In 1631, the accessories to "Fier lockes" made in London included "keyes" which could only be wheel lock spanners. Firelocks undergoing Tower proof in 1703 seem to have had snaphance locks, but in 1854 the *Artillerist's Manual* described the official exercises for "Flint Firelocks" and "Percussion Firelocks."   w.r.

FLARE PISTOL

Flare pistols are basically a device to ignite and control the phenomenon of fire, and its resulting smoke, for the purpose of a signal. Pyrotechny is the art of fire, and the broad term "pyrotechnics" includes flare pistols, fireworks for exhibition, display and/or military signaling.

Long before recorded history, fire and smoke were used by primitive man for what we now would define as a signal; that is, a sign to give notice of something, issue a command, or to take other concerted action that had been agreed upon. Early in the eighteenth century, as firearms and gunpowder gained in popularity and replaced the earlier weapons, it was apparent that the underlying principle, with its fire, smoke and noise, was also valuable for purposes of communication.

During the middle part of the eighteenth century the French were leaders in many branches of science, and far advanced in the art of pyrotechny. A high degree of skill in the art was developed under the monarchy, and this was carefully fostered by the government which, through the ordnance department of the army, conducted a long series of tests and experiments for the determining and perfecting of all the processes involved. Careful records were kept and remain available today. In addition to the fact that the French had already attained a high degree of proficiency in pyrotechny at this period, their interest was further stimulated by the contributions of Father d'Incarville, a Jesuit priest who, while serving as a missionary in China, interested himself in the study of fireworks, and brought back to Europe a detailed knowledge which he placed at the service of his fellow countrymen in France.

It was the military, in France and elsewhere, who developed the art of pyrotechnics along the technical and scientific lines practised at the present time. The devices used were many and varied, and of course crude by the standards of today. However, we must bear in mind that the art developed slowly, keeping pace, as it were, with scientific developments in general.

Flares, flare pistols and similar pyrotechnic devices are direct descendants of the rocket – that most curious projectile, which is complete in itself, needing no cannon or gun to launch its flight.

In the latter part of the eighteenth century and the beginning of the nineteenth, there was great activity on the part of those enthusiastic over pyrotechnic devices as war instruments. A rocket corps was even made part of the British Army. Rocket missiles were used against Americans in the War of Independence and also in the War of 1812 at Fort McHenry and elsewhere. They were frequently employed in battles on the continent of Europe. This period witnessed many other inventions, adaptations and improvements in the art, but this development gradually ceased as the great improvements in other departments of ordnance rendered it essentially ineffective by comparison. However, in recent years rockets have again found preeminent places in the world's military arsenals (see ROCKET GUN).

But another variation in the use of rockets was destined to no such uncertain future during the early nineteenth century. Their value for signaling at night was realized, and rockets soon became a necessary part of the equipment of all military forces, whether on land or sea, as they remain to this day. The art of pyrotechnics, then, was slowly developing during this nineteenth-century period with the main emphasis on its use for signaling and communications. It was mostly employed by the military, although some commercial adaptations should at least be mentioned, for they were used early and continue in use today: railway and aircraft signals, ship-to-ship and ship-to-shore signals, are a few examples.

The earliest specialized pistols for firing flares known to the writer comprise those made for the United States Army and Navy during the American Civil War. Both models utilized the percussion ignition, and both had brass frames and tubes to hold the signal flares, but the navy model had brass grips and a long straight frame while the army model had wooden grips and a short, sharply curved frame. It should be noted, however, that some of the navy pattern dated 1861 are marked "U.S. Army". Thus, during the first year of the war both services apparently used the same model. Navy specimens are known bearing dates as early as 1861 and as late as 1872. All army pistols examined have been dated 1862, but a signal manual of 1879 describes them as still in use. In reality, these pistols were merely torch handles. The flares burned in their holders and were not propelled into the air. Thus it was necessary for the signaler to hold his pistol aloft until the full course of lights had burned. The lights themselves were invented by B. Franklin Coston, and consisted of a series of twelve combinations of red, white and green lights patented by the inventor's widow on April 5, 1859. In the 1870's a "needle gun" ignition was devised to fire these Coston flare cartridges but was apparently never put into production, in the United States at least.

An important advance in flare signaling came in 1877 with the invention by Lieutenant Edward W. Very, an American naval officer and ordnance expert, of a system of signal lights that could actually be propelled from a pistol and burn high in the air. This not only relieved the

signaler from holding the pistol throughout the performance but placed the flares at a much higher elevation so
that they could be seen from greater distances. Very's
system of signaling was adopted and used by almost all
armies and navies, and remains in use today with only
minor changes in some of the manufacturing techniques
to improve the pistol and cartridges. In Very's system,
balls or stars of red, green or white fire are shot from the
pistol in groups denoting numbers having a code significance. A cartridge holds the signal star, or stars, which
are propelled about three hundred feet, burning for six
to eight seconds, the ignition taking place about fifty
feet from the muzzle of the pistol. The cartridge is about
one inch in diameter and three to five inches long, depending on the particular loading. Diameters and lengths vary
slightly in different countries. Some early designs utilized
ten gauge sizes, but the one inch or twenty-five mm. was
the most popular. A 1½-inch size appeared in the First
World War and was also used in the Second World War,
but the twenty-five mm., because of size and weight, remained the logical and popular size. Signal cartridges are
similar to shotgun shells in appearance. Signal pistols
resemble an ordinary pistol with handgrips and barrel,
or barrels, of about six inches long. The principal difference lies in the size of the bore and the thin barrel walls.
Flare pistols have one, two, or three barrels, and hinge or
break to load and extract the cartridges. The firing pin
of the pistol indents the primer in the signal cartridge
base, igniting the propelling charge in the base of the
cartridge and thus firing the signal into the air to the
height prearranged for detonation.

The cartridge consists of a case, usually cardboard
with a metal base, but sometimes all metal or an aluminum alloy. A primer is in the base. The propellent charge
is about twenty-five to fifty grains of black powder. On
top of the charge are the wads and loading – stars, balls
of fire, or other grouping, as desired. The loading of each
cartridge is designated on the top of the cartridge, which
is sealed against dampness, usually with paraffin. Loading
and various combinations are numerous. A typical example is as follows:

White Star

Saltpeter	65.9%
Black Antimony	16.5%
Sulphur	16.5%
Meal Powder	1.1%

Red Star

Chlorate of Potash	71.9%
Strontium Carbonate	18 %
Powdered Orange Shellac	9 %
Lampblack	1.1%

Green Star

Barium Chlorate	90%
Powdered Orange Shellac	10%

Actual ingredients of pyrotechnics have changed little
over the years, but procedures and manufacturing techniques have kept pace with the over-all developments in
ordnance materials. Flare pistols of light-weight metals
are being developed, and synthetics and plastics used in
the loadings and cases of cartridges. Modern signals burn
better and longer, and the colors are more intense.

G.B.J.

Illustrations: pages 276–7.

FLINT

See: GUNFLINT.

FLINTLOCK

A term first recorded in 1683, in Turner's *Pallas Armata*,
when it seems, like snaphance, to have been applied indiscriminately to any type of gunlock that ignited the
charge by means of the sparks produced by a spring-
actuated cock striking a piece of flint against a vertical,
pivoted striking-plate (steel, hammer, or, in later dialect,
frizzen). Some writers and collectors confine it to the form
that has the steel and pan cover combined, reserving
snaphance for the form on which these parts are separate,
an artificial distinction first made by Meyrick in the early
nineteenth century. In 1939 Torsten Lenk, in his *Flintlåset*, defined the flintlock as a snaphance that has the steel
and pan cover combined *and* a sear operating vertically
to engage in two notches – giving respectively half cock
(safety) and full cock – in a tumbler attached to the inner
end of the cock spindle. This is the form of lock that was
in general use from the time when the term flintlock is
first recorded. Lenk's definition has been increasingly
adopted, and is the one used here. Some writers, in def-
erence to the nineteenth-century classification, call the
lock so defined the "true" or "French" flintlock.

The origins of the flintlock are still slightly obscure.
Snaphances were already being equipped with a tumbler
linking the mainspring and cock in the sixteenth century,
while at least one Italian example of the second half of
the century, in the Artillery Museum, Turin, has a combined steel and pan cover. It can be shown that these features, combined with a vertically operating sear engaging
in notches in the tumbler, were in use in France before 1615.
The evidence for this is provided by a flintlock gun made
for Louis XIII, now in the Renwick Collection at Tucson,
Arizona, which bears a mark ascribed with virtual certainty to Jean le Bourgeoys of Lisieux in Normandy,

who died in 1615. Earlier than the Renwick example, however, is another flintlock gun from the collection of Louis XIII, in the Hermitage, Leningrad, which is signed in full by Jean's brother, Marin le Bourgeoys. If the tradition that this belonged to Henri IV is correct, it must date from before 1610. In any event, it is the earliest flintlock known, and there is therefore some reason for regarding its maker as the inventor of the system.

Though it seems probable from the above that the flintlock was invented in the first decade of the seventeenth century, it came into general use only very slowly. The few recorded flintlocks dating from before *ca*.1630 are all associated with the French court, and there is, in fact, no evidence to show that the lock was made outside France before *ca*.1640. But by the 1660's it had virtually supplanted the snaphance in all the major European countries except Italy and Spain. In certain areas of Italy the snaphance and the national form of miquelet remained popular. In Spain the flintlock was always considered inferior to the miquelet, so much so, indeed, that true flintlocks of Spanish make are almost unknown, except on late military arms. Elsewhere, from the late seventeenth century until the early nineteenth century, the supremacy of the flintlock remained unchallenged. Even after the invention of the percussion system, it was supplanted only slowly in the West, while in many primitive communities it has retained its popularity to the present day.

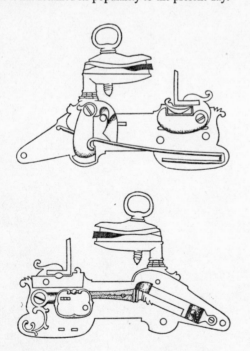

Miquelet lock, exterior and interior views

The early flintlock had a flat lock plate, often attached by two screws, instead of the three used for the contemporary snaphance. The cock, too, was flat and of rectangular section, often with a lateral piercing in which the lower end of the jaw screw moved: it was attached to the tumbler by a bolt with a nut on the inside. A feature, borrowed from the snaphance, that is found only on the earliest flintlocks is a small stop, or buffer, screwed to the plate in front of the cock, which it was designed to

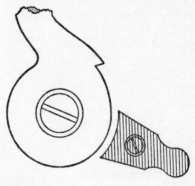

The buffer

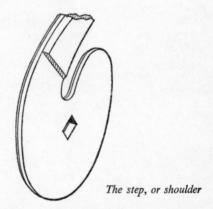

The step, or shoulder

prevent from descending too far. This was replaced after *ca*.1630 by a step, or shoulder, cut in the inner face of the cock, which performed the same function by catching on the top edge of the plate. The steel – a term that on the flintlock is often applied to the steel and pan cover together – acted against a V-shaped feather spring on the outside of the lock plate, as on the snaphance. On a few locks dating from before *ca*.1650 the steel-spindle is equipped with a tumbler that acts on a spring inside the plate.

About 1650, a new method of attaching the cock was introduced. The tumbler was now fitted with a square shank which projected through the lock plate into a corresponding hole in the cock, the two being held together

Plate 3

Wheel lock rifle, ornamented over its whole surface. The barrel and lock plate are engraved with the Virtues and figures emblematic of abundance amidst floral scrolls, while the stock is veneered with carved ebony enclosing panels of carved staghorn. The staghorn panels, which are executed with exceptional skill, depict hunting subjects and numerous figures of Turks, doubtless referring to the wars with the Turks in southeastern Europe. The carved stock is attributed to Peter Opel of Regensburg. South German, early seventeenth century. From the collection of Prince Fugger, Schloss Babenhausen.

Victoria and Albert Museum, London.

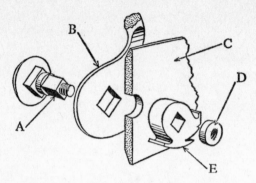

Method of attaching the cock before ca.1650
A. *Bolt*
B. *Cock*
C. *Lock plate*
D. *Nut*
E. *Tumbler*

achieved its final mechanical form. All subsequent developments were only refinements that left the basic construction unchanged.

In the 1650's the cock assumed the graceful "swan-necked," or "gooseneck," form that was to remain the most popular one for the rest of the flintlock's history, although military arms were often still fitted with the pierced cock, known in the eighteenth century as a "throat hole" cock. The 1650's also saw the beginning of a fashion, originating in Paris, for rounding the surfaces of the cock and lock plate. This survived until almost the end of the eighteenth century, though flat cocks and lock plates, usually with beveled edges, which came into favor again in the 1690's, were more common after about 1750.

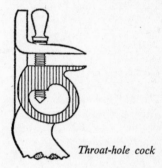

Throat-hole cock

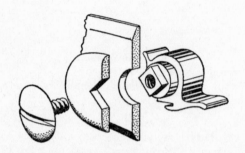

Method of attaching the cock after ca.1650

Among the refinements added to the flintlock mechanism, mention must be made of the following:

(a) The detent. This was a small pawl attached to the tumbler which prevented the sear from catching in the half cock notch (or bent) as the cock fell. It is first recorded on French firearms of the late seventeenth century, but it did not come into wide use until the second half of the eighteenth century.

The bridle

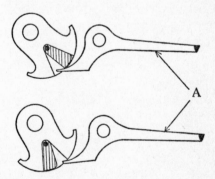

on the outside by a central screw. Another feature that appeared at the same time was a small bracket or bridle screwed to the inside of the plate to act as a bearing for the tumbler, which had hitherto been supported by the cock pivot only. With these improvements the flintlock

The detent – position at half cock (above) and fully cocked
A. *Sear*

(b) From about 1770 a roller bearing was sometimes fitted to the steel-spring or to the steel itself. This reduced friction so that the steel flew back more quickly and produced more sparks. The same period saw the introduction of a small swivel linking the mainspring to the tumbler, also to reduce friction. Both features became common after about 1785.

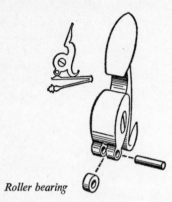

Roller bearing

(c) Many flintlocks from about 1780 onwards were fitted with waterproof pans. These had a raised rim over which the pan cover fitted like the lid of a box, while the curved fence behind the pan – designed to protect the shooter's eye – was pierced with a small drain-hole.

(d) Though a flintlock was theoretically safe when at half cock, many examples were fitted with an additional safety device. The earliest of these was the dog catch (see DOG LOCK) which, though rare after *ca*.1700, survived until the middle of the eighteenth century. From *ca*.1720 onwards the commonest safety catch was a sliding bolt which locked the cock. On box-lock pistols (see below) this was frequently combined with a device for securing the steel in the closed position, both often being operated by moving the trigger guard forward.

In 1812, Joseph Manton of London patented his gravitating stop, a device designed to prevent a gun from being fired accidentally while being loaded at the muzzle. It consisted of a small weighted lever made in one with a pawl and pivoted to the lock plate. When the gun was held with the muzzle upwards, the weight on the lever caused the pawl to engage in a notch in the cock, so lock-

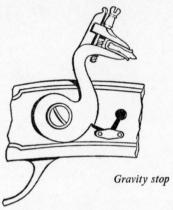

Gravity stop

ing it; when the gun was moved into any other position, the weight withdrew the pawl.

Finally, certain special forms of flintlock must be mentioned:

(a) The box lock. On this the mechanism is held, as in a box, between two plates, normally made in one with the breech. The cock is usually mounted centrally on top, and is itself shaped and notched at the bottom to perform the functions of a tumbler, though examples with the cock at the side as on the standard lock do occur. A pair of pistols of *ca*.1660 by Harman Barne of London, in an English collection, are fitted with box locks of a kind, but they are isolated examples at this date. The true box lock was introduced in the

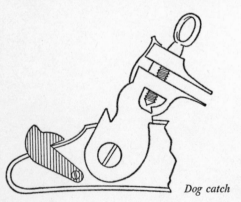

Dog catch

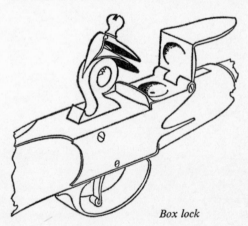

Box lock

early eighteenth century, and was subsequently widely used on pistols, especially pocket pistols.

(b) A rare group of late-seventeenth-century pistols, probably all made by the Cloeter family of Grevenbroich in Germany, have slender all-metal stocks with the lock mechanism mounted externally on the left. The cock is mounted in the normal manner but its spindle passes right through the stock.

(c) The screwless lock. In about 1783 the London gunmaker Jonathan Hennem devised a flintlock on which all screws, except those on the cock, were replaced by pivots secured with springs. This was taken up by the British Board of Ordnance, but was not adopted for service. Instead, experiments were made with an entirely new screwless lock devised in 1785 by another London gunmaker, Henry Nock. This was a form of box lock, in that the mechanism was mounted between two plates, the inner one of which was secured by a front catch. In dismantling, the catch was released and the plate removed; the various parts of the mechanism were then lifted off their respective pivots. Though taken into only limited service, this was mechanically one of the finest flintlocks ever made.

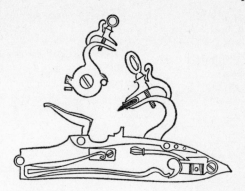

Madrid lock

is, however, found on late-seventeenth and eighteenth-century Scottish firearms.

(e) The concealed lock. Found on a group of German guns of the second quarter of the eighteenth century, this is completely concealed within the breech. The steel, which can be opened for priming, is actually a

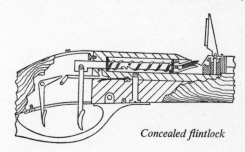

Concealed flintlock

lid covering the housing of the lock. The cock is thrust forward from the rear by a spiral spring, like a piston, and strikes the flint on the under surface of the steel.   C.B.

Illustrations: pages 39–40, 42–3, 107–9, 152 (plate 4), 233 (plate 5), 252 (plate 6), 301 (plate 7), and endpapers.

Blair, Claude, *European and American Arms*, London, 1962.

Hayward, J. F., *The Art of the Gunmaker*, 2 vols, London and New York, 1962–64.

Lenk, Torsten, *Flintlåset, dess Uppkomst och Utveckling*, Stockholm, 1939.

Peterson, Harold L., *The Treasury of the Gun*, New York, 1962 (*The Book of the Gun*, London, 1963).

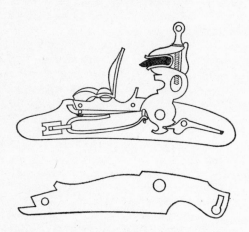

Nock's patent screwless lock

(d) The "Madrid" lock. Though this resembled a flintlock externally it was, strictly speaking, a development of the miquelet. The mechanism was equipped with two horizontal sears which projected through the lock plate and engaged respectively with a lug on the breast of the cock (half cock) and another on its tail (full cock). The lock, which is first recorded *ca.*1700, was confined almost exclusively to Spain and those parts of Italy under Spanish influence. A rather similar mechanism, derived independently from the snaphance,

See also: BOURGEOYS, MARIN LE; DOG LOCK; ENGLISH LOCK; MIQUELET; SAFETY DEVICE; SCANDINAVIAN SNAP LOCK; SCOTTISH FIREARMS; SNAPHANCE; SPANISH FIREARMS.

FORSYTH, ALEXANDER JOHN

Alexander John Forsyth was born in 1768 at Belhelvie, Aberdeenshire, where his father, James Forsyth, was minister. On his father's death in 1791 he took over the ministry, which he held for the rest of his life.

A keen shot and an enthusiastic chemist and mechanic, he was aware of the failings of the flintlock gun then in use. Inspired by the reports of Edward Howard, the scientist, on the use of fulminating powders, he began experiments to devise the first percussion lock. In 1806 he gained the support of Sir Joseph Banks, who persuaded Lord Moira, the Master General of the Ordnance, to allow Forsyth to conduct official, but secret, experiments at the Tower. In 1807 he completed his famous "scent-bottle" lock, so named because it had a magazine of fulminate shaped like a scent bottle, which replaced the old priming pan and by an ingenious action allowed a small portion of the powder to be detonated by a hammer. Official trials of the lock at Woolwich were, however, a failure, and the Ordnance withdrew its support after paying Forsyth his expenses of over £600.

Forsyth then patented his lock and set up a gunmaking firm, Alexander Forsyth & Company, at 10 Piccadilly. Such were the terms of his patent that he was able to take legal action against gunmakers like Joseph Manton who had developed other percussion locks, and it was not until the expiry of his patent that the ultimate form of percussion lock using a percussion cap could be successfully introduced. Nevertheless, when Forsyth heard that the Ordnance was replacing its flintlocks with percussion cap arms in 1840, he claimed compensation as the inventor of the percussion system. Although the Ordnance did not dispute that, they maintained that he had had no part in the invention of the percussion cap. At first, therefore, in 1842, they awarded him the small sum of £200. After his death in 1843, as a result of public demand, the further sum of £1,000 was divided among his surviving relatives.

H.L.B.

Illustration: page 41.

Blackmore, Howard L., *British Military Firearms, 1650–1850*, London, 1961.

Reid, Major General Sir A. J. Forsyth, *The Reverend Alexander John Forsyth and his Invention of the Percussion Lock*, Aberdeen, 1909.

See also: PERCUSSION SYSTEM.

FOWLING PIECE

A fowling piece is a smoothbore gun designed to fire a number of pellets at one time, for use in hunting small game, especially birds. During its early history it was frequently called a birding piece. More recently it has become known almost universally as a shotgun.

The practice of firing a charge of small shot when hunting small game was in vogue at least as early as the middle of the sixteenth century, though it was not always looked on with favor. An English law of 1549, for instance, forbade the firing of "hayl-shot or any more pellets than one at a time" with specific references to practices in shooting birds. Apparently this was designed to protect churches, houses and dovecots which had suffered from the indiscriminate shooting of enthusiastic fowlers. Bullet molds of the latter part of the century provide cavities for a number of different sized pellets, and references abound to "swan shot," "goose shot," and similar terms.

At first there was little or no specialization in sporting firearms. The pellets might be fired from any of the standard smoothbore guns of the era. Even heavy military weapons might be used. An excellent series of engravings of hunting scenes by Johannes Stradanus published in 1578 illustrates a variety of matchlock guns in use for different forms of fowling. Apparently, shot may even at times have been fired in the early large-calibered rifles.

In the beginning, the hunting of birds with firearms seems to have been principally the pursuit of the lower classes, who increased their food supply both through consuming the birds themselves and through preventing them from consuming crops. Wealthier sportsmen at first apparently considered birding only a form of target practice. Then it became a sport in itself, and it was this increased interest by those able to afford special weapons which brought about the development of the specific birding piece.

Probably the first of the specialized fowling pieces were the well-known English long fowlers of the early seventeenth century. These were huge weapons with barrels ranging sometimes to five or six feet in length. Ballistic theory of the period held that the longer the barrel, the greater the charge of powder that could be burned effectively, and hence the longer the range and the flatter the trajectory of the shot, all desirable qualities in the hunting of waterfowl for which these arms were produced. These great long guns were designed primarily to be fired from blinds near flyways and feeding areas. Their primary era of popularity (in England and America at least) lasted until about 1750. Market fowlers of the nineteenth century clung to the long weapons, however, and the punt guns of that period and more recent years may be considered direct descendants.

The long fowler remained relatively unchanged throughout its period of popularity. Ignition systems changed from English locks and dog locks to true flintlocks and finally to percussion. The stock shapes were modified in keeping with the era, and the muzzle moldings disappeared. To the end, however, it remained a long heavy arm of the simplest construction.

Shorter birding pieces developed in England at almost the same time as the long fowler, however. These were used for more mobile field fowling and can usually be distinguished from the arquebuses or calivers of the period by a slight flare at the muzzle emphasized by ornamental moldings. It was in the design of these lighter arms that real changes and improvements are to be found. Throughout Europe, and to a certain extent in America, gunsmiths turned their attention to producing finely balanced guns with light barrels of just the right length to consume the charge of powder properly. Improvements in ignition were sought as well as more rapid fire and greater accuracy.

Developments were slow until almost the end of the eighteenth century. Then a series of improvements followed each other in rapid succession. The key to the series was Henry Nock's patent breech of 1787. This device, which brought about more rapid and efficient ignition by detonating a small quantity of powder in a chamber be-behind the main charge, made guns shoot farther. Because the powder burned more rapidly it was also possible to shorten barrels from the previous standard of forty inches for a sporting gun to thirty-two or even thirty inches. Shortening the barrels made the guns still lighter, and this in turn made the side-by-side double-barreled fowling piece practical. A few had been made earlier, but their weight and clumsiness had prevented them from becoming popular. Now they became a major factor in the sporting scene. Joseph Manton, the great English gunsmith of late flintlock days, made them still more popular with the elevated sighting rib, patented in 1806, which made aiming easier and put their accuracy on a par with the single-barreled fowler at thirty to sixty yards. For greater distances the single gun was still supreme.

Fowling pieces followed the pattern of other arms in changing to the new percussion ignition. By 1830 almost all were made for the percussion cap, most with standard side locks with the mainspring mounted in front of the hammer, but a few with the newer back-action lock. By 1850 the back-action had become the more popular, but as late as 1884 some guns were still being made with the older side locks.

By this time, however, the muzzle-loading shotgun was already obsolete. In 1812 Johannes Samuel Pauly had patented his break-open breechloader and its cartridge of wrapped cardboard with a metal head, foreshadowing the modern single-loading breechloaders. In 1836, Lefaucheux took development a step further with his double-barreled pin-fire shotgun which opened at the breech on an under hinge and closed against a solid standing breech. A lever beneath the barrels released the catch. By the

1860's improved versions of the breech-loading shotgun using center-fire cartridges had appeared, and by the late 1870's hammerless models with top release levers and snap-closing latches were offered for sale. The choke bore was also perfected about mid-century. A short portion of the bore near the muzzle was constricted to concentrate the shot so that the pellets would travel in a tighter group for a longer distance and thus increase the effective range of the arm. This completed a development begun almost a century before. Added to the hammerless center-fire action, it produced what was virtually the modern single-loading shotgun.

Although all of these improvements had taken place and fine hammerless shotguns were being offered for sale by leading dealers throughout Europe and America, public acceptance was slow, and the second half of the nineteenth century witnessed the simultaneous use of a wide variety of fowlers ranging from the standard percussion-cap muzzle-loader through various versions of the side-hammer cartridge guns to the completely enclosed hammerless.

Acceptance of the repeating and automatic shotguns has been equally slow. The first repeaters began to appear in the 1880's, with Christopher Spencer's patent for a pump action version as one of the first. Real popularity, however, has come only with the present century, and there are many purposes for which the standard singleloaders are still preferred because of their lighter weight and their choice of two differently bored barrels if desired.

Although the original purpose of the fowling piece or shotgun was the hunting of birds and small game, many other uses have developed over the years, The use of larger shot, such as buckshot or even a single slug, has widened the target possibilities of the arm. In some localities it is widely used for hunting deer. The use of buckshot has also served to make it a formidable weapon as well as a hunting gun. The scattering of the shot compensated for poor aiming, and so American stagecoach guards welcomed the shotgun as the successor of the blunderbuss. The Wells Fargo Company armed its guards with a special short-barreled 10-gauge double gun made in England, and many peace officers carried similar weapons for riot work, where a spread of shot was desirable. Even today prison guards favor them for many purposes, and the sawed-off shotgun of the gangster became almost a legend during the 1930's. H.L.P.

Illustrations: pages 45, 277–8.

Ducharte, Pierre-Louis, *Histoire des Armes de Chasse et de Leurs Emplois*, Paris, 1955.

George, John N., *English Guns and Rifles*, Plantersville, S.C., 1947.

Greener, William W., *The Breech-Loader and How to Use It*, 9th edition, London, 1906.

Greener, William W., *The Gun and Its Development*, 9th edition, London, 1910.

Peterson, Harold L., *The Treasury of the Gun*, New York, 1962 (*The Book of the Gun*, London, 1963).

Serven, James E., "The Shotgun" in *Gun Digest*, 17th annual edition, 1963.

See also: BALLISTICS; CALIBER; LEFAUCHEUX; MANTON, JOSEPH; NOCK, HENRY; PAULY, JOHANNES SAMUEL; PIGEON GUN; PUNT GUN; SHOT; SPENCER, CHRISTOPHER M.

FUSEE/FUSIL

An anglicised version of the French *fusil*, meaning a flintlock musket which, when it was first introduced, was lighter and more convenient than the contemporary matchlock musket. The word fusee came to mean a light musket, and an English reference to "fuzees or long carbines" in 1680 seems to be an accurate contemporary description of certain weapons issued to fusiliers, grenadiers, sappers, sergeants and other selected troops until the mid-nineteenth century. In 1773, the young Prince of Wales and his brother Frederick received small "Fuzees... made in proportion to Musquets," which suggests that size and caliber were then the important points of difference between the standard musket and the smaller, handier, fusil or fusee.   w.r.

GALLERY GUN

Some gallery guns use an explosive as a propellant; others use air.

Gallery guns firing explosives are in two categories. First, there are the cheaply made small-caliber repeating rifles, seen at places of amusement, which may be dismissed from further consideration. Second, there are the fine single-shot weapons formerly found in public shooting galleries and in the private salons of France.

The public shooting galleries were primarily for target practice by any who felt they might have to engage in a duel with pistols. The pistols might be the shooter's own, or the property of the shooting gallery. They were mostly percussion cap, smoothbore, and of high quality. Many were of superb craftsmanship, and they shot where they were pointed. The galleries attempted to simulate conditions that would be met on what was called the field of honor. The target was normally the figure of a man, and

the shooter held his pistol pointed at the floor until it was signaled that he might raise it and fire. Sometimes the target was on edge to the shooter until the handkerchief was dropped, when the target turned, much as bobbing targets are turned in today's rapid-fire pistol matches. Collectors call such pistols "target-duelers."

Firearms used for target practice in salons might be these same large-caliber target-duelers, but they were more often of small caliber, less than accurate, and intended for shooting at shorter ranges. In such guns the powder charge, if any, was minimal. Many of these indoor target arms used as a propellant only the fulminate in a percussion cap or, in the case of breechloaders, the equivalent charge for the tiny rim-fire cartridges that contain no gunpowder – the .22 BB, the .22 CB, as well as the 4 mm. and 6 mm. cartridges designed for indoor target shooting.

The indoor target pistols were not always of as conventional construction as the target-duelers. Sometimes a breech-loading pistol would chamber a holder which contained the nipple for the percussion cap.

This idea of a holder became established with the *Zimmerstutzen*, the German indoor target rifles which shoot the 4 mm. rim-fires charged with the fulminate only. The barrel is bored to a depth of 6–8 inches at the muzzle end and the holder, loaded with its little cartridge, is inserted at that distance from the muzzle. A long striking rod extends back to the hammer. *Zimmerstutzen* rifles are regularly of Schuetzen pattern and are equipped both with double set triggers and with peep sights adjustable for windage and elevation.

Some percussion-cap long guns made for indoor shooting similarly employed a long rod to strike a percussion cap set on a nipple fixed in the center of the barrel only six inches from the muzzle.

Gallery guns were by no means all firearms. Many were spring-air guns, designed for passing amusement, and to be found in public galleries in populous areas. Such gallery air guns usually employed a spring mechanism that was incapable of great compression.   L.W.

Illustration: page 278.

Smith, Walter H. B., *Gas, Air and Spring Guns of the World*, Harrisburg, Pa., 1957.

Winant, Lewis, *Early Percussion Firearms*, New York, 1959, and London, 1961.

Wolff, Eldon G., *Air Guns* (Milwaukee Public Museum Publications in History, No. 1), Milwaukee, 1958.

GARAND, JOHN C.

Born on January 1, 1888, at St. Rémi in the province of Quebec, John C. Garand moved to Connecticut in 1898.

He began work in a cotton mill at the age of twelve, and showed his mechanical genius by obtaining the first of his many patents at the age of thirteen. After some machine-shop and welding experience, he was employed by a tool manufacturer as a tool and gauge maker. He later worked for other manufacturers as a machine and gauge designer.

The outbreak of the First World War found him in New York City, at which time he became interested in gun design. He submitted a design for a light machine gun in 1916 and was employed by the National Bureau of Standards to work on this design. His work attracted the attention of the Army Ordnance Corps, and he transferred to Springfield Armory in November 1919. He remained at Springfield Armory for thirty-four years, retiring in 1953. He still resides in Springfield, Massachusetts.

Garand's outstanding achievements have been in the design of semi-automatic rifles. His first effort in this field produced the primer-actuated T1920 rifle. Garand's second rifle design, the Model 1921, was also a primer-actuated arm, as was his Model 1924. In 1929, his gas-operated T3 semi-automatic rifle was submitted for testing. This rifle was similar to the later M1 rifle, but was chambered for the .276 Pedersen cartridge. In 1931 a caliber .30 version of this rifle was developed, and this evolved into the M1, which was adopted by the United States Army in 1936.

Garand developed the first semi-automatic military rifle, produced in millions and used as a basic shoulder weapon.   J.E.S.

Hatcher, Major General Julian S., *Hatcher's Book of the Garand*, Washington, D.C., 1948.

See also: GARAND RIFLE.

GARAND RIFLE

A gas-operated, magazine-fed weapon adopted by the United States Army on January 9, 1936. The nomenclature of the weapon is Rifle, Caliber .30, M1. The two sniper versions of this rifle are the M1C and the M1D. The Garand rifle works on the gas impingement system (see AUTOMATIC ARMS) and is loaded with an eight-round *en bloc* clip which is ejected when the last round is fired; it has a turning bolt with two frontal locking lugs. The rear sight is an aperture type adjustable for windage and elevation. The M1 weighs 9.5 lb. and is 43.6 inches long with a 24-inch barrel; muzzle velocity is 2,750 feet per second with the ball cartridge.

Over five million M1 rifles were made by Springfield Armory, Winchester, Harrington and Richardson, and International Harvester. The Garand is being replaced in United States service by the 7.62 mm. M14 rifle.   J.E.S.

Illustration: page 207.

Hatcher, Major General Julian S., *Hatcher's Book of the Garand*, Washington, D.C., 1948.
Smith, Walter H. B. and Joseph E., *The Book of Rifles*, 3rd edition, Harrisburg, Pa., 1963.

See also: GARAND, JOHN C.

GAS GUN

Gas guns may be defined as those using as a propellant any gas except air or those gases resulting from an explosion of gunpowder.

Modern gas-powered arms all use liquified carbon dioxide (CO_2), supplied in steel cartridges similar to those made for home soda bottle charging.

Carbon dioxide was known by 1834 in all its modern forms as a gas, or compressed to a liquid or a solid ("dry ice"). In that year, the Danish inventor Peder Rasmussen apparently experimented with a carbon dioxide repeating gas gun.

A variety of other gases and combinations have been tried, including:

Steam. About 1500 A.D., Leonardo da Vinci designed a steam-powered cannon. Other inventors built successful steam cannon as late as the American Civil War in 1863. All proved impractical in the field, and no steam-powered small arms are known.

Hydrogen. In 1849, John Edington (Spec. 549, British) proposed carburated hydrogen and air as a propellant. In 1887, De Penning and Smith obtained British patent 2,864 to use "combined vapours of water and oil or fats for propellants."

The diesel effect. In the early 1920's Herr Ronnebeck obtained German patent No. 203,076 to increase the power of spring-type air guns. He utilized the heat generated by the sudden compression of air at the instant of firing to explode a mixture of light oil and air, thereby increasing velocity, with erratic results.

Ether-air. A recent German system uses an ether atomizer to inject ether gas into spring-type air guns, utilizing the diesel principle, thereby doubling the velocity. Again, results are erratic.

Dry ice gas system. In 1943 the use of CO_2 gas, solidified by greater pressure into solid form (carbon dioxide ice), was tested by R. J. Monner of Denver, Colorado. He produced a bolt-action repeating rifle, in which the propellant stayed intact for months. The arm would fire thousand of shots at 700 feet per second with heavy bullets, but was never produced commercially.

The only practical system was that of Paul Giffard, a French engineer, who in 1859 patented the modern pneumatic air gun, and in 1889 the modern CO_2 gun complete in every detail except for the present use of the "soda bottle" cartridges. Giffard used a small, exchangeable, refillable gas cylinder. His gun drew a great deal of attention, and was considered by some to be a weapon to end war.

Modern air and gas arms are accepted today as excellent target arms and shooting trainers. Their war use was prohibited by the Geneva Conference years ago, although a few especially constructed specimens were utilized by various espionage agencies during the Second World War.

Most gas guns are manufactured and used in the United States, being preferred to air guns for greater ease in loading and shooting. They also handle more like standard firearms. The pressure in a liquid gas gun remains nearly constant for a much greater number of shots than does that of a pneumatic air gun, resulting in more uniform velocity and accuracy.

The use of gas guns in Great Britain is restricted by the firearms laws covering all pneumatic arms, permitting general use only of the lower-powered, spring-operated, compressed-air guns.

In 1958, the Crossman Arms Company of Freeport, New York, produced a curious smoothbore arm of caliber .50, to shoot gas-operated hypodermic syringes in the form of darts $3\frac{1}{4}$ – $4\frac{3}{4}$ inches long – the cap-chure gun. Filled with medical solutions to tranquilize, paralyze or innoculate wild animals or cattle, these arms are finding increased use by animal handlers and police, to whom their sale is restricted.

Underwater spear guns, using carbon dioxide cartridges, were introduced by the Crossman Arms Company in 1958.

Special guns for trick film effects, such as knife-throwing and the accurate shooting of arrows, spears or fake bullets at close ranges, are all of individual design and most use compressed air from tanks, although some of them do use gas.   P.W.

Smith, Walter H. B., *Gas, Air and Spring Guns of the World*, Harrisburg, Pa., 1957.

Wesley, L., *Air-Guns and Air-Pistols*, New York and London, 1955.

Wolff, Eldon G., *Air Guns* (Milwaukee Public Museum Publications in History, No. 1), Milwaukee, 1958.

GATLING, RICHARD JORDAN

Richard Jordan Gatling was born on September 12, 1818, in Hertford County, North Carolina, where the first Gatlings emigrating from England had settled, about 1700.

His father was a successful planter and inventor, and young Gatling soon demonstrated his own mechanical ability when at the age of twenty-one he patented a rice-sowing machine.

In 1844 he began manufacturing agricultural implements in St. Louis and soon expanded his operations to include plants in Springfield, Ohio, and Indianapolis, Indiana.

The Civil War provided Gatling's springboard to fame. On November 4, 1862, he was granted United States Patent No. 36,836 for a rapid-fire gun. The first model was only a crude forerunner of the gun he soon perfected, the prototype of one of the most remarkable firing mechanisms of all ordnance history – the Gatling gun.

Continued improvements brought another patent in 1865, and twelve guns were manufactured that year in Philadelphia. After official acceptance by the United States Army in 1866, Gatling received his first large order from the military – 100 guns.

For the next thirty years Gatling worked on improvements, and conducted many firing exhibitions throughout Europe and South America. By now the gun had reached a firing rate of 1,200 rounds per minute. Gatling later sold the patent rights to the Colt Patent Fire Arms Manufacturing Company.

After an unsuccessful attempt to develop a new gunmetal alloy, Gatling returned to agricultural implements and invented a motor-driven plow in 1900. While on a business trip to arrange for manufacture of the plow, he was stricken by influenza and died on February 26, 1903.

                                                G.M.C.

See also: GATLING GUN.

GATLING GUN

The first Gatling gun was designed by Dr. Richard J. Gatling in 1861 as a special objectives weapon to defend buildings, causeways and bridges. In 1862 Gatling demonstrated his first working model, which was fundamentally the Ager principle improved by the multi-barrel arrangement of the Ripley gun.

This weapon was crank-operated with six revolving barrels equally spaced around a central shaft. Each barrel had its own bolt, and cocking and firing were performed by cam action through a gear-drive arrangement.

Gatling constantly improved the various models of his machine gun. Type 11 of the 1862 model added copper-cased rim-fire ammunition to replace the paper cartridges and percussion caps originally used. The United States Army officially adopted the Gatling in 1866, after it had been chambered for the caliber .50 army-rifle ammunition.

The Gatling gun saw service in many armies and a number of wars, and was chambered for almost every contemporary caliber military ammunition. It was adapted for electric-powered, and later gas, operation, and achieved a firing rate of 3,000 rounds per minute before being abandoned as obsolete in 1911.   G.M.C.

Illustration: page 183.

Chinn, Colonel George M., *The Machine Gun*, 4 vols, Washington, D.C., 1951–55.

Serven, James E., *Colt Firearms, 1836–1960*, Santa Ana, Cal., 1954.

See also: GATLING, RICHARD JORDAN.

GAUGE

See: CALIBER.

GRAS RIFLE

The French Model 1874 (Gras), caliber 11 mm. (.433), bolt-action single-shot rifle was designed by Captain Basile Gras (1836–1904), who presented it to the Commission at Douai in May 1873. The Model 1874 was a modification of the Chassepot rifle adopted in 1866. The general lines of the Chassepot were retained, while the barrel and breech mechanism were modified to take a center-fire metallic cartridge, which replaced the "self-consuming" one formerly used. The overall length of the Model 1874 without bayonet is 51.25 inches, and of the four-grooved barrel 32.5 inches. The weight without bayonet is 9 lb. 11 oz. The Model 1874 épée bayonet has a brass pommel, wooden grips and a straight 20½-inch blade T-shaped in cross section. The scabbard is steel. The

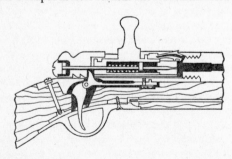

Cross section of the action of the Gras rifle, Model 1874

musketoon Model 1874 has a turned-down bolt handle. The trigger guard, butt plate and three bands are brass. Its total length is 27.25 inches. No bayonet was provided for the musketoon. A carbine Model 1874 was also produced. The Model 1878 Kropatschek rifle, caliber 11 mm., incorporated the Model 1874 breech assembly with a tubular magazine fitted in the stock under the barrel. This arm, used by the French Navy, served as the prototype for the Model 1886 (Lebel) rifle.   L.A.W.

Farrow, Edward S., "Gras Rifle" in *Farrow's Military Encyclopedia* (3 vols), Vol. 1, New York, 1885.

"Gras, Basile" in *La Grande Encyclopédie* (31 vols), Vol. 19, Paris, 1886–1902.

Hicks, Captain (later Major) James Ernest, assisted by André Jandot, *Notes on French Ordnance, 1717–1936*, Mount Vernon, N.Y., 1938.

See also: LEBEL RIFLE.

GREENER, WILLIAM

William Greener, of Newcastle and Birmingham, who died in 1869, was certainly one of the best known gunmakers of his day. He acquired his reputation more from his literary and administrative activities than from great

William Greener's expanding bullet

inventive genius in the field of firearms development. Even so, he did make an important discovery in this direction when, in 1835, he produced his self-expanding rifle bullet. Unfortunately, its possibilities were not at the time appreciated by the authorities, but later, in 1857, he was awarded £1,000 for this first public demonstration of the principle that was later to become so well known as Minié's system.

He turned his natural talent towards many different ends, ranging from the patenting of the first electric light in England to the design of a water-ballast, self-righting lifeboat. Nevertheless, he was concerned with the inefficiency of most muzzle-loaders then in use, and did much to expose the defects of the service smoothbore musket. Though his efforts to improve muzzle-loading shotguns were generally successful, he was, in 1852, entirely unable to produce a military muzzle-loading rifle of sufficient merit to take part in the trials that led, eventually, to the introduction of the Pattern 1853 rifled musket.

As an author he was fairly prolific. The most important of his books were *The Gun* (1835), *The Science of Gunnery* (1841), and *Gunnery in 1858*, but he still found time to do much towards the better organization and administration of the gun trade. He was succeeded by his son, W. W. Greener, who staunchly upheld the family's literary reputation but who, unlike his father, turned his inventive talent towards the perfection of the breechloader.   C.H.R.

GRENADE LAUNCHER

Shortly before 1600, a development in military firearms took place that was to have little effect on the course of any battle for the next three hundred years. The hand mortar, introduced to throw grenades farther than a man could by the strength of his arm, came into use in several parts of Europe. There is no record of where the first was made, but surviving examples from the end of the sixteenth century are German, fitted with locks made in Nuremberg. Their stocks were based on the butt of the contemporary musket, and a standard wheel lock fired the charge in the constricted powder chamber of a short, stubby mortar barrel.

In their wars against the Danes between 1657 and 1660, the Swedish infantry fired small grenades mounted on tubes that fitted their musket barrels. These tubes were filled with an incendiary compound that served as a fuse. In theory, the burning time of the fuse corresponded to the time of flight of the grenade.

In 1681, a variation of the original type was invented by John Tinker, a British Ordnance fire-worker, as "a new way of shooting Handgranadoes out of small Morterpeeces." Four years later 50 were made at a cost of £5.10s. each, compared with about 17 shillings for a common musket. Two firearms in the Tower of London may be part of this order. Both are engraved with the Royal Cipher of King James II (1685–88) on flintlocks that are ingeniously made to fire charges either in the barrel or in the 2.75-inch diameter chambered cup that forms the root of the butt. To fire the mortar cup, the musket is propped on its (plugged) muzzle and on a pivoted steel rest. The hinged wooden end to the butt is dropped to open the steel cup, which is then loaded like any other mortar and primed at an opening behind the cock. A sliding shutter is raised before firing.

Two short grenade mortars in the Kungliga Armémuseum, Stockholm, now consist only of short cups with constricted chambers and sockets fitted with grub screws for attachment to a staff or stand. The powder in the small, scalloped pans was ignited by match. They are difficult to date but are probably from the end of the seventeenth century and may be the direct antecedents of a *mortier à grenade* shown in Surirey de Saint-Rémy's *Mémoires d'Artillerie*, 1702. This, the invention of a French artillery officer, looks very like a modern infantry mortar but has a short cup barrel set on a tubular spike with a second tube as a prop.

By 1728, a grenade gun combining a detachable cup with a musket or carbine was in use in Britain and elsewhere. The cup's hollow socket was fastened to the muzzle by a screw thread, a spring catch or an L-shaped slot such as held the contemporary bayonet. A stout muzzle ring positioned the cup and acted as a stop. A tight wad was rammed home over the blank charge, the grenade loaded in the cup, lit, and shot out – if all went well – by the force of the discharge. Examples with 2.6-inch diameter cups, dated between 1728 and 1747, are preserved in the Tower of London Armouries. One has a steel lug for a pivoted support, another is dated 1740 and is engraved on the barrel ROY^L ARTILLERY.

Of the same period is another type, reminiscent of the sixteenth-century hand mortars, in which the stubby mortar barrel is mounted directly on to a short, thick gunstock. An important group of these in the Bernisches Historisches Museum, Switzerland, have their flintlocks tilted downwards to bring the pans in line with their touchholes. In contrast, a 3-inch bore, steel-barreled mortar by John Hall the younger of London, and a 2-inch brass French mortar by (? Simon) Jourson, both *ca.*1740, have their locks set level. The Berne series is of particular interest, as several are cast with the arms of notable Swiss families and the finest have cast or chiseled ornamental bands. Two are of 2.16-inch diameter and thirteen others have bores between 2.79 inches and 3.07 inches.

Yet another variant is a French pattern with the usual brass mortar cup engraved with the French Royal Arms, the date 1747 and the arms of the Comte d'Eu (1701–75), Grand Master of Artillery. Instead of a gun butt, each has a long, curved stock which the firer tucked under his right arm, with its spiked end stuck into the ground. With his left hand he gripped a hinged handle and with his right he fired the charge. These *grenadiers* shot their 2.1-inch diameter grenades *ensabotées*, that is, set on wooden bases which acted as additional wads.

A common fault with all grenade dischargers of the seventeenth and eighteenth centuries was their dependence on the efficiency of the lock ignition. Once the loaded grenade was lit, a misfire was likely to lead to a fatal accident, and at least one recorded comment calls for a hand mortar in which this hazard could be reduced by using the flash of the discharge to light the grenade fuse, as in the Swedish grenades mentioned above. Presumably the failure to achieve this essential safeguard led to the disuse of hand mortars about the middle of the eighteenth century.

The Russo-Japanese War marks the renaissance of the grenade with Martin Hale's grenade being adopted by the Japanese. A "rodded" version of it was used from rifle dischargers. The development of a reliable time fuse and cartridges permitted a revival of interest in the discharger which was subsequently adopted throughout the world in the early twentieth century.   w.r.

Illustrations: pages 279–80.

Blackmore, Howard L., *British Military Firearms, 1650–1850*, London, 1961.

GUERILLA GUN

An improvised weapon made by guerilla forces, or a modification of a standard firearm to facilitate its use by guerilla forces. Because of the availability of shotgun shells in the civilian economy and the fact that their low pressure does not require the relatively high-yield steels used to construct rifles, guerilla guns are frequently made to use shotgun shells.

In the Philippines during the Second World War guerillas constructed a number of shotguns from a heavy piece of wood and two pieces of pipe. A nail through the wood served as a firing pin. The piece of pipe bearing the shotgun shell was pulled back, causing the nail to strike the primer of the shotgun shell. Guerilla guns captured from the Mau Mau in Kenya included some made of light steel pipe with lead bolts using the .410 shotgun shell.

North Korean guerillas who infiltrated behind the United Nations lines frequently carried cut-down weapons. As an example, Mosin-Nagant rifle actions cut to within several inches of the receiver were recovered. A favorite guerilla weapon was the United States caliber .30 carbine with the barrel cut to five or six inches and the butt stock cut off behind the pistol grip.   j.e.s.

See also: LIBERATOR PISTOL.

GUNFLINT

The snaphance, or some other early snapping lock, was the first ignition system for firearms which utilized a gunflint, the wheel lock having used iron pyrites to strike the spark. Therefore, since the snaphance was invented during the sixteenth century, it follows that for a period of almost 250 years gunflints were an important adjunct to the firearms industry.

Undoubtedly, much effort was expended in trying to devise efficient ways of providing raw flint to the knappers so that they could convert the nodules into pieces of the requisite size and shape with the least amount of labor and waste. We do not yet know just how the first gunflints were made, but by about 1650 a distinct type had evolved which can best be described as a "gunspall" rather than a "gunflint," since it was typically made of chert instead of flint, and each one was an individual spall struck from the surface of the nodule. Though some flint nodules were utilized at this time, they, as well as the chert nodules, appear to have been float gathered from the glacial drifts of northern Europe. A careful examination of these gunspalls indicates that they were most probably struck from the surface of small nodules, well rounded by either water or glacial action, by a pick-like hammer which would deliver its stroke as a concentrated blow at one spot and thereby produce spalls of a fairly uniform size and shape. These individual spalls were then dressed by

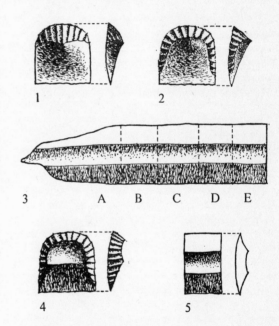

1 *and* 2. *Typical forms of the gunspall*
3. *Blade struck from a prepared core of flint, in the process that supplanted the gunspall. The blade was then broken at the dotted lines, producing flints B, C and D. The ends, A and E, were discarded – E being unusable on account of the bulb of percussion on its reverse side, which resulted from the blow of the knaprer's hammer when the blade was struck from the core.*
4. *Typical French gunflint*
5. *Typical English gunflint*

secondary chipping, and a rounded or "gnawed" heel, or back, resulted. Because this rounded back is also characteristic of the French gunflints which immediately supplanted the gunspall, it is ordinarily assumed that these early gunspalls were of French manufacture. It must be emphasized, however, that no documentary evidence has yet been found to support this supposition.

In an attempt to develop a more efficient means of production, a new technique was introduced during the first decade of the eighteenth century and was well established by about 1750, resulting in the production of the conventional gunflint of later years. Actually, this was not a new technique, but a rediscovery of the Neolithic system of striking long blades from a prepared flint core, and then breaking these blades into shorter lengths to produce the individual gunflint. The need for a dependable source of supply of flint of uniform quality led to the systematic mining of this material both in England and on the Continent. The English mines at Brandon, Savenham, Tuddenham, and Mindenhall are reputed to have been reopened by about 1686, and they certainly were in operation by 1700. At about the same time, the French opened mines in the departments of Loire et Cher, Yonne, and Indre, while the Russians are reported to have obtained their flint from Podolia in Poland.

By 1789 the Russian Army was producing gunflints at the comparatively modest rate of 45,000 per month, which may explain why very few of them got into world trade channels. By way of contrast, in 1793 the French had over 30,000,000 gunflints in storage in and around St-Aignan, and were carrying on a lively commerce with Holland, Spain, England, and the United States.

American archeologists have been puzzled to find that the honey-yellow French gunflints with rounded heels outnumber the black, sharply angular English flints in the ratio of approximately nine to one, even on British camp sites of the period of the American War of Independence, but recent documentary revelations now explain why the French dominated the trade up to the year 1800. Apparently, British gunflint production increased markedly at about that time, for these same archeologists find that the British army camp sites during the War of 1812 reveal that almost fifty per cent of the gunflints used by them then were of their own manufacture. By the close of the flintlock era, about 1850, both British and American trading posts in the Indian country were stocking English gunflints almost exclusively.

The *Ordnance Manual* of the United States Army, published in 1850, specified the parts of the gunflint as follows: "The *edge* or *bevel*, the *back*, the *sides*, the *face*, slightly convex, and the *bed*, or lower face, slightly concave". In the same paragraph the statement is made that "a good flint will last for more than fifty fires," and that

they were "issued to troops in the proportion of one flint to twenty rounds."

The revival in recent years of the sport of shooting muzzle-loading rifles has again raised the question of the proper manner in which a gunflint should be mounted in the cock. A careful reading of the literature of the flintlock era indicates that the flints were actually placed either way in the cock, depending upon both the degree of curvature of the individual flint and the user's inclination. In most instances it is probably best to place the edge uppermost, since that increases the length of its rake against the frizzen. However, in some locks it is possible to get so long a rake that the spark has started to cool before striking the pan.

In placing the gunflint in the vise of the cock there are really only three important things to remember. (1) Cushion the flint in the jaws with either a thin sheet of lead or a piece of leather. *Never* use paper or cloth for this purpose, since either can easily catch and hold a spark. (2) Line up the inner side of the flint so that it will just miss the barrel. (3) Adjust the edge so that it will strike the frizzen squarely.   T.M.H.

Hamilton, T. M. (compiler), "Indian Trade Guns", *The Missouri Archaeologist*, Vol. 22, 1960.

GUNPOWDER

True gunpowder (also called black powder) is an intimate mixture of saltpetre or nitre (potassium nitrate, KNO_3), suphur (S) and charcoal (consisting mainly of carbon, C) in proportions by weight of approximately 75 of saltpetre, 10 of sulphur, and 15 of charcoal, this composition being standardized for British gunpowder in 1781. For use in rockets and fireworks the proportion of charcoal is increased. The rate of burning of gunpowder is slower at lower atmospheric pressures. A distinction is drawn between the burning of gunpowder when used as a propellant, when the motive gas is generated relatively slowly, and when used for blasting, when the gas is developed very rapidly. A true high-explosive is unsuitable for use in firearms, since it would burst the piece.

The saltpetre and sulphur must be carefully purified. The charcoal is made from common deciduous woods such as beech, birch, willow, or alder, the last two being preferred. The wood is carbonized at a relatively low temperature and for some sporting powders a brown or red incompletely carbonized charcoal is made by heating with superheated steam under pressure. Advantages have been claimed for particular woods, but the suitability of a charcoal for making gunpowder depends mainly on the temperature of carbonization.

The charcoal and sulphur are first milled together, then

the nitre is added and the damp mixture milled under rollers, then pressed into a cake in a hydraulic press. The cake is broken and sieved to grains of suitable size, which may be glazed with blacklead, and the powder is dried. For blasting purposes the potassium nitrate is sometimes replaced by the cheaper sodium nitrate (Chile saltpetre), but powder made from this becomes damp in a moist atmosphere and is therefore unsuitable for use with firearms.

The earliest kind of gunpowder was in the form of a very fine powder, and it had several disadvantages. It tended to become damp on exposure to moist air, when it was useless. This was especially evident with gunpowder used on board ship, and this disadvantage continued until the beginning of the nineteenth century, although various expedients were adopted to overcome it, such as mixing the powder with powdered quicklime. The gunpowder was also stored in waxed canvas bags, and in some cases, even, the materials were stored separately and mixed only just before use.

A method of reducing the absorption of moisture was to form the gunpowder into grains, the so-called corned gunpowder. This was invented fairly early, probably in the fifteenth century; some earlier kinds which were more properly called "lump" gunpowder were not true corned powder. Another method which was tried was to heat the powder till the sulphur melted, when the hard mass so formed did not absorb moisture. This, however, was a dangerous process. The use of corned powder was first made possible in practice when guns were cast which were of sufficient strength to withstand the higher pressures which result from the burning of corned powder.

In the nineteenth century the gunpowder used for cannon was formed into pieces called "prism" gunpowder, consisting of hexagonal prisms of definite sizes, and the composition was also somewhat modified. Prism powder and brown gunpowder continued in use as propellants until they were replaced by smokeless powder based on compositions of guncotton and nitroglycerine.

A survey of the various compositions of gunpowder shows great variations until the eighteenth century, and in some cases, even then, different compositions were used, e.g. in France, for cannon, muskets and pistols. The ratio saltpetre:sulphur:charcoal given by Roger Bacon about 1260 was 7:5:5. English gunpowder about 1350 was 6:1:2, German at about the same date 4:1:1, and 22:4:5 about 1400. Prussian gunpowder in 1774 was 8:1:1, but in 1800 it was the same as the English of 1718, 75:10:15. Swedish powder of 1827 was 75:15:10. The English powder had the same composition for all kinds of arms, the difference being only in the size of the grains.

In the burning of gunpowder the oxygen in the nitrate burns the sulphur and charcoal. The chemical reaction is complicated, but is approximately represented by the equation:

$$2KNO_3 + S + 3C = K_2S + N_2 + 3CO_2$$

The gaseous product also contains some carbon monoxide (CO) as well as nitrogen and carbon dioxide, and the solid product (including that in the smoke) contains potassium carbonate (K_2CO_3) and sulphate (K_2SO_4) as well as potassium sulphide, the last giving rise to the smell of a discharged firearm and to fouling of the breech and barrel.

In modern explosives such as the propellant cordite and high explosives such as nitroglycerine and trinitrotoluene, the oxygen is contained in the molecule of the substance and there is no solid residue from the explosive itself.

The place and date of the invention of gunpowder have been the object of much investigation and discussion. Sulphur and charcoal were known in antiquity, and the problem concerns the discovery of saltpetre. This is not a natural mineral product as common salt is, but is formed by the slow oxidation of organic matter containing nitrogen by atmospheric oxygen in presence of basic substances such as potassium carbonate in the form of wood ashes and lime in the form of old mortar. The oxidation is brought about by micro-organisms and is carried out in nitre-beds, which are supplied with organic nitrogen in the form of manure or urine. The product must then be carefully purified and any calcium nitrate in it converted into potassium nitrate. The process is still carried out in India, but elsewhere potassium nitrate is made from the cheaper native sodium nitrate (Chile saltpetre).

It is believed that saltpetre was not known in antiquity. What is called *nitron* by Greek authors and *nitrum* by Latin is not nitre but soda (the "nitre" in the Authorised Version of the Bible should be "soda," as in modern translations). Saltpetre became known in Europe about 1250, when it is mentioned by Roger Bacon and Albertus Magnus. It seems probable that their knowledge was derived from Latin translations of Arabic works. Both saltpetre and gunpowder are described in a Latin work called the *Book of Fires* (*Liber Ignium*) attributed to Mark the Greek (Marcus Graecus), but it is a translation not of a Greek but of an Arabic work made about the time of Roger Bacon and Albertus Magnus. It was probably from similar works that their knowledge was derived.

The *Liber Ignium* gives recipes for gunpowder as well as for incendiary compositions such as "Greek fire," which was based on light petroleum and did not contain saltpetre. It also distinguishes between propulsive burning as in rockets and explosion in suitable containers ignited by a fuse. The use of saltpetre for cooling water is described in Arabic medical works of about 1250 or rather earlier. It has been supposed that gunpowder was invented by Roger Bacon. In his *Opus Majus*, completed in 1268, he describes the explosion of gunpowder, and in his *Opus Tertium*, composed about the same time or a year or two later, Bacon gives the composition of gunpowder. This is also given, with the name of charcoal in the form of an anagram, in Bacon's *De Secretis Operibus Artis et Naturae*, which may have been written about 1248, although this has been disputed. A work attributed to Albertus Magnus (who died in 1280), *De Mirabilibus Mundi*, gives the same recipes as the *Liber Ignium*.

In the *Opus Majus* Bacon first gives a description of Greek fire, which he thought contained saltpetre, petroleum, naphtha, etc. True Greek fire did not contain saltpetre. He then says that sounds like thunder and flashes in the air can be made by means of a little of a rightly prepared material no bigger than a thumb, which can destroy whole cities and armies. He says:

"We have an example of these things in that children's toy which is made in many parts of the world, viz. an instrument made as large as the human thumb. From the force of the salt called saltpetre so horrible a sound is produced by the bursting of so small a thing, viz. a small piece of parchment, that we perceive it exceeds the roar of strong thunder and the flash exceeds the greatest brilliancy of the lightning."

In the *Opus Tertium* Bacon says:

"By the flash and combustion of fires, and by the horror of sounds, wonders can be wrought, and at any distance that we wish, so that a man can hardly protect himself or endure it. There is a child's toy of sound and fire made in various parts of the world with powder of saltpetre, sulphur and charcoal of hazelwood. This powder is enclosed in an instrument of parchment the size of a finger, and since this can make such a noise that it seriously distresses the ears of men, especially if one is taken unawares, and the terrible flash is also very alarming, if an instrument of large size were used, no one could stand the terror of the noise and flash. If the instrument were made of solid material the violence of the explosion would be greater."

In the *De Secretis Operibus Artis et Naturae* Bacon says:

"Thou shalt take saltpetre, *luro vopo vir can utriet*, and sulphur, and by this means make it both to thunder and to lighten."

The anagram has been solved to mean "willow charcoal." In another place in the work Bacon gives the proportions of the materials.

Albertus Magnus gives a recipe for "flying fire" (*ignis volans*):

"Flying fire. Take one pound of sulphur, two pounds of willow charcoal, and six pounds of saltpetre, which three things grind finely on a marble stone. Then put as much as you wish into a paper case to make flying fire or thunder. The case for flying fire should be long and thin and well filled with powder, that for making thunder short and thick and half-filled with powder."

As stated, this recipe is practically the same as one in the *Liber Ignium*. The "flying fire" has been thought to mean a rocket, although a roman candle is possible.

It seems that saltpetre was something new when the *Liber Ignium* was written, since it gives a definition of it:

"Note that saltpetre is a mineral of the earth and is found as an efflorescence on stones. This earth is dissolved in boiling water, then purified and passed through a filter. It is boiled for a day and a night and solidified, and transparent plates of salt are found at the bottom of the vessel."

The purification of saltpetre by wood ashes, containing potassium carbonate, which precipitates deliquescent calcium salts from the saltpetre solution, has been thought to be mentioned obscurely by Bacon. It is given in the Arabic work of Ḥasan al-Rammāh.

Arabic treatises of about 1225 describe incendiary compositions of the type of Greek fire, but not gunpowder. A work by Ḥasan al-Rammāh, probably written about 1280, quotes earlier authors, describes the purification of saltpetre, and gives many compositions for fireworks which are described as Chinese. It does not describe true gunpowder. An Arabic author Ibn al-Bayṭār, who died in 1248 and was well acquainted with Indian and Persian drugs, calls saltpetre "snow of China" (thalj al-Ṣīn), and it seems reasonable to assume that knowledge of saltpetre and incendiary mixtures containing it came to the Arabs from China. True gunpowder is another matter. Another Arabic work of uncertain date, perhaps of 1300–1350, describes the use of gunpowder as a propellant. Cannon were known in Europe by that time, the earliest representation of one being in an Oxford manuscript written in 1326.

From the late fifteenth century a legend was in circulation that gunpowder and firearms were invented by a German monk called "Black Berthold" (Berthold Schwartz), reputed to have lived in the fourteenth century, but gunpowder was known to Roger Bacon a century before this, and the modern view is that Berthold is a purely fictitious person. A German military treatise called the *Feuerwerkbuch*, written about 1420 by an unknown author, describes the materials used in making gunpowder, the methods of making ordinary gunpowder and special powders, incendiary compositions, and guns and shooting. It mentions "white gunpowder" in which, apparently, charcoal was replaced by starch. Later works mention a "noiseless gunpowder," which was probably fictitious. All kinds of useless materials such as camphor, sal ammoniac, and mercury, are described in books of recipes. The composition of gunpowder is also variously given, usually with too little saltpetre.

It has been said above that knowledge of powders containing saltpetre may have reached the Arabs from China. Incendiary mixtures containing saltpetre are described in a Chinese work dated 1044, the *Wu Ching Tsung Yao*. In the form of this now available there are pictures of European cannon of the seventeenth century, which may have been added to an older form, since they are not described in the text itself. The *Wu Ching Tsung Yao* uses the name *huo yao* for what has been called gunpowder, but true gunpowder is not described in it. Saltpetre is called *hsiao shih* and it is possible that this was known in China some time before this. The recipes contain various materials, and although what has been translated "bombs" occurs in it, the *huo yao* was rather "proto-gunpowder" than true gunpowder.

A recipe in the *Wu Ching Tsung Yao* reads:

"Grind together with a pestle and sift 14 oz. of Chin-chou sulphur, 7 oz. of K'o sulphur, 2.5 lb. of saltpetre. Grind together 1 oz. of realgar [red arsenic sulphide], 1 oz. Ting powder [?] and 1 oz. massicot [lead oxide]. Powder 1 oz. of dry lacquer. Roast to bits or powder 1 oz. hemp roots, 1 oz. bamboo roots. Boil to a paste 0.5 oz. beeswax, 0.1 oz. clear oil, 0.5 oz. t'ung oil, 14 oz. pine pitch, 0.1 oz. heavy oil. Mix all together evenly, bind with hemp, smear with pine pitch and throw by a catapult."

This is an incendiary, although it contains the constituents of gunpowder. Another recipe of a similar kind specifies saltpetre, sulphur and charcoal with various resins, oils, wax, etc., the mixture being smeared over a ball and kindled to make a rumbling noise, flames, and smoke.

In accounts of 1132 a fire lance apparently containing an incendiary powder is mentioned, in 1221 what is called a "bomb" of pig iron which exploded like a thunderbolt, and in 1259 a bamboo tube containing powder and bullets. These suggest that some kind of explosive powder was known then. We are now getting near the time when gunpowder was known in Europe.

The standard Chinese work on explosives is the *Wu Pei Chih*, written by a military expert in 1628, a time when gunpowder and firearms were well known in Europe and these were known to the author. Like most Chinese works it begins with a legendary history attributing inventions to mythical emperors or officials of the remote past, and

European translators of Chinese works were seriously misled in taking this information at its face value. They stated, for example, that gunpowder and firearms were known in China before the beginning of the Christian era.

The *Wu Pei Chih* contains, as would be expected, several recipes for gunpowder:

"Fire powder: saltpetre 5 lb., sulphur 1 lb., charcoal 1 lb. [This would be a good mixture.] Grind well, moisten with spirits and shape into pellets.
Lead [bullet] powder: Purified saltpetre 40 oz., sulphur 6 oz., willow, calabash or egg-plant-stalk charcoal 6 to 8 oz. Grind well with a little water and dry in the sun. It is useful to add a spider skin.
Cannon powder: Saltpetre 10 oz., sulphur 6 oz., calabash or bamboo charcoal 3 oz., orpiment [yellow arsenic sulphide] 1 oz., realgar 0.5 oz."

It would seem that true gunpowder appeared in China during the Mongol period (1260–1368) and since it was known to Roger Bacon in Europe in about 1250 it is, at present, uncertain whether knowledge of it came to Europe from China by way of the Arabs, or the reverse. The probability is that it was invented in China, since the recipes in the *Wu Ching Tsung Yao* are on the way to it, and it seems unreasonable to assume that no development of them took place. The Mongol dynasty followed the Sung (960–1279, overlapping with the Mongol), in which the *Wu Ching Tsung Yao* was compiled, and in which other accounts of military weapons which might involve explosives, barely mentioned above, also occur. The part played by the Arabs is probably more important than was thought not long ago, but the exact details of the transmission of a knowledge of gunpowder from the East to Europe is still very obscure.

The suggestion has been made that gunpowder originated in India. In that country there was a clever metallurgical technique and chemical works are fairly early. The assumption that chemical knowledge reached India from the Arabs is not very probable. The processes differ from those in Arabic works, and the use of plant materials in metallurgy, as in making steel, is characteristic of India. There would seem to be a relation here with the use of such materials in the recipes in the Chinese *Wu Ching Tsung Yao*, but this should not be stressed too much, since there was an extensive Chinese pharmacology based on vegetable drugs.

Saltpetre was probably known fairly early in India and hence it might have been expected that gunpowder was discovered there. The dating of Sanskrit works is mostly difficult or uncertain. Supposed references to gunpowder in early works are now recognised as mistaken. Two Sanskrit works, the *Śukranīti* and the *Nītiprakāśikā*, which describe gunpowder and firearms, have been supposed to be early, but there is every reason to think that in their present form they are relatively late. Some of the recipes in them resemble those in the *Wu Ching Tsung Yao* and the possibility of borrowing in one direction or the other cannot be excluded. Too little research has been done on both Chinese and Indian sources to allow of any very great feeling of satisfaction to be felt as to our knowledge of either, and what work has been done has mostly been by students not sufficiently acquainted with military and technical information, which is indispensable for a proper understanding of them. In the case of Chinese works, especially, the wrong technical terms have been used in the translations.

The information summarised above seems to suggest that a knowledge of saltpetre and its use in making incendiary compositions originated in China soon after 1000 A.D. and passed to the Arabs. True gunpowder was known in China only in the Mongol period and may have been discovered in Europe between 1225 and 1250, although the evidence for this is lacking.   J.R.P.

Davis, T. L., *The Chemistry of Powder and Explosives*, New York, 1943.

Marshall, A., *Explosives*, 2 vols, London, 1917–32.

Partington, J. R., *A History of Greek Fire and Gunpowder*, Cambridge, England, 1960.

See also: SMOKELESS POWDER.

GUNSMITH

For many years this term has been used to describe the trade of a maker of small firearms. The inaccuracy of the word lies in the fact that guns were only partially made by a smith. The verb "smith," according to *An American Dictionary of the English Language*, Springfield, Massachusetts, 1848, means "to fabricate out of metal by hammering." Its use in English is similar to the Swedish word *smida*, the Danish *smider*, and the German *schmieden*. It is the proper suffix for words describing such trades as silversmithing, blacksmithing, and coppersmithing. It is obvious that the barrel and the lock were forged and the men who produced them have been properly called barrelsmiths and locksmiths. Other craftsmen involved in the production of a gun were cabinet-makers and wood carvers, brass founders, and engravers. In the production of special types of arms, like Scottish pistols, the work of a silversmith was also required. It is evident that, because of the variety of trades involved in the production of a firearm, the word gunmaker might be used more logically than gunsmith. However, since the word gunsmith has been customarily used to describe the trade of the man who made guns, it will be used here with this meaning.

The true definition of the word gunsmith is further confused by the fact that the word is very loosely used to describe the work that these craftsmen performed during the various stages in the development of gunmaking. The Cominazzi are called gunsmiths, although they are reputed to have made only barrels. The riflemaker on the Pennsylvania frontier is called a gunsmith, and it is believed that he made an entire gun. A man who worked in Leman's rifle factory in Lancaster, Pennsylvania, in the late nineteenth century, was called a gunsmith, but he filed only a few parts of a gunlock. It is obviously difficult in a short survey to describe precisely the work which the trade involved.

The problem of describing the work done by a gunsmith will be handled in this article by utilizing an old list of procedures which appears in the gunshop of the Castle Museum in York, England. The content of the statements suggests that each process was performed by an individual craftsman, and these craftsmen were probably engaged in the production of arms for military use. Such specialization was possible only in a large arms-producing area such as Birmingham, but the work was essentially the same regardless of where it was done or how many men were involved. The absence of terms suggesting the use of power machinery indicates that most of the work was done by hand. The museum's list is italicized and the author's explanation follows.

BARREL FORGER
Barrels are forged from three square bars of iron.

The use of three-square (i.e. triangular in cross-section) bars of iron for making gun barrels is a new procedure to the author. Before the days of rolling mills such a shape would have been difficult to produce; however, there must have been a logical reason for using this form to forge the long strip of metal used in making barrels. Over the years there were many variations in the procedure of forging and welding a barrel; however, a standard procedure is described by Espinar in his *Arte de Ballestería y Montería* in 1644, by Acton in his *Essay on Shooting* in 1789, and by Henry and George Landis, who describe the practice of Pennsylvania barrelmakers in the nineteenth century, in volume seven of the Pennsylvania Folklore Society, published in 1942. The Acton account follows:

"To form a barrel in the manner generally practised, the workmen begin by heating and hammering out a bar of iron into the form of a flat ruler, thinner at one end than another, the length, breadth, and thickness of it being regulated by the intended length, diameter, and weight of the barrel. This oblong plate of metal is then, after repeated heating and hammering, turned round a cylindrical rod of tempered iron, called a mandril,

Plate 4

Pair of snaphance pistols made by Matteo Acqua Fresca of
Bargi, near Bologna, probably for a member of the Medici
court. The barrels, though signed by Acqua Fresca, were
made by the Brescian master, Francino, whose signature is
stamped underneath. The mounts, entirely of steel, are
chiseled with masks and engraved with scrolls. The carved
ebony stocks are profusely inlaid with floral scrolls in silver
wire. Italian, *ca*.1690.

Collection of R. T. Gwynn.

whose diameter is considerably less than the intended bore of the barrel. The edges of the plate are made to overlap each other about half an inch, and are welded together by heating the tube in lengths of two to three inches at a time, and hammering it with very brisk but moderate strokes upon an anvil having a number of semi-circular furrows in it, adapted to the various sizes of the barrels . . . These heatings and hammerings are repeated until the whole barrel has undergone the same operation, and all of its parts are rendered as perfectly continuous as if it had been bored out of a solid piece. Musket barrels and those for ordinary fowling pieces are forged of Swedish iron, that which comes from Russia being too coarse to be wrought into barrels."

The early production of iron in America provided an ample supply of charcoal iron for gun barrels of all types. Many furnaces and forges were set up in Pennsylvania where gunsmiths and gun factories were located in the eighteenth and nineteenth centuries.

BARREL-BORER AND FILER
The roughly forged barrels are then bored and smoothed inside and the outside is filed smooth.

The boring operation was preceded by annealing the barrel in a gentle heat and slowly cooling it before clamping in the vise of the boring mill. The boring operation is described in *Gunnery in 1858* by Greener:

"Boring and grinding gun barrels generally take place under the same roof: the borer occupying a very small shop, the grinder a larger one. Two men and two boys are generally found in a shop. There are four benches, to each a spindle, in which there is an oblong hole to receive the end of the boring bit. The barrel is secured on a sort of carriage, which is at liberty to traverse the whole length of the bench. A boring bit is then selected of suitable size; it is put into the spindle, and the point introduced into the end of the barrel. A sort of lever is then taken and hooked on a kind of a staple, or a piece of hooked iron (a number of which are fixed in one side of the bench the whole length) and passed behind the carriage to force it up to the bit; this is removed and fixed again until, by forcing the carriage, the boring bit has passed through the whole barrel. During this operation a stream of water is kept playing on the barrel to keep it cool. A bit of larger dimensions is next introduced and passed through, then others of still larger dimensions until the whole of the scales or blacks are entirely bored out, or until the barrel has become so large in bore as to preclude any further boring with safety."

The barrel drills seen by the author resembled a modern augur bit except that two spurs on the outer diameter of the spiral cut away the excessive metal instead of the ends of the spirals, which are sharpened to cut wood. The final rod passed through the barrel had a square shape with the edges ground to provide a scraping action rather than the cutting action of the earlier bits. The earliest boring mills were operated by hand, later by water power, and finally by steam power.

The exterior of the barrel was finished in a variety of ways depending on the time and place the work was done. In the earliest time most of the finishing was probably done "free-hand" on a large grinding wheel. A view of a grinding device in the Diderot *Encyclopedia* indicates that barrels were ground with a lateral motion of the stone over the barrel rather than the perpendicular motion later used by gunsmiths in America on their octagonal rifle barrels. The index plate on the end of the lateral grinding device determined the shape (octagonal to round) of the finished barrel. Because of the wide circulation of these encyclopedias, no doubt many craftsmen knew of this method and used it as long as barrels were ground.

After machine lathes were equipped with a lead screw, some of the barrels were roughly ground on stones and finished on the lathe. Small plugs were fitted into the bore and the barrel was set in the lathe between the live and dead centers. This operation was efficient, but dangerous, for long barrels sometimes developed a whip and were subsequently ruined.

Files and abrasives were used for the final finishing of the barrels.

After the bore and the exterior of the barrel were finished by one of the accepted methods, it was ready for the breech plug, if it was a smoothbore. However, if the barrel was to be rifled, a very important operation remained to be done. Cutting the grooves in a rifle barrel was a very tedious task, and one in which the skill of American craftsmen compared with that of Europeans.

Rifling was done on a long bench made of a heavy plank about eight or ten feet long. One end of the bench was supported by two splayed legs and the other end was attached to a wall. On one half of the bench two eyes were installed into which the barrel was rigidly fastened by tightening setscrews in the top of each eye. On the other half of the bench a sliding frame was installed, about fifteen inches wide and forty-eight inches long. A long cylinder of wood, about six inches in diameter, was located in the center of this frame and on one end a free swinging handle was placed. The rifling cutter was in a steel rod and the rod was attached to the other end of the cylinder. Ribs were mounted on the long side of the cylinder in the same spiral pattern as the intended grooves for the barrel.

A forward thrust of the handle caused the cylinder to

move forward and rotate through an index plate, which was permanently attached to the top of the bench. The cutting tool on the far end of the cylinder and rod followed the spiral motion of the cylinder through the index plate and cut a groove on the inside of the barrel. Subsequent thrusts brought the groove to the desired depth, after which the barrel was given a partial turn and the previous operation repeated until the barrel was fully rifled. Finally, a lead plug covered with oil and a powdered abrasive was used to polish the interior of the barrel.

LOCK BODY AND FURNITURE FORGER
The body blank, fore-end blank, trigger plate, and trigger guard blanks, lock plates, and working parts of the lock are forged by this man.

The man who forged the lock plate and the iron mountings of guns was obviously a smith, but his tools were of a more refined nature than those of the man who forged the barrel. To produce these small gun parts there must have been a number of small hearths located in the gun factories at Birmingham, or possibly individual craftsmen worked at small forges in their homes in the neighboring areas of Wolverhampton and Willenhall. The silver mountings for guns were probably made by silversmiths; however, such mountings are rare in comparison with the number found of iron and brass.

Some mountings for muskets and most of those for sporting arms were made by a founder who worked in brass. Patterns for these parts were usually made of wood and then placed in a two-piece box filled with dampened sand. After the pattern of wood had been cleverly removed from the sand, molten brass was poured into the cavity and allowed to solidify. Mountings usually consist of a butt plate, trigger guard, trigger plate, fore-end cap, and lock bolt plate.

FURNITURE AND ACTION FILER
The body is filed and finished and the fore-end, trigger plate, trigger guard, and lever are filed down.

Most of the mountings, either cast or forged, had slight irregularities on the edges which had to be removed for ease in handling and to facilitate fitting to the stock. This work did not require a high degree of skill and was probably done by apprentices.

RIBBER AND BREACHER
The ribs, lumps, and loops to barrels are fitted and the complete barrels are joined to the body.

The work of this man was obviously concerned with applying the finishing touches to the barrel. Instructions for fitting the breech plug are precisely presented in the *Encyclopedia Perthansis, or the Universal Dictionary of Knowledge* (published in Perth about 1780):

"The first tool used in the forming of the breech-screw is a plug of tempered steel, somewhat conical, with threads of a male screw upon its surface, and by workmen termed a screw tap. This being introduced into the barrel from left to right and back again, until it has marked out the first four threads of the screw, another less conical tap is introduced; and when this has carried the impression of the screw as far as it is intended to go, a third one nearly cylindrical is made use of scarcely differing from the plug of the breech intended to fill the screw thus formed in the barrel. The plug itself has its screw formed by a screw plate of tempered steel with several female screws, corresponding with the taps employed for forming the threads in the barrel; 7 or 8 threads are sufficient for a plug, they ought to be neat and sharp, so as to completely fill the turns made in the barrel by the tap."

Loops were fastened to the bottom of the barrel so that the barrel could be pinned to the stock, and a rib was attached to the barrel in case the gun did not have a full stock, or if two barrels were fastened together.

LOCK-FILER
The locks are now filed from forgings and the locks are built up in a roughly finished state.

The fine workmanship found on the front and back of old gun locks was the result of this man's work. Only hardening and final polishing remained to be done after the filer was finished with the parts. This work might have been done by apprentices who were well along in their progress toward the final stage of journeyman.

STOCKER
The fitting of the action and the locks and fore-ends into the stock blank made of walnut is the next process.

The first consideration in making the stock must have been the type of wood to be used. The traditional wood for gun stocks was walnut; however, some very early guns had stocks of pear wood, snake wood, cherry wood, or apple wood, and some pistols had stocks of ebony or ivory. American gunsmiths were partial to maple for gun stocks. Scottish pistols had stocks of brass or iron.

If a sporting gun was to be made, some consideration was given to the length and drop of the stock. Specifications for the butt would vary, according to the needs of a small man with short arms or a tall with long arms. Stocks for military guns were doubtless made from one pattern.

SCREWER TOGETHER
Temporary screws called "slave screws" are now made and used for building up the gun.

After the inletting for the mountings was finished, they

were fastened to the stock by this man, using temporary screws so that the final ones would be perfect and intact. The need for this preliminary fitting with screws is easily understood, particularly when the elaborate screwheads used on early fine guns are examined. No impaired screws could be used on fancy guns, and there was probably no excuse for burred screw slots on military guns.

MAKER OFF
The stock is finished and the fore-end polished.

The work of this man on military arms was not very intricate, but on fine sporting guns it was of a very critical nature. The forming of the graceful contours of the stock was in his hands and the carving on various parts of the stock required workmanship of the highest caliber. Elaborately ornamented guns were carved around the breech tang, the ramrod pipe, the trigger guard, butt plate, and on the cheek side of the butt. It is possible that this craftsman also did some of the fine inlaying on stocks, using ivory, horn, brass, and silver.

STRIPPER AND FINISHER
This man takes the gun to pieces and replaces the "slave screws" with permanent ones.

This work required little skill but probably a great deal of patience.

LOCK FINISHER
The lock is stripped down and the working parts polished and hardened.

This work on the lock was of a highly specialized nature and was very critical, because the perfect functioning of the lock depended a great deal on the skill of this craftsman. This work was well done, for in the writer's experience few lock springs have been found to show evidence of improper hardening or inefficient action after centuries of use.

ENGRAVER
Cuts into the metal various designs.

The expression "cuts into the metal various designs" is a very modest statement of one of the most exacting arts practised by men who worked on guns. It demanded a combined knowledge of metals and aesthetics; and this work, along with that of the woodcarver, determined, to a large extent, the artistic quality of the arm. The work of the metal chiseler was closely allied to that of the engraver and, in the era of the wheel lock gun, both trades were probably practised by one man.

POLISHER AND HARDENER
Strips down the gun again and hardens the fore-end body, trigger plate and lever.

This man case-hardened various parts to minimize wear and resist abrasion. The work was less exacting than that of the man who tempered springs.

BROWNER
The barrels were browned by rusting them with acid, removing the rust with wire brushes, and finally dipping them in hot water and polishing.

Browning barrels was probably a more exact art than this statement suggests. The process was used by many men from many nations and some of their products have survived into the last half of the twentieth century for collectors to admire. If anyone cares to brown a barrel, he had better seek more detailed directions than are provided above.   H.J.K.

Acton, John (attrib.), *An Essay on Shooting*, London, 1789.

Blair, Claude, *European and American Arms*, London, 1962.

Greener, William, *Gunnery in 1858*, London, 1858.

Hayward, J. F., *The Art of the Gunmaker*, 2 vols, London and New York, 1962–64.

See also: BLUING; BROWNING; DAMASCUS BARREL; DECORATION OF FIREARMS.

GUNSTOCK

See: STOCK.

H

HACBUTT/HACKBUT/HAGBUT/ HAQUEBUT

Most authors who have studied period arms give to the terms arquebus and hacbutt the same meaning. Nevertheless, there exists documentary evidence to prove that the two arms in question, though related to each other, are different. It is the belief of many students that the word hacbutt derives from the German *Hakbuchse*, or "hook gun," and was literally a gun with a hook; that is, one of the heavier portable firearms with a hook on the underside of the barrel which could be placed over a wall or similar support to help absorb some of the recoil. The Landshut illustrated inventory of 1485 tends to confirm this interpretation.

One of the first references to the hacbutt seems to be that of Olivier de la Marche (1426–1502) writing on the artillery of Duke Charles of Burgundy: " . . . the duke is able to draw upon three hundred pieces of artillery in battle, besides countless hacbutts and culverins."

The hacbutt existed in three forms: a heavy weapon on a support, a powerful weapon with a sling, and a portable weapon.

In his edict of May 26, 1527, Francis I allowed for a considerable improvement in the pay of the hacbuttiers in relation to the arquebusiers: ". . . the arquebusiers will have, besides their fixed emolument, one solz each month, and the hacbuttiers ten solz." According to a practice, apparent in numerous edicts dealing with questions of arms, the size of the monthly payment is always relative to the efficiency and cost of the arms. It can be inferred therefore, from the text of May 26, 1527, that the hacbutt was more effective than the arquebus.

The last references to the hacbutt date from the middle of the sixteenth century: this type of weapon would therefore have been used from *ca*.1475 to *ca*.1550.　　CL.B.

Illustration: page 33.

Bosson, Clement, "Que sait-on de l'Haquebute?" in *Armes Anciennes*, Vol. 2, No. 1, Geneva, 1957.
Peterson, Harold L., *Arms and Armor in Colonial America, 1526–1783*, Harrisburg, Pa., 1956.

See also: ARQUEBUS.

HAIR TRIGGER

See: SET TRIGGER.

HALL, JOHN H.

John Hancock Hall was born on January 21, 1778, in Portland, Maine. His ancestors included many distinguished doctors, lawyers, ministers, and fine craftsmen. In 1812 he is reported one of the owners of the sloop "Yankee," built for privateering in the second war with Great Britain. It is thought he designed the "Yankee" and that she was lost on her maiden voyage because of an improperly designed keel.

As a young man, Hall joined the militia, and in 1814, when the British threatened the Portland area, he was on active duty as a lieutenant in Captain Shaw's company of Portland Light Infantry. Hall said his service in the militia aroused his interest in firearms, and he sought means to facilitate their loading and improve their accuracy. He said the only breechloading method he knew was the turn-off barrel method used on pocket pistols. He designed a rising receiver action which he patented on May 21, 1811, in partnership with William Thornton of Washington, D.C.

Hall set up a shop on Richardson's Wharf in Portland, where he manufactured sporting rifles and shotguns for civilian use. In 1813 he received an army order for one hundred rifles, but was unable to complete it before the war ended. In 1816 he proposed to the War Department to construct rifles of his plan with uniform and completely interchangeable parts, provided he received a contract large enough to justify erecting a factory with water power and the necessary machinery. However, the army ordered only two hundred rifles, for tests by field troops, and these Hall constructed in 1817 in the usual manner.

In 1818 Hall went to the national armory at Harpers Ferry, at the invitation of the government, to prepare new models for further tests. On March 19, 1819, he received a contract to supervise the manufacture of one thousand rifles of his pattern. He was rated an Assistant Armorer at Harpers Ferry at a pay of $60 per month and a royalty of $1 per rifle. After almost five years spent in constructing tools and machinery, Hall completed the contract in 1824. These were the first firearms manufactured in quantity in a national armory with all parts uniform and interchangeable.

Hall received additional contracts and established a rifle factory at Harpers Ferry, working constantly to improve the quality of his guns and machines. In 1840 he took leave of absence, and died the following year in Huntsville, Missouri.

Hall's firearms were never popular, the most serious criticism being the leakage of fire and gas at the joint between barrel and receiver, which was disconcerting to the shooter. Hall's great achievement was in making the parts of his rifle interchangeable: according to a report in 1827, by government arms inspectors who were familiar with the American arms industry, Hall's achievement was unique. Present day studies by industrial and arms historians may reveal that Hall was the true father of the interchangeable parts system of manufacture.　　C.R.G.

Fairbairn, Charlotte Judd, and Patterson, C. Meade, "Captain Hall, Inventor" in *Gun Report*, October and November 1959.

See also: HALL BREECH-LOADING ARMS.

HALL BREECH-LOADING ARMS

This system of loading at the breech was patented by John Hancock Hall of Portland, Maine, and William Thornton of Washington, D.C., on May 21, 1811.

The charge was placed in the chamber within a breechblock pivoted on the frame. When depressed, the breechblock formed a butt joint with the rear of the barrel. The breechblock was secured in the firing position by a spring latch engaging the under side of the stock. The flintlock mechanism was mounted on the top of the breechblock, and the sights were offset to the left on the rear of the barrel. The bore was tapered from breech to muzzle to permit the use of a slightly oversized ball which formed a tight gas check.

Hall established a shop on Richardson's Wharf in Portland where he manufactured pistols, rifles, and single- and double-barreled fowling pieces for sportsmen. Surviving specimens indicate that Hall styled them after the popular Kentucky pattern. Hall's military rifle of 1817, made for United States Army trials, was a caliber .54 flintlock with a 33¾-inch octagonal barrel rifled with eight deep grooves. It was rounded at the muzzle to take a socket bayonet. The stock extended just short of the muzzle.

In 1818 Hall made new models of his guns at the Harpers Ferry Armory, and after extensive tests he received a contract in 1819 to supervise their manufacture at the Armory. The rifles produced under this and subsequent contracts are designated by modern collectors "U.S. rifle, Model 1819 (Hall's)."

In the first Model 1819 rifles, the rifling – sixteen tight grooves – extended to the muzzle as in conventional rifles. However, about 1828 the muzzle was reamed out smooth to a point just below the front sight, giving the rifle the appearance of a smoothbore. Some of the earlier pieces appear to have been altered, because some have been found with faint traces of original rifling showing in these last few inches.

Hall rifles were also made by Simeon North of Middletown, Connecticut, who received contracts in 1828, 1829 and 1835. These, too, had interchangeable parts, and correspond with those made by Hall at Harpers Ferry.

The Hall carbine adopted in 1833 was the first United States firearm made in quantity with the percussion ignition system. It was a smoothbore, caliber .64 arm fitted with a triangular rod bayonet which was recessed under the stock and could be extended for use. This model was manufactured by Simeon North. In 1836, the caliber was reduced to .52, and the barrel was rifled and shortened from 26⅛ inches to 21 inches. In 1838 the carbine was again modified. The rod bayonet was eliminated, the receiver catch was replaced by an elbow-shaped device, and some were made in caliber .64 with rifled barrels. In 1840, the elbow-shaped device was replaced by a fishtail lever. The barrel was shortened to 21 inches and rifled. In 1841 the fishtail lever was replaced by a side lever. All these carbines were manufactured by Simeon North. Hall made only one model at Harpers Ferry, and this, interestingly, was flintlock.   C.R.G.

Illustrations: page 44.

Fairbairn, Charlotte Judd, and Patterson, C. Meade, "Captain Hall, Inventor" in *Gun Report*, October and November 1959.

Fuller, Claud E., *The Breech-Loader in the Service*, Topeka, Kan., 1933.

Gluckman, Colonel Arcadi, *United States Muskets, Rifles and Carbines*, Harrisburg, Pa., 1959.

Huntington, Major R. T., "Hall Breech-loading Firearms" in *Gun Report*, December 1956.

Huntington, Major R. T., "The Model 1841 Hall Rifle" in *Gun Report*, January 1957.

Peterson, Harold L., *The Treasury of the Gun*, New York, 1962 (*The Book of the Gun*, London, 1963).

See also: BREECHLOADERS; HALL, JOHN H.

HAND CANNON

The hand cannon is distinguished from the arquebus by its stock on tiller, which is not constructed for firing from the shoulder, and by its ignition, which required the direct manual application of fire to the touchhole. The hand cannon, also called the "powder shaft," was derived from the original cannon: a large tube supported by and attached to a wooden frame. When it became possible to make the tube light enough for one or two men to carry, an extension of wood or iron was added so that the holding and handling of the weapon became easier.

The hand cannon consisted of a strong tube of iron, bronze or copper, closed at the back end, with a vent or touchhole on top of the barrel at the breech. The marksman fed the powder, the wad and the projectile through the muzzle, and the charge was fired with the aid of a lighted match or hot wire thrust into the touchhole. It can be inferred from the operation that two men were needed to handle this weapon, one to aim it, the other to fire it. Early illustrations, however, frequently show both tasks performed by one man.

Military authors acknowledge as the first document concerning the use of firearms in Europe the text of the "Riformagioni" of Florence (February 11, 1326). This document is an authorisation granted by the government of Florence to the priors, to the gonfalonier and to twelve good men to delegate one or two "masters" to have made iron cannon balls and "canones de metallo" which were to be used for the defense of the republic. (Original text: *Études sur le Passé et l'Avenir de l'Artillerie* by Favé, Vol. III, Paris, 1862, p. 72.)

However, Major Angelucci quotes a document of 1281 containing the following terms: " . . . Une squadra grande de Balestrieri e scoppettieri del conte Guido di Montefeltro" (Angelo Angelucci: *Documenti inediti per la storia delle armi de fuocco italiane*, Turin, 1869, p. 17).

The *scopettieri* are firearms bearers, in all the texts where this term appears. According to this document, the portable firearm would have been used in Italy from the last three decades of the thirteenth century.

There is no known description to give us an idea of the construction of the hand cannon. Fortunately, there exist pictures on documents which can be dated with certainty.

The work of Konrad Kyeser, dated 1405, entitled "Belliforte," shows a hand cannon consisting of a barrel reinforced by four rings and lengthened by a wooden stock. The weapon is as high as the soldier's shoulder. (This MS. is preserved in the library of Göttingen University, cod. MS. phil. 63; reprod. E. Wagner, Z. Drobvna and J. Durdik: *Medieval Costume, Armour and Weapons*.)

A manuscript previously in the possession of the "Feldzeugmeisters von Hauslab" at Vienna shows several soldiers. Five of them have in their hands a fire tube fixed to a stock which reaches to half way along the barrel. Two seem to be holding the weapon in a firing position, propped on the crook of the left arm, the right hand serving as a support at the place where the stock joins the barrel (reprod. W. Hassenstein: *Das Feuerbuch von 1420*, Munich, 1941, p. 164).

The mounted figure in armor shown in a drawing dated 1449 from the library of Count Wilczeck at Vienna has just lit the charge of his weapon: the iron stock extends behind the barrel (reprod. *op. cit.* p. 163), and is held against the breastplate of the horseman.

The manuscript of Marianus Jacobus, of the same date, shows a hand cannon resting on the shoulder of the soldier. Since the weapon is held in both hands, the firing must have been the job of an aide (reprod. *op. cit.* p. 169).

A wood engraving from the manuscript *Rudimentum Noviciorum* (Lübeck, 1475) shows two armor-clad marksmen in action. When the shot is fired, the stock extension of the barrel passes under the left arm of the marksman (reprod. Robert Held: *The Age of Firearms*, Harper, New York, 1957, and Cassell, London, 1959, p. 24).

Surviving hand cannon are rare; nevertheless, the general form of those which have been found – mainly excavated pieces – is very similar to that shown in the manuscripts. One of the oldest, preserved in the German National Museum, is that called "Tannenberg," the name of the castle under the ruins of which it was discovered, in what remained of the cistern. Since the castle of Tannenberg, in Hesse, was destroyed in 1399, the arm must be of earlier date than this. It is a bronze, octagonal tube weighing 1,235 gm., totalling 32 cm. in length and with a bore of about 18 mm. (*Zeitschrift für Historische Waffenkunde*, Vol. III, p. 97).

The Copenhagen Arsenal possesses an arm known as "Vedelspang," a place to the south of Schleswig where it was found under the ruins of a castle constructed in 1416 and destroyed in 1426. The cannon, which measures 21 cm., is extended by a long iron staff; the bore is 18 mm. (reprod. *Guide to the Royal Danish Arsenal Museum*, Copenhagen, 1953, p. 13).

Lastly, there are the hand cannon dating from before the time of firing from the shoulder, in the Historical Museum of the town of Pilsen (*Zeitschrift für Historische Waffenkunde*, Vol. II, p. 266), in the German Museum of Nuremberg (*ibid.* p. 166), in the Berlin arsenal (*ibid.* p. 387), in the Museum of Art and History at Geneva (*Les Musées de Genève*, September 1953), and in the Historical Museum at Hamburg, as well as in the Swedish State Historical Museum and the Royal Armory.

It has already been noted that no text in existence gives an exact description of the hand cannon. Contemporary sources deal only with the manageability of the arms.

Thus, in one of the inventories preserved at the Arsenal of Bologna, dated 1397, one reads as follows: ... *VIII sclopos de ferro de quibus sunt tres a manibus* (eight iron "escopettes" three of which are hand ones – *Études sur le Passé et l'Avenir de l'Artillerie* by Prince Louis-Napoléon Bonaparte, Paris, 1846, Vol. 1, p. 364). A reference of 1383 mentions seven reinforced cannon, four of them large and three portable (Inventory of the fortresses of Artois, cited by V. Gay, *Glossaire Archéologique 1*, p. 274). Another of 1417 refers to "one hand cannon, seven hundred arrows..." (Reg. de la Cloison d'Angers, No. 54, cited by V. Gay, *op. cit.*) This hand cannon, better designated by the term fire tube, which describes it fairly well, became the original arquebus when it was fitted with a firing system which the marksman could operate himself and with a butt which enabled him to hold it against his shoulder, cheek, or chest, and aim. "Mechanical" firing became possible as soon as a pan to contain the fuse powder and a clip to hold the match were added to the arm.

At what date did the hand cannon become able to be fired mechanically from the shoulder? Several documents provide an answer to this question. One is the inventory of the Arsenal of Landshut, dated 1485 (*Zeitschrift für Historische Waffenkunde*, Vol. II, p. 281): on one of the pages is a hand cannon shown with a long stock and the caption "Aeltere Handtpuchsen." Another picture shows arquebuses, already with the stock supporting the barrel, and a butt, which, although admittedly crude, nevertheless merits the name. The inscription is "Handtpuchsen So im Kassten sein." This document is proof of firing from the shoulder, but not yet of a means of mechanical firing. The latter is proved in a document dated 1500, the *Codex Monacensis 222*, pl. 61, of the Munich National Museum: this page contains a view of the arsenal and depicts arquebuses resting horizontally on two metal eye bolts fixed in beams. The butts are the original ones. Five of the thirteen weapons are equipped with serpentines, or clamps, for holding and moving the match (W. Hassenstein, *op. cit.*, p. 168).

It is difficult to imagine the hand cannon being useful in open warfare; it was much more useful during a siege, the attack and defense being easily able to use a supported weapon. Until Monthléry (1465), Commines put only archers into the field in the armies of Burgundy and France. It is scarcely conceivable that hand cannon were of use in open warfare against a mobile enemy until the modifications began which changed them into a type of arquebus. One can thus accept the completed change as dating from the last three decades of the fifteenth century. At this period, in 1474, the first mention of an organized shooting match for firearms occurs: ". . . ordered to award three prizes, each to the value of six florins, one for the crossbowmen, one for the archers, and one for the culveriniers" (Geneva, Reg, du Conseil, August 2, 1474, transl. from Latin). This shooting competition for firearms, comparable with the precision shooting matches often described for bow and crossbow, could have taken place only after the system of sighting had been made effective by the two improvements mentioned above.

CL.B.

Illustrations: page 33.

Blair, Claude, *European and American Arms*, London, 1962.

Peterson, Harold L., *The Treasury of the Gun*, New York, 1962 (*The Book of the Gun*, London, 1963).

Wagner, E., Drobvna, Z., and Durdik, J., *Medieval Costume, Armour and Weapons*, London, n.d. (English translation by Jean Layten from German edition, Prague, 1957).

See also: ARQUEBUS; HACBUTT; MATCHLOCK.

HARMONICA GUN

Taking its nickname from the well-known musical instrument, this unusual gun was but another attempt to produce a repeating arm. In this instance the chambers were placed side by side in a sliding horizontal bar. The guns were equipped with a single barrel, or on some guns the chambers were of sufficient length to form their own barrels, much in the style of a pepperbox. Usually in firing the loaded block moved horizontally, both double-action or manually, from left to right as each chamber was fired. The number of chambers in the block varied from four to ten or more. This type of arm was made, and achieved its greatest popularity, during both the percussion and early cartridge periods. Calibers were varied. The harmonica principle was employed not only on handguns but on long arms as well. Best known of the harmonica handguns are those by Jarré of France, while the Kendall rifles of the United States are typical of the harmonica mechanism.

H.C.L.

Illustration: page 179.

Logan, Herschel C., *Hand Cannon to Automatic*, Huntingdon, W.Va., 1944.

Winant, Lewis, *Firearms Curiosa*, New York, 1955, 2nd edition 1961, and London, 1956.

HARPERS FERRY

Small-arms manufacturing plant and arsenal established by George Washington in 1796, at Harpers Ferry, Virginia (now West Virginia), at the confluence of the Potomac and Shenandoah rivers. The site was named after a ferry established by Robert Harper in 1747. Though the construction of the shops, warehouses, barracks and quarters was begun in 1796, the first year's production of 243 muskets patterned on the French Model 1763 was recorded in 1801. With the training of personnel, construction of facilities and accumulation of materials such as seasoned walnut for stocks, the Armory rapidly expanded its production until it averaged over 10,000 muskets and rifles annually, with some 75,000 small arms kept in the arsenal reserve.

On the night of April 18, 1861, faced with imminent capture by Confederates, the Armory and its arsenal were set afire by the guard commander, Lieutenant Roger Jones, who managed to destroy some 20,000 stands of arms and machinery before retreating across the Potomac with his detachment of forty-five men. However, the Confederates managed to salvage some of the machinery, complete arms and musket parts for later use.   A.G.

HARPOON GUN

See: WHALING GUN.

HARQUEBUS

See: ARQUEBUS.

HENRY, BENJAMIN TYLER

B. Tyler Henry was born in Claremont, New Hampshire, on March 22, 1821. A machinist, Henry devoted almost all of his adult life to work on firearms. His apprenticeship was served with J. B. Ripley & Company, gunsmiths of Claremont and patentees of a "waterproof rifle" which has been described as an intermediate step between the Hall breech-loading flintlock and the Spencer cartridge repeater. It was never popular, but it did provide Henry with a knowledge of the problems of breech-loading and repeating arms. After brief service with several other gun shops, including the Springfield Armory, he joined N. Kendall & Company in 1842, just before they became Robbins, Kendall & Lawrence.

At the Robbins, Kendall & Lawrence Armory, Henry first came in contact with the repeating system he was later to perfect into the Henry rifle. This was Walter Hunt's "volitional repeater" as improved by Lewis Jennings, which the shop began to produce in 1850. Here also he met Daniel B. Wesson and later Horace Smith who were developing their Volcanic arms as a further improvement on the Hunt. When the New Haven Arms Company was organized by Oliver Winchester to manufacture the Volcanic rifles and pistols, Henry joined the firm and supervised production.

While in this position Henry devised the improvements which led to the Henry and later to the Winchester rifles. Ammunition had been one of the major drawbacks of the Hunt, Jennings and Volcanic arms. Thus Henry began experimenting with a .44 rimfire cartridge in 1858 and soon perfected it. Then he altered the Volcanic rifle to fire the new ammunition. A patent was granted in 1860, and the Henry rifle was put into production in time to see some service, especially with the western armies, during the Civil War. It was an excellent arm. With minor changes it became the first Winchester rifle in 1866. At that time Henry left Winchester's employ and operated a machine shop in New Haven until his death on June 8, 1898.   H.L.P.

Parsons, John E., *The First Winchester*, New York, 1955.

Peterson, Harold L., *The Treasury of the Gun*, New York, 1962 (*The Book of the Gun*, London, 1963).

Williamson, Harold F., *Winchester, the Gun that Won the West*, Washington, D.C., 1952.

See also: HENRY RIFLE; HUNT, WALTER; REPEATING ARMS; SMITH, HORACE; WESSON, DANIEL B.; WINCHESTER.

HENRY RIFLE

The Henry rifle was a refinement of the repeating system developed by Walter Hunt, Lewis Jennings, Horace Smith and Daniel Wesson. It retained the tubular magazine beneath the barrel and the lever action of its predecessors, but was improved by radically different ammunition, a new bolt, and a firing pin with a divided head designed to strike both sides of the cartridge rim at once and so avoid the chance of a misfire caused by a dead spot in the priming ring. The magazine held fifteen .44 caliber rounds, and a sixteenth could be loaded in the chamber. Army tests indicated a reasonably skilled shooter could fire 120 rounds in 340 seconds, an average of one shot every 2.9 seconds, including reloading time. Henry obtained his patent on October 16, 1860. Production began at the New Haven Arms Company plant early in 1862 and terminated in 1866. An estimated 13,500 were made.

                                         H.L.P.

Illustrations: page 180.

Parsons, John E., *The First Winchester*, New York, 1955.

Williamson, Harold F., *Winchester, the Gun that Won the West*, Washington, D.C., 1952.

See also: HENRY, BENJAMIN TYLER; HUNT, WALTER; REPEATING ARMS; WINCHESTER.

HEURTELOUP, BARON CHARLES-LOUIS-STANISLAS

Born in Paris in 1793, Heurteloup graduated in medicine in 1823. After some years of research he published a medical treatise in 1827, received an award of 5,000 francs for his work in 1828, and then moved to London, where he made his home and patented his first firearms designs.

The patent of May 22, 1834, described a breech-loading cartridge gun and the prototype of the primer for which Heurteloup became famous. The primer was a tube "of soft metal or other substance" filled with his detonating compound, and was fed through the butt to the nipple by a toothed wheel that turned automatically on cocking. When struck by the adjustable cutting and striking head of the cock, the primer was cut off and sealed an instant before the section on the nipple exploded. A similar patent was granted in Paris on October 11, 1834, and both appear to be based on the earlier design by L. de Valdahon, which used a straw filled with priming.

In a booklet that he wrote in 1836, Heurteloup used the name *koptipteur* – from the Greek "to cut" and "to strike" – for a new lock with its cock striking upwards against priming fed along a channel under the fore-end. Quick to use, the primer had obvious advantages over the percussion cap. The gun performed well in British Ordnance all-weather trials in 1836 and 1837, but it was too revolutionary, and despite its relative simplicity was rejected by the British. The muskets of the British trials and the arms issued to the Belgian *Chasseurs-Éclaireurs du Royaume* in 1842 are of a design patented in Paris in 1837 and in Belgium in 1838.

Correspondence in *The Times* described massive trials at St. Petersburg in early 1841, and an example of Heurteloup's British patent of September 9, 1841, is dated in that year and has a Russian military inscription. It has not been possible, however, to establish whether the arms went into service in Russia in any numbers.

This last Heurteloup design was a standard flintlock musket with a *koptipteur* cock and a dispenser holding a coiled, 80-ignition tape primer above the lockplate. The primer, which resembled Maynard's patent of 1845, was fed on to the nipple by a wheel turned by the forefinger. This lock was also rejected, and no more were offered by the Baron who was then described by George Lovell as "a gentleman of very first rate mechanical talent and untiring perseverance." The Baron died in 1864.   W.R.

Illustration: page 41.

Heurteloup, Baron Charles-Louis-Stanislas, *Mémoire sur les Fusils de Guerre*, Paris, 1836.
Reid, William, "The Firearms of Baron Heurteloup" in *Journal of the Arms and Armour Society*, Vol. 3, No. 3, London, September 1959.

See also: PERCUSSION SYSTEM.

HOLSTER

A holster is a case intended to hold a pistol. While the exact date of introduction is not known, in all probability the holster appeared soon after the advent of the pistol itself, in Europe early in the sixteenth century. The English term holster and the Dutch word *holster*, both in the same sense, were in common use in the seventeenth century.

Holsters may be placed in two general categories: saddle holsters, and those for wear upon the person. The earliest holsters were designed for attachment to a horseman's saddle and, for some three centuries following, holsters were generally of this type. Holsters appear to have been attached occasionally to the baldric during the eighteenth century. It was, however, only in the middle of the nineteenth century, contemporaneously with the transition in handguns from singleshot to revolver, that saddle holsters generally gave way to those intended for wear on the person, commonly on the waist belt.

The form of the holster proper has almost always been that of a tube (often called a pipe), enlarged toward the mouth to admit the trigger guard and, as necessary, portions of the lock mechanism. Leather has been, in all periods, by far the most used substance in holster construction, though other materials, such as textiles, wood, and rubber, have been introduced at various times. The holster, from an early period in its history, has often served as a point of attachment for various items related to the pistol, such as tools, powder flask and bullet pouch, or fixed ammunition.

Both saddle and belt holsters were nearly always provided with a substantial covering – cap, hood, or flap – as long as the ignition system of the pistol was subject to damage from moisture. Since the introduction of metallic ammunition, the holster flap, where retained, has tended to be abbreviated, often being simply a narrow strap to guard against loss of the pistol. Only, as a rule, in holsters designed for military service has the tendency been to retain a sizable flap.

Before the introduction of the revolver, saddle holsters were frequently made in pairs. Such pairs were commonly connected by a centerpiece, which rested across the pommel, with the holsters themselves depending at each side. When it was desired to carry only one pistol on the saddle, a pouch was often substituted for the second holster, to contain items such as horseshoes or currycomb and brush.

Saddle holsters often bore ornamentation, sometimes of the most elaborate sort. Brass tips at the muzzle ends of the holsters were common. Holster covers, which at times were very large, might be decorated with braid and embroidery. Covers of fur, such as bearskin, were sometimes used. Fur covers, in addition to their decorative value, gave protection to a rider if he were thrown against the pommel.

The belt holster apparently had no one place of origin. Rather, it seems to have come into use in various parts of the world at practically the same time. Belt holsters were in use to some extent in the American West as early as the middle 1840's; a decade later they were common there. In the middle 1850's all Russian cavalrymen carried the pistol in a belt holster. In 1856, the Chief of Ordnance of the United States Army observed that, in the American service, while "horse pistols" were still carried on the saddle, "Colt's revolvers of the light pattern are carried in a pouch, or half-holster, attached ... to the waist belt." The first patent for a belt holster, one designed for the Colt, was granted in England in 1857.

A sliding belt loop has been the means most commonly

1. *Saddle holsters for wheel lock pistols, early seventeenth century, and wheel lock saddle holster shown in position*
2. *Saddle holsters for flintlock pistols, eighteenth century*
3. *Belt holster for Adams revolver*
4. *Belt holster for Luger pistol*
5. *Shoulder holster and harness*
6. *Saddle holsters for Colt Walker revolvers*

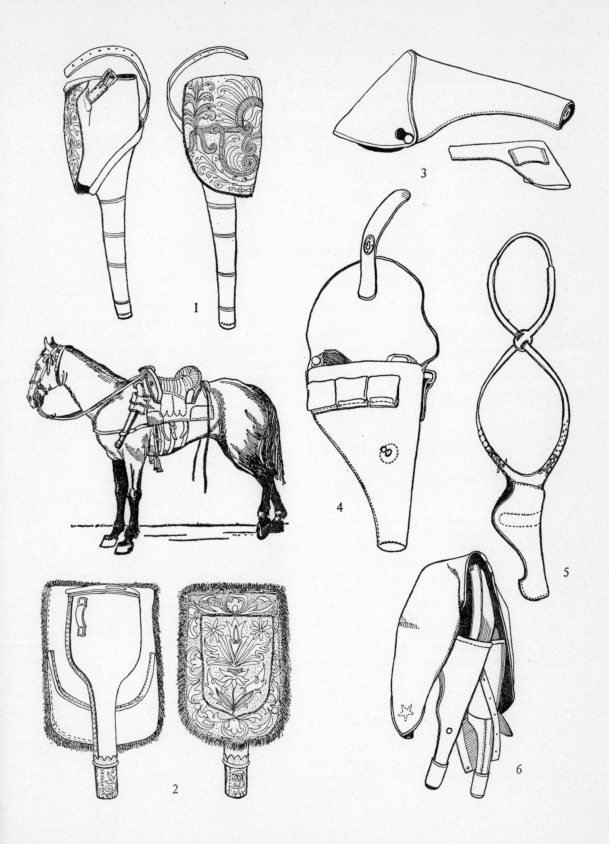

used for attaching the holster to a waist belt. Many other methods have been devised, however, such as the familiar wire hanger, devised in 1901, for insertion in the eyelets in a web belt. In addition, the holster has been carried on the person in numerous ways other than on the waist belt, the modern shoulder holster being a good example. In this, a strap loop passes over the shoulder and the holster itself is suspended between the arm and the body. Some shoulder holsters are designed as a spring clip to hold the pistol, rather than as a leather case of the traditional type.   J.S.H.

Peterson, Harold L., *Arms and Armor in Colonial America, 1526–1783*, Harrisburg, Pa., 1956.

Stone, George Cameron, *A Glossary of the Construction, Decoration and Use of Arms and Armor in All Countries and in All Times together with some Closely Related Subjects*, Portland, Me., 1934.

HOTCHKISS, BENJAMIN BERKELEY

Benjamin B. Hotchkiss, the American inventor and manufacturer, was born at Watertown, Connecticut, on October 1, 1826. Following a high school education and an apprenticeship as a machinist he entered his father's hardware factory, and soon began to produce the innovations in firearms and ammunition that made him famous. The first of these was a projectile for rifled artillery, patented in 1855. With later improvements it became one of the most widely used rifle projectiles of the American Civil War. This projectile, plus fuses of his own design, established him as an important munitions designer and manufacturer.

Among the firearms designed by Hotchkiss was a revolving cannon or quick-firing gun which was adapted for both land and naval use. It was operated by a hand crank, but, unlike the Gatling which it superficially resembled, the barrels locked in place and remained stationary for firing. This gun was developed while Hotchkiss was in France during the Franco-Prussian War and is supposed to have been inspired by the Montigny mitrailleuse.

In 1875, after his return to the United States, Hotchkiss invented a magazine repeating rifle with a bolt action. The patents for this arm were promptly purchased by Winchester, and it was manufactured in both sporting and military models.

Throughout this period Hotchkiss had continued to work on the improvement of artillery projectiles and the establishment of manufacturing plants. By 1882 the B.B. Hotchkiss Company had its headquarters in the United States and branches in Austria, England, France, Germany and Russia. He was working on a new machine gun design when he died, in Paris, on February 14, 1885. It

remained for others to develop and perfect the machine gun which bore his name.   H.L.P.

Chinn, Colonel George M., *The Machine Gun*, 4 vols, Washington, D.C., 1951–55.

See also: AUTOMATIC ARMS; MACHINE GUN; REPEATING ARMS.

HUDSON'S BAY FUKE/HUDSON'S BAY GUN

See: TRADE GUNS.

HUNT, WALTER

Walter Hunt, inventor and machinist, was born in Martinsburg, New York, on July 29, 1796. In 1826 he moved to Brooklyn to manufacture a flax-spinning machine he had invented. The project collapsed for lack of capital, and Hunt began an endless round of experiments and inventions, many of which might have made him a fortune if he had had the money or business ability to exploit them properly. Among them were a heating stove, an ice boat, a nail-making machine, a fountain pen, a forest saw, a safety pin, and a sewing machine. The sewing machine was very similar to Howe's successful model of a few years later. Hunt had not patented his device, however, and so lost all rights to it.

In the firearms field, Hunt is best known for his invention of a bullet and of a magazine rifle to fire it. The bullet boasted a hollow base large enough to hold a propellant charge and closed by a cork with a hole to transmit the flash from a separate primer. This bullet, patented in 1848, was followed the next year by a gun with a tubular magazine under the barrel. Called a "volitional repeater" by Hunt, it was the direct ancestor of the Winchester rifle which still retains the magazine and some other internal features. Lacking the capital to develop his gun, Hunt sold the rights to it to the first of a series of companies which eventually came under Winchester's control. He died in New York City on June 8, 1859.   H.L.P.

Illustration: page 179.

Peterson, Harold L., *The Treasury of the Gun*, New York, 1962 (*The Book of the Gun*, London, 1963).

Williamson, Harold F., *Winchester, the Gun that Won the West*, Washington, D.C., 1952.

See also: HENRY, BENJAMIN TYLER; REPEATING ARMS; WINCHESTER.

I

INDIAN GUNS

It would be quite accurate to say that the guns used by the American Indian, from the times of the early settlers to the end of the Western plains wars, covered very nearly all the styles and types made in America in that period, and indeed, many that were made abroad.

The uncivilized savage was not long in learning that the white man's firearm would be of inestimable use to him, for both hunting and warfare. Quite naturally, he set about obtaining this weapon, and over a period of time this was accomplished by gift, barter, theft and capture.

During the so-called French and Indian wars, and later during the War of Independence, Indians were extensively used as mercenaries, and were liberally furnished with arms by their respective principals.

In ensuing years, French, English and American fur trade companies bartered weapons for furs, and the justly famous trade gun came into prominence; in fact, it was a prominent Indian weapon for almost 150 years. The story of Indians trading a pile of beaver skins to the height of the barrel for one of these guns has been proved aprocryphal, incidentally.

The Indians paid well for the trade gun, and it, in turn, was the only gun designed specifically for Indian usage. Sometimes called the northwest gun or Hudson's Bay fuke, it was a full-stocked flintlock smoothbore of approximately .58 caliber, which could readily be adapted to firing with a single ball and wad, or loaded with shot and used as a shotgun.

Its general-purpose usage was an obvious advantage to the Indian, who was far removed from sources of supply. These sturdy flintlocks, coupled with a reasonable amount of powder and lead, kept him in a self-reliant position for extended periods of time.

With the advent of percussion ignition, and later of cartridge weapons, many Indians still preferred the flintlock trade gun for the reasons mentioned, and also because of its reliability. It was a well made weapon.

It was also of inexpensive construction, and the Indian refused to accept substitutes or inferior copies. He demanded, for some reason still not clear to historians – although it may be merely a carry-over from the design of the earliest arms – a serpent or dragon sideplate, and known proofmarks and makers' names also carried considerable importance.

English makers controlled the market for a long period, with Barnett, Chance, Sargent, Wheeler, Parker-Field and Hollis being prominent suppliers.

The American Fur Trade Company encouraged American makers, who included Deringer, Henry, Leman and Tryon, but they never were as successful as the English.

The Belgians and the French made trade guns, and a number of the Belgian pieces were infringements of their English counterparts in that they used slight variations of makers' names to win Indian approval.

Some of these escaped the detection of the Indian, but others were disdainfully rejected because they were of inferior quality.

Decoration of these weapons – and any other the Indian might come by – was usually in the form of designs set in the stock with brass tacks, the tacks being obtainable at almost all trading posts on the frontiers, and also from the small trunks carried by emigrants.

The designs were often formed in the particular owner's concept of "good medicine." Such was his interest in tacked designs that some English exporters even shipped guns for this trade which were pre-tacked, so to speak, and others were furnished with small oval mirrors set in the stock.

The Indian gave virtually no thought to the care or maintenance of his weapon. Either it fired or it didn't. A broken stock caused him to bestir himself to the point where the break was mended with wet rawhide sewn around the fracture. When this dried and shrank, it made, strangely enough, a very satisfactory repair. Many of the guns extant today have this form of repair.

Barrels were sometimes shortened to carbine length for running buffalo on horseback. The cut-off portion was often fashioned into a tent peg or hide scraper. Butt plates, too, were frequently removed and made into scrapers.

As pointed out, many other types of firearms were used by Indians. Guns captured from the military were extensively used, as were those taken from settlers, trappers and emigrants – along with their scalps, in many cases. Pistols showing Indian usage are relatively rare.

The Sharps "Old Reliable" rifle, the Hawken and the Leman, all types preferred by the buffalo hunters, were favorites of the savage. The Sharps carbine, the Spencer, Springfield and Remington of military usage, all found their way into Indian hands.

The Henry and Winchester repeating rifles were obtained largely by illicit trade with unscrupulous post traders, but some were actually issued by governmental officials, ostensibly for hunting purposes, to Agency Indians.

No people knew the fallacy of such practices better than the cavalry commanders in the field. General Custer was vociferous in his demands that all such types of illicit trade be curtailed. As a result, he met his initial downfall at the hands of Washington politicians in the Grant cabinet. A few weeks later, he met his death on the banks of the Little Bighorn river, when many of the very weapons he had objected to were turned against him, annihilating his immediate command.

Public reaction was so great that the Ordnance Department was required to examine a selection of captured Indian weapons at the Springfield Armory to ascertain whether Indian fire power was superior to that of the military.

What this board neglected to point out was that the greatest carnage in the Custer battle resulted from captured military weapons being turned on the remaining soldiers with much more telling effect than that from weapons owned by the Indians. It reported merely that Indian guns were not superior, and that some were in such a state of disrepair that they could not be made to fire at all. The white man was not as ingenious in this respect as his red counterpart!

Indian guns were, and are, colorful because the Indian made them so, and their use in the westward movement will probably never be forgotten in American history.

                                              J.S. DU M.

Illustrations: pages 214–16.

du Mont, John S., "Collecting Indian Guns" in *The American Rifleman*, July 1958.

Ewers, John C., "The Northwest Trade Gun" in *Alberta Historical Review*, Spring 1956.

Hanson, Charles E., Jr., *The Northwest Gun* (Nebraska State Historical Society Publications in Anthropology, No. 2), Lincoln, Neb., 1955.

Hanson, Charles E., Jr., *The Plains Rifle*, Harrisburg, Pa., 1960.

Parsons, John E., "Gunmakers for the American Fur Company" in *The New York Historical Society Quarterly*, New York, April 1952.

Parsons, John E., and du Mont, John S., *Firearms in the Custer Battle*, Harrisburg, Pa., 1953.

Russell, Carl P., *Guns on the Early Frontiers*, London, and Berkeley and Los Angeles, Cal., 1957.

See also: TRADE GUNS.

J

JACOB, JOHN

John Jacob, born in 1812, was the fifth son of the vicar of Woolavington in Somerset. He was educated at home by his father and then entered the East India Company's college at Addiscombe. In 1828 he was commissioned second lieutenant in the Bombay Artillery.

After distinguished service in the Afghan War, he was given command of the Scinde Irregular Horse, and for the first time brought peace to the frontier districts under his control. From then on Jacob devoted his life to their administration, and instituted vast agricultural and civil engineering projects, including the construction of a town which was to bear his name, Jacobabad.

He was also interested in firearms and invented a system of four-groove rifling using a conical studded bullet which could be fitted with an explosive head. After several years of experiments, which he described in his booklet *Rifle Practice*, he designed a military rifle for this bullet weighing 10½ lb, with double barrels 24 inches long of 32 bore. It was sighted up to 2,000 yards and was supplied with an elaborate sword bayonet with a 30-inch blade. Although this rifle was rejected by the government, two infantry regiments, raised by Jacob just before his death in 1858 and known as Jacob's Rifles, were armed with it.

                                              H.L.B.

Jacob, John, *Rifle Practice*, London, 1855.

Shand, A. I., *General John Jacob*, London, 1900.

JAEGER RIFLE

The jaeger rifle derived its name from the German word *Jäger*, meaning hunter. It usually refers to the typical European flintlock hunting rifle used principally during the eighteenth century.

It originated from the efficient, short, heavy-barrel wheel lock rifle which had been popular in Germany for many years. About 1665 two gradual changes took place, the adoption of the flintlock system and the change in the shape of the butt so that the gun could be fired comfortably from the shoulder instead of being held to the cheek. These changes produced the jaeger, which existed with slight change until approximately 1850. From about 1820 on, the percussion ignition system was used.

The jaeger was the big game hunting rifle of the aristocracy, game keepers and foresters. It had widespread use in the Jäger and Light Infantry rifle battalions of central and northern Europe. It was in this capacity that the rifle received its first serious use on the battlefield. Many were taken to America during the Revolution by the so-called Hessians.

The jaeger was imported by German immigrants to Pennsylvania in the early eighteenth century, where frontier gunsmiths eventually transformed it into the Kentucky rifle.

The jaeger served as the model for the first military rifles to be adopted by England, France, Russia and the Scandinavian countries.

A typical good quality mid-eighteenth-century jaeger has a 30-inch octagonal barrel of about .60 caliber, rifled with seven grooves. Its full stock, with some relief carving, had a cheek piece and a sliding patch-box cover. The furniture was of brass or iron. The average weight was 7¾ lb.

B.W.M.

Illustrations: page 102.

JESSEN, NIELS STAAL

Danish gunmaker, iron cutter and chaser, born on May 22, 1797, the son of Squire Claus Seidelin Jessen of Asserstrup (Lolland). He was apprenticed to the gunmaker Gaetcke in Schleswig on December 12, 1818, received a trade license in Slagelse on May 12, 1821, and then worked as a gunmaker at Sjaellandske Jaegerkorps (Zealand Corps of Chasseurs) from 1827. He was head of the Small Arms Factory of the Danish Navy (Christiansholm, Copenhagen) from September 27, 1829. He resigned from the service in 1862, and died on June 25, 1880.

Jessen became a gunmaker at a very interesting period in the technology of arms. The useful percussion cap had recently been invented, and breechloaders were being constructed, among other things, to facilitate loading of the rifle. These breechloaders, however, were usually not gasproof, and it was still debatable whether the problem of loading the rifle was not more likely to be solved by a new muzzle-loading system.

Jessen was one of those believing in the future of the muzzle-loader. His proposal may remind one of the Brunswick oval gun, though the Brunswick rifle was only figuratively an oval gun, being in fact a rifle with two broad opposed grooves and an oval-shaped muzzle.

Jessen went much further, by taking up again the old idea of making the ball as an elongated bolt. Its cross section corresponded exactly with that of the barrel, both in form and size. Jessen chose the simplest cross section, the oval, which others had thought of before him, but which had never actually been made. The oval cross section, of course, wound down the barrel, just as other grooves. Loading was easy, and no forcing was necessary.

The Jessen oval rifle became known during the World Exhibition in London in 1851, to which he had sent an oval gun. After the exhibition the gun was bought by the Army Ordnance Corps in England, and it is now kept at the Tower of London. There is no doubt that the Jessen gun inspired the well-known English gunmaker Charles Lancaster to make the oval-rifled gun which he submitted in 1852 as a proposal for a new military rifle.

Although the Lancaster oval gun was not accepted, the type became important, as his oval-rifled guns became very common, and were well thought of. A few years later the production of oval guns was also taken up in the United States, although as breechloaders. The barrels of these Greene rifles were made on machines bought from Lancaster.

F.A.

Askgaard, Finn, "N.S. Jessen's Ovalgevaerer" [N.S. Jessen's oval guns] in *Vaabenhistoriske Aarbøger*, Vol. 7, Copenhagen, 1954.

See also: RIFLES AND RIFLING.

JEZAIL

The jezail is an Afghan gun with a slender, curved butt stock. It is distinguished from the so-called Afghan stock (actually from Sind) by its narrow oval butt. Originally

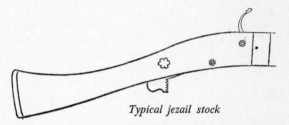

Typical jezail stock

jezails were matchlocks, but many were converted to flintlocks, usually by the substitution of a British-made lock. Some were rifled, and most were fitted with an A-shaped barrel support.

H.L.P.

Egerton, Wilbraham, *An Illustrated Handbook of Indian Arms*, London, 1880.

Stone, George Cameron, *A Glossary of the Construction, Decoration and Use of Arms and Armor in All Countries and in All Times together with some Closely Related Subjects*, Portland, Me., 1934.

See also: AFGHAN STOCK; ASIATIC FIREARMS.

K

KALTHOFF

A name given to a magazine repeater developed by a family of gunmakers, originally living in Solingen, Germany, from where a number of its members spread over most of Europe. Best known are Wilhelm Kalthoff, who in 1640 obtained a patent in Paris; Peter Kalthoff, who had a Dutch patent of 1641 and who lived in Denmark from 1646 until his death in 1672; Caspar Kalthoff, who worked with the Marquess of Worcester in London from 1628 until his death in 1664; and his son of the same name, who worked in Moscow in 1658–65, or perhaps longer.

A construction used by all these gunmakers is a magazine system where the movement in the horizontal plane of the trigger guard transports the powder from a magazine in the butt to the breech. This fundamental element in the system must have been invented before the family began to disperse, but later the construction was improved in different ways by the various members of the family and by other gunmakers copying the basic idea.

Guns of the Kalthoff system may be divided into three groups, according to the form of the breechblock:

Firstly, a group with a box-shaped square breechblock moving horizontally at right angles to the barrel; secondly, a group with a cylindrical breechblock turning on a vertical axis; and finally, a third group with a cylindrical or quarter-cylindrical breechblock with an axis parallel to the center line of the barrel.

The first type is probably that mentioned in Peter Kalthoff's patent of 1641. The Tøjhusmuseet, Copenhagen, has about fifty of these guns, the oldest being dated 1645. The guns are stated to have been used by a company of the Danish Foot Guards in 1658. Others were made in the Netherlands by H. Bartmans in 1641, and Cornelis Coster, of Utrecht, in 1652.

Of the second type, there are guns by Caspar Kalthoff, father and son, made respectively in London and Moscow. A number of Dutch gunmakers also made such guns, among them Harman Barne, working in London about 1650, Jan Flock from Solingen, working in Utrecht, and Cornelis Kant in Amsterdam. Other makers of this type are Berselli in Rome and Cousin in Paris.

Finally, the third type was made by Heinrich Habrecht in Schleswig and Alexander Hartingk, probably a German, shortly after 1650.   A.H.

Illustration: page 177.

Hoff, Arne, *Aeldredansk Bøssemageri* [early Danish gunmakers], 2 vols, Copenhagen, 1951 (with summary and captions in English).

See also: REPEATING ARMS.

KENTUCKY RIFLE

Kentucky rifle is a name popularly applied to a distinctive American arm. It was a graceful and accurate muzzle-loading rifle made during the eighteenth and nineteenth centuries. Other names given it have included the "long rifle," "American rifle," and "Pennsylvania rifle." The earliest of these rifles were copies of those brought by immigrants from central Europe to America. The characteristics of the imported rifle were slowly changed until a new rifle was evolved. There is no evidence that this new rifle had a specific name until the second decade of the nineteenth century when it became known as the Kentucky rifle.

The name of the rifle suggests that it was made in Kentucky, but that state has never been known as a center for the production of firearms. Rifles were first made in Pennsylvania because the German immigrants who settled there had used rifles in Europe and knew how to make them. Later rifles were made in many of the original colonies and in Ohio. They became famous for their performance on the frontier as weapons for hunting big game, played a minor role in the French and Indian wars, an important one in the American War of Independence, and a somewhat lesser role in the War of 1812. It is true, however, that riflemen from the Ohio River Valley played a brilliant part in Jackson's victory at the Battle of New Orleans in 1815. A ballad was written about their proficiency in this battle and the poet suggested that all of them were from Kentucky. The error in this statement indicates that "Kentucky" was selected for its rhythmical value rather than for historical accuracy, but the name Kentucky rifle caught the popular imagination. Since that time all rifles with long octagonal barrels and stocks of maple have been generically referred to as Kentucky rifles.

Although there was some overlapping of the various periods of production, the span of years in which rifles were made can be divided into three segments. The first period, called the transition period, started at some unknown date in the first half of the eighteenth century and terminated about the time of the American War of Independence. Rifles made in the earliest portion of this period were probably very similar to the rifles which were brought to America from Europe. It is obvious that gunsmiths slowly introduced new features, such as longer octagonal barrels and stocks of maple wood instead of walnut wood which had been used on the European guns. Near the middle of the century some of the craftsmen invented a patch-box cover of sheet brass which was attached to the stock with a hinge. These three features usually identify a rifle as a product of an American craftsman. Virtually a new rifle had been created by the time of the American War of Independence to meet the needs and taste of a new nation.

The second period of rifle production in America has been aptly called, by Joe Kindig, Jr., in his standard book on that era, the Golden Age of rifle making. This period started soon after the close of the War of Independence and terminated in about 1825–30 when the percussion lock came into general use. Most of the fine American rifles were made in this period.

The superior workmanship on rifles at this time was due to a number of factors. Men who had previously been engaged in warfare for a number of years might now turn to hunting big game with a fine rifle. An economy geared to normal living, rather than warfare, might provide adequate funds for the purchase of a beautiful rifle.

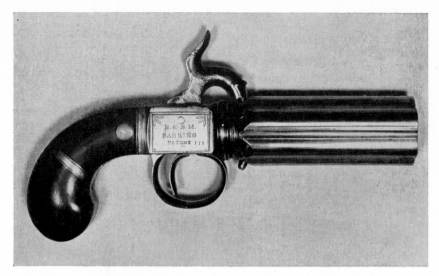

Pepperbox made by
B. & B. M. Darling,
the first pepperbox
patented in the
United States.
*Collection of
Frank R. Horner.*

Double-action pepperbox
by Allen & Thurber.
*Collection of
Frank R. Horner.*

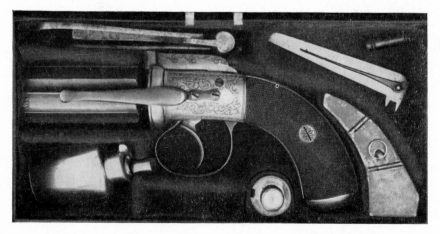

Cased British pepperbox
with belt hook and
sterling silver frame.
*Collection of
Robert Abels.*

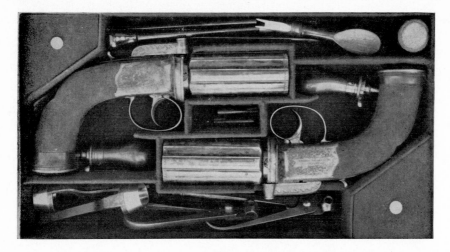

Cased British
pepperboxes made by
Westley Richards.
*Collection of
Robert Abels.*

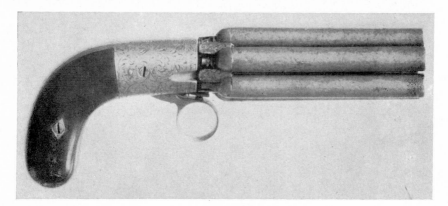

Belgian mariette
pepperbox.
Arms Museum, Liège.

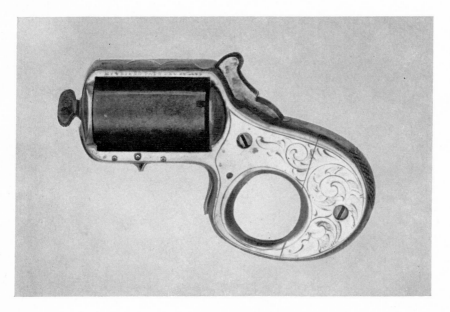

"My Friend"
knuckle-duster
made by James Reid.
*Collection of
Herschel C. Logan.*

Venetian matchlock
revolving pistol.
*Doge's Palace
Museum, Venice.*

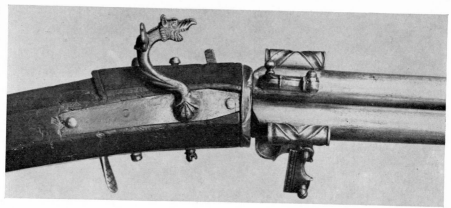

Snaphance revolver, seventeenth century. *Winchester Repeating Arms Company.*

Collier patent flintlock revolver. *Armouries, Tower of London.*

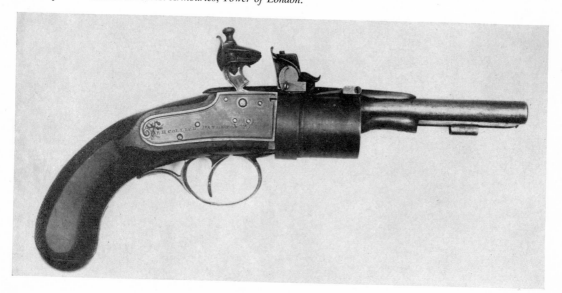

Colt third model Drago⟨
the Old Model Army Pist⟨
presentation-engraved w⟨
solid silver straps a⟨
plain ivory gri⟨
engraved on back str⟨
"Col. F. M. Milliki⟨
Collection of John S. du M⟨

Colt Old Model Navy Pistol, 18⟨
the barrel and action engraved w⟨
conventional scrollwo⟨
Presented to Benito Juar⟨
President of Mexi⟨
Collection of John S. du M⟨

Prototype Puckle gun of iron.
Armouries, Tower of London.

Presentation-engraved and silver-inlaid Texas size Colt Paterson revolver, with shell-carved ivory grips.
Collection of John S. du Mont.

BELOW Colt 1860 Army Model, the New Model Army Pistol; rare variation, 8″ B.B.L., with full fluted or "cavalry" cylinder; presentation-engraved, with silver and gold plating, and carved relief Mexican eagle ivory grips; implements silver-plated. *Collection of John S. du Mont.*

Robert Adams double-action
revolver, 1851.
*Winchester Repeating
Arms Company.*

Lefaucheux pin-fire revolver.
Smithsonian Institution.

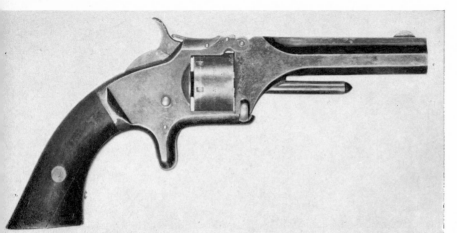

Smith & Wesson revolver no. 2.
Smithsonian Institution.

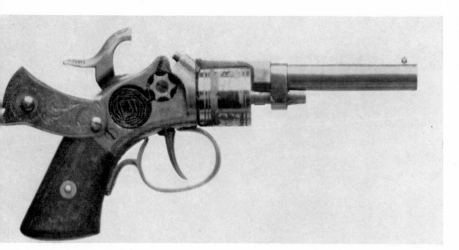

Walch revolver, firing
superposed loads.
Smithsonian Institution.

Massachusetts Arms Co.
revolver with
Maynard tape primer.
Smithsonian Institution.

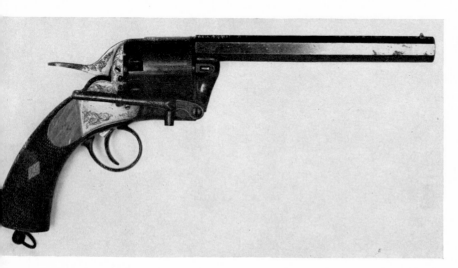

James Webley's
"Longspur" revolver,
second model.
Armouries,
Tower of London.

Webley center-fire revolver, Royal Irish Constabulary model of 1883. The frame is stamped ARMY & NAVY C.S.L. *Armouries, Tower of London.*

Copy of Webley "British Bulldog" revolver by Forehand & Wadsworth, U.S.A. This model was widely copied in Belgium, France, Germany, Spain, and the United States. *Armouries, Tower of London.*

Webley-Fosbery automatic revolver. *Winchester Repeating Arms Company.*

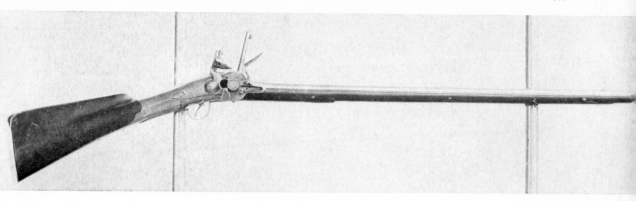

Italian Lorenzoni flintlock repeater,
showing the lever pulled halfway back.
Smithsonian Institution.

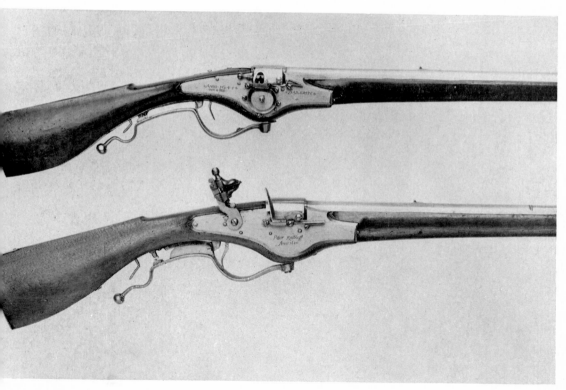

Kalthoff wheel lock magazine rifle, dated 1645, and
Kalthoff flintlock magazine rifle, dated 1646.
Tøjhusmuseet, Copenhagen.

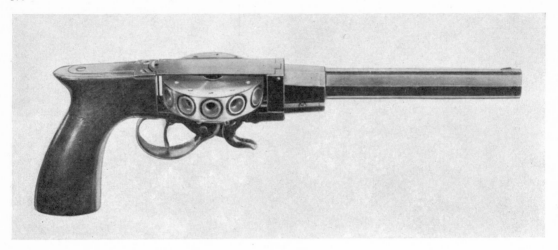

Cochran "Monitor" revolver, caliber .36.
Smithsonian Institution.

Sharps four-barreled pistol, caliber .32.
Smithsonian Institution.

Hunt rifle, caliber .54, 1848.
Winchester Repeating Arms Company.

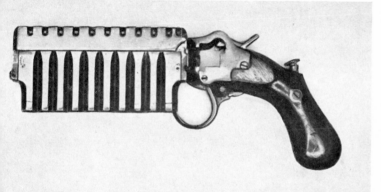

Jarré harmonica gun.
Collection of Henry M. Stewart.

Lancaster four-barreled
repeating pistol, caliber .455.
Smithsonian Institution.

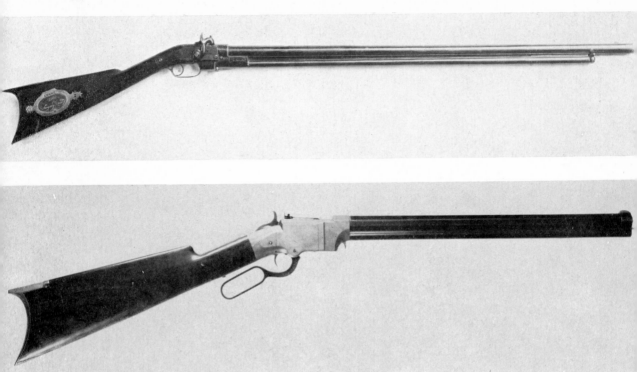

Jennings repeating rifle, caliber .54. (TOP) and
Volcanic repeating carbine, caliber .32. *Smithsonian Institution.*

Iron-frame Henry rifle and brass-frame Henry rifle.
Winchester Repeating Arms Company.

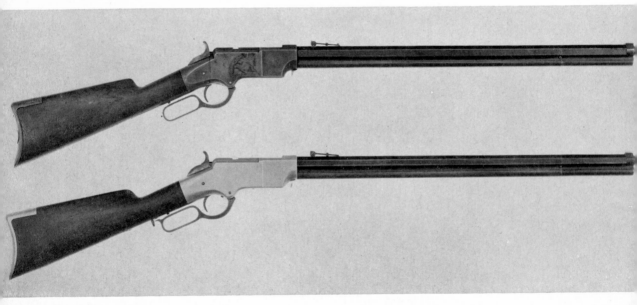

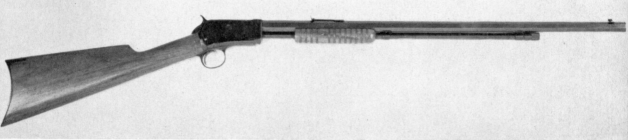

Winchester rifle, Model 1866.
Winchester Repeating Arms Company (TOP) and
Winchester pump-action repeating rifle, Model 1890.
Smithsonian Institution.

Internal view of Spencer mechanism.
Smithsonian Institution.

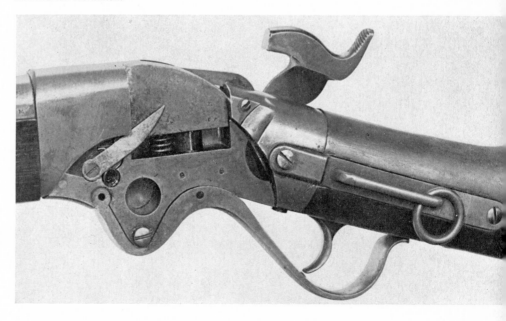

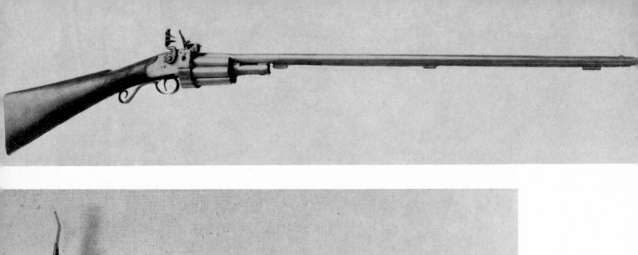

Swiss Vetterli rifle.
Museum of Art and His
Geneva.

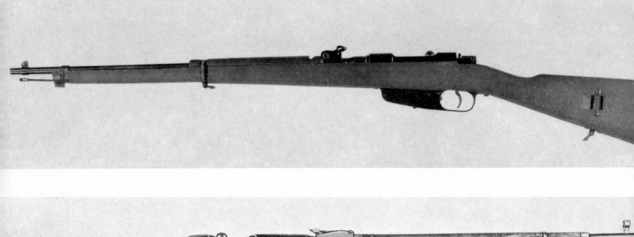

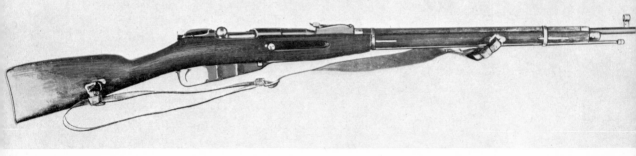

ler revolving musket.
sonian Institution.

Chambers repeating musket.
The Rotunda, Woolwich.

Gatling gun, U.S. Model 1865.
Smithsonian Institution.

n Mannlicher
no rifle,
m. M1891.

an
-Nagant rifle,
mm. M1891/30.

Danish organ espignolle on field carriage, *ca.*1840, with supplementary charged pipes in the two long boxes on the carriage; caliber 20 mm. *Tøjhusmuseet, Copenhagen.*

Billinghurst & Requa battery gun, M1862, caliber .50; also known as the "Eureka" battery gun. *Springfield Armory.*

And finally, a surplus of gunsmiths, particularly in Pennsylvania, produced a highly competitive business climate which resulted in the production of these accurate and elaborate rifles.

It has been pointed out that a true American rifle had been created by the time of the War of Independence, and the reader should be aware that the rifle after that was largely a refinement of the earlier gun. The octagonal barrel was lengthened to forty-two or forty-six inches, and the bore was reduced from a caliber of .60 to .50. This long barrel was mounted in a stock of curly maple which replaced the stocks of plain maple used on the earlier guns. The stocks were often carved on the cheek side of the butt with scrolls, geometric patterns, and, in some rare cases, animals. This carving in relief compares favorably with similar work done on fine furniture made in Philadelphia, New York, and Newport. Two side plates were added to the earlier two-piece patch box; all of which were beautifully engraved and perfectly fitted to the stock. The extravagant workmanship often included silver escutcheons for the barrel pins and an eight-pointed star, or other device, inlaid on the cheek piece. The name of the gunsmith was often engraved on the top facet of the barrel between the rear sight and the breech plug. A silver plate was provided on the wrist of some guns for the engraving of the owner's initials. Two types of locks were used on the guns of the period. One had a plain lock plate with one or two lines filed behind the cock and the other had an engraved lock plate. The plain type is thought to have been made in Germany; the engraved plates were made in England. In the early part of the nineteenth century a few American lockmakers supplied locks for Kentucky rifles. The rifle of the period after the War of Independence was not an elegant gun, by contemporary European standards, but it was an attractive, accurate arm made by artisans in the primitive workshops of America.

It has been noted that rifles were made in many of the original colonies, and it is logical to discover that gunsmiths in different areas developed styles or patterns peculiar to the area in which they worked. Rifles made in the state of New York are slightly different from those made in Pennsylvania, and the craftsmen of Salem, North Carolina, used designs for their guns which are typical of the region. The degree of specialization was so great in Pennsylvania that many patterns were evolved there, many of which are typical of the respective counties in which rifles were made. Some of the typical details are an elliptical wrist on the guns of Northampton County, a Roman nose on the guns of Berkshire County, the daisy patch-box finial on guns of Lancaster County, and the unique lock plates found on guns made in Bedford County.

The final phase of rifle production took place after the invention of the percussion lock. This invention, combined with the use of faster-burning powder and the factory production of guns, caused a general deterioration in the craft of gunmaking.

The general characteristics of the late rifle included an octagonal barrel, often reduced to thirty-four or thirty-six inches in length, and a bore reduced to a caliber of .40. On rare occasions the caliber was reduced to .25. The stocks were made of plain maple and some were artificially grained to simulate the curly maple used in earlier rifles. In the final stage of rifle production stocks were usually made of walnut. Brass mountings were reduced in size to conform to the smaller stocks and they were more sparsely engraved than in the preceding period. The long rectangular patch box was dropped for a smaller one which was either round or elliptical. Relief carving was continued on a few guns with percussion locks but the incised technique was more frequently used on late guns that were carved. Most of the lock plates were engraved, and frequently the name of the lockmaker appears on the middle of the lock plate, in front of the hammer.

Although inlays were used to decorate guns with flint locks, the art of inlaying reached its apex in the percussion era. The earlier escutcheons for the barrel pins were retained and to them were added inlays on each side of the wrist, on the cheek side of the butt, on the lock and side-plate panels, and on the fore-stock between the lock panel and the ramrod tail pipe. Shapes such as hearts, teardrops, diamonds, half-moons, and fish were widely used. A few of the so-called Pennsylvania "hex signs" were inlaid on some guns. Some rifles have as many as thirty to forty inlays scattered over the stock. It is obvious that this gun with a plain stock, or one with indiscriminately scattered inlays, was a less attractive gun than its predecessor; but it was an accurate gun and was priced within the reach of most men who wanted to own one.

Throughout the flint and percussion periods a few Kentucky pistols were made by the men who made rifles. These handguns had octagonal barrels (frequently rifled) of iron or brass, stocks of maple, and flint or percussion locks. Few of them were carved, and regional differences are not generally noticeable. Most of them were made in Pennsylvania, but a few are known to have been made in other areas where rifles were made.

Throughout the last half of the nineteenth century rifles were made by a few individual craftsmen, but the large portion of the product was made in factories such as Leman's in Lancaster and the factory of Brown and Hirth in Pittsburgh. The disappearance of big game and the importing of double-barreled shot guns for small game forced the factories to close their doors. Kentucky rifles continue to function in small muzzle-loading rifle meets, but the major use of the rifle today is for exhibition as a museum relic.   H.J.K.

Illustrations: page 103, and endpapers.

Dillin, John G. W., *The Kentucky Rifle*, revised edition, Wilmington, Del., 1959.

Kauffman, Henry J., *The Pennsylvania-Kentucky Rifle*, Harrisburg, Pa., 1960.

Kindig, Joe, Jr., *Thoughts on the Kentucky Rifle in its Golden Age*, Wilmington, Del., 1960.

Peterson, Harold L., *Arms and Armor in Colonial America, 1526–1783*, Harrisburg, Pa., 1956.

See also: RIFLES AND RIFLING.

KENTUCKY WINDAGE

See: BALLISTICS.

KNUCKLE-DUSTER

See: COMBINATION WEAPON.

KRAG, OLE H.

Ole H. Krag was born at Gudbrandsdalen, Norway, in 1837. He entered the Norwegian army and was commissioned at the age of twenty. Initially he served in the artillery, but soon transferred to small-arms work. A captain in 1870, he was assigned to the Kongsberg Arms Factory; in ten years he became the director of the factory. In 1895 he was made a colonel and Master General of Ordnance, at which time he enlarged the Kongsberg plant and the Raufoss ammunition plant. Krag retired from the army in 1902, but remained active in arms design, producing an automatic pistol design three years before his death in 1912.

The Krag-Peterson developed in conjunction with a Swedish engineer – Axel Peterson – was the first of Krag's rifle developments. The rifle has a modified Martini-type action with a tubular magazine in the fore-end. It was chambered for the 12.77 mm. rim-fire cartridge and was adopted by the Norwegian navy in 1877. Few of these rifles were made.

The bolt-action Krag-Jørgensen (see KRAG RIFLE), by far the best known of Krag's designs, was developed during the 1880's in conjunction with Erik Jørgensen, the chief armorer at Kongsberg. The rifle was first adopted by Denmark in 1889; a modified version was adopted by the United States in 1892, and by Norway in 1894. The United States government paid the inventors one dollar royalty for each rifle and carbine produced.

Although Krag produced a limited number of designs, his bolt-action rifle was one of the most successful guns of its time and was one of the few foreign gun designs ever adopted by the United States government.   J.E.S.

See also: KRAG RIFLE.

KRAG RIFLE

A bolt-action, magazine fed rifle developed by Ole H. Krag and Erik Jørgensen at the Kongsberg Arms Factory, Norway.

Its bolt has a single frontally mounted locking lug with a guide rib which serves as a safety lug. The five-round magazine has a side-mounted loading gate and is loaded with loose rounds. The loading gate on the Danish Krag pivots forward, while those of the Norwegian and American Krags pivot horizontally. The Danish M1889 originally had a half-cock-type safety, but was later fitted with a rotary lever-type safety. The American and Norwegian Krags have a Mauser-type leaf safety.

Denmark adopted the Krag in 1889, chambered for the Danish 8 mm. round – 8 × 58R. In 1892 the Krag was adopted by the United States in caliber .30–40 and in 1894 by Norway in 6.5 × 55 mm. American models of the Krag are: rifle 1892, rifle 1896, carbine 1896, Cadet rifle, rifle 1898, carbine 1898, carbine 1899, and caliber .22 gallery practice rifle M1898.   J.E.S.

Illustration: page 106.

Gluckman, Colonel Arcadi, *United States Muskets, Rifles and Carbines*, Harrisburg, Pa., 1959.

Hicks, Major James Ernest, *United States Firearms, 1776–1956*, Beverley Hills, Cal., 1957 (revised edition of Hicks's *Notes on United States Ordnance*, Vol. 1, Mount Vernon, N.Y., 1940).

Smith, Walter H. B. and Joseph E., *The Book of Rifles*, 3rd edition, Harrisburg, Pa., 1963.

See also: KRAG, OLE H.

L

LANCASTER, CHARLES W.

Charles William Lancaster was born in 1820, the eldest son of Charles Lancaster, the well-known London gunmaker. He quickly showed himself to be a very clever mechanic as well as a skilled craftsman and excellent shot. Through his employment under his father, who in 1843 was appointed gunmaker to Prince Albert, the younger

LAWRENCE, RICHARD S. – LEBEL RIFLE

Lancaster had the ear of the great, and managed, in 1846, to interest the Duke of Wellington in an improved rifle of his own design. The limited employment of the Lancaster-Brunswick rifle in the Cape of Good Hope paved the way, in many senses, for the later adoption of the Minié rifle.

As early as 1848 he conducted important experiments with small-bore rifles of .451 and .500 caliber which later had considerable effect on the course of development of military rifles. But his chief passion and major contribution to firearms was the perfecting of the oval-bore system of rifling. He was exceedingly unlucky in failing to secure the general introduction of his system, which was ultimately declared to be the best suited to large-bore rifles, (see RIFLES AND RIFLING) though he was successful in securing its adoption for the Royal Engineers' carbines. Much of his effort went into ordnance experiments: indeed, his oval-bored cannon, used in the Crimean War by both the army and the navy, were probably the first rifled ordnance to be employed by the British on active service. He patented more than a score of firearms improvements in his lifetime, including, in 1852, the earliest successful center-fire sporting breechloader, and was recognised as one of the leading firearms authorities of his day. He died suddenly in London on April 24, 1878.   C.H.R.

Illustration: page 179.

See also: RIFLES AND RIFLING.

LAWRENCE, RICHARD S.

Practical machinist, master armorer and armory superintendent, born at Chester, Vermont, on November 22, 1817. After his boyhood near Watertown and short army service, Lawrence went to Windsor, Vermont, where from 1838 he spent four years with N. Kendall & Co., learning the firearms-manufacturing trade. In 1843 Lawrence became Kendall's partner in a custom gunshop. S. E. Robbins joined them in 1844 to establish the firm of Robbins, Kendall and Lawrence. On February 18, 1845, the firm received a government contract for 10,000 Model 1841 percussion rifles at $11.90 each, duration five years. The contract was finished with eighteen months to spare. Kendall was bought out in 1847, and the firm continued as Robbins & Lawrence. On January 5, 1848, they received an additional contract for 15,000 Model 1841 rifles, and also undertook to manufacture privately 5,000 Jennings rifles as well as pepperbox percussion pistols.

The firm exhibited in London in 1851, with a resultant contract for 25,000 Enfield rifles and a promise of a further order for 300,000. Encouraged, the firm undertook a contract to make 5,000 Sharps carbines at their Windsor shop and 15,000 Sharps rifles and carbines at

a new factory to be established in 1853 at Hartford, Connecticut, where Lawrence went that year to operate the plant. The large Enfield contract failed to materialize and the firm, heavily involved in preparations for the order, failed in 1855.

Lawrence remained in charge of the Sharps plant in Hartford, which remained under Sharps company stockholders' control and continued operations until 1881. Not the least of Lawrence's achievements in arms development in the transition period from muzzle-loader to breechloader, was his introduction in 1851 of the grooved bullet lubricated with tallow, thus doing away with excessive leading of the barrels which affected their accuracy. He also developed a breech-loading firearm, a primer and rear sight for the Sharps rifles and carbines, and a flanged-plate gas check, as well as barrel-drilling and rifling machinery. He died at Hartford, Connecticut, on March 10, 1892.   A.G.

LEBEL RIFLE

The French Model 1886, caliber 8 mm. (.315), bolt-action rifle, commonly called the Lebel, was the first smallbore and smokeless-powder rifle to be adopted by a major world power. The Model 1886 derived its popular name from Lieutenant Colonel Nicolas Lebel (1838–91), a member of the commission instituted in 1884 to produce an arm capable of using a smokeless-powder rimmed cartridge, developed by the chemist Vieille and Captain Desaleux. The Kropatschek tubular magazine was adopted, with a few modifications, and held eight cartridges.

Cross section of the action of the Lebel rifle, Model 1886

Improvements were made in 1893, including a stronger receiver, a hole bored in the movable bolt head for gas escapage in case of primer rupture, rear sight alterations, and a stacking prong added to the muzzle cap. The receiver was marked "Modèle 86/93." The overall length without bayonet is 51.7 inches, and of the four-grooved barrel 31.5 inches. The Model 86/93, without bayonet, weighs 9.21 lb. In 1897, the magazine plunger was modified to allow the magazine to accommodate, without jamming, the pointed "balle D" cartridge designed by Desaleux, and adopted in 1896 to replace the snub-nosed Model 1886 cartridge. The Model 1886 épée bayonet has a grip of German-silver and a straight, quadrangular blade 20¼ inches long.   L.A.W.

Hicks, Captain (later Major) James Ernest, assisted by André Jandot, *Notes on French Ordnance, 1717–1936*, Mount Vernon, N.Y., 1938.

"Lebel, Nicolas" in *La Grande Encyclopédie* (31 vols), Vol. 21, Paris, 1886–1902.

Ommundsen, H., and Robinson, Ernest H., *Rifles and Ammunition and Rifle Shooting*, London and New York, 1915.

Textbook of Small Arms, H.M. Stationery Office, London, 1929.

See also: GRAS RIFLE.

LEE, JAMES P.

James Paris Lee was born in Scotland on August 9, 1831, emigrated to Stevens Point, Wisconsin, by way of Canada, and founded the Lee Firearms Company at Milwaukee, Wisconsin, to manufacture a single-shot, side-swinging breech rim-fire carbine patented by him on July 22, 1862. 1,000 were ordered by the War Department in 1865, but were rejected, owing to a misunderstanding as to caliber difference between the specifications and the chambering.

In 1874, Congress appropriated $10,000 for the manufacture of a Lee falling-block single-shot military rifle, and Lee moved to Springfield, Massachusetts, to oversee its limited production at the Springfield Armory. Only 145 were made, since single-shot arms were already becoming obsolescent. From Springfield he moved to Hartford, Connecticut, to superintend the manufacture of his later, more successful, military arms, a number of which were tested by Ordnance Boards of 1872, 1878, 1882, 1891 and 1895 for the United States armed services. Among these arms were the magazine Remington-Lee and the Winchester-made Lee "straight-pull" bolt-action arms, accepted by the United States Navy.

Lee held seven major United States patents for breech-loading arms granted between 1862 and 1879: Nos. 35,941, 54,744, 114,951, 116,068, 122,470, 122,772; and No. 221,328 for a magazine arm. Born in Scotland, educated in Canada and an American by choice and adoption, Lee was one of the world's foremost arms inventors and designers, ranking with Browning and Maxim. His greatest contribution to firearms design was undoubtedly the development of the box magazine located below the action, first manufactured in his Navy rifle of 1879 and soon imitated throughout the world on almost all bolt-action

rifles. In addition to his design of arms for American use, he was associated with the British Lee-Enfield and Lee-Metford magazine-loading systems. He died at Short Beach, Connecticut, on February 24, 1904.   A.G.

See also: LEE RIFLE.

LEE RIFLE

This United States Navy "straight-pull" magazine rifle, caliber 6 mm. (.236 inches) using a 112 grain, jacketed bullet with a muzzle velocity of 2,550 feet per second, was based on the designs of the famed arms inventor James P. Lee, and manufactured by the Winchester Repeating Arms Company of New Haven, Connecticut, under patents of October 10, 1893, January 30, 1894 and October 8, 1895.

The rifle was remarkable chiefly for its straight-pull bolt action, clip loading and extremely small caliber. The 27¼-inch barrel was rifled with six grooves. The rifle weighed 8½ lb.

The full-length stock had a pistol grip and a hand guard from the receiver to the lower band. On the upper band was a bayonet stud for an 8⅓-inch blade bayonet. A blade front sight and a flat-leaf rear sight were set into the hand guard. The five-shot vertical magazine was integral with the arm. The arm operated both opening and closing by a straight pull of the bolt handle backward and a push forward, locking the bolt without rotation. Rearward action of the bolt extracted and ejected the fired shell and cocked the mechanism. Forward motion of the bolt stripped a cartridge from the magazine and fed it into the chamber. When loaded, the gun could be opened only by a downward push of the bolt release. The safety lock on the left of the receiver operated against the tension of the mainspring.

The rifles made for the navy in 1896, on a contract for 10,000 arms, after acceptance by a board of officers in 1895, were marked on the receiver "USN," arm number, "NCT," anchor and Winchester marking, including patent dates.

These arms were the last of the Lee rifles accepted by the navy, the first being the .45–70–405 Remington-Lee rifles, Model 1879, of which they acquired three hundred.
                                                        A.G.

Gluckman, Colonel Arcadi, *United States Muskets, Rifles and Carbines*, Harrisburg, Pa., 1959.

See also: LEE, JAMES P.

LEFAUCHEUX

Two Frenchmen, father and son, bore a name known throughout the world of firearms – Lefaucheux. M. Lefaucheux the elder received a French patent in 1835 which covered the first really practical breech-loading shotgun and its special cartridge. The latter, since known as a pin-fire cartridge, had a paper case with a brass head formed like a cup. A percussion cap was placed inside the head, resting against the lower side. A small metal pin entered the opposite side of the head, passed through it and fired the cap when struck by the gun's hammer. The gun had a breech which opened by tipping the barrel downward on a hinge. The action was held closed by a locking lever which turned in a horizontal plane and engaged a lug on the bottom of the barrel in its T-slot.

The new breechloader was an immediate success, though its cartridge was not quite satisfactory at first. As it lacked internal reinforcing, a heavy charge sometimes caused failure around the pin hole.

The son, Eugène G. Lefaucheux, patented a revolver in 1845. This used an improved version of his father's cartridge.

The Lefaucheux revolver is possibly the type of handgun that has been most widely made by gunsmiths and arms factories around the world. The center of its production was in Europe, where Belgium, France and Spain produced it for decades, in numbers which must have run to a million or more.

The Lefaucheux revolver was at any rate the commonest European type of the nineteenth century. It was popular in all Latin America and to some extent in the United States, though the system was never manufactured there. However, several American ammunition factories made pin-fire cartridges in shotgun as well as revolver sizes. In Europe the revolver cartridges were made in 5, 7, 9, 12, and 15 mm. sizes, while the shotgun shells came in a wide range, from four-gauge down to thirty-two, as well as shot loads for the revolver calibers. During the American Civil War, considerable quantities of Lefaucheux revolvers were purchased in Europe by both sides.   B.R.L.

Illustration: page 174.

See also: CARTRIDGE; FOWLING PIECE.

LEMAT REVOLVER

Jean Alexandre François LeMat, French-born physician and colonel on the staff of the Louisiana governor, was granted an American patent in October 1856 for a two-barrel pistol combining features of both revolver and shotgun. A nine-shot .42 caliber cylinder, aligned to a standard barrel, revolved upon a central "grapeshot" barrel of .63 caliber. A movable hammer nose fired either barrel at will.

Under a partnership with Pierre Beauregard, later a famous Confederate general, some three hundred were made in New Orleans. These bear only the inventor's name. Despite approval by a military board, the revolver was never officially adopted by the United States and the partnership was dissolved.

In 1861, after securing patents in the principal foreign countries, LeMat, with Charles Girard as partner, contracted with the Confederate Army and Navy for all his products and removed to France. Here, some 2,200 additional guns were made with no break in serial numbers. These pistols bear the Paris address.

In 1864, manufacture was removed to Birmingham, England. Despite misleading serial numbers, only some 1,000 additional revolvers were made there, marked "Le-Mat & Girard's Patent." With the fall of the Confederacy activities ceased. All percussion revolvers can be considered Confederate.

After the war manufacture was resumed in France but with pin- and center-fire cartridge ignition. Such guns were widely used in connection with French penal colonies.

Occasionally encountered are percussion carbines and small-sized revolvers made on the "grapeshot" principle. The former were for the Confederate Army and the latter exclusively for the Confederate Navy.   W.A.A.

Illustration: page 213.

Albaugh, William A., III, Benet, Hugh, Jr., and Simmons, Edward N., *Confederate Handguns*, Philadelphia, 1963.
Albaugh, William A., III, and Simmons, Edward N., *Confederate Arms*, Harrisburg, Pa., 1957.

See also: CONFEDERATE FIREARMS.

LEVER ACTION

Lever action is a term applied to firearms in which a lever, usually the trigger guard, is manipulated to open and close the breech. Normally the guard is pivoted at its forward end and is swung downward in an arc, then returned. In early and simple forms, this merely raises and lowers the breechblock, exposing the chamber. It is necessary to insert the cartridge and cock the hammer with separate motions. In more highly refined repeaters, the motion of the trigger guard ejects the expended cartridge, loads another in its place, and cocks the piece.   H.L.P.

LEWIS, ISAAC NEWTON

Born in New Salem, Pennsylvania, on October 12, 1858, I. N. Lewis devoted his entire life to a military career, specialising in weapon design. Upon graduation from the United States Military Academy in 1885 he was commissioned in the artillery, which facilitated his study of ordnance material. He invented a number of electrical fire-control devices and related apparatus, but is best remembered for the Lewis depression position-finder of 1891 and the Lewis machine gun of 1911.

A disability forced Lewis' retirement from the army in 1913, and he turned his attention to the commercial production of his machine gun. Since the United States Army had refused his gun, he went to Liège, Belgium, to organize a corporation to manufacture it. At the outbreak of the First World War he transferred to Birmingham, England, and produced thousands of his guns there for the British and French armies. Eventually the United States also adopted the arm. The Lewis machine gun was a light air-cooled weapon, and was generally recognized as one of the best of the war. It was the first machine gun ever fired from an airplane (1912), and it was adapted for ground and naval use as well.

After the war Lewis continued his experimentation and manufacturing activities until his death in Hoboken, New Jersey, on November 9, 1931.   H.L.P.

Illustration: page 202.

Chinn, Colonel George M., *The Machine Gun*, 4 vols, Washington, D.C., 1951–55.

See also: MACHINE GUN; TURRET GUN.

LIBERATOR PISTOL

During the Second World War, the United States Office of Strategic Services desired a gun for arming resistance forces in enemy-occupied territories. It had to be light, inexpensive, and delivered in a hurry. Army Ordnance designed a pistol to meet these specifications, a contract was let to the Guide Lamp Corporation, and a million completed arms were produced within thirteen weeks, the last delivery being made in August 1942. These guns have been called liberator pistols because of their planned use by resistance forces.

Liberator pistols were crude but effective arms. Except for the 4-inch length of steel tubing that served as a smoothbore barrel and the die-cast mechanism, they were constructed throughout of sheet steel stampings with a few steel pins and coil springs. All of the materials were chosen from the "non-strategic" category. The various elements were held together by folded seams, rivets and welds. As finished, they were single-shot arms without either an extractor or ejector. The empty cartridge case had to be pushed out with the aid of a wooden rod inserted through the muzzle.

Each pistol was delivered in a paraffin-coated box complete with a sheet of instructions, ten rounds of caliber .45 ammunition housed in the grips, and the wooden rod for ejecting the spent cartridge cases. The pistol weighed less than a pound.   H.L.P.

Illustration: page 114.

Waite, M. D., "Liberator Gun" in *The American Rifleman*, June 1954.

LÖBNITZ, NICOLAI JOHAN

N. J. Löbnitz, the Danish gunmaker and inventor, was born in 1798 and died in 1867 in Copenhagen.

Coming from a family of military gunmakers, Löbnitz learned his profession from his father and in 1823 invented a pill-lock breechloader which won him a royal grant for two years' traveling abroad. After his tour through Europe he made his masterpiece in 1828 and was given a job as military gunmaker in Copenhagen. Soon he became gunmaker to the king's advisor in matters of small arms and thus became acquainted with all the actual problems in the field. In 1842 he was made Royal Gunmaker, but in 1851 he handed over his workshop to his stepson and was nominated Government Comptroler at the Kronborg gun factory.

On August 11, 1833, Löbnitz patented a breech-loading mechanism in which a lever with an eccentric axle moved the barrel forward where it could then swing up, leaving the mouth of the chamber open to be loaded. His next patent, in 1838, concerned an underhammer percussion lock in which the hammer was released by pressure on the inside of the trigger-guard. A number of arms with this lock were made, most of them for tape primers. In 1841 a system of military firearms with the Löbnitz under-hammer lock was provisionally introduced in the Danish Army, consisting of a muzzle-loading musket and rifle, a breech-loading rifle for non-commissioned officers, a breech-loading carbine and cavalry pistol, and a smooth-bore muzzle-loading cavalry pistol. Only a few hundred of each of these types were made, and only the breech-loading cavalry arms saw active service in the war with Prussia in 1848. In that year, however, a system of percussion firearms of the usual type was adopted in Denmark, to the great disappointment of Löbnitz.

About 1835, after some experiments with air guns, Löbnitz constructed an air machine gun for stationary use. A pump worked by a crank handle placed on two big flywheels created a pressure of 30 atmospheres in the air chamber below the rifle. The rate of fire was 80 rounds a minute with killing power at about 60 yards distance.

In 1849, Löbnitz took up experimenting with ammunition for the so-called espignolle, a multiple-shot weapon with superimposed loads invented by A. A. F. Schumacher, and he constructed a new cartridge with which it was possible to load the espignolle in the field. The ignition took place from the muzzle by means of a friction primer. During the Danish-German war of 1864, Löbnitz made a 20-barreled organ-espignolle firing 300 rounds in about a minute. Ignition was produced by a kind of pin-fire primer. Organ-espignolles were used in the battle of Dybbøl where they were all taken by the Prussians, and after the war the whole system was abandoned.   A.H.

See also: ESPIGNOLLE.

LORENZONI REPEATING SYSTEM

One of the earliest attempts to produce a repeating magazine firearm is accredited to the mid-seventeenth-century Florentine gunmaker, Michele Lorenzoni. The system probably dates earlier, but bears the Italian's name because European students first observed the action in a gun bearing his signature.

In this system the butt contained two magazines, one for powder and one for the ball. A smaller magazine for priming powder was attached to the lock. To load, the shooter held the gun muzzle up, and then, pulling back on a lever attached to the left side of a cylindrical breech-block, aligned two cavities in the block with openings in the magazines in the butt. The shooter then held the muzzle down, whereupon ball and powder fell into the block cavities and were then conveyed to the barrel chamber by returning the lever to the original position. This lever movement also primed the pan and cocked the gun.

Among others to use this system were the Englishmen Abraham Hill (1664), John Cookson (ca.1670–80) and Henry Mortimer (1780–1855). In America, John Pim of Boston is believed to have used the system in 1722. In 1756, another Bostonian, John Cookson, possibly a son of the English Cookson, made guns of the Lorenzoni type. His name was adopted by American students to identify the action. In the nineteenth century the system again appeared in the English Hulme rifle of 1807 and in A.D. Perry's United States patent of 1849.   C.R.G.

Illustration: page 177.

Hayward, J. F., The Art of the Gunmaker, 2 vols, London and New York, 1962–64.

Peterson, Harold L., Arms and Armor in Colonial America, 1526–1783, Harrisburg, Pa., 1956.

Peterson, Harold L., The Treasury of the Gun, New York, 1962 (The Book of the Gun, London, 1963).

See also: REPEATING ARMS.

LOVELL, GEORGE

George Lovell, born in 1785, entered the service of the British Ordnance at the age of sixteen. In 1805 he was promoted to Clerk of the Cheque, at North Yarmouth, and in 1816 he became Storekeeper of the new arms factory at Enfield. He soon showed enthusiasm for the design of military firearms, and in 1823 helped to produce a double-barreled flintlock carbine for the Cape Cavalry. His clear and concise reports on the production of arms won the approval of the Board and the Master General, and from 1831 he took charge of the Ordnance percussion experiments, producing some converted percussion muskets and pistols for the navy as early as 1832. He continued to supervise the trials of many experimental firearms, but it was his own converted pattern arms which were finally adopted. In 1838 he recommended the adoption of the musket ball as standard for all arms, and he designed a musket, a rifle and a carbine with a new back-action percussion lock for the purpose. The musket became known as the Pattern 1838, the carbine was named after Queen Victoria and the rifle's official title of Lovell's Improved Brunswick rifle was soon shortened to the Brunswick.

Lovell's great work was recognised by his appointment as Inspector of Small Arms in 1840. From then until his retirement in 1854, he was responsible for the design and production of most of the firearms of the British Army and Navy and other armed forces. These included sergeants' muskets, a carbine and sword bayonet for sappers and miners, a cavalry pistol, a yeomanry carbine, another double-barreled carbine for the Cape and a heavy naval rifle. He abandoned his back-action lock in 1842 in favor of a side- or front-action lock which was fitted to all later models of his arms. Two unusual weapons made for the

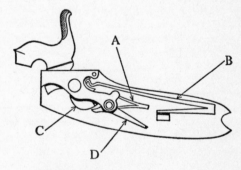

Lovell's first back-action lock, interior view
A. *Sear spring*
B. *Mainspring*
C. *Tumbler*
D. *Sear*

Irish police were a carbine with a bayonet locking in its scabbard and a pocket pistol for plain-clothes men. A knowledge of French and German enabled him to follow continental experiments closely, and he visited all the great arms centers of Europe, bringing back examples of the latest inventions. It was mainly due to his efforts that the Minié rifle was adopted in 1851. His last task was to organise the production of the Enfield rifle and to prepare the way for the full-scale introduction of machinery at Enfield.

His insistence on a high standard of workmanship for contract-made guns earned him the enmity of the gunmakers. However, when he died, in 1854, he had ensured that the British soldier was the best armed soldier in the Crimea.   H.L.B.

Illustration: page 104.

Blackmore, Howard L., *British Military Firearms, 1650–1850*, London, 1961.

See also: BACK-ACTION LOCK ; BRUNSWICK RIFLE.

LUGER, GEORGE

George Luger was born at Steinach in the Austrian Tyrol in 1848. He served in the Austrian Army for a short time and worked with Ferdinand Ritter Von Mannlicher after leaving the army. His first efforts in conjunction with Mannlicher included the conversion of the Austrian Werndl rifle into a magazine arm, and design of a semiautomatic rifle. In 1891 he moved to the Ludwig Loewe firm (later DWM) in Berlin. Shortly thereafter Hugo Borchardt came to Loewe with an automatic pistol design. Borchardt had emigrated, at an early age, to the United States where he had secured many patents on firearms. Borchardt's pistol was produced by Loewe in 1893 but was not a commercial success. Luger took over the design, making it lighter and simpler. In 1898, the first Luger pistol was tested by Switzerland. In 1899 an improved model was tested, and Switzerland adopted the Luger in 1900.

Luger made a practical and popular weapon out of a complex design. Luger pistols have been manufactured in millions and have been the service arms of at least nine countries. Luger died at the age of seventy-four.   J.E.S.

Datig, Fred, *The Luger Pistol*, revised edition, Beverley Hills, Cal., 1958.

See also: LUGER PISTOL.

LUGER PISTOL

A semi-automatic, recoil operated hand weapon developed by George Luger from a design of Hugo Borchardt. It is sometimes called the Parabellum pistol, Parabellum being the telegraph code of the firm – DWM – by which it was originally produced.

The Luger action consists of a toggle-joint-type breech mechanism which opens vertically upon recoil of the barrel and is normally fed by an eight-round, removable, in-line box magazine. Barrel lengths vary from $3\frac{5}{8}$ inches to 24 inches, the most common being 4 inches. Most models have fixed rear sights, but long-barreled models have tangent-type sights adjustable for elevation. Many models are fitted with mounting lugs for shoulder stocks, the first one so fitted being the 1902 carbine model. All models have a safety mounted on the left rear of the frame.

Switzerland adopted the first military Luger in 1900. This pistol had a 4.75-inch barrel, was chambered for the 7.65mm. Luger cartridge (sometimes called .30 Luger) and was fitted with a grip safety. A commercial version of this weapon was also manufactured, and in 1900 the United States purchased a quantity of 7.65 mm. Lugers for service test. They were not approved by the army. In 1902, a commercial model Luger chambered for the newly developed 9 mm. Parabellum cartridge was introduced. In the same year appeared the first Luger carbine, which had an 11.75-inch barrel and a wooden fore-end, and was chambered for the 7.65mm. cartridge. In 1904 the German Navy adopted the Luger in 9mm. Parabellum with a six-inch barrel; this weapon led to the most famous Luger, the German Army 9mm. Pistol Model 08 (1908). This weapon, with a four-inch barrel and no grip safety, was the standard German service pistol of the First World War and was used in large quantities in the Second World War.

About 1906, the leaf-type recoil spring in the Luger was replaced by a coil spring. In that year the rarest of the Lugers was made. This is the caliber .45 Luger made for the United States Army pistol tests of 1907; only two of these weapons are believed to have been made. The grip safety was not fitted on many Lugers after the 1906 model. During the First World War, a fully automatic version of the Luger was produced by the Germans in limited quantity; a special 32-round drum magazine – frequently called the snail magazine – was designed for the weapon. This weapon proved unsatisfactory, and few were made.

The Luger has been used by Brazil, Bulgaria, China, Finland, Germany, Holland, Iran, Luxembourg, Norway, Portugal, Switzerland, and Turkey. Manufacturers were: DWM, Erfurt Arsenal, Mauser, Krieghoff, and Simson, in Germany; the Swiss government arsenal at Bern; and Vickers, in England.   J.E.S.

Illustration: page 204.

Datig, Fred, *The Luger Pistol*, revised edition, Beverley Hills, Cal., 1958.
Jones, Harry E., *Luger Variations*, Los Angeles, 1959.

See also: LUGER, GEORGE.

M

MACHINE GUN

Machine gun is a term loosely applied to a number of rapid-firing weapons. Normally they are too large to hold while firing, and require a mount or carriage, and usually the services of two or more men are necessary to operate them efficiently. They may be either single-barreled or multibarreled, air- or water-cooled, and fed from a belt or a magazine.

Modern machine guns are automatic weapons, but this is the culmination of a long evolutionary process. From the third century B.C. – when Dionysius, Tyrant of Syracuse, is reputed to have attempted to improve upon the bow with a machine called a *polybolus* for shooting arrows in rapid succession – man has sought to produce a long-range, rapid-firing weapon for military purposes. After the invention of firearms the first attempt lay in the direction of volley guns, firing a large number of shots at one time. These were achieved by mounting a series of barrels parallel to each other on a beam and firing them simultaneously by igniting a powder train that passed over their touchholes. Because the parallel barrels reminded some viewers of the pipes of an organ they came to be known as organ batteries or death organs. They were also called ribaudequins. With more ingenuity, the beams holding the gun barrels were fastened together to form triangles or squares pivoting around a central axis. In this manner, the barrels on one side of the square or triangle could be fired, the block rotated, a powder train quickly laid, and the barrels on the next side discharged, thus giving almost the effect of a repeating arm. In various forms, these batteries were popular from the middle of the fourteenth century until well into the sixteenth.

Truly repeating machine guns, however, came much later. Among the milestones in their development were guns on the roman-candle principle, such as the seven-barreled swivel guns invented by Joseph Chambers and used during the War of 1812, and the orgelespignolles

of Captain A.F. Schumacher, used by the Danish Army and Navy until 1870. In these arms a burning fuse set off one charge after another, delivering an impressive number of shots in a short time, but impossible to stop, once the fuse had been ignited, until the last charge had exploded. James Puckle's gun of 1718 might also be considered a direct ancestor of the modern machine gun, for it was a repeating arm, indeed a revolver, of large caliber and mounted on a tripod. Thus it was intended to deliver a rapid fire in precisely the same manner as the machine gun of today, albeit not so rapidly or efficiently – and it was crank-operated with each shot fired separately, not fully automatic.

It was not until the nineteenth century that real strides were made towards perfecting the modern machine gun, and improvements in ignition, including the percussion cap and later the metallic cartridge, provided the keys to this success. In 1829 the first patent using the term "machine gun" was issued by the United States to Samuel L. Farries of Middletown, Ohio, and this grant seems to imply that the term was to be assigned to any mechanically operated weapon of rifle caliber and above, regardless of whether the energy necessary for sustained fire was derived manually or from some other power source.

Other developments followed rapidly. In the 1850's Sir James S. Lille of London attempted to combine both the multibarrel and the revolving chamber systems. He arranged twelve barrels in two rows with a revolving cylinder of twenty chambers to the rear. Each chamber had to be aligned manually and then fired with a percussion cap. On July 8, 1856, the United States issued a patent to C. E. Barnes of Lowell, Massachusetts, for a crank-operated machine cannon that was the forerunner of a whole series of crank-operated weapons. The gun's locking system employed a toggle-joint arrangement that rammed a fixed charge home. Gas pressure from the explosion in the chamber was used to cock the hammer for the next round.

Ezra Ripley, of Troy, New York, took advantage of the paper cartridge developed by Samuel Colt and the Ely brothers of England to patent a machine gun. Ripley achieved sustained volley fire by a compact firing assembly that allowed the gunner to fire one shot, or the whole volley, by a quick turn of the handle.

During this period, the military ordered little more than the conventional small arms. For this reason, guns like the Ripley were of little or no interest to firearms producers. The military would not consider such guns and civilians had no use for them.

Perhaps the weapon most in keeping with the militarily acceptable idea of producing volley fire was the Requa battery. This .58 caliber gun was built late in 1861 by the Billinghurst Company of Rochester, New York. It had twenty-five barrels mounted flat on a light metal platform. The sliding-breech mechanism was operated by a lever and the barrels were loaded by light steel cartridges positioned on special clips. The Requa battery did not employ paper cartridges inserted in the steel cases. Instead, each cartridge case was loaded by hand with loose powder, and a patched ball was used in the belief that it gave the weapon greater accuracy.

The next machine gun to be used by the United States was the Ager, better known as the "Coffee Mill" gun. The nickname was derived from the fact that its crank operation from a hopper feed located on top of the gun closely resembled the contemporary kitchen coffee grinder. Using a revolving-type action, the Ager fired a caliber .58 Minié-type bullet through a single barrel at a rate of 120 rounds per minute.

In 1862 Richard J. Gatling, physician, inventor and manufacturer, patented a weapon that was destined to make history in no small way. This was the Gatling gun, the only weapon in history to progress from black powder to smokeless and from hand power to full automatic and then to power-driven operation without a change in its basic operating principle.

The weapon was the logical result of the trends portrayed in the Ager and Ripley guns. Gatling combined the best principles of both and overcame their most objectionable features. His successful results caused him to be credited generally with being the father of the hand-operated machine gun.

There was still one great weakness, however – that the gunner had little or no control over the placement of the individual shot.

One solution to this problem was the volley system, strongly favored by European armies, in which a number of barrels were grouped in a plane, either parallel or in stacks.

To impress military authorities and advertise an improved means of delivering the universally used grapeshot, European inventors called their firing mechanisms "mitrailleuse," meaning "grape shooter," or, more literally, "grapeshot shooter." By this name they hoped to imply that theirs was a system for controlling the dispersion of grapeshot.

The weapons of this quarter of a century were all manually operated. Since it was always necessary for a gunner to aim the piece, there seemed to be no reason why he should not also furnish the power to feed and fire the gun. Mechanical advantage was utilized to enable the individual soldier to maintain sustained fire with a minimum effort. During the latter part of this era, the weapons reached such a high degree of efficiency that it was believed that there was nothing left to be improved. They were accepted as "invincible reapers of death."

However, the world did not reckon with a young American inventor named Hiram S. Maxim, who for the first time combined the words "automatic" and "machine gun."

He accomplished this by using the power of the recoil forces generated from the explosion of the powder charge in the cartridge to produce the entire cycle of operation. The simple mechanism he originated as a first attempt worked so successfully that to this day the famous Maxim automatic machine guns have remained basically unchanged.

There have been, to date, only two known means of successful automatic operation that can be derived from the energy generated by the exploding powder charge: (a) the rearward thrust of the recoiling mass; and (b) pressure generated in the bore by the expanding gas of the progressive burning charge.

The former is known as recoil actuation, while the latter is labeled gas operation. All known means used in making an automatic weapon complete a full cycle fall into this broad classification, whether the mechanics employed are reciprocating or rotary.

The recoil-operated type of weapon can be further broken down into two distinct classifications: short and long recoil. Gas operation, however, seems to have no limit in its application. For instance, the residual pressure remaining in the bore a few milliseconds after the projectile has cleared is called blowback, implying a type of recoil operation. In reality it is but another form of gas operation.

In the long recoil system, barrel and breechblock move rearward for a distance slightly greater than the over-all length of the cartridge. The barrel is driven back to firing position by a return spring which allows the extractor on the face of the breechblock to remove and eject the cartridge case. The block then moves forward, cocking the firing mechanism and picking up a new cartridge from the magazine.

In the short recoil system perfected by Maxim, the barrel and block move rearward together for only a fraction of an inch. This allows the residual gas pressure in the bore to drop to a level where the bolt may be opened without danger of rupturing the cartridge case and jamming the weapon.

At this point the barrel and block separate and the block continues rearward, extracting and ejecting the spent case as it goes. On its return trip it cocks the firing mechanism, picks up a new cartridge from the magazine, and drives the barrel back to firing position.

In the plain blowback system, the barrel remains stationary and the mere inertia of the bolt and the resistance of its return spring delay the operation until the critical stage of gas pressure has passed. After the bullet has cleared the barrel, the operation of the bolt is the same as in the short recoil system.

This unusual power supply has been exploited to such a degree that it takes at least four distinctly different classifications to cover the application of this method of utilizing residual pressure for completing a cycle of operation. These are (a) pure blowback (Bergmann); (b) retarded blowback (Schwarzlose); (c) delayed blowback (Scotti); and (d) advanced primer ignition (Becker). Each system is strictly adaptable to certain types of actions and is utterly impractical other than for a specific purpose.

However, the most common method of employing the energy created by the gas of the exploding propellant is to tap the barrel and let the expanding gas be brought to bear on an actuating device such as a piston, lever, etc. The system is universally referred to as "gas operation," erroneously implying that this is the only way gas pressure is utilized as a source of power.

The first successful gas-operated automatic machine gun was perfected by John M. Browning in 1890. The Colt Machine Gun, Model 1895 (Mark 1), designed by Browning, was the first fully automatic machine gun purchased by the United States government, and was first used in combat by the Marines at Guantanamo Bay, Cuba, in 1898.

The gas-operating mechanism can take many forms. The most commonly used device consists of a simple gas cylinder and a piston which is driven rearward to transfer its energy to the bolt by direct impact.

The methods used for transferring energy from the piston to the gun-operating mechanism are also extremely diverse in form and function. Instead of transferring energy directly to the bolt, the piston itself sometimes moves through a very short stroke and transfers its energy indirectly by impinging on an intermediate sliding member or lever.

In the gas-operated system called muzzle-blast actuation, no actual tapping of the bore is necessary. After the projectile has emerged, some of the gases are trapped in an expansion chamber screwed on to the muzzle of the weapon and actuate the piston to complete the operating cycle.

Generally speaking, there are only five known practical applications for accomplishing sustained fire in an automatic weapon: (a) short recoil; (b) long recoil; (c) gas pressure in the bore bled off externally through an orifice (gas operation); (d) residual pressure remaining in the bore a few milliseconds after the projectile has cleared (blowback); and (e) blast energy generated by the expanding gases after being released from the barrel at the muzzle end (muzzle-blast actuation).

These are considered the basic principles, and from these simple variants of power more than 3,000 patents have been issued on operational features of machine guns since Maxim's first recoil patent in 1884.   G.M.C.

Illustrations: pages 172, 183–4, 201–3, 283, 339.

Chinn, Colonel George M., *The Machine Gun*, 4 vols, Washington, D.C., 1951–55.

See also: AUTOMATIC ARMS; BROWNING, JOHN M.; CHAMBERS SYSTEM; ESPIGNOLLE; GATLING GUN; HOTCHKISS, BENJAMIN BERKELEY; LEWIS, ISAAC NEWTON; MAXIM, HIRAM; MITRAILLEUSE; REPEATING ARMS.

MAGAZINE ARMS

See: REPEATING ARMS.

MANNLICHER

The first Mannlicher rifle manufactured in quantity was the Austrian 11mm. M1885. This straight-pull bolt-action rifle had a vertical in-line box magazine with the clip functioning as part of the magazine. The clip was ejected from the top of the action as the last cartridge case was ejected. The bolt locked by a wedge which dropped from the bottom rear of the bolt. The Austrian M1886 was basically the same as the 1885, but the clip dropped out of the bottom of the magazine when the last round was loaded; this system was used in all later Mannlicher rifles with in-line magazine systems. The M1888 and 1888/90 Austrian Mannlichers are basically the same as the 1886, but are chambered for the 8mm. Austrian cartridges – 8 × 50R.

The 1890 Austrian Mannlicher carbine introduced the straight-pull bolt with forward-locking lugs on a rotating bolthead. The M1895 rifle, short rifle and carbine are similar to the M1890.

The M1892 6.5mm. Dutch and Rumanian are the first turning-bolt Mannlichers produced in quantity. They have two-piece bolts with forward-locking lugs. Rumania adopted a slightly modified version in 1893, as did the Dutch in 1895. In 1893, Switzerland adopted a Mannlicher carbine which had a staggered box-type magazine loaded with a six-round charger. In 1903, Greece adopted a 6.5 mm. Mannlicher with the rotary spool Schoenauer-type magazine. Mannlicher-Schoenauer sporters have similar actions. All of the Mannlicher-type turning-bolt rifles, with the exception of the Hungarian Model 35, cock on opening of the bolt.

Mannlicher pistols include the M94, M96 (M1903) and M1900. The 1900 was the only Mannlicher pistol that was manufactured in quantity.   J.E.S.

Illustration: page 182.

Smith, Walter H. B., *Mannlicher Rifles and Pistols*, Harrisburg, Pa., 1947.

Smith, Walter H. B. and Joseph E., *The Book of Rifles*, 3rd edition, Harrisburg, Pa., 1963.

See also: MANNLICHER, FERDINAND RITTER VON.

MANNLICHER, FERDINAND RITTER VON

Ferdinand Ritter Von Mannlicher was born at Mainz, Germany, in 1848 and moved to Austria at an early age. He was educated as an engineer and was Chief Engineer of the Austrian Northern Railroad for some time before becoming associated with the Austrian Arms Company at Steyr. His first design, a turning-bolt repeating rifle, appeared in 1880 but was not particularly successful. After several other turning-bolt designs, he introduced in 1884 his first straight-pull design (see BOLT ACTION) which led to the Model 1885 11mm. Austrian service rifle – the first of his popular designs. This straight-pull rifle was the first to have the Mannlicher magazine system: the loaded cartridge clip is inserted in the fixed vertical box-type magazine and functions as part of the magazine. The 1885 model went through several modifications, and in 1890 a new Mannlicher straight-pull carbine with frontal locking lugs was adopted by Austria. A slightly modified model was adopted by Austria in 1895, and represents the last of Mannlicher's straight-pull designs.

In 1888, Germany adopted a turning-bolt rifle with a Mannlicher-type magazine; shortly afterwards (1892) Mannlicher developed the first of his turning-bolt rifles with his magazine system. This rifle was adopted in 6.5mm. by Holland and Rumania. In 1887 he designed a rotary spool magazine; this development was perfected by Otto Schoenauer. This type of magazine was and still is used in the Mannlicher-Schoenauer sporter and the Savage M99 rifle. It was also used in the Greek M1903 rifle and the American Johnson semi-automatic rifle. In 1900, Mannlicher introduced a turning-bolt rifle with rotary spool-type magazine.

Mannlicher designed a large number of automatic and semi-automatic weapons, many of which introduced novel features which are in use today. His designs in this field were frequently failures because of the shortcomings of the ammunition and metals of his day. Of all his automatic designs, only the M1900 pistol can be considered a success.

Mannlicher designed over 150 models of automatic and repeating firearms; his designs included gas, recoil and blowback operated weapons. His contributions to firearms design were outstanding and frequently ahead of their time.   J.E.S.

Smith, Walter H. B., *Mannlicher Rifles and Pistols*, Harrisburg, Pa., 1947.

See also: BOLT ACTION; MANNLICHER.

MANTON, JOSEPH

Joseph Manton was born in Grantham, Lincolnshire, in 1760 and was, like his brother John, one of the most famous London gunsmiths of his day. He was already married and established in his shop in Davies Street, Berkeley Square, by April 1792, when his first patent was granted. He retained his shop until, despite the proportionately high prices he charged for his fine craftsmanship – his best guns had platinum touchholes and hydraulically tested barrels – he failed in business, going bankrupt in 1826. He later moved to New Road and to Burwood Place before settling at the address in Holles Street where his sons continued in business until 1840.

Manton's two major contributions to firearms design were his patent breech, which allowed muzzle-loading sporting guns to be made more graceful in shape, and his elevated rib which simplified the sighting of double-barreled guns. Among his lesser innovations were a deep, V-shaped priming pan; his "gravitating stop" safety (see SAFETY DEVICE); and a sear which produced a musical note instead of the usual crisp click. Patents for pellet and tube primers, of 1816 and 1818 respectively, led to litigation with Forsyth, who won both cases. Although Colonel Peter Hawker suggests that "Poor Joe Manton – the life and soul of the trade" was the first to produce guns using copper caps, this is not borne out by the evidence.

"Old Joe" died in London on June 29, 1835, and his family placed over his grave in Kensal Green cemetery an epitaph written by his friend and customer Hawker, who referred to Manton's "unrivalled genius."   W.R.

Illustrations: page 278.

Teasdale-Buckell, G. T., *Experts on Guns and Shooting*, London, 1900.

See also: FORSYTH, ALEXANDER JOHN; FOWLING PIECE; PERCUSSION SYSTEM; TUBE LOCK.

MARTIAL ARMS

A martial arm is any weapon designed for military use. In modern circles there has been some attempt at further refinement by using the term "primary martial" to designate those arms specifically adopted as official by a given nation, made at a national armory, or purchased in large numbers under an official contract which called for formal inspection and approval. Other arms designed for military purposes but purchased by individual military units or states, or produced in only experimental quantities, have been classed as "secondary martial."

The first small arms to appear were all intended primarily for military use and thus may be considered martial. Specialized arms for hunting and personal defense came later, probably not until the sixteenth century when new ignition systems and an increased interest in firearms caused the whole field to develop rapidly. As this specialization developed, the standard military arm became a matchlock smoothbore of large caliber for infantry. The musket, a heavy arm designed to be fired from the shoulder with the muzzle supported by a rest, probably appeared between 1525 and 1550, and the Spanish Duke of Alva is usually credited with having brought it to prominence. During the second half of the century its use spread throughout Europe. Lighter armed troops carried shorter matchlocks of smaller bore which could be fired without a rest and which were frequently called either calivers or arquebuses, depending upon the period and country of their use. As the years passed, the musket itself gradually grew shorter and lighter. By 1625 all real differences between it and the caliver had disappeared, and the latter name dropped from use while the term musket came to be applied to all smoothbore military long arms.

The matchlock remained the standard ignition system for military long arms throughout Europe until almost 1700. Wheel locks were too expensive for general issue. Only élite corps and princely bodyguards carried them as a rule, except in America where the settlers' dependence upon their arms caused the more efficient lock to be used for military purposes in some quantity during the first half of the seventeenth century. The various flint systems were applied to military long arms and issued to selected units by most nations of Europe during the middle 1600's, but only in America did they become standard much before the end of the century, at which time the true flintlock was adopted almost universally in western Europe except in Spain and Portugal.

Once the flintlock was adopted, it remained standard until the early 1840's. Several nations, including France, Great Britain, Sweden, and the United States, had begun to issue percussion arms to special troops in the 1830's, but the complete adoption of the new system took place in the following decade.

Breechloaders appeared early among martial arms, but their acceptance was slow. Henry VIII's pistol shields of the middle 1500's may perhaps be considered the first. Next came the Chaumette in France in the 1720's, the Crespi in Austria, and the Ferguson in England, all issued to small units. The Hall rifle adopted by the United States was the first breechloader to become a standard arm, and others followed in rapid succession with such notable examples as the Dreyse and Chassepot bolt-action arms of 1848 and 1866. Generally speaking, the years from 1866 to 1873 mark the abandonment of the muzzle-loader and the supremacy of the breechloader throughout Europe and America.

The first repeating martial arms were probably the Kalthoff magazine rifles, issued to selected Danish troops in the 1640's. Thereafter, experiments were made from time to time with various forms of repeaters with little success until the revolver and the Spencer magazine rifles and carbines of the American Civil War proved themselves reliable and practical arms for military purposes. The experiences of that war, plus the spectacular use of Winchester repeaters by the Turks at the Battle of Plevna in 1877, stimulated all nations to study the use of such arms. Generally the bolt action was preferred to the lever action of the Spencer and Winchester, because it could be operated more readily by a soldier lying prone. James P. Lee and Ferdinand Ritter Von Mannlicher developed their box magazines, and by the mid-1890's almost all the armies of the western world had adopted some form of bolt-action rifle with a box magazine. Semi-automatic and fully automatic arms followed rapidly for special purposes, becoming standard for many weapons during the Second World War.

Rifles for military use first appeared upon the scene about 1611, when some Danish troops were armed with them. Thereafter almost all nations of Europe boasted some riflemen in their military establishments at various periods, and Americans performed spectacularly with their long rifles during the War of Independence. Nevertheless, the length of time required to load a rifle as compared to a smoothbore, as well as other difficulties, prevented the rifle from becoming more than an auxiliary weapon. It was not until these defects were corrected, about 1850, that the rifle became dominant and completely superseded the smoothbore for all but a very few specialized martial arms.

The martial pistol has had a shorter history than the military long arm. It was the wheel lock that made the pistol a practical weapon, and its use for warlike purposes seems to date from the mid-1500's. For a brief time it was extensively used, especially by the German horsemen, and almost eliminated the use of the sword. This situation was short-lived, however, and the pistol was relegated to a supporting role until the increased firepower afforded by the revolver again increased its importance. Except for the fact that they began as wheel locks, martial pistols generally paralleled the advances of long arms as they changed to flintlocks and then to percussion. There the similarity ends, however, for repeating arms in the form of the revolver were adopted for handguns well before they became standard for shoulder weapons. The United States began to issue revolvers to its cavalry in 1847, and European nations followed shortly thereafter. There were a very few single-shot breechloading pistols, but they were never widely used or issued outside the Scandinavian countries. The revolver has remained the standard martial pistol for several nations to the present time, although semi-automatic and fully automatic pistols have been adopted by many since the turn of the century.

Most students and collectors of martial arms are interested in tracing the weapons of one specific nation or era and in recognizing various models in detail. Generally speaking, the standardization of military arms has followed the history of the nation. Older nations such as Great Britain and France standardized their arms at an early date. In Great Britain the process began during the reign of William and Mary and continued during that of Queen Anne. By the accession of George I, military long arms were well standardized and pistols were reasonably so. In France the first official musket model was adopted in 1717, the first pistol in 1733. The United States adopted its first official musket model in 1795, its first pistol in 1799. In the newer nations such as Germany and Italy, weapons were standardized first by the various individual principalities, then by the nation as a whole after unification. The study of these various models is a highly specialized subject, which has an extensive literature. Some of the most useful titles are listed below.   H.L.P.

Alm, Josef, *Arméns Eldhandvapen Förr och Nu*, Stockholm, 1953.

Blackmore, Howard L., *British Military Firearms, 1650–1850*, London, 1961.

Bottet, Maurice, *Monographie de l'Arme à Feu Portative des Armées Françaises de Terre et de Mer de 1718 à Nos Jours*, reprint, Paris, 1959.

Boudriot, Jean, *Armes à Feu Françaises, Modèles Réglementaires*, 1717–1836, Paris, 1961, 1964.

Eckardt, Werner, and Morawietz, Otto, *Die Handwaffen des Brandenburgisch-Preussisch-Deutschen Heeres, 1640–1945*, Hamburg, 1957.

Gluckman, Colonel Arcadi, *United States Martial Pistols and Revolvers*, Buffalo, N.Y., 1939.

Gluckman, Colonel Arcadi, *United States Muskets, Rifles and Carbines*, Harrisburg, Pa., 1959.

Hicks, Captain (later Major) James Ernest, assisted by André Jandot, *Notes on French Ordnance, 1717–1936*, Mount Vernon, N.Y., 1938.

Hicks, Captain (later Major) James Ernest, *Notes on United States Ordnance*, 2 vols, Mount Vernon, N.Y., 1940.

Lewis, Colonel Berkeley R., *Small Arms and Ammunition in the United States Service, 1776–1865*, Washington, D.C., 1956.

Reynolds, E. G. B., *The Lee-Enfield Rifle*, London, 1960.

Smith, Walter H. B. and Joseph E., *Small Arms of the World*, 6th edition, Harrisburg, Pa., 1960.

See also: AMUSETTE; ARISAKA RIFLE; AUTOMATIC ARMS; BAKER RIFLE; BERTHIER RIFLE; BREECH-LOADERS; BROWN BESS; BRUNSWICK RIFLE; CARABINE À TIGE; CARBINE; CARCANO RIFLE; COMMITTEE OF SAFETY MUSKET; CONFEDERATE FIREARMS; FERGUSON RIFLE; FUSEE/FUSIL; GARAND RIFLE; GRAS RIFLE; GRENADE LAUNCHERS; HALL BREECH-LOADING ARMS; KRAG RIFLE; LEBEL RIFLE; LEE RIFLE; LIBERATOR PISTOL; LUGER PISTOL; MACHINE GUN; MANNLICHER; MARTINI-HENRY; MAUSER; NEEDLE GUN; PEDERSEN DEVICE; RIFLE MUSKET/RIFLED MUSKET; RIFLES AND RIFLING; ROCKET GUN; ROSS RIFLE; SCHEEL, F. W.; SHARPS RIFLES AND CARBINES; SNIDER RIFLE; SPENCER RIFLE; TOWER; VETTERLI RIFLE.

MARTINI-HENRY

In 1866, the British War Office, aware that the Snider rifle was only a stop-gap arm chosen because of its suitability for the conversion of existing stocks of muzzle-loading rifles, set up a special committee to choose an entirely new breech-loading rifle. Their recommendation, a rifle with a smaller caliber of .45, combining the breech mechanism of Friedrich von Martini, an Austrian lace manufacturer, with the barrel of Alexander Henry, the Edinburgh gunmaker, was adopted in April 1871.

The Martini action, patented in 1868, was a modification of the American Peabody action, in which a falling block was operated by the trigger guard. Whereas the Peabody had a side hammer and firing pin and was designed for a rim-fire cartridge, the Martini utilised a spring-compressed pin running through the middle of the block, suitable for a center-fire cartridge. Lowering the trigger guard automatically opened the breech, worked the ejector and cocked the firing pin.

The Henry rifling consisted of seven grooves with a right-hand uniform twist of one turn in twenty-two inches. The depth of the grooves was progressive for the first eleven inches from the breech and was then of uniform depth to the muzzle.

The standard rifle, which was made with a long and short butt, was just over four feet long, weighed approximately 8½ lb. and was sighted up to 1,450 yards. Carbines made for cavalry and artillery weighed a pound lighter and, with a shorter barrel, had a range up to 1,180 yards. Of the carbines, only the artillery model was armed with a bayonet – a sword bayonet with a long, straight blade. With the rifles, line regiments were provided with a socket bayonet similar to the Snider, but sergeants and rifle battalions carried a curved sword bayonet. A similar bayonet issued to the naval forces had a cutlass guard. The Martini-Henry was superseded by the Lee-Metford rifle in 1891.   H.L.B.

Illustration: page 47.

See also: BREECHLOADERS.

MATCH

The common form of match was the slowly burning cord used by musketeers and cannoneers to ignite their weapons during the matchlock period. At best it was an uncertain and hazardous means of ignition.

There were two general types of match, known as slow match and quick match. The quick match was used mostly as a fuse for fireworks and for setting off charges of powder for demolition purposes. Both were made from tow, a ropelike twist or cord made from flax, cotton or hemp.

For making slow match, this cord was soaked in a saturated solution of nitre (potassium nitrate), then dried. Such cord burned at the rate of about an inch per minute. Slower rates could be obtained by diluting the strength of the nitre solution.

Quick match was made similarly, except that while still moist, the cord was rolled in mealed black powder. Such match burned much faster – about a foot per minute. When used for fireworks, quick match was usually enclosed in a small paper tube for protection and to reduce the hazard in its use.   B.R.L.

MATCHLOCK

The matchlock constituted the first mechanical device for firing. It consisted of an arm called the serpentine which gripped the match between its two jaws; by means of a trigger, a simple leverage system lowered the serpentine, thrust the glowing end of the match which it held into the pan fastened to the side of the barrel, and fired the priming powder which it contained.

For this improvement, so important to firing, to be posssible, two modifications of the hand cannon were

necessary: the addition of a pan to hold the priming powder, which replaced the match in setting off the powder charge inside the barrel, and the addition of the serpentine, holding the match and thus freeing the hand of the shooter or his aide.

These original matchlocks did not as yet include the leverage system worked by a trigger and indeed did not have true "locks." Instead, the serpentine was a simple S-shaped arm pivoted in its center, the lower end serving as a handle by which the shooter moved the device manually. For this reason, many students place arms of this sort in a category between the hand cannon and the true matchlock.

An interesting variant of the early matchlock is illustrated in the *Codex Monacensis 222* of Munich, dating from approximately 1500. If the arquebuses in this document are carefully examined, the serpentine can be clearly seen, but no trigger is indicated. One can conclude from this that a trigger of traditional form does not exist, its absence being confirmed by examination of the two arquebuses of the Basle Historical Museum (Inv. Nos. 1905, 4498 and 1905, 4498a). The lock of these two exceedingly rare weapons functions as follows: when pressure is applied to the head of a rod attached to a trip lever, the latter disengages and the serpentine, no longer held back, falls towards the pan. They have, in other words, what many firearms writers call a button trigger. Furthermore, the marksman firing from the shoulder in the *Codex Monacensis* has placed his left hand just under the serpentine with a clearly visible movement of the fingers, corresponding exactly to the pressure on the head of the rod. With this system the serpentine was lowered by means of its own weight assisted by a spring. These snapping matchlocks were popular for only a brief period in Europe during the early sixteenth century, but they served as the model for the matchlocks made in Japan until about 1850. The matchlock with a lever trigger, similar to that on the crossbow, was also already developing. A primitive form is shown in the *Codex Germanicus 597*, dated 1475. During the sixteenth century a trigger similar to that on modern arms was developed which acted upon the serpentine through a sear mechanism. Such triggers could be made smaller and enclosed within a trigger guard for safety. In this form the matchlock was used, at least for military purposes, until the eighteenth century.

The match, which fired the fuse powder in the pan, underwent little modification during the long period it was in use. The precise description which Surirey de Saint-Rémy gives of it in his *Mémoires d'Artillerie* (1697) can thus be applied to the original match: "... a good match should be made of flax or hemp tow."

Tow is the name given to the waste arising from the

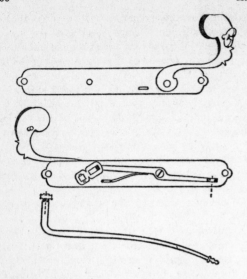

Early matchlock with lever trigger – exterior (above) and interior views

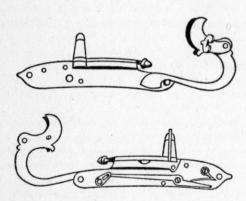

Late matchlock with sear trigger – exterior (above) and interior views

separation of long fibres, during the combing of the flax or hemp.

Saint-Rémy's explanation continues "It must be spun into three strands of medium width, and each covered separately with pure hemp . . . It must be washed, well glazed and well tightened . . . It must burn well so that one piece, four or five inches in length, lasts one hour if possible . . . It must make a good, hard coal which finishes in a point and which stands up to being pressed against something."

When the serpentine was lowered, the lighted end of the match reached to the middle of the pan; this result was obtained by "proportioning" the tow. This term, which consistently occurs in instructions about the handling of the arquebus and musket, meant that the length of the match had to be regulated, before firing, by a trial firing with the pan empty.

The Spaniards seem to have been the first to understand the advantages of the organized tactical use of the matchlock arquebus. At Pavia, in 1525, six or seven hundred Spanish arquebusiers enfiladed the flank of Francis I's cavalry, and thereby ensured the defeat and capture of the French king.

During its long career, the matchlock was improved by the addition of a pan cover and a small vertical screen protecting the marksman's eye against the flash of the priming powder.

Finally, attention should also be drawn to Vauban's invention in 1688 of the lock combining in one single piece the serpentine of the musket and the cock of the flintlock, so that the match and gunflint worked together, thus doubling the chances of accurate firing.

Outside Europe the matchlock continued in use, especially in China, India and Japan, until modern times (see ASIATIC FIREARMS).   CL.B.

Illustrations: pages 34–5, 171, 209–10, and endpapers.

Blair, Claude, *European and American Arms*, London, 1962.

Hayward, J. F., *The Art of the Gunmaker*, 2 vols, London and New York, 1962–64.

Peterson, Harold L., *Arms and Armor in Colonial America, 1526–1783*, Harrisburg, Pa., 1956.

Peterson, Harold L., *The Treasury of the Gun*, New York, 1962 (*The Book of the Gun*, London, 1963).

See also: ARQUEBUS; MATCH; MUSKET.

MAUBEUGE

Situated in the ancient province of Flanders, near the Belgian border, Maubeuge owes its name (formerly Malbodium) to a double monastery for men and women founded in the seventh century by St. Aldegonde, daughter of an Austrasian lord.

In the thirteenth century, the inhabitants of Maubeuge already enjoyed the benefits of a town charter. The painter Jean Gossart, known as "Mabuse," was born there about 1470. The town was ceded finally to France by the treaty of Nijmegen (1678), and in 1685 Vauban surrounded it with imposing fortifications, parts of which exist today. It was at Maubeuge that Captain Coutelle staged the first military aeronautics trials, in 1794. Because of this, the town was equipped as a center for guided

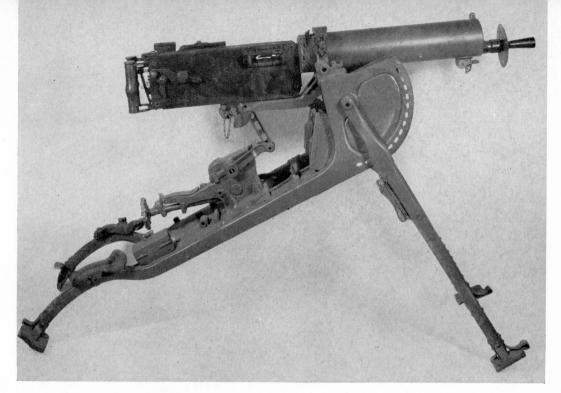

German Maxim machine gun, 7.92 mm. Model 1908.

Browning gas-operated machine gun, 6.5 mm. Model 1914,
made by Colt for Italy in the First World War.

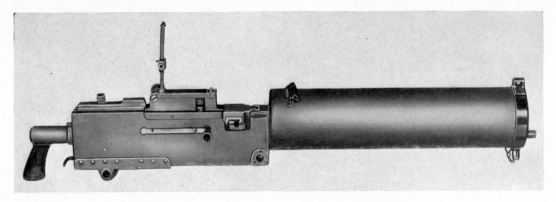

U.S. Browning machine gun, caliber .30 M1917A1.

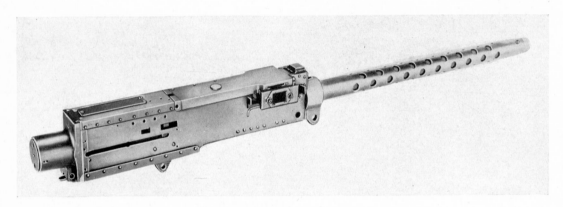

U.S. aircraft machine gun, caliber .50 M3, a Browning type.

British Lewis gun, caliber .303 Mark I, 1915.

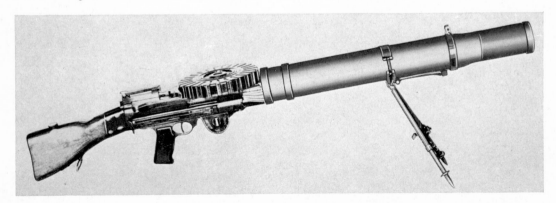

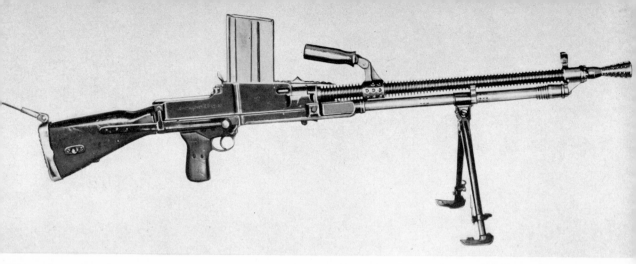

Czechoslovakian light machine gun, 7.92 mm. Model 1926.

German machine gun, 7.92 mm. Model 42.

Pedersen device, automatic pistol, caliber .30, of 1918;
right top view (ABOVE) and bottom side view.

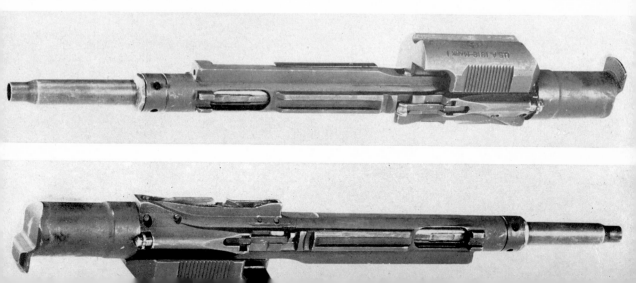

Browning automatic pistol,
7.65 mm. Model 1900.

German Luger pistol,
9 mm. M1908.

U.S. submachine gun,
caliber .45 M1928A1 (Thompson).

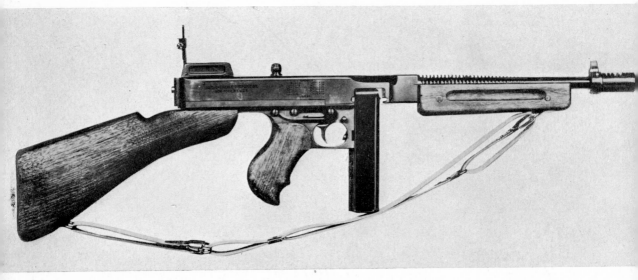

German submachine gun,
9 mm. Model 38.

U.S. submachine gun,
caliber .45 M3A1.

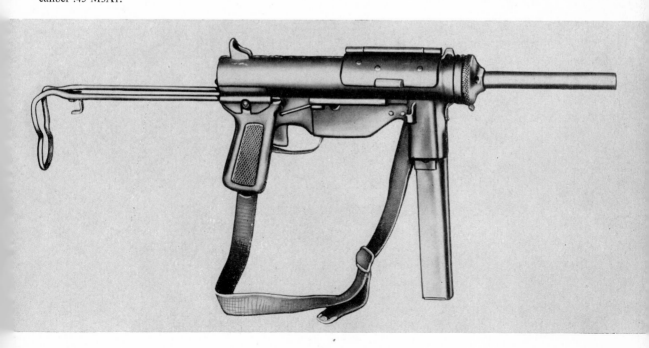

German assault rifle, 7.92 mm. Model 44.

U.S. Browning automatic rifle, caliber .30 M1918A2.

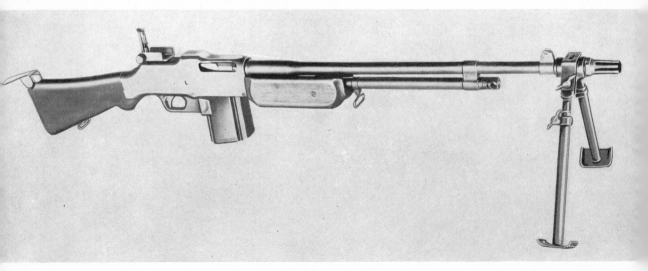

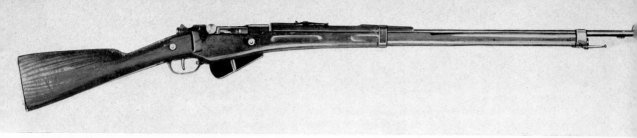

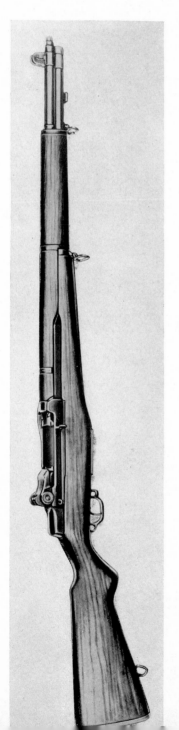

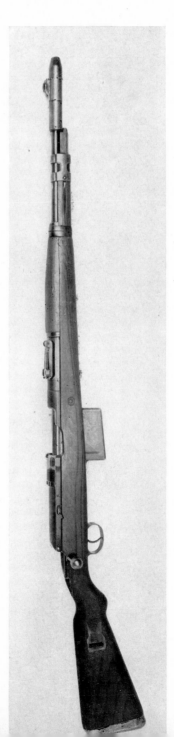

U.S. Garand rifle,
caliber .30 M1.

German
semi-automatic
rifle, 7.92 mm.
Model 41(M).

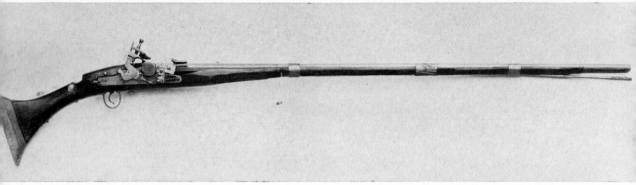

Algerian gun with snaphance of Dutch type.
Danish National Museum, Copenhagen.

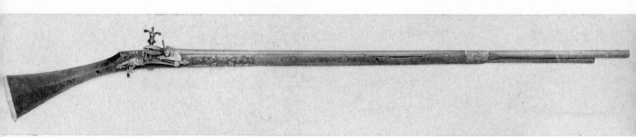

Kabyl gun with British military flintlock, early nineteenth century.
Danish National Museum, Copenhagen.

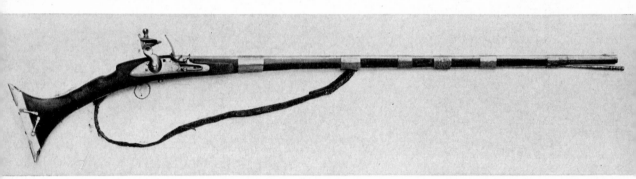

Kabyl gun with typical miquelet lock.
Danish National Museum, Copenhagen.

Four Japanese matchlocks.
Winchester Repeating Arms Company.

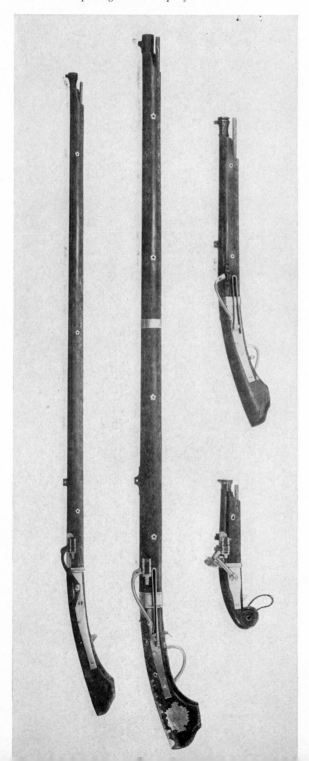

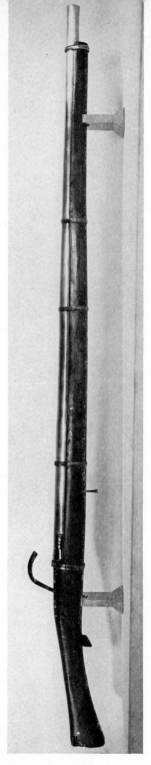

Chinese matchlock.
*Winchester Repeating
Arms Company.*

210

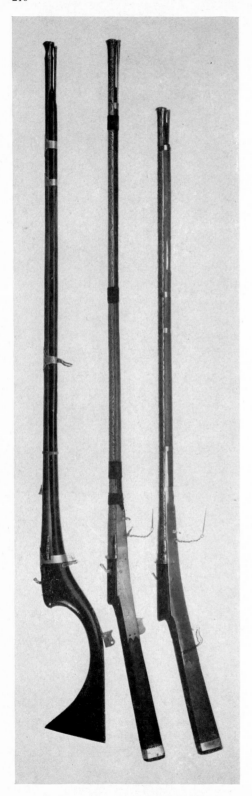

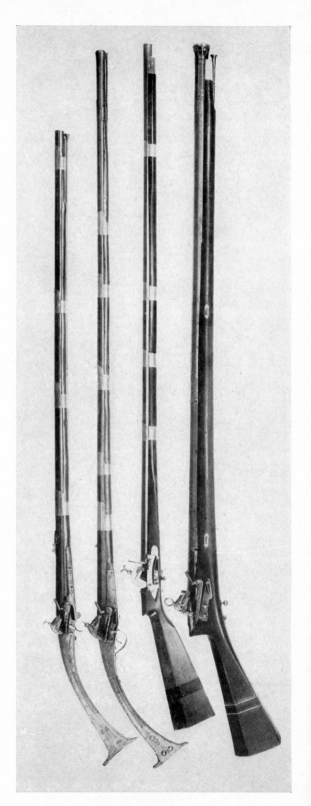

Three Indian matchlocks. The first has an
Afghan stock, and the other two
have stocks similar to the Turkish style.
Winchester Repeating Arms Company.

Two Balkan miquelets and two Turkish miquelets.
Winchester Repeating Arms Company.

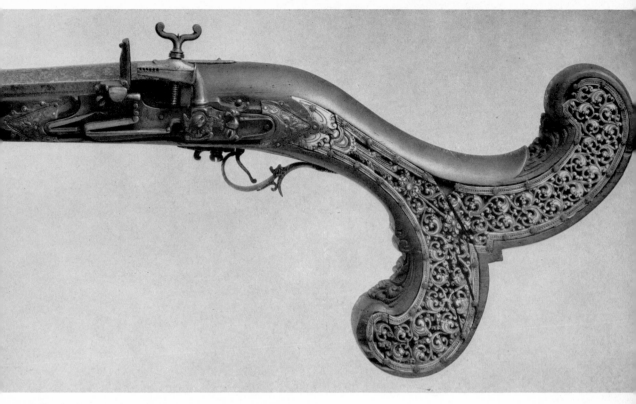

Miquelet from Ceylon with typical butt and left-hand lock.
Metropolitan Museum of Art, New York.

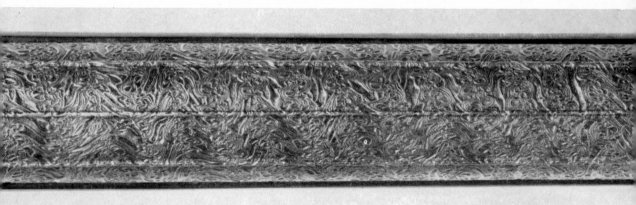

Detail of Damascus barrel of Indian flintlock gun, *ca.*1650.
Wallace Collection, London.

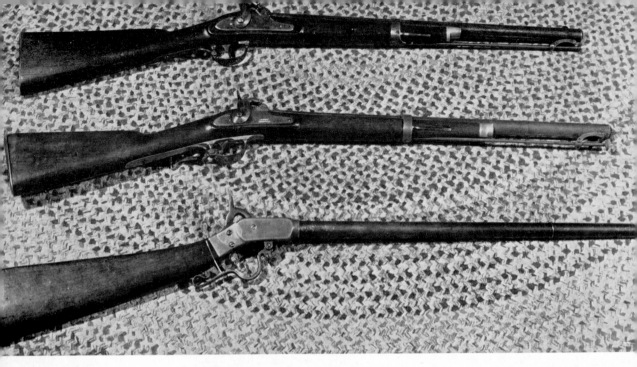

Three Confederate carbines:
copy of U.S. Model 1855,
made by Hodgkins, Macon, Ga.,
unmarked except for serial; copy
of U.S. Model 1855, made by
J. P. Murray, Columbus, Ga.,
and so marked; brass-framed
breechloader, made by
Read, Danville, Va.
Collection of William A. Bond.

Confederate copy of Colt, marked
"Leech & Rigdon, CSA";
grip carved "C. H. Milner,
Dublin, Texas".
Collection of Robert Krumdich.

Confederate brass-framed
copy of Colt, made by
Griswold & Gunnison, Ga.
*Collection of
William A. Albaugh, III.*

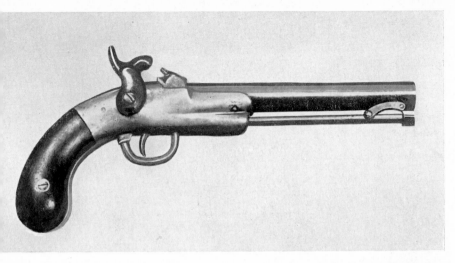

Confederate brass-framed single-shot pistol, made by Garrett & Co., Greensboro, N.C., who also made the Tarpley carbines. *Collection of William A. Albaugh, III.*

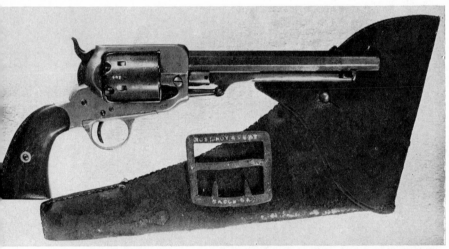

Confederate brass-framed copy of Whitney, made by Spiller & Burr, Atlanta, Ga., with original holster. *Collection of William A. Albaugh, III.*

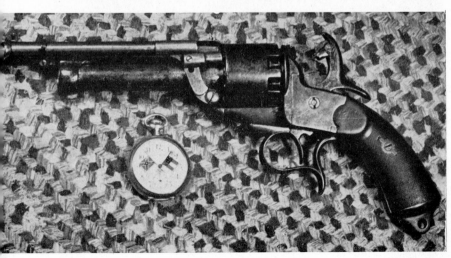

LeMat's "grapeshot" revolver. The loading lever is on the left-hand side. The hammer nose is depressed to fire the lower, "grapeshot" barrel. *Collection of William A. Albaugh, III.*

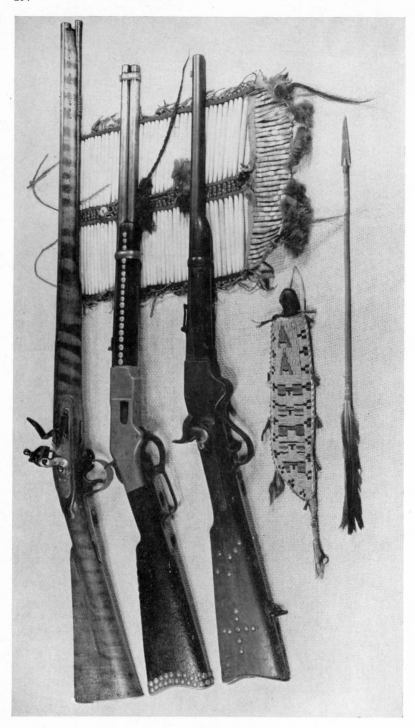

Three Indian guns:
Barnett flintlock trade musket;
Winchester Model 1866
carbine, caliber .44;
Spencer repeating carbine,
U.S. cavalry issue, caliber .52.
Collection of John S. du Mont.

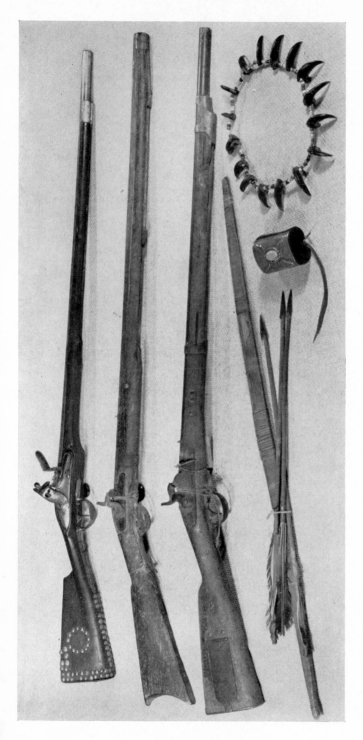

Three Indian guns:
French military flintlock musket,
no maker's name;
Leman rifle converted to percussion;
Whitney U.S. Model 1841 musket,
1855 alterations.
Collection of John S. du Mont.

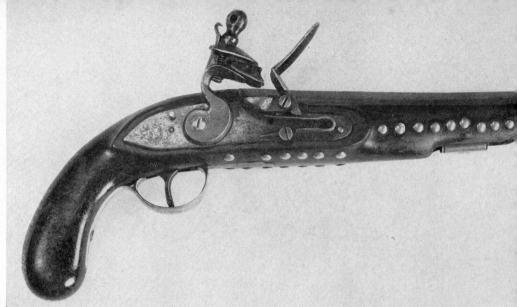

English flintlock pistol
"Chief's Grade."
*Collection of
John S. du Mont.*

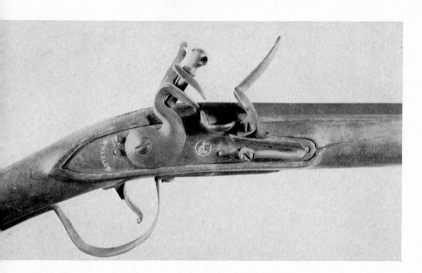

Early northwest gun made by Wheeler,
with fox-in-circle view mark on lock.
*Museum of the Fur Trade Collection,
Chadron, Neb.*

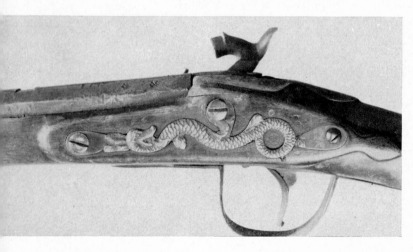

Serpent or dragon side-plate on northwest g
made by W. Chance & Son, Birmingham.
*Museum of the Fur Trade Collection,
Chadron, Neb.*

balloons; the hangars were taken down during the German occupation (1940–44).

The royal manufactory of arms was established in 1704. After 125 years' activity, in 1830, it was transferred to Châtellerault, a town which, since the year 1815, had had the manufactory of side arms that was previously at Klingenthal.   CL.B.

MAUSER

Rifles and pistols designed by Peter Paul Mauser, or weapons copied from these designs. The single-shot German 11mm. M1871 was the first successful Mauser rifle design. In 1884 the M71/84, a conversion of that weapon to tubular magazine loading, was adopted. The first modern Mauser was the 7.65mm. Belgian M1889; this rifle had the one-piece bolt with frontal-locking lugs which was to become the Mauser hallmark, and an in-line five-round box magazine loading with a five-round charger. The next significant Mauser design was the 7mm. Spanish M1893, the first Mauser with a staggered box magazine. The German 7.92mm. M1898 was the most successful of all Mauser designs, and most later Mausers are merely slightly modified copies of this weapon. The '98 was the first Mauser to cock on the opening of the bolt, to have extra large gas escape holes in the bolt, and to have a receiver ring with an enlarged diameter and a bolt sleeve lock. It also included a number of earlier improvements.

Mauser also developed a successful recoil operated military automatic pistol which was introduced in 1896. This weapon has a ten-round magazine placed ahead of the trigger guard and is loaded with ten-round chargers. Most models of this pistol are chambered for the 7.63mm. (caliber .30) pistol cartridge.   J.E.S.

Illustration: page 48.

Olson, Ludwig E., *Mauser Bolt Rifles*, Beverley Hills, Cal., 1957.
Smith, Walter H. B. and Joseph E., *The Book of Rifles*, 3rd edition, Harrisburg, Pa., 1963.

See also: MAUSER, PETER PAUL.

MAUSER, PETER PAUL

Peter Paul Mauser was born at Oberndorf, Württemberg, on June 27, 1838. His father was an armorer at the Royal Württemberg Arms Factory, as were his brothers. He started working at the arms plant full-time in 1852; he was conscripted in 1859 and served in the army for a few years. Upon returning to Oberndorf, he collaborated with his older brother Wilhelm in the development of a breech-loading cannon; this design was never adopted. In 1865, he developed a modification to the bolt system of the Dreyse needle gun. He and Wilhelm, who was to act mainly as business agent for his brother, were not successful in interesting Prussia, Austria or Württemberg in the development. An American, however, Samuel Norris, became interested, and financed the design of a similar modification for the French Chassepot. The brothers moved to Liège, Belgium, and Paul continued his design work. Norris was unable to obtain financial backing, and broke his contract with the Mausers after a patent was issued in 1868 on a Mauser-Norris rifle.

In 1871, Prussia adopted the first successful Mauser design. This single-shot bolt-action rifle, chambered for a black powder 11mm. cartridge, was the foundation stone of the great Mauser firm. In 1873, the Mausers opened a plant in Oberndorf; this plant burned down shortly afterwards, and Mauser bought the Royal Württemberg Arms Factory after that state had ordered 100,000 M71 rifles. Paul Mauser worked out a number of designs to convert the M71 into a magazine rifle. In 1880 he introduced a tubular magazine for the rifle, and this was accepted by Prussia in 1884 as the M71/84. Other famous models, the Belgian M1889, the Spanish M1893, and the German M1898, followed, and the Waffenfabrik Mauser became one of the largest and richest gun companies in the world.

In addition to rifles, Paul Mauser designed several revolvers, the Mauser 7.63mm. military automatic pistol and a number of semi-automatic rifles. He died in May 1914, at the age of seventy-six, after having designed what many people believe were the best bolt-action rifles of their time.   J.E.S.

Olson, Ludwig E., *Mauser Bolt Rifles*, Beverley Hills, Cal., 1957.

See also: BOLT ACTION; MAUSER.

MAXIM, HIRAM

Hiram Stevens Maxim was born on February 5, 1840, at Brockway's Mills, near Sangerville, Maine. His family was of French Huguenot descent. Driven out of France, the family fled to Canterbury, England, and later emigrated to Plymouth County, Massachusetts.

At the age of fourteen Maxim was apprenticed to a carriage maker. He studied whatever scientific books he could find, and, with a natural talent for drawing and painting and a facility for handling tools, he soon became adept at several trades.

After a variety of jobs, ranging from draftsman to bartender, Maxim settled down in 1865 with an instrument maker in Boston. Recognizing the future of electricity as a source of light, Maxim opened his own business, the Maxim Machine Company, where he perfected a reliable light bulb using carbon.

On a visit to Europe in 1881, Maxim became intrigued with the fact that almost every inventor in Europe was attempting to perfect some sort of machine gun.

Maxim later stated that the idea for his machine gun arose from his observance of the tremendous recoil force exerted by existing shoulder weapons.

Maxim set up a workshop in London, where he later became a British subject and was knighted by the Queen. Between 1883 and 1885 he patented practically every conceivable method of obtaining automatic fire.

The principle he decided to be most logical was what is known today as the short recoil system. Maxim's weapons were adopted by every major power in the world at one time or another between 1900 and the First World War.

Maxim died in New York City on November 24, 1916.

G.M.C.

Illustration: page 201.

See also: AUTOMATIC ARMS; MACHINE GUN.

MAYNARD, EDWARD

Edward Maynard was born on April 26, 1813, at Madison, New York, the son of Moses and Chloe Butler Maynard. After a preparatory course at Hamilton Academy, Maynard entered the United States Military Academy in 1831 but resigned the same year because of frail health. He then studied civil engineering and anatomy. In 1836 he moved to Washington, D.C., where he practised dentistry for the major portion of his life. He developed many important techniques and invented a number of instruments that are still used in that profession. His patients included several presidents, cabinet officers, members of Congress and many prominent military officers. Despite his outstanding achievements and honors received in the field of dentistry, he is best remembered for his contributions to the development of firearms.

Maynard patented in 1845 a mechanical system for priming firearms similar to the modern toy pistol using a roll of caps. This system was used by the United States Army in converting flintlock muskets to a percussion system and for the new-pattern arms that were adopted in 1855.

The Maynard type of primer was also used on the Jenks, Sharps and Symmes carbines and revolvers manufactured by the Massachusetts Arms Company. In 1851 and 1859 Maynard patented a simple, efficient breech-loading action combined with a brass cartridge which was used for nearly half a century by sportsmen through-

out the world. The Maynard breech-loading carbine was also purchased by the Union Army during the Civil War.

In 1858 and 1865, Maynard also submitted to the army several designs for converting muzzle-loading arms to a breech-loading system.

The Maynard double gun patented in 1865 was a successful effort to join two gun barrels in such a way that they might expand or contract endwise, independently of each other.

Maynard's contributions to the fields of dentistry and ordnance won him many honors. The King of Prussia made him a chevalier of the Military Order of the Red Eagle, the King of Sweden awarded him the Great Medal of Merit, and Tsar Nicholas I offered him the post of Court Dentist. He was awarded many testimonials by the leading scientific societies of the world. He died in Washington, D.C., on May 4, 1891.

C.R.G.

Illustrations: pages 48, 175.

METFORD, W. E.

Probably the most important British rifle designer of the nineteenth century was William Ellis Metford. Born on October 4, 1824, he was first destined for the career of a civil engineer on the railways, but an illness he contracted in India during the Mutiny became chronic and compelled his retirement. Thereafter he was free to devote almost all his time to rifle experiments, though he always remained a keen astronomer and a versatile inventor, devising such things as a lock-picking gadget, an improved theodolite and a gem facet cutting machine.

His earliest important contribution to small arms development came in 1852 when he invented the projectile that is now more commonly known as the Pritchett bullet, from the name of the gunmaker whom he approached to manufacture it. In 1854 he discovered "flip" – a phenomenon which explained much that had previously baffled those striving for extreme precision in shooting. The chief outcome of his earlier years, however, was a marked improvement of the service rifled musket. For this he designed an explosive projectile that was later adopted by the British government, as well as his hollow-nosed bullet, which proved the salvation of this slow pitched rifle and the means of ensuring its extended military career as the Snider.

Important though this work was, his later perfecting of a system for small-bore military and match, muzzle- and breechloading rifles deserves most attention. From 1865 onwards his ultra-shallow-grooved rifles firing hardened bullets steadily defeated all rival types until they completely dominated the prize lists. During the 1880's he gave frequent and important assistance to the War Office, and more than anyone else was responsible for the success of the .303 Lee-Metford. He died on October 14, 1899.

C.H.R.

Fremantle, T. F., and Brunel, H. M., "Memoir of William Ellis Metford" in *Proceedings of the Institution of Civil Engineers*, May 1900.

Metford, William Ellis, *The Metford Muzzle-loading and Breech-loading Match and Military Rifle*, Bristol, *ca.* 1876.

See also: RIFLES AND RIFLING.

MINIÉ, CLAUDE-ÉTIENNE

Born in Paris on February 13, 1804, Minié joined the French Army when very young and reached the rank of captain in the *Chasseurs d'Orléans* after serving in several campaigns in Africa. He was then encouraged to offer his projected improvements in bullet design and barrel and cartridge manufacture to the *Comité d'Artillerie*. In 1849, his method of expanding a bullet to fit the grooves of a rifle barrel was published and was quickly adopted for the élite troops of many European nations and of America. At this time he refused to protect his design with a patent and resisted the money and high rank offered by the Russians, who wanted him to enter their service. From his own grateful government he received 20,000 francs and a staff appointment to the Vincennes school of musketry.

In 1858 Minié retired from the army to found a school of musketry and an arms factory in Cairo at the request of the Viceroy of Egypt. He was created an Officer of the Legion of Honour in 1868. He is said to have traveled to America in the following year to work on the Remington productions, but this cannot be confirmed and seems to be unfounded. He died in Paris on December 14, 1879.   W.R.

See also: BULLET; MINIÉ BALL; RIFLES AND RIFLING.

MINIÉ BALL

Rifled guns had been used for many years before they were generally adopted for military use. They took too long to load and so were not considered suitable for combat. A system was needed to permit rapid loading and still ensure that the ball would fit the rifle grooves properly when fired.

The system most generally used was that perfected by a French officer, Captain Claude-Étienne Minié, though others, notably Captain Gustave Delvigne, had established the principle. Many nations adopted Minié-type rifles in the early 1850's. This rifle had grooves which deepened progressively from muzzle to breech. The cylindro-conical bullet had three grooves, usually filled with tallow, and a conical cavity in the base. In the original, this was plugged with a sheet-iron cup which the powder gases drove into the bullet, expanding it. British and American experiments with slightly modified designs soon indicated that no plug was necessary, but the British continued to insert boxwood plugs because they prevented damage

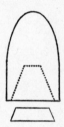

American adaptation of the Minié ball (left) as designed by James H. Burton
British version of the Minié ball, the Pritchett bullet (right), showing plug of boxwood

to the projectile in packing. The bullet diameter – less than the bore – permitted it to drop down the barrel when loading. The Minié system made for faster loading and had the considerable practical advantage at the time that most smoothbore muzzle-loaders could be converted to it. The shallow grooves did not weaken them seriously.

B.R.L.

Peterson, Harold L., *The Treasury of the Gun*, New York, 1962 (*The Book of the Gun*, London, 1963).

See also: BULLET; CARTRIDGE; MINIÉ, CLAUDE-ÉTIENNE; RIFLES AND RIFLING.

MIQUELET

The name miquelet is derived from Catalonian. Its use, as applied to the Spanish flintlock, was not contemporary, and the term seems to have appeared no earlier than the late nineteenth century.

The lock is characterized by a combined battery-pan cover, or frizzen, and a horizontally operating sear which, traversing the lock plate, acts directly on the heel or toe of the cock. Other features which exist in the earliest Spanish examples and have become associated with the miquelet lock in general are characteristic only of the majority of these locks. These are the large external V-shaped mainspring, the externally mounted cock with no internal tumbler, the bridle supporting the cock screw, the upper cock jaw with its guide pin which passes through

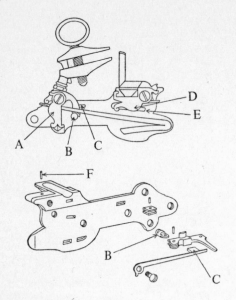

Typical Spanish miquelet lock, representative of the period ca.1640–ca.1800

A. *Cock bridle*
B. *Half cock sear*
C. *Full cock sear*
D. *Battery bridle*
E. *Battery spring*
F. *Fiel*

a hole in the lower jaw, and the ring-headed thumbscrew for tightening the jaws upon the flint. The fact that all of these features are common to one version of the earliest Scandinavian snaplock suggests the possibility of its introduction into the Peninsula by way of Spanish Flanders. Thence it could have passed to the Spanish possessions of Sardinia and the Kingdom of the Two Sicilies. An alternative theory holds that the lock originated in Italy. In any event, its progress must remain conjecture, for in no country can its presence be established any earlier than in Spain, where it was called, perhaps with considerable truth, "the Spanish lock."

The Spanish lock seems to have made its appearance during the second or third decade of the seventeenth century, although a version of the snaplock had been known in Spain at least as early as 1580. The earliest examples extant (which can be dated with certainty only between 1621 and 1641, although they probably more nearly approach the earlier date) are of Madrid manufacture and besides the above features include a lock plate contoured to provide a minimum surface upon which to mount the various parts; a striated striking face dovetailed to the body of the battery; a full cock sear only,

which retains the toe of the cock while the mainspring passes beneath and acts against the heel; a V-shaped battery spring similar to that of the conventional flintlock, mounted forward of the mainspring; and *fieles* on both cock and battery screws. *Fieles*, small pins which passed through holes drilled in the threaded ends of these screws and corresponding holes in the lock plate, served to secure the screws against loosening due to the movement of the parts they retained. They disappeared shortly after mid-century, and in subsequent locks screws were sometimes secured by striking their ends with a punch in order to spread the threads. Improvements in threading seem to have obviated the need for these measures in the latter half of the seventeenth century.

An early method of scoring the battery face disappeared about the same time as the *fiel*. In this method, the striations appeared as ridges raised above the face rather than as a series of grooves. This is found only in combination with the separate battery face which continued, with recessed striations, to enjoy a limited popularity until the nineteenth century. Otherwise, striations were cut directly into the battery or, as in Madrid, often were not used.

A half cock sear was introduced before 1644 in the form of a short round finger, notched to receive the toe of the cock. With the lock at half cock, the toe in this notch prevented the sear from being withdrawn and accidentally igniting the piece. When the trigger was pulled with the lock at full cock, this and the flat, full cock sear retracted simultaneously, allowing the cock to fall.

Apparently by *ca.*1636, the forward-mounted battery spring was reversed, reduced in size, and mounted directly under the pan where it was concealed by the battery-screw bridle.

Contemporary with the above lock existed a variation called *agujeta*. In its original form it differed from the earlier miquelet in the arrangement of its internal mechanism; externally, its full-cock sear engaged the heel of the cock while the half-cock sear operated in the normal manner against the toe which was forced downward by the lower arm of the mainspring. Fitted with a dog catch, this model was long manufactured in Ceylon, undoubtedly introduced by the Portuguese before 1658. While seventeenth-century Spanish examples are almost unknown, this lock, without the dog catch, was produced well into the eighteenth century both in Spain and in southern Italy. It became known in Spain during this period as *a la romana*. Almost identical with the conventional Spanish lock was the *calzo atrás* or "rear sear" lock, differing from the former only in having its full-cock sear contact the cock heel, while the arrangement of the mainspring remained the same.

In Brescia, the influence of the earliest Spanish lock is

evident in the continued use there of the forward battery spring until the final quarter of the seventeenth century.

A distinct rear sear miquelet lock with a dog catch flourished briefly in Ripoll during the third decade of the seventeenth century. The lock plate had the same deep drop as the Ripoll wheel lock. Earlier models had a projection on the outside of the battery to facilitate opening the pan, while on all models the battery was actuated by a leaf spring. The *fiel* was not used. However, from the earliest period, the ordinary miquelet also was known here where it was characterized in most cases by its fluted cock and battery bridles.

With the succession of the Bourbons to the Habsburg throne in 1700, the influence of French gunsmithery invaded the Spanish court where it resulted in the creation of a bastardized version of the miquelet lock made in imitation of the French flintlock. Outwardly identical to the flintlock, the cock was attached to a tumbler, useless because the two sears, in miquelet fashion, traversed the lock plate to engage the breast and heel of the cock. Popular only in Madrid, where it was termed *a la moda*, it endured for more than a century, falling into disuse during the Peninsular War (1808–14).

During the postwar years in Spain, foreign innovations such as the waterproof pan and friction-reducing roller bearings on cock and battery were adapted to the miquelet lock until, about 1825, the system was finally abandoned, in favour of the increasingly popular percussion system. It left traces in North Africa and the Near East, where both versions of the Ripoll miquelet lock had been introduced early in the seventeenth century and remained in vogue for almost three hundred years.   J.D.L.

Illustrations: pages 210–11, 272–3.

Buttin, Charles, "L'Arquebuserie de Ripoll" in *Armes à Feu et Armes Blanches*, 1914.

Martínez de Espinar, Alonso, *Arte de Ballestería y Montería*, Madrid, 1644.

Neal, W. Keith, *Spanish Guns and Pistols*, London, 1955.

Peterson, Harold L., *The Treasury of the Gun*, New York, 1962 (*The Book of the Gun*, London, 1963).

See also: AFRICAN FIREARMS; ASIATIC FIREARMS; SPANISH FIREARMS.

MITRAILLEUSE

The mitrailleuse, or "grape shooter," was originally invented by Major Fafschamps of the Belgian Army in 1851. He offered his weapon to Joseph Montigny, a noted Belgian engineer, who persuaded the French Emperor, Napoleon III, to adopt the weapon in 1867.

The Montigny gun consisted of thirty-seven rifled barrels mounted in a wrought-iron tube. It was loaded by an iron plate bored with thirty-seven matching holes. The firing mechanism was operated by a hand crank, and the gunner could fire from one to thirty-seven rounds with a single turn. The average rate of fire was about 12 bursts, or 444 rounds, per minute.

The gun was manufactured behind closed doors and was the famous "secret weapon" of the Franco-Prussian War. Its first combat trial, however, proved its inefficiency.

If the mitrailleuse had been used against rifle fire, it might have been successful; but the military command insisted on matching it against field artillery, where it was completely outclassed. The Prussians also used a mitrailleuse-type weapon, the Feld gun, with twenty-four barrels mounted in parallel rows, but it was considered mechanically unreliable.

The mitrailleuse lasted less than a year before total failure in action necessitated its abandonment. The name, however, is still used in France to refer to a machine gun.   G.M.C.

Chinn, Colonel George M., *The Machine Gun*, 4 vols, Washington, D.C., 1951–55.

MOSIN-NAGANT RIFLE

A bolt-action, magazine-fed rifle developed by Colonel S. I. Mosin, of the Imperial Russian Arms Plant at Tula, and Nagant of Belgium.

It has a two-piece bolt with dual locking lugs mounted on a removable bolthead. The five-round magazine is an in-line type and protrudes below the stock. It can be loaded with a five-round charger or single cartridges. The safety is awkward, in that the cocking piece must be pulled to the rear and rotated to the left. The Russian rifles use a triangular section bayonet which locks on to the barrel; the M1944 carbine has a folding bayonet.

The 1891 was the first Mosin-Nagant to be adopted by Russia; this model was followed by the Dragoon model rifle, carbine M1910, rifle M1891/30, carbine M1938 and carbine M1944. It has also been used extensively by Finland in models 1891, 27, 28, 28-30, and 39. All of these weapons are chambered for the 7.62mm. Russian (7.62 × 53R) rimmed cartridge. The Mosin-Nagant is obsolete in the U.S.S.R., but is still used in some other Communist countries.   J.E.S.

Illustration: page 182.

Smith, Walter H. B. and Joseph E., *The Book of Rifles*, 3rd edition, Harrisburg, Pa., 1963.

Smith, Walter H. B. and Joseph E., *Small Arms of the World*, 6th edition, Harrisburg, Pa., 1960.

MUSKET

A military firearm fired from the shoulder. In the beginning it was heavier and of bigger bore than the caliver, and the musketeer supported its weight on a forked rest when shooting. The musket was introduced during the first half of the sixteenth century. Thereafter the heavier shoulder arms used by the infantry came to be known as muskets, and the name continued in use until the end of the nineteenth century. Originally the word referred to a matchlock arm, and in France at the end of the seventeenth century was used in contradistinction to the flintlock *fusil*, a gun with a combined match- and flintlock being known as a *fusil-mousquet*. In the eighteenth and nineteenth centuries, "musket" was generally used to indicate a smoothbore military arm of large caliber intended to be fired from the shoulder.

The earliest recorded reference to the name is in the Spanish title of a book, *Ballestas, Mosquetes y Arcabuces*, said by bibliographers to have been published in Naples in 1537. The musket as described above was probably in use by this time, as soldiers escorting the Emperor Charles V in 1530 are represented as carrying rests with their heavy shoulder arms.   W.R.

Illustrations: pages 40, 84 (plate 2), 101 and endpapers.

See also: ARQUEBUS; FUSEE/FUSIL; MARTIAL ARMS; RIFLE MUSKET/RIFLED MUSKET.

MUSKETOON

A type of musket with a short, smoothbore barrel and large bore; by inference, a soldier armed with a musketoon. The term was loosely used, and no satisfactory definition is to be found in contemporary descriptions that range from "short bastard snaphaunce musquetts" (1688) to the shortest kind of blunderbuss (1772).   W.R.

MUZZLE BRAKE

A muzzle brake is a hood-like extension attached to the muzzle of a firearm to reduce the recoil of the piece when it is fired. It does this by trapping and changing the direction of the escaping gases from the powder charge. Experiments with such a device on cannon were carried out by the United States Ordnance Department as far back as the turn of the century, and muzzle brakes have been applied with varying success to different types of sporting and military arms ever since.

The most efficient muzzle brakes are those which block all the gas and turn it straight back. This subjects the shooter to an intolerable blast directly in his face and an increase in the sound of the report to his ears. Most muzzle brakes, therefore, direct the gases to the side. This is much less efficient, but it avoids injury to the user.

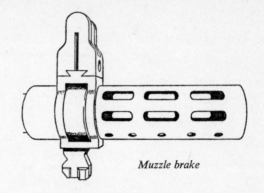

Muzzle brake

Another form of muzzle brake is one which traps the gases and then releases them gradually. This is the principle upon which silencers operate, so that such devices are in effect muzzle brakes as well. They are bulky and comparatively complicated, however, and in most countries they are rigidly controlled by law. Thus they have not been applied for their muzzle-braking effects alone. The slotted hoods are much simpler, smaller, and not subject to the same restrictions.

Generally speaking, muzzle brakes have been considered only for heavier guns. The recoil of small-caliber arms is too slight to require such a device.

At one time it was thought that the muzzle brake was effective in combating the tendency of the muzzle of an automatic arm to climb in firing. For this reason many submachine guns have been equipped with them. However, thorough tests have revealed that although there is a slight practical effect in this direction it is too slight to be of any real value.   H.L.P.

Harrison, Colonel E. H., "Muzzle Brakes" in *The American Rifleman*, May 1957.

N

NEEDLE GUN

The needle gun is a form of percussion firearm in which a striking needle is driven through the base of a cartridge and against a primer located within the cartridge. The first needle guns were muzzle-loading, but most were breech-loading. Needle guns were invented and first manufactured in Germany, where their use had far-reaching results. For a time, France also relied on needle guns to arm her foot soldiers. The German and French needle guns – and more especially their cartridges – were quite different from one another, in construction and in appearance.

Best known of the needle guns are the Dreyse, Chassepot, Needham, and Chatauvillard, in that order.   L.W.

Illustration: page 46.

Barber, Edward C., *The Crack Shot*, New York, 1871.
Blanch, H. J., *A Century of Guns*, London, 1909.
Busk, Hans, *The Rifle: And How to Use It*, London, 1860.
Greener, William W., *The Gun and Its Development*, 9th edition, London, 1910.
Marks, Edward C. R., *The Evolution of Modern Small Arms and Ammunition*, London, 1898.
Ommundsen, H., and Robinson, Ernest H., *Rifles and Ammunition and Rifle Shooting*, London and New York, 1915.
Winant, Lewis, *Early Percussion Firearms*, New York, 1959, and London, 1961.

See also: BREECHLOADERS; CARTRIDGE; CHASSEPOT, ANTOINE ALPHONSE; DREYSE, JOHANN NIKOLAUS VON.

NIPPLE PRIMER

A nipple primer was used occasionally by sportsmen of the mid-nineteenth century to clear the channel of a percussion cap nipple that had become clogged. The technique consisted of inserting a few grains of gunpowder into the nipple and firing again with a new cap. The resulting explosion would normally open the passage to the interior of the bore. Since the opening in the top of a nipple is small, it was a difficult task under field conditions to introduce the powder. Thus special primers were developed to assist in the operation. The simplest forms consisted of a small funnel shaped to fit the nipple. More elaborate types added powder magazines and prickers which could be used in teasing the powder into the hole. Occasionally other devices were also attached, including cappers and even dog whistles. Documentary evidence and surviving specimens would seem to indicate that such primers were never widely popular.   H.L.P.

Bedford, R., "Percussion Nipple Primers" in *Journal of the Arms and Armour Society*, Vol. 4, No. 3, September 1962.
Riling, Ray, *The Powder Flask Book*, New Hope, Penn., 1953.

See also: PRIMER.

NOBEL, ALFRED BERNHARD

Alfred Nobel was born in Stockholm, Sweden, on October 21, 1833. When he was nine his family moved to St. Petersburg where his father manufactured such diverse commodities as mines, torpedoes, firearms and agricultural implements for the Russian government. In 1850 Nobel visited the United States to study with the Swedish inventor John Ericsson. Upon his return he began experiments with nitroglycerine, but continued accidental explosions caused him to turn his attention to less powerful explosives. In 1863 he produced dynamite experimentally. Blasting gelatin followed in 1876 and with it came the gelatin dynamites. Then, in 1887 and 1888, he patented nitrocellulose and a form of smokeless powder from which cordite was later developed. His patents (129 in all) and his manufacturing ventures brought him a fortune, most of which was used as directed in his will to establish the Nobel Prizes for service to mankind. He died at San Remo, Italy, on December 10, 1896.   H.L.P.

See also: SMOKELESS POWDER.

NOCK, HENRY

Henry Nock, born in 1741, was by trade a lockmaker and in 1770 first approached the British Ordnance with a new musket lock. In 1775, with William Jover and John Green, he patented a covered flintlock with an ingenious smoke tube. The following year he began supplying arms to the

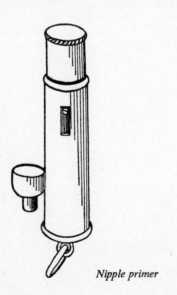

Nipple primer

East India Company, including some Ferguson rifles. The Ordnance followed by giving him contracts for gun locks and in 1781 granted him a monopoly for the supply of the famous seven-barreled volley guns to the Royal Navy.

Turning his attentions to the sporting market, Nock established a shop in Ludgate Hill, London, in 1784, and purchased his freedom of the Gunmakers Company. Many magnificent sporting guns, some with the seven barrels of his naval weapon and others with clever revolving and repeating actions, were made under his direction, and led to the development of a special breech which he patented in 1787.

He was a prolific maker of pistols, and there are probably more pistols in existence to-day bearing his name than that of any other maker of this period. They were made in all possible combinations of barrels: single barrels ranging from vest-pocket miniatures up to long holster and dueling weapons; two- or three-barrel combinations with rolling-tap or sliding cut-off actions; four-barrel duck-foot mob pistols; and six- and seven-barrel volley and revolver pistols. For the Ordnance he designed a cavalry pistol with a detachable butt in 1783 and ten years later a very powerful double-barreled pistol for the Royal Horse Artillery.

All these achievements were recognised by his appointment in 1789 as gunmaker-in-ordinary to the King. From a group of workshops in the Whitechapel area he continued to supply large quantities of military arms to the Ordnance and the East India Company, and to design gunmaking tools, gauges and machinery, for he was not only the greatest gunmaker of his time but a great engineer. With the encouragement of the Duke of Richmond, he conducted a series of experiments that produced his screwless enclosed lock, for which he was awarded £100 by the Ordnance in 1786, and culminated in 1790 with the musket which was intended to be the new standard arm of the British Army. Known as the Duke of Richmond's pattern and using the Nock lock, it was the finest flintlock musket ever produced, but it was costly and difficult to make, and only Nock could be entrusted with its manufacture. After only a few thousand had been made the project was abandoned at the commencement of the Napoleonic Wars. But the Nock lock, easily dismantled yet sturdy and durable, was fitted to many government carbines and pistols and to volunteer rifles.

In 1802 Henry Nock was elected Master of the Gunmakers Company. He died two years later, and his business was continued by his son-in-law and foreman, James Wilkinson, the founder of the present firm of Wilkinson Sword.   H.L.B.

Illustrations: pages 43, 339.

Blackmore, Howard L., *British Military Firearms, 1650–1850*, London, 1961.

See also: VOLLEY GUN.

NORDENFELT, THORSTEN

Swedish financier, 1842–1920, founder of companies producing machine guns and quick-firing ordnance.

The earliest and best known Nordenfelt machine gun was designed in 1872 by Heldge Palmcrantz, a Swedish engineer, but was manufactured and marketed by Nordenfelt. One of the most successful of the manually operated weapons, it had from one to twelve barrels fixed in a rectangular frame and was operated by a lever on the right-hand side. This lever was drawn back to cock the firing mechanism, at the same time ejecting the empty case. A forward movement chambered a new round, and, at the end of the lever's travel, fired it. A tall rectangular magazine or hopper was positioned on top of the gun, the cartridges falling by gravity into slots behind the chamber.

The guns were produced in various sizes from rifle caliber to one inch, the latter firing hardened steel bullets as they were mainly for anti-torpedo-boat use.

In the 1890's Nordenfelt, in partnership with Hiram Maxim, formed the Maxim-Nordenfelt Gun and Ammunition Company. The firm had only a short existence, its production being mainly confined to rifle-caliber Maxim guns together with the 37 mm. pom-pom. In 1897, Nordenfelt, who up to this time had been established in London, formed a company in Paris to manufacture a new machine gun invented by Captain Bergman, a Swedish army officer who is not to be confused with Theodore Bergmann, the German designer of automatic weapons. This 1897 gun was water-cooled and belt-fed, and had the unusual distinction of giving automatic or manually operated fire at will. It achieved only limited success.

A.N.K.

NORTHWEST GUN

See: TRADE GUNS.

ORGAN BATTERY

See: VOLLEY GUN.

ORIENTAL FIREARMS

See: ASIATIC FIREARMS.

P

PALM PISTOL

Guns belonging in this classification are an unusual type; held in the palm of the hand, they are fired by the act of squeezing, or compressing the fist. This ingenious method has also given them the appellation of squeezer pistols.

Types of arms comprising the palm pistols take various shapes: from the Webber single-shot tube with a hard rubber knob on one end, to the round watch-like shape of the Chicago and Minneapolis palm pistol, a seven-shot, double-action repeater. This gun has a flat cylinder, with chambers radiating out like the spokes of a wheel.

Between these two extremes were the Shatuck Unique with four chambers bored through one solid barrel block, which tipped down to load, and the five-shot French Gaulois squeezers bearing a slight resemblance to the later automatic type of arms, having one barrel through which the cartridges were fired. Cartridges in the latter were held vertically within the grip.

In firing, the barrel of both the Webber and the Chicago palm pistols protruded between the first and second fingers. The Gaulois was held in the hand much as one would hold a normal gun. The four-barrel block of the Unique extended between the forefinger and the thumb.

Most palm pistols worked on the principle that when the main spring was contracted enough by the squeezing action, the hammer or firing pin became disengaged and moved forward to fire the cartridge. In the Unique pistol, the firing pin itself revolved to strike the edge of the rimfire cartridges. On the other palm or squeezer pistols, the hammer moved only in a horizontal position to detonate the cartridges, as they were brought into alignment by the action of cocking, or as they were raised into position by a magnetic spring, as in the Gaulois pistols.

Perhaps the most unusual of the palm pistols is the one known as the "Little All Right." Resembling a tiny revolver, minus the grip, it too was held in the palm of the hand. Its small five-shot cylinder was revolved and the concealed firing pin activated by a squeezing action of the forefinger on a folding trigger on the top side of the short barrel.

The calibers of palm pistols ranged from .22 up to the .410 caliber of some of the modern gas pistols.

Countries in which palm pistols were produced in the greatest number included Belgium, France, and the United States. The greatest period of popularity for these unusual arms was during the 1890's. That they were designed for personal defense is evident from the name "the Protector" given to one such arm.   H.C.L.

Illustrations: pages 114–15.

Logan, Herschel C., *Hand Cannon to Automatic*, Huntingdon, W.Va., 1944.

Winant, Lewis, *Firearms Curiosa*, New York, 1955, 2nd edition 1961, and London, 1956.

See also: TURRET GUN.

PATRON

See: CARTRIDGE BOX.

PAULY, JOHANNES SAMUEL

Johannes Samuel Pauly, later known as Jean Samuel or Samuel John, was born near Berne, Switzerland, in 1766. He was granted a ten-year *brevet* in Paris on September 29, 1812, for the world's first center-fire, breech-loading guns and pistols to use a self-obturating cartridge with a soft brass head containing a depression to hold a primer of percussion compound. The report on trials of the lifting-breech and drop-barrel weapons, which were a half-century ahead of their time, put them in "the front rank of hunting arms known up to the present time." The advantages cited – double-loading impossible, facility in unloading, practically weatherproof action, quickly loaded when on the move – had important military applications, but the Emperor Napoleon was not convinced. The gun with which Pauly fired what was then a phenomenal number of shots – twenty-two in two minutes – remained no more than an interesting curiosity to sportsmen, who bought it in various models and some quantity from Pauly's associates and successors, Prélat, Roux, Pichereau and Lefaucheux. Surviving examples include fine shotguns, civil and military pistols and at least one seven-barreled volley gun.

By August 4, 1814, Pauly was in London, and had patented a mechanism to ignite the powder in his cartridge by a blast of air heated in a tiny cylinder by a violent compression from a spring-loaded piston. Following his patents for waterproof fabric and a balloon called the "Dolphin," the abortive attempt to build which cost the gunmaker Durs Egg £10,000, came the compressed-air ignition patent of May 14, 1816. This enlarged on the 1814 hand firearms designs and described cannon igniters and ingenious breech-loading cannon.

The following year, the British Board of Ordnance refused a trial to a dangerously impractical mortar intended to shoot explosive shells. The rejection of his percussion lock for cannon was equally unequivocal after a disastrous trial held on August 21, 1818. Pauly's spirited but hopeless request for a second chance is the last surviving record of an outstanding contributor to the development of firearms. His death, presumably about 1820, would certainly not be unrecorded had his inventive genius been matched by commercial acumen.   W.R.

Illustrations: pages 45, 116.

Reid, William, "Pauly, gun-designer" in *Journal of the Arms and Armour Society*, Vol. 2, No. 9, London, March 1958.

See also: BREECHLOADERS; CARTRIDGE; FOWLING PIECE.

PEDERSEN DEVICE

A semi-automatic mechanism which could be inserted into a modified United States Springfield M1903 rifle to enable it to fire caliber .30 pistol cartridges. The device was developed by J. D. Pedersen in 1917 and was produced secretly as the "U.S. pistol caliber .30 M1918."

The device consists of a blowback-type action with a barrel of the same size and shape as the caliber .30 Springfield case (30–06) and a forty-round magazine. The Springfield bolt was removed and the device inserted, converting the rifle into a semi-automatic weapon firing 80-grain bullets at 1,300 feet per second. If it were desired to fire caliber .30 rifle cartridges, the rifle bolt could be inserted after the device was removed. The modifications to the rifle consisted of a rectangular hole cut into the left receiver wall as an ejection port, and a modified sear and cut-off. Springfield rifles so modified were stamped Mark 1.

In 1918, 500,000 Pedersen devices were ordered; 65,000 were completed at the end of the First World War and the remainder were cancelled. After the First World War, the United States Army decided that the device was impractical and stocks were destroyed.   J.E.S.

Illustration: page 203.

Hatcher, Major General Julian S., *Hatcher's Notebook*, Harrisburg, Pa., 1947.

See also: AUTOMATIC ARMS.

PELLET LOCK

See: PERCUSSION SYSTEM.

PENNSYLVANIA RIFLE

See: KENTUCKY RIFLE.

PEPPERBOX

In the terminology of collectors, a pepperbox is a multi-barreled firearm in which each barrel is fired separately by a single striker. Some students refine the term still further and insist that the barrels must revolve, while others will also accept as pepperboxes those guns in which the hammer or firing pin moves, or in which the flash may be directed to individual barrels by some other means, such as a valve controlling a number of vents. Both groups, however, insist that the barrels must be grouped around a central axis, not arranged in a line as in some harmonica guns. Those pepperboxes with rotating barrels are technically revolvers by definition. They are grouped here only because modern common usage normally restricts the term revolver to an arm with a single barrel and a revolving cylinder. This is a purely arbitrary distinction, but it is useful and generally recognized.

If the strictest pepperbox definition is applied, requiring that the clustered barrels must revolve, the history of the type can be traced back no further than the mid-sixteenth century. During the second half of that century both wheel locks and snaphances were manufactured with varying numbers of barrels which could be revolved so that each, in turn, came under the dog head or cock. After 1600 the number of such arms increased rapidly, if the record of surviving specimens is any indication. None of these forms was entirely successful, however. They suffered from the same drawbacks as the single-barrel revolvers of their eras, especially the difficulties concerned with providing safe, quickly available priming for each barrel. As in the case of the cylinder revolver, it was not until the advent of the percussion system, in the first quarter of the nineteenth century, that the pepperbox became a practical and popular weapon.

Even then, development was slow. The first of the percussion pepperboxes were probably made in the 1820's, and the barrels were undoubtedly revolved by hand, in the same manner as the majority of the earlier forms. Some of them in fact, seem to be adaptations of the then popular two-barrel turnover pistols, with two additional barrels fastened alongside the originals so that all could pivot under the hammer. Some time after 1830, the barrels were made to turn automatically as the hammer was cocked. This was not a sudden or radical innovation. John Dafte, for one, had made flintlock revolvers which operated in this manner during the seventeenth century. Other English and Continental makers subsequently produced similar guns, and perhaps some had made them earlier. Probably because of this situation, European pepperbox manufacturers did not attempt to patent their systems for rotating the barrel block automatically, and so it is impossible to establish a definite date for the introduction of such arms either in England or on the Continent. In America, however, the brothers Benjamin and Barton Darling did obtain a patent on their system for automatic rotation of the barrels on April 13, 1836, the first to be granted for a pepperbox in the United States and a definite indication of the date of the introduction of the system into that country. It is generally believed that the same general system became popular in Europe at about the same time.

The second major improvement in pepperboxes came hard on the heels of the mechanically rotating barrels. All of the early versions of the arm had been single-action, requiring the hammer to be cocked manually for each shot. Then, in 1837, Ethan Allen of Massachusetts obtained a United States patent for a double-action lock which made his pepperboxes the fastest-firing handguns in the world, far better known and more popular than the Colt revolver for more than a decade. Loaded and primed in advance, one of these double-action pistols could be drawn and fired in a single motion. The bar hammer was streamlined so that there were no rough contours to catch in the belt or clothing, and the charges in the extra barrels gave assurance that there were shots in reserve if the first should miss – both factors which added to the weapon's appeal. Double-action pepperboxes probably appeared in Europe at about the same time, but once again there are no patents by which the date can be firmly established.

Among the American revolving pepperboxes, the best known are those made by Ethan Allen in the various partnerships which he formed with relatives, such as Allen & Thurber and Allen & Wheelock. For a time, in fact, the name Allen became almost synonymous with that form of gun, just as Colt did for revolver. Other notable American makers included the Darlings, Blunt & Syms, Stocking, W. W. Marston (as Marston & Knox or Sprague & Marston), and the Manhattan Arms Company. Many of their pepperboxes closely resembled the Allen with its usual top hammer, but some, like the Blunt & Syms, were underhammer guns, and others manufactured by Thomas K. Bacon were not only underhammers but continued to offer manually turned barrels.

In Europe, the variation was far wider. Most American pepperboxes were made with from four to six barrels. In Europe ranges of from three to twenty-four barrels have been recorded. Daggers and belt hooks, features which would make any American pepperbox a rare specimen, are found on a number of European examples. Fine workmanship and decoration are also European characteristics. In America the arm was looked upon as primarily utilitarian. Such engraving as is encountered is largely uninspired, and a specimen with ivory grips or decorative carving is most uncommon. Even casings of the pistol and its accessories are unusual. Although many European pepperboxes are also of plain workmanship, high quality workmanship with fine engraving and the use of expensive materials are far more common than on American specimens.

Most of the major European gun manufacturers who worked between 1830 and 1860 made pepperboxes. In England Joseph Lang, J. R. Cooper and James Purdey were especially noteworthy, as were the Rigbys in Dublin. Joseph Manton made eighteen-shot pepperboxes, some of them with only six nipples so that each cap fired three barrels simultaneously. Manton also produced some specimens with dagger blades that could be screwed into the butt instead of into the muzzle where most such blades attached. On the Continent, the best known of the pepperboxes were those of the Mariette system patented in Belgium in 1837 and produced widely in both Belgium and France. These are immediately recognizable by their ring triggers and partially concealed hammers and also by the fact that the barrels, often of Damascus twist, are made separately and screwed into a standing breech which contains the powder chambers and nipples.

Despite the fact that the percussion double-action revolving pepperbox was a fast-firing gun, and although it placed a number of shots at its owner's disposal, it had some serious drawbacks which eventually caused it to be superseded by the single-barrel revolver. For one thing, it was difficult to aim. On many, the hammer was directly in the line of sight, and on all the trigger pull was heavy, and the barrels were revolving during the first part of the pul. Also, in common with all multi-barreled arms, pepperl boxes had a tendency to become muzzle-heavy in large calibers. This was especially noticeable in models with eight or more barrels, and it must have taken an extremely strong wrist to hold a pistol with twenty-four barrels steady while the trigger was pulled. Because of these factors the revolver began to overtake the revolving pepperbox in popularity during the 1850's and had almost completely supplanted it by 1860.

There were, however, some cartridge pepperboxes with revolving barrels which achieved a degree of popularity. Chief among these were those models of James Reid's "My Friend" knuckle-dusters without a barrel, of which some 13,500 were made between 1866 and 1883 (see COMBINATION WEAPON). Remington had also manufactured a cartridge pepperbox with revolving barrels based on a patent by William Elliott during 1861 and 1862, but less than a thousand were produced before it was superseded by another model, also based on an Elliott patent, in which the barrels remained stationary while a striker mounted in the frame revolved to fire each of the four barrels in turn.

If one accepts the broader definition of a pepperbox, which includes those arms in which the clustered bar-

rels remain stationary while the hammer or other detonator moves, then the history of such arms is much longer
and the variety of types is much greater. In fact, if one
includes a burning match or hot wire held separately in
the hand as a moving "detonator," it may be claimed that
pepperboxes have been made with every major ignition
system since the development of firearms. In the Tower of
London there is a two-handed mace of the type called a
holy water sprinkler with three hand cannon barrels
mounted in its head, each with a separate touchhole so
that each could be fired in turn by the same "detonator."
This weapon is first mentioned in an inventory of 1547,
but such arms may be earlier still. There are one or two
more primitive hand cannon in existence, probably of
fifteenth-century European origin, and the type has continued until modern times in China, where clusters of
three or four wrought-iron barrels were fastened together
and provided with a socket for attachment to a stick or
tiller to serve as a primitive form of stock. Again, each
barrel was fired separately by applying a burning match
to its touchhole.

It was during the flintlock period, however, that pepperboxes with the selective firing of stationary barrels actually
achieved some degree of popularity. These were normally
pistols with three or four barrels and a valve system which
could direct the flame from the priming pan to the selected
charge. Two common methods were employed, and sometimes they were combined. One comprised a pan divided
into sections with a sliding cover which exposed only one
part at a time. The other made use of a revolving valve
reminiscent of a water faucet, and thus often called a
tap-action, which directed the flame of the priming to the
proper barrel.

During the percussion cap era many pepperboxes were
made with stationary barrels and revolving hammers.
George Leonard patented such an arm in the United
States in 1849, and it was manufactured in quantity by
Robbins & Lawrence until about 1855.

Christian Sharps also patented a percussion cap pepperbox with a revolving striker, but it was his four-barreled
cartridge version that achieved popularity. Sharps patented
the latter pistol in 1859 and some 129,000 of them were
made in various models before production ceased about
1874. Both American and European manufacturers copied
the Sharps system with its sliding barrel block which moved
forward for loading the cartridges and its revolving firing
pin on the nose of the hammer, but none could compare
with the Sharps in popularity during the second half of the
nineteenth century. The closest was the Remington-Elliott
four-barreled pistol mentioned above, of which an estimated 50,000 were made between 1863 and 1888.

Even during the present century, cartridge pepperboxes
have been patented and manufactured. The two most

important ones were both designed by Oscar F. Mossberg of Chicopee Falls, Massachusetts. The first, patented
in 1906, was a squeezer palm pistol manufactured by the
C. S. Shatuck Arms Company, and known as the Shatuck
Unique (see PALM PISTOL). The other, patented in 1920,
was more conventional in appearance and was produced
by Mossberg himself. Both had four barrels drilled from
a solid block, which tipped down to load, and a rotating
hammer. To all intents and purposes, these were the last
of the pepperboxes.   H.L.P.

Illustrations: pages 115, 169–70, 178.

Winant, Lewis, *Pepperbox Firearms*, New York, 1952.

See also: ALLEN, ETHAN; COMBINATION WEAPON;
REVOLVER; SHARPS, CHRISTIAN.

PERCUSSION CAP

See: PERCUSSION SYSTEM.

PERCUSSION SYSTEM

"Percussion" is from the Latin *percutere*, meaning "to
strike smartly or with violence." Pianos, drums, cymbals,
all sounded by tapping or crashing, are percussion instruments; guns discharged by striking a cap or primer
are percussion firearms. Today's firearms, which have
priming in a cartridge head, are in fact percussion firearms – but it is customary to limit the term "percussion
gun" to those, mostly muzzle-loading, which employ a
separate copper cap or other primer. The earliest percussion guns – those having fulminate loose, or in tubes, or
in tiny lumps – were known only as detonators.

The Rev. Alexander John Forsyth, M.A., LL.D., who
was born in Belhelvie, Scotland, in 1768, and died there
in 1843, invented the percussion system of firearms
ignition – but not the percussion cap.

For four hundred years, roughly from 1400 to 1800, the
priming in firearms was gunpowder, ignited either by
being touched with flame (or some hot substance such as
a glowing wire), or by sparks generated by the rubbing
together of flint or pyrite and steel.

Then came Forsyth – and in another forty years almost
all firearms had their charges ignited by the detonation of
fulminate.

Doctor Forsyth liked hunting and fishing, and working
on mechanical and chemical problems. He knew that attempts were forever being made, in England and on the
Continent, to use a fulminating mixture in place of gunpowder in a gun barrel. In hunting waterfowl, Forsyth's
flintlock often missed birds that dived with the flash and

were safely submerged when the shot struck. He tried to conceal the flash with a hood over the lock, but he still missed. He then began a series of experiments, using fulminate not as a propellant but simply as a substitute for fine gunpowder in the pan of his flint gun. He learned that fulminate in an open pan would not be set off by sparks. When he tried igniting the fulminate with a light blow rather than by sparks he became convinced he was on the right track, but that he must have a lock that would confine the fulminate and direct its explosion through the touchhole. He made a successful lock in 1805 and fitted it to a fowling piece which he used for a season.

About a year later, Forsyth had the gun in London, where it was examined by Lord Moira, Master General of Ordnance. Lord Moira arranged that Forsyth should undertake further work leading to the development of a sturdy lock suitable for use on muskets.

Forsyth obtained leave of absence from the Aberdeen Presbytery and set up his headquarters in the Tower. Improved locks, for muskets and also for cannon, together with a dependable fulminate mixture, were produced under Forsyth's direction – and then Lord Moira was succeeded by John Pitt, second Earl of Chatham, as Master General of Ordnance. Lord Chatham was brother to William Pitt, the Prime Minister of England, but historians assert that he lacked the fine qualities of his brother, and was given to unwise decisions. He ordered Forsyth to take himself and all his "rubbish" from the Tower.

James Watt, the steam engine inventor, gave his valuable help in the drawing up of patent specifications, and Forsyth applied for a patent. British Patent No. 3,032 for the year 1807, always thereafter recognized by the high courts as a basic patent, was granted to Forsyth for his invention of percussion ignition.

With the great James Purdey as his gunsmith, Forsyth began the manufacture of guns fitted with his lock. The manufactory with Forsyth's name continued in business for some ten years after his death.

The first Forsyth detonators were fitted with what collectors call scent-bottle locks. The scent-bottle magazine was followed by the sliding magazine. Both locks kept fulminate confined and safe from damp, and allowed a single priming to be quickly deposited in the touchhole, where it would be detonated by the hammer's fall. In the first model, turning the scent-bottle served to prime for shot after shot; in the later models, priming was effected by sliding the magazine back and forth. Either magazine contained about forty primings.

After the percussion system was adopted by the British Army in 1839, the House of Commons belatedly made awards to Forsyth to acknowledge the importance of his invention. An award of £200 was paid to Forsyth himself; later, after his death, a further £1,000 was apportioned among three surviving relatives.

The significance, and even the fact, of Forsyth's invention, was then almost forgotten until 1929, when a group of collectors, historians and sportsmen, supported by military and gunsmith organizations, had a handsome memorial made. This was a fitting tribute, a bronze tablet placed in the Tower and inscribed as having been erected by admirers of Forsyth's genius.

Forsyth's invention had to do with muzzle-loaders; its principle was not applied to any extent to breechloaders until shortly before the appearance of modern metallic cartridges. (For accounts of such percussion breechloaders, see BREECHLOADERS and specific names.) But it is a fact that, only five years after Forsyth obtained his patent, Johannes Samuel Pauly invented, patented, and manufactured a workable breechloader firing a fully self-contained cartridge.

Once the practicability of the Forsyth invention became known, all the gunmakers in Europe were either copying or modifying the Forsyth lock – although they perhaps belittled it in public. The innovations, often adjudged infringements in England, were largely short-lived (except for the copper cap – which is quite another matter) but they deserve mention, albeit brief.

Some followers of Forsyth built locks with magazines to supply multiple primings, but for the most part the locks were without magazines and renewal of priming by hand was necessary at each shot.

The finest competitive guns built with magazines for fulminate may have been those produced by LePage of Paris. Detonators with magazines for priming were invented in England by Lieutenant Colonel Henry Shrapnel, Westley Richards, Joseph Egg, and others.

Perhaps the first successful competition to the Forsyth locks was provided by the patch locks. These single-priming locks, with fulminate in flattish cakes between pieces of waterproofed paper set on stubby nipples, were in use before metallic caps were devised.

Almost as early as patch locks were locks that had fulminate in pellets, varnished or waxed. Pellet-lock guns were developed throughout Europe, and in the United States where they were called punch locks.

Joseph Manton, "King of the Gunmakers," patented a pellet lock in 1816, and then, in 1818, an entirely different and more successful type of detonating lock. This, the tube lock, was to be widely used by other gunmakers in England and on the Continent. Manton's tube primer was a cylinder of thin copper, less than an inch long and of a pencil-lead's diameter, filled with fulminate. The hammer on an 1818 Manton gun struck across the middle of the tube, detonating the fulminate and giving sure ignition in all weather conditions.

In guns by a few makers, the tube was thrust into an oversize nipple and was detonated by a blow on its end.

Then there was the Sharps, whose priming was in an incredible two-piece metal wafer, and there were the Maynards and the Heurteloups which had hammers that moved long strips of fulminate on cocking and cut off small bits on descent. These last were all developed after the invention of the percussion cap, which came soon after the first patch-lock and pellet-lock guns.

The percussion cap which is pressed on a perforated cone for ignition is, as is the primer of today's guns, a short tube closed at one end and coated inside with fulminate.

The first patent for a copper cap was granted in France to Prélat, French patent no. 900 of July 29, 1818. Prélat was not its inventor; he was a copier of inventions of nationals of other countries. The invention was claimed for Durs Egg, Hawker, Purdey, Shaw and others.

Invention of the copper percussion cap opened the way to safe, dependable repeating firearms, until then always impracticable, and also spurred on the search for accuracy. Pepperboxes depending on caps for ignition, soon followed by revolvers, came into wide use within a score of years. With the transfer of the primer to a cartridge head, the development of repeating and self-loading arms came fast.   L.W.

Illustrations: page 41.

Barber, Edward C., *The Crack Shot*, New York, 1871.

Blackmore, Howard L., *British Military Firearms, 1650–1850*, London, 1961.

Blanch, H. J., *A Century of Guns*, London, 1909.

Busk, Hans, *The Rifle: And How to Use It*, London, 1860.

Cline, Walter M., *The Muzzle-Loading Rifle Then and Now*, Huntingdon, W.Va., 1942.

Deane, John, *Deane's Manual of the History and Science of Firearms*, London, 1858, and Huntingdon, W.Va., 1946.

George, John N., *English Guns and Rifles*, Plantersville, S.C., 1947.

Greener, William W., *The Gun and Its Development*, 9th edition, London, 1910.

Hawker, Colonel Peter, *Instructions to Young Sportsmen in all that relates to Guns and Shooting*, London, 1844.

Logan, Herschel C., *Hand Cannon to Automatic*, Huntingdon, W.Va., 1944.

McKee, Thomas Heron, *The Gun Book*, New York, 1918.

Marks, Edward C. R., *The Evolution of Modern Small Arms and Ammunition*, London, 1898.

Ommundsen, H., and Robinson, Ernest H., *Rifles and Ammunition and Rifle Shooting*, London and New York, 1915.

Peterson, Harold L., *The Treasury of the Gun*, New York, 1962 (*The Book of the Gun*, London, 1963).

Pollard, Captain H. B. C., *A History of Firearms*, London, 1926.

Roberts, Ned H., *The Muzzle-loading Cap Lock Rifle*, 3rd edition, Harrisburg, Pa., 1947.

Sawyer, Charles Winthrop, *Our Rifles*, Boston, Mass., 1920.

Tennent, Sir J. Emerson, *The Story of the Guns*, London, 1864.

Winant, Lewis, *Early Percussion Firearms*, New York, 1959, and London, 1961.

PETRONEL

A short firearm of medium caliber used in the sixteenth and seventeenth centuries, primarily by mounted soldiers; a carbine. From the French dialect *petrinal* "of the breast or chest," presumably a reference to its being held to the chest when shooting. In modern usage, a short gun with a sharply curved butt is denoted.   W.R.

PIGEON GUN

The shooting of pigeons released from traps, though of earlier origin, became popular in England about the year 1810. Each trap, of which there were five or more, consisted of a shallow box sunk in the ground with a sliding lid, the shooter being positioned between twenty-one and twenty-five yards distant. A cord attached to the lid of the box was held by an assistant, standing near, who released the bird on a signal from the shooter.

Pigeon shooting developed rapidly from a simple trial of shooting skill to a fashionable sport in which large sums of money were wagered. By 1820 special pigeon guns were being produced. Normal double-barreled sporting guns had been used at first, but the specialized pigeon gun differs from these, being usually single-barreled and of large bore, usually 10 but sometimes 8 bore or even larger. As heavy a charge as was consistent with accuracy and comfort was used, generally No. 4 shot. The guns are frequently not fitted with ramrods, a separate loading rod being used for the purpose.

A typical pigeon gun of about 1825 in the Armouries of the Tower of London has a 10-bore barrel $34\frac{1}{2}$ inches in length and weighs 7 lb. 7 oz. It is a finely made tube-lock by William Reavell of London. No ramrod is fitted, the short fore-end being capped with a silver scallop shell.

Tube locks gave very sure and quick ignition, and pigeon guns were frequently fitted with them for some years after the introduction of the normal percussion cap.

By 1860 the large-bore guns described above went out of fashion, and normal sporting guns took their place, although the charge tended to be heavier than those used in normal game shooting. Muzzle-loaders continued to be frequently used until well into the 1870's, as they were considered by many shooters to be harder hitting than breechloaders.

Pigeon shooting, though no longer permitted in Britain or America, continues as a sport in France and Spain. The guns used are sporting guns of normal type, although any form of magazine arm is usually discouraged.

A.N.K.

PILLAR BREECH

Pillar breech is a term often applied to the *à tige* muzzle-loading rifle system invented by Colonel Louis Étienne Thouvenin of France. It was characterized by a steel pillar fastened to the center of the breech plug and projecting into the bore. In loading, the powder filled the space around the pillar which protruded above the charge and provided an anvil against which the loose-fitting bullet could be flattened by heavy blows of the ramrod, until

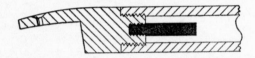

Cross section of pillar breech

it spread out and entered the grooves of the rifling. The pillar breech was adopted for the French service in the early 1840's and was copied for a short period in Great Britain as well as in other Continental countries. Inaccuracy resulting from the distortion of the bullet, and sometimes from a bent or broken pillar as well, caused the *à tige* system to be abandoned in favor of the expanding bullet systems of Minié, Burton and others for the rapid loading of muzzle-loading rifles.

H.L.P.

See also: CARABINE À TIGE; RIFLES AND RIFLING.

PILL LOCK

See: PRIMER.

PIN-FIRE

See: CARTRIDGE; LEFAUCHEUX.

PISTOL

The term pistol denotes a small firearm which can be held and fired with one hand. Several theories have been advanced concerning the origin of the word. Most prominent is one which suggests that the pistol originated in Italy and took its name from the city of Pistoia where it first became popular. Another argues in favor of a Bohemian origin, deriving the name from the word *pistala* which meant pipe or whistle; and there have been other suggested derivations.

Whatever the origin of the word, the pistol appeared soon after the development of the first effective wheel lock in the early sixteenth century. Until the invention of the wheel lock, such a weapon had been impractical. Matchlock pistols were made in Japan, but with the arguable exception of the breech-loading Italian gunshields of about 1545 in the Tower of London and a single matchlock revolver in Venice, no European matchlock pistol survives. Once it had appeared, however, the pistol quickly became the favored personal firearm of men of rank and mounted soldiers. By 1549, men-at-arms in the French Army carried a pair of pistols at their saddlebows and, singly or in pairs, pistols have remained throughout history the most popular firearm for cavalry. Although occasionally used for hunting, and very popular as a target weapon, the pistol has always been essentially a gun for close-quarter shooting – light, portable, fast to use, and accurate enough at short range for all practical purposes.

W.R.

See also: ALL-METAL ARMS; AUTOMATIC ARMS; BAR PISTOL; BREECHLOADERS; DAG; DERINGER PISTOL; DUELING PISTOL; FLARE PISTOL; LIBERATOR PISTOL; LUGER PISTOL; PALM PISTOL; PEPPERBOX; REPEATING ARMS; REVOLVER; SUICIDE SPECIAL.

PLAIN RIFLE AND PLAINS RIFLE

"Plain rifle" was the descriptive designation used by gunmakers and gundealers of the nineteenth century for muzzle-loading rifles made without embellishments or refinements. The quality of plain rifles is illustrated by the following quotation from a catalogue published by the Great Western Gun Works of Pittsburgh, Pennsylvania, in the 1870's: "We do not warrant the plain rifles as being very fine or accurate long-range shooters. They are good, plain, durable guns, and for many purposes will do as well as could reasonably be expected for the price." The catalogue offered plain rifles for all purposes with bores from 50 gauge to 200 gauge (.46 to .29 caliber) and with barrels from 30 to 40 inches long.

"Plains rifle," on the other hand, is a generic term for muzzle-loading rifles made expressly for use on the plains of the western United States during the approximate period 1800–1875. It is not a contemporary term, and is

Plate 5

Pair of flintlock saddle pistols made by Les La Roche in
the Galleries of the Louvre for Louis XV, King of France.
These pistols rank among the most richly decorated ever
made. The barrels are divided into two parts, that towards
the breech being chiseled with mythological subjects
against a gold ground, while that towards the muzzle is
encrusted with figures in chased gold against a brightly
blued ground. The steel mounts are chiseled in unusually
high relief with subjects from classical mythology and the
walnut stock is carved and inlaid with gold wire, incorporating the cipher of Louis XV. Their maker was Jean
Baptiste La Roche, *Arquebusier du Roi*, assisted by his son.
French, *ca.*1760.

Victoria and Albert Museum, London.

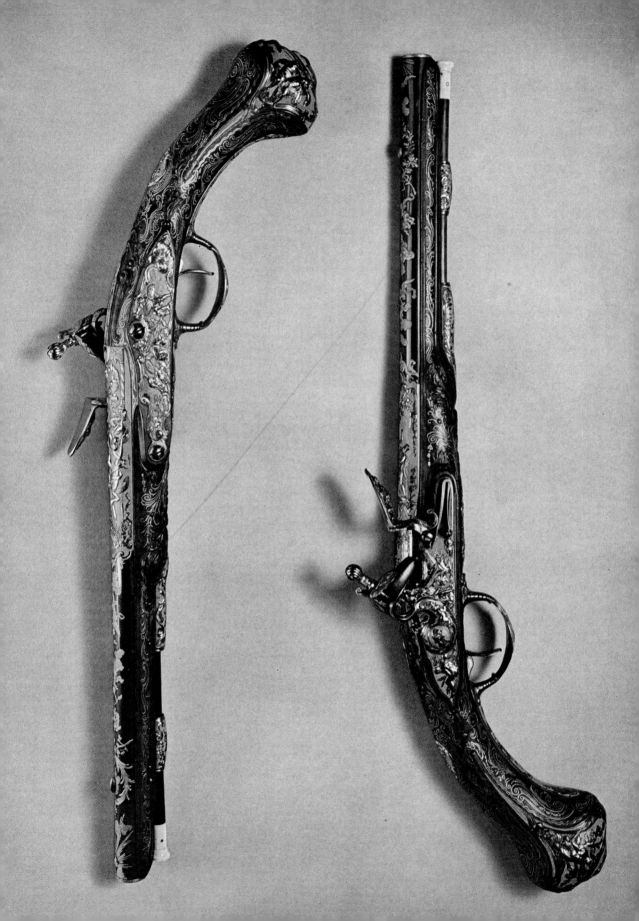

believed to have been originated by American arms collectors in the twentieth century. Contemporary writers usually referred to these rifles as Mountain Rifles or Hawkins Rifles; less frequently they were called Missouri Rifles or Buffalo Rifles.

Most of the plains rifles were made in St. Louis, Missouri. They were adapted from the long-barreled flintlock Kentucky rifles developed during the eighteenth century in Pennsylvania and carried to the American frontier in great numbers after 1800. As exploration and settlement progressed in the prairie regions beyond the Appalachian Mountains, riflesmiths began modifying the basic Kentucky design to provide shorter rifles for mounted use, with larger bores and heavier barrels for powerful long-range loads. Many of the early nineteenth-century flintlock rifles made by Tennessee and Kentucky gunsmiths show varying degrees of such adaptation, but the real development of a new and distinctive design was the work of Jacob and Samuel Hawken of St. Louis in the period 1820–30.

The Hawkens were brothers, and sons of Christian Hawken, a skilled maker of Kentucky rifles at Hagerstown, Maryland. Jacob was born in Hagerstown in 1783 and is believed to have opened a shop in St. Louis around 1815. Samuel was born in Hagerstown in 1796. After spending a few years at Xenia, Ohio, he moved to St. Louis and became Jacob's partner in 1822. Until Jacob's death in 1849, the firm was known as J. & S. Hawken. Samuel continued to operate the business alone until 1862, stamping his products "S. Hawken, St. Louis."

At the height of their popularity on the American frontier, the rifles made by J. & S. Hawken were the most widely accepted and most typical plains rifles. The first models were flintlocks, but percussion models appeared very early. Stocks were of plain hard maple stained very dark and fitted with oval cheekpieces. The octagon barrels were one inch or slightly more in thickness with rifled bores of .50 to .54 caliber, having a very slow twist. All furniture was iron, including flat barrel wedges, forestock tips, Kentucky-style butt plates, and scrolled iron trigger guards made in integral units with double-set triggers. Patch boxes and ornamental inlays were seldom used. Breech tangs were made long and strong to reinforce the wrist of the stock. Percussion models generally had nipple lugs welded on the barrel which seated into a semicircular cut in the top edge of a typical American percussion side lock. The average barrel length was 36–38 inches. Later rifles were often of the half-stocked style with two flat barrel wedges and a ramrod rib under the barrel. A few Hawken rifles with fancy patchboxes were made on special order, and Samuel Hawken made a few rifles with the full patent type of breech, which permitted the barrel to be hooked into a recessed breech iron held to the stock by screws. All Hawken rifles were made full and strong in every part. Average weight varied from nine to fourteen pounds.

These guns shot a half-ounce patched round ball with charges ranging from 75 to 200 grains of coarse black powder. The trajectory was very flat for muzzle-loaders and the high velocities attainable made these guns very desirable for buffalo hunting and Indian fighting. The accurate and effective range exceeded 200 yards. The Hawkens supplied their rifles to General Ashley's Rocky Mountain Fur Company and to thousands of free trappers. On the western frontier "Hawkins rifle" eventually became a popular term for any heavy, long-range hunting rifle.

Samuel Hawken went to Denver in 1859 for his health and kept a gunshop there for two years. His son, William Stewart Hawken, was both a trapper and a gunsmith and also worked in Denver for a time. J. P. Gemmer, a Hawken foreman, bought the St. Louis shop when Samuel retired in 1862 and continued to operate the business until 1915.

The Hawkens had little competition in St. Louis during the period of the profitable beaver trade from the Rocky Mountains. Plains rifles were made on a small scale during the 1840–48 period by Tristram Campbell, who often worked for the Hawkens; by Frederick Hellinghaus, who moved to California about 1848; by Reno Beauvais, a St. Louis jeweler whose family worked in the Indian trade; and by T. J. Albright, who became a prominent sporting goods dealer.

Horace E. Dimick established a gunshop in St. Louis in 1849, and his heavy iron-mounted plains rifles attained a good degree of popularity with frontier scouts and hunters. Dimick rifles were made in many patterns, but the plains types generally had walnut half-stocks, percussion locks, heavy barrels of .50 to .60 caliber and iron furniture including a spur-type trigger guard and separate double-set trigger. Barrels were fastened to the stocks with two flat wedges with German-silver escutcheons. From 1849 until 1864 the firm was known as H. E. Dimick & Company; from 1865 until Dimick's death in 1873, his guns were simply marked "H. E. Dimick, St. Louis."

Gunmaking in St. Louis experienced a business boom when the gold rush to Colorado began in 1859. The new makers of plains rifles during the period 1860–70 included Adolphus Meier, Meyer Friede, Frederick Schwarz, Thomas Gibbons, Henry Folsom and John Blickensdorfer. Plains rifles by these makers were usually of .54 caliber, half-stocked, mounted in iron or brass, and generally similar in style to those made by S. Hawken and H. E. Dimick.

Pennsylvania riflemakers offered strong competition to the St. Louis makers of plains rifles, but the majority of the eastern guns were sold to Indian traders and the smaller hardware dealers. The firm of Tryon in Philadelphia supplied heavy flintlock "Indian rifles" of plains style to the United States government in the 1850's and also to the great St. Louis trading firm of Pierre Chouteau Jr. & Co. In the period 1860–75, James Henry & Son sold many heavy iron-mounted halfstocks to western traders and dealers. Henry rifles varied in caliber from .44 to .60 and were stocked in walnut with locks and breeches similar to those used on the British Enfield rifles of the period. However, the great majority of the plains rifles made in Pennsylvania were produced by Henry E. Leman of Lancaster. Until about 1875, he furnished large quantities of plain heavy flintlock and percussion Indian rifles to Indian agents, independent outfitters and such important trading firms as Pierre Chouteau Jr. & Co. and Robert Campbell & Co. The typical Leman rifles had heavy octagonal barrels 32 to 38 inches long, calibers from .50 to .65, artificially striped maple stocks, single triggers, plain brass fittings and distinctive brass cap boxes with finials in iris design. The locks were of Leman manufacture with rolled engraving and squared tails.

Many less prolific riflesmiths made plains rifles on the frontier. Notable examples are the heavy hunting rifles made for scouts and Indians by Carlos Gove, John P. Lower and Morgan Rood in Denver, Colorado, during the 1860's, and the fancy German-silver mounted halfstocks made in the 1845–60 period by Stephen O'Dell in Natchez, Mississippi, Other known plains rifle makers include Benjamin Mills, Harrodsburg, Kentucky; Josh Griffith, Louisville, Kentucky; H. A. Lyon, Sioux City, Iowa; M. Wallerich, Independence, Missouri; and Jasper Adalmon Maltby, Galena, Illinois (period 1850–60).

After the Civil War, heavy, powerful, single-shot Sharps and Remington rifles using center-fire cartridges soon took the place of muzzle-loaders for buffalo shooting, and Winchester and Spencer rim-fire repeaters became the popular light rifles. By 1875 the few plains rifles still in use were nearly all in the hands of hostile Indians. Ten years later the muzzle-loading rifle had been virtually abandoned in western America.　　　　　C.E.H.

Illustration: page 106.

Hanson, Charles E., Jr., *The Plains Rifle*, Harrisburg, Pa., 1960.

Russell, Carl P., *Guns on the Early Frontiers*, London, and Berkeley and Los Angeles, Cal., 1957.

POPINJAY

A popinjay is a figure of a bird, often a parrot, set on a pole as a mark to shoot at. Homer described a white dove fastened to the top of a ship's mast as a target for the archers of Achilles.

From a live or modeled pigeon-sized bird set on a mast, a church tower or a high pole, the popinjay's size evolved to both larger and smaller forms. The targets shot at by the shooting guilds of Dresden and other cities were sometimes as big as 13 feet by 8 feet, occasionally made in the form of an imperial eagle. The bird was shot at with crossbows or large-bore rifles. The flat wooden bird was made of numerous pieces of various shapes and sizes, each with its value. The shooter's score depended on the total points of the pieces he shot off. It is thought that very heavy, long-barreled, wheel lock rifles of good quality were used for this highly specialized sport in the seventeenth century. The weight of the rifle meant that it had to be supported. Some have trunnions fitted to make them steadier when held in a rest.

At the other end of the scale are the little brass birds shot at to this day by Belgian crossbow clubs. These tiny targets, not much bigger than a man's finger-joint, are raised on a pole 55 metres high and shot at with very heavy crossbows using blunt bolts.

The form of the seventeenth-century popinjay is perpetuated in a number of charming prize collars. From the collar hung a silver popinjay to which each year's winner added a tiny gun or crossbow of the same metal.　　　W.R.

PORTE TACHE

A porte tache, or flask carrier, was a strap designed to carry a powder flask and a bullet pouch, and sometimes a spanner for wheel locks. Normally this strap was attached to the waist belt on the right side and hung straight down. It was most popular during the late years of the sixteenth century and the opening years of the seventeenth.　　　H.L.P.

POTTET, CLEMENT

Clement Pottet invented a breech-loading arm with a cartridge, for which he received a French patent in 1829. The cartridge had a removable base with a pocket for a detonating mixture, usually fulminate of mercury. It did not have its gas seal formed as do modern cartridges, by expansion of a thin metal case. Rather, it had a base made like a stopper, ground to fit the breech of the gun. This system was not very popular and had a short life.

However, Pottet obtained another patent in 1855. This was of lasting importance, being the immediate ancestor of the modern shotgun shell. In fact, there have been few important changes in the shot shell since Pottet's invention. His cartridge had a base made like a short metallic cartridge case – a thin metal cup with a rolled edge. This cup had a center recess at the back to receive a percussion

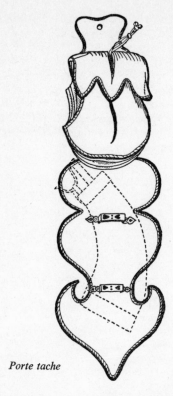

Porte tache

cap. A cylindrical tube of paper was inserted into the base and held in place by a tight-fitting wad pushed down inside. The cap cavity contained a small anvil, shaped like a tiny shield, against which the primer or cap was fired by a blow from the hammer.

G. H. Daw obtained a British patent in 1861 which covered a shotgun cartridge. This has been considered by many as the first modern shot shell, but it differed from Pottet's only in the shape of the anvil in the primer pocket. The first metallic-cartridge breechloader used by the British government – the Snider, caliber .577 – used the Pottet cartridge head in its first type of ammunition, the Mark 1.   B.R.L.

Winant, Lewis, *Early Percussion Firearms*, New York, 1959, and London, 1961.

See also: CARTRIDGE; FOWLING PIECE.

POWDER FLASK AND
POWDER HORN

The powder flask in its most comprehensive definition may be considered as any receptacle or container that may be advantageously adapted to carry powder for use in priming or charging any firearm. The flask was not indigenous to any nation, state, or community. Its progressive development in its myriad forms was the result of the use of suitable and available materials and the skill of the maker to satisfy the requirements of use. The date and character of the first container of powder is lost in antiquity, but it may properly be assumed that it originated in some crude form with the advent of the use of gunpowder as a propellant. Undoubtedly the first containers were of generous and bulky proportions to supply the large charges for cannon or for priming. As to form, one may only speculate that the powder was first carried in a wooden cask, a bag made of hide, a package of sorts, or in large purse-like leather pouches.

True powder flasks made their appearance during the early part of the fifteenth century, and were principally for charging and priming hand and shoulder weapons. The size was varied according to the desire of the maker and user, and flasks were rarely identical in form, finish, or workmanship. Each was made by an individual craftsman from readily obtained materials such as gourds, roots, and tusks, bones or horns of animals. Those flasks made from the horns of animals were closed at the bottom with hide, wood, or other material, and frequently the roundness of the natural horn was distorted to present a rectangular section. A simple plug of bone or wood was used as a stopper at the outlet or nozzle end.

In the early part of the sixteenth century gradual improvements in the closing and opening of the nozzle began to appear with a simple mechanical addition to the existing types. This mechanical improvement primarily supplied a convenient means of closing the nozzle with a spring-operated cap at its end. Then followed a second type of closure: a spring-pivoted gate at the base of the nozzle or at the top of the body of the flask. This method of closure in effect was used throughout the existence of the powder flask. Finally the two systems of closure, the spring-actuated cap at the nozzle and the spring cut-off at the base of the nozzle, were used in concert. The consideration of obtaining a fixed charge undoubtedly brought this last combination into existence. This same basic principle was later used by Hawksley and other nineteenth century makers, and in G. & J. Hawksley's catalogue specimens featuring this principle of double closures were advertised "to insure accuracy of charge" – this coming three hundred years after the appearance of the system on the early flasks.

Basically, the powder flask had now progressed to satisfactory shapes of large and small containers for carrying, respectively, the loading charges and the priming charges. Its use in either size was confined to hand and shoulder arms, with only exceptional use for priming cannon. From the last half of the sixteenth century through the seventeenth and eighteenth centuries, mechanical innovations were relatively few; but the forms, the materials, and the character of decoration gave full play to the talents of craftsmen, artists, armorers, soldiers, hunters, and tinkerers.

It is through these years that the magnificently carved, sculptured, jeweled, inlaid and curiously wrought body designs reflect the high point of art and skill. These centuries have given to collectors the prize gems in a galaxy

of materials and treatment: carved antlers and wood, hard leather, pearl inlays, silver niello, ormolu, precious metals in filigreed overlays, carved ivory and bejeweled surfaces, tusks, tortoiseshell, and Damascus steel with gilt inlay. The artistic accomplishments of artisans and artists of many nations have left a record through this period of personal achievement in creating flasks for royalty, for élite troops, for wealthy sportsmen, and for military figures of prominence. These collectors' treasures, embellished with silk and woven cords and tassels, created to some

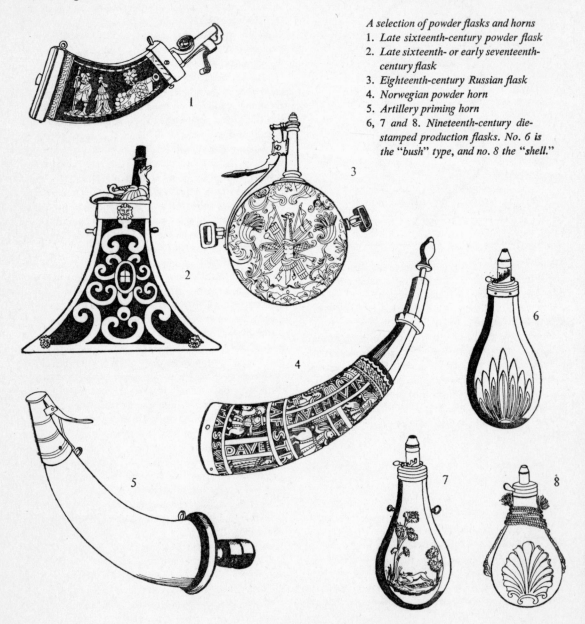

A selection of powder flasks and horns
1. *Late sixteenth-century powder flask*
2. *Late sixteenth- or early seventeenth-century flask*
3. *Eighteenth-century Russian flask*
4. *Norwegian powder horn*
5. *Artillery priming horn*
6, 7 and 8. *Nineteenth-century die-stamped production flasks. No. 6 is the "bush" type, and no. 8 the "shell."*

degree a status symbol. Many of these exceptionally lavish products were used on formal and state occasions and only rarely in dispensing powder in combat or in the hunting field. These rarities of the collector's world are most frequently found today in the important museums, and only occasionally in private collections.

Paradoxically, the simple, easily obtained, and waterproof cow horn with its core removed, closed at the bottom with wood or other substance, and with a plug at the nozzle, became the standard form of powder flask for hunters and the military in England, on the Continent, and in America early in the eighteenth century. The well used and meaningful work flask of cow horn was frequently engraved with fanciful designs, maps, battle actions, ships, and scenes touching upon the home life of the user. Many of these somewhat commonplace horns, plain or decorated, were laid aside as family heirlooms, later to become collectors' prizes.

The die-stamped metal flasks most generally known to the collectors of today began to make their appearance about the beginning of the nineteenth century. It is interesting to note that the catalogue of Thomas Sykes of Sheffield and London, ca.1800, exhibits some flasks made of horn with turned wood bases and metal measuring tops, listed for "Military-Light Infantry." Undoubtedly the first of these nineteenth century flasks, of horn and/or metal, were supplied to the American market by British makers for the military as well as the hunter. The British makers of horn ink pots and metal workers were admirably equipped to make the flasks throughout the nineteenth century, and it was by these makers that impetus was given to a rapidly growing but short lived specialty. Although James Dixon and Sons was certainly not the first of the production makers, the firm is believed to have been the earliest actively to solicit business from the American government, as early as the 1830's, and it is also recorded that the firm awaited contracts not only from the military but also from the civilian trade. Peter Frith and Sons, G. & J. Hawksley, and Thomas Sykes, the latter being the original patentee of the so-called patent top for flasks (August 4, 1814, No. 3,828), were all well known not only throughout the British Isles but also in America and on the Continent. The principal French makers were Caron, Boche, and Gosset. The beginning date of American production may be said to be about the middle of the nineteenth century. The two names standing out most prominently among these production makers in America are the American Cap and Flask Company and John Matthewman.

The material of these flasks was most frequently brass or copper, but a number of styles were made in zinc and tin, with comparatively few produced in pewter. The finer flasks often made for fine-cased sporting weapons or pairs of pistols were occasionally executed in sterling silver. The Dixon firm was particularly skilful in making individual flasks by casting them in silver in high relief and finishing them by hand. Flasks were at times covered with pigskin or morocco leather. The ardent hunter welcomed the use of the leather-covered metal flask for a number of reasons: it did not rattle in the pocket to alert game, and it was comfortable to handle on frosty mornings in the field. In regular use it did not show scratches or tarnish, nor did it take on the shabbiness of a metal flask that was used from day to day. Collectors will infrequently find flasks made entirely of leather, but these are, nearly always, shot flasks and should not be considered as true powder flasks.

The flasks of copper, brass, and even those of tin were most frequently treated with lacquer and attractively brought to a fine finish. These finishes were somewhat distinctive, and the expert collector, from long association with flasks, is often able to detect the finishes peculiar to various makers. Hawksley and Dixon excelled in their very beautiful lacquer finishes on ordinary flasks of first quality. The range of colors in these lacquers ran from light browns through the russets and dark browns and into the very deep purplish browns.

The sizes of the flasks varied from the very small ones that would hold a single charge for a dainty muff pistol or a slightly larger flask for priming, or for more generously charging small pistols, through an increasing range of sizes for pistols, rifles and shotguns. On these flasks there was a variety of chargers: the fixed charger, the common or fast top charger, the screw-off charger, and a great many innovations down to the French plunger types known as self-charging. These latter were infrequently copied by American makers.

The nineteenth-century flasks were not often fashioned of unusual materials, except perhaps the tribal flasks of Africa, those of the islands of the South Seas, and of Japan. Flasks from these faraway places were of course seldom of a production nature, but were made from various exotic materials such as sea shells, the stomachs of camels, and large nuts, often brilliantly painted with significant symbols and designs, all to the taste and desire of the individual maker.

In the regular grade of flasks and those of better grade, britannia metal was frequently used for the tops and chargers, and this material appeared to be one of the best that existed throughout the nineteenth century for the purpose at hand. It was used most frequently in the flasks made in England; American manufacturers used it only occasionally in their best quality flasks. Notwithstanding the rather limited materials of the principal nineteenth-century flasks, the tremendous variety of decoration and subtle differences in contour of these are worthy of the collector's most careful attention and study. Unquestionably these many variations in form and decoration were primarily brought about by active competition between producers at home and abroad seeking to win the favor and patronage of shooter and hunter.

The metal powder flasks of the last century should be seriously considered as to their variations in purpose, in function, in form, and in decorative treatment. In order to interest the most casual reader in this very broad field and especially to guide the serious collector in his desire for specialization, arbitrary groups or classifications, with pertinent comments and brief explanations, are listed as follows.

Plain. Those which carry no decoration on their surface and whose most intriguing attributes are the nuances of form.

Fluted and Beaded. Displaying flutings and/or beading accents vertically covering the body of the flask.

Shell and Bush. Decorated by a stylized form of shell or bush as a sole or major embellishment.

Overall. On which the designs, in repetitive application, cover the entire surface of the body. The decoration presents wicker and woven basket effects, stars and circled dots, rope mesh, lozenges or diamonds, fleur-de-lis, etc.

Panel. Containing a sole central motif, or one complemented subordinately by a border or surrounding decoration. Among these would be included representations of single pistols, figures, stylized and geometrical designs, or allegorical subjects.

Oak Leaf. In which the leaf and acorn is prominently presented in part as a border or background or in complete surface coverage.

Dead Game. Whereon are depicted trophies of the hunt, both fowl and animals of the field, hanging singly or in groups.

Foliage. Those showing the use of the bud, flower, leaf, stem, and tendril as decorative elements.

Medallion. Including the flasks with an applied central motif as well as those having a central shield or medal-like design impressed in the body. Either type generally features portraits, figures, or scenes.

Bird. These display principally or in subordinate detail one or more birds other than the eagle, namely, a variety of game birds, falcon, peacock, stork, etc.

Eagle. The American national bird used in successful and popular design by the makers in the United States and abroad to attract the American user.

Colt. These should be of absolute Colt revolver association, either bearing the name of Colt in some form or being clearly identified in their use with Colt arms.

Sloping Charger. Specimens of this group could, by reason of decorative design, fall into other appropriate classifications, but the unusual collector interest in the sloping charger makes it advisable to keep them within a special category.

Martial. Made for and by the United States, and made by other governments for the use of army, navy, and militia. The rare Hall rifle flask falls within this group.

Dog and Hunter. On these appear decorations either of dogs, hunters, or both, as a main pictorial element.

Deer. Deer, elk, stag or other similar antlered game of the family *cervidae* are mainly featured.

Horse and Other Animals. Representations of the horse, buffalo, lion, boar, bear, fox, monkey, and squirrel being prominent in detail.

Leather Covered. An interestingly wide range, particularly of pocket flasks in varying forms, combine in this category.

Horn. Includes divers forms, charging arrangements, sizes and sorts, that have bodies of natural horn or of a transparent nature bearing the archaic name of lanthorn horn. Many of these lanthorn horn flasks were skilfully embossed with scenes and occasionally were inlaid with silver and pearl.

Materials. Flasks of bearskin, die-pressed rawhide, tortoiseshell, hard rubber compounds or caoutchouc and many other materials deviating from the norm.

Shapes. These would include the entwined dolphin forms, the "gunstock," the violin shapes, and all of the curiously irregular contours.

Charging Variations. The Austrian side arm graduated plunger charger, the self chargers, the double chargers, combination cappers and flasks, and the many unusual and special arrangements for measuring and charging.

Modern. Those of recent manufacture made in comparatively small quantities to suit the requirements of present day muzzle-loading enthusiasts. These have rarely been made on a significant production basis and are frequently "tinkered" to suit individual requirements. Perhaps the originals, unaltered, may prove to be an interesting collecting entity in the not too distant future. The facsimiles and reproductions of Dixon of England made from the recently found old dies could properly be included in this category, as should the reproductions made by a few of the American manufacturers.

Caveat Emptor. A collector's catch-all for fakes, re-works, or improvisations. To include flasks that are purposely made to deceive or to suit the whim of the thoughtless collector. In this group should be included those flasks that are made of parts from other flasks and that cannot be considered as homogeneous.

With the résumé of classifications of the last but most fertile period of the powder flasks, the milestones of a transitory product have been passed and concisely reviewed. Rapid technical advances have long since brought the self-contained cartridge into universal use, so that the powder flask is today of historical interest only.   R.R.

Illustration: page 270.

Grancsay, Stephen V., *American Engraved Powder Horns, a study based on the J. H. Grenville Gilbert Collection*, New York, 1945.

Lucas, Fred. W., *Appendiculae Historicae, or, Shreds of History Hung on a Horn*, London, 1891.

Riling, Ray, *The Powder Flask Book*, New Hope, Penn., 1953.

Stone, George Cameron, *A Glossary of the Construction, Decoration and Use of Arms and Armor in All Countries and in All Times together with some Closely Related Subjects*, Portland, Me., 1934.

See also: SCOTTISH FIREARMS.

POWDER HORN

See: POWDER FLASK.

POWDER TESTER

All powder testers made use of the same fundamental principle. That is, to cause a given amount of powder to do work, and measure the result, which could then be compared with the results of the tests of other lots of powder in the same tester. Three designs were basic, and had wide use. These were elaborated into many variations, the earlier testers being simple, and later ones more sophisticated.

Most popular of all was the disc, or wheel, operating against a resistance, usually a spring. Second was the vertical ratchet, in which the explosion of the powder raises a weight. And last was the V-spring, or quadrant, in which the force of the detonation compresses a spring. All of these will be examined in more detail later on.

The need to know the strength of a lot of powder was a matter of prime importance. There was little or no knowledge of the importance of the purity of the ingredi-ents, and the resultingly poor product was often made even worse by deliberate adulteration. Coal dust was often used, which is almost inert under such conditions, and difficult to detect. Impure chemicals usually meant the presence of chlorides instead of chlorates. Chlorides absorb moisture from the air; the difficulty of keeping common salt (sodium chloride) dry in humid weather is known to everyone.

A gun left loaded overnight with poor powder would almost certainly miss fire on a damp morning, with all the attendant trouble of having to draw the charge, clear the pan and touchhole, and start again. And in the face of an enemy, or out hunting, this was not always possible. A device to measure the merit of a sample of powder was, therefore, a most valuable accessory.

The first mention of a powder tester in print seems to be by William Bourne, in his *Inventions and Devices very Necessary for all Generalles and Captaines* (London, 1587), and it appears that the device was known and in use at that time.

Other early references are by Joseph Furttenbach, in *Halinitro-Pyrobolia* (Ulm, 1627), and, perhaps the best known, Surirey de Saint-Rémy's *Mémoires d'Artillerie* (Paris, 1697). Saint-Rémy's remarks are so widely known and have been so often quoted that he has even been given credit for the invention of the powder tester.

The military, dealing with the need for larger charges for cannon, used test mortars, first devised by the English gunner, Nye, in 1647. These are outside the scope of this article, but there is a fine one at the entrance to the Birmingham Gun Barrel Proof House, and a very fine series of these mortars at the Tøjhusmuseet, Copenhagen, which can be consulted by those interested. The French, in an ordinance dated September 18, 1686, published a regulation stating that a three-ounce sample of powder must cast a sixty-pound ball from a government test mortar a distance of at least 50 *toises* (320 feet), and enforcement of this regulation secured for the French an enviable reputation, in the late seventeenth and eighteenth centuries, for the quality of their powder.

Among the earlier testers encountered are simple types, with what we refer to today as "match" ignition. Probably they were originally ignited with a coal or hot wire, although the slow match, of course, was in common use. These date from the late seventeenth to early eighteenth centuries. The English style was often referred to as the "Queen Anne" type. French examples of the same period differ only in details. Many French match testers exist in which the barrel is vertical, and the disc is mounted above the base plate, between the barrel and the handle. Both these types were readily portable, reasonably accurate and convenient to use.

The ease of handling pistol-like testers brought many

with more sophisticated ignition systems, such as the snaphance, and of course it was to be expected that the Spanish would use the miquelet. The French preferred the true flintlock. This design saw very wide use over a large part of the eighteenth century. There are many interesting variations, such as a reversed tester mechanism, and all-metal construction.

A design of which many were made was the covered wheel. These are found in both match and flintlock ignition forms, and this pattern also formed the basis for one of the most successful combinations.

Danish, French, German and Italian pieces may be identified from signatures, usually on the lock plate, although occasionally the wheel is also inscribed, and, of course, there are many others, not signed or otherwise marked, which are difficult to assign to any specific country of origin. Perhaps it is best, in such cases, merely to say "European."

As an interesting footnote, so far as the writer's research has extended, the only authenticated American powder tester is Mexican (in the Southwest Museum, Los Angeles). There are no known Russian or Oriental testers, and the only Scottish testers seem to be of English (Birmingham) origin. Apparently the Scottish smiths who produced the lovely all-metal pistols so highly prized by collectors made no testers, but were content to import them.

The popularity of the box lock in the later part of the eighteenth and early nineteenth centuries brought many testers built with this construction. These are the ones most frequently found of all, in both flint and percussion forms. So many examples are so nearly identical that it seems probable that the Birmingham gunmakers furnished parts to gunsmiths through the length and breadth of the British Isles, which were then finished up, and signed as the work of the local smith. Many of these are of brass. The earlier examples of the box lock tester used an external resistance spring, but nineteenth-century English testers of this type were often made with an internal resistance, a coil spring inside the disc, which was made thicker in order to accommodate the necessary cavity. The Liège makers, as might be expected, produced their own very similar versions of the box lock testers, often of iron, in both flint and percussion forms, types that were very popular on the Continent.

In addition to the readily portable pistol-type testers already described, others, also using the disc, were made, designed to be used while resting on a work bench or table. A Swiss tester of the seventeenth century has its index in roman numerals. And while many testers were plain and workmanlike, some were quite ornate.

By far the greatest number of powder testers were those that used the registering wheel or disc, but this method was by no means the only possible solution to the problem. The earliest tester extant is a vertical ratchet type, at the Kunsthistorisches Museum, Vienna. It was illustrated in Wendelin Boeheim's *Handbuch der Waffenkunde* (Berlin, 1890), and there are a number of variations on this theme, such as the magnificent bronze Italian match-type tester at the Metropolitan Museum of Art, New York, which is regarded as dating from the seventeenth century. A modification of the same construction with flintlock ignition is mounted on a pistol stock with ivory butt plate. This fine specimen is Dutch, also seventeenth-century, and is signed with the maker's initials on the interior of the lock plate.

The third tester system that saw extensive use was the "V-spring," or quadrant, form. These are found in all three ignition systems: match, flint and percussion, although the V-spring type dates from the late eighteenth century to the middle of the nineteenth. The coming of the percussion era did not do much to ameliorate the problem of powder quality, which was not really solved until nearly the middle of the century, and we find powder testers being made as late as 1855, the latest known example being of V-spring form.

Many of the flint and percussion examples came from the shop of Guillaume Berleur, of Liège. Some are signed, while others carry inscriptions such as "Eprouvette de la Poudre," while still others, obviously from the same hand, are unmarked. Characteristic of Berleur's careful workmanship is the index, which runs from one to eighty, with the fifth and tenth divisions neatly marked with arrow points.

In addition to the testers designed solely for testing, there are also combinations; that is, the powder tester combined with some other accessory. These are, without question, the rarest of all, and surviving examples are few. The largest group of these are the combinations of match-type testers, wheel lock spanners and adjustable powder measures that were used in the seventeenth century. This design is an adaptation of the covered wheel. Many of the larger national collections in Europe have examples of this combination. There is a good series at the Tøjhusmuseet, Copenhagen; others at the Generaal Hoefer Museum, Leiden; and a number at the Carolino-Augusteum, Salzburg. Most of these are so very similar it seems possible that they all originated in the same shop, although diverse national origins are claimed for them. Again, it may be that they were developed independently at a number of places at much the same time, but this seems unlikely.

Very similar in all respects is the same type of match tester, with adjustable powder-measure handle, simply omitting the spanner shank. These probably followed right after the preceding group, since the wheel lock, which required the spanner, was largely superseded by other lock forms by the end of the seventeenth century.

Another practical combination is that of the powder tester and tinder lighter.

The pieces chosen to illustrate this chapter are all of the more widely used types. It would be possible to go on at considerable length, describing and picturing more of the many ingenious devices that have been developed to help gauge the merit of gunpowder, but such detail is beyond the scope of a brief general survey.   P.J.W.

Illustrations: pages 345–7.

Wolf, Paul J., "Powder Testers at the Royal Ontario Museum" in *Journal of the Ontario Arms Collectors' Association*, Vol. 1, No. 1, Toronto, Ontario, June 1957.

Wolf, Paul J., "Some Segalas Variations" in *Journal of the Arms and Armour Society*, Vol. 3, No. 8, London, December 1960.

Wolf, Paul J., four articles on powder testers in *The American Arms Collector*, Towson, Md.: "Those most frequently found," January 1958; "More Testers Using the Disc," April 1958; "Those not Using the Disc," July 1958; and "The Combinations," October 1958.

PRIMER

In 1807, Alexander John Forsyth patented a means of using detonating mixtures for igniting gunpowder. Before that, firearms had been discharged either by applying flame or a hot iron directly to the charge, or by causing sparks from flint or pyrites and steel to ignite a supplemental charge in a separate pan, which then communicated the flame to the chamber. Forsyth's detonating composition was used in bulk, a small portion being measured out mechanically, then confined in the pan till struck and detonated.

Soon after Forsyth's development, other gunmakers, mainly in England, began to devise means of incorporating the detonating mixture into small unit containers for convenience in applying to the gun and to avoid the considerable hazard inherent in handling such materials in bulk. These devices were the beginning of the modern primer. One of the first forms was the patch, a little wafer of composition held in a striker which was placed in the hammer nose. Patch locks were commonly applied to shotguns. They worked well but were not water resistant.

Joseph Manton patented a pill lock in 1816, which used a small pellet of priming material. This was placed in a corresponding recess in the lock, where it was struck by a plug fastened to the nose of the hammer. Though such locks were not much used in England, they were extensively employed in the United States, where Dr. Samuel

Guthrie claimed to have invented them, after about 1830. Often called punch locks, they were used on pistols, revolvers, and both single-shot and revolving rifles. The tiny pills were usually coated with a metallic foil to make them water resistant. J. Miller and William Billinghurst were noted makers of cylinder rifles using such ignition.

Manton, Westley Richards, and others, produced locks using a tiny metal tube to hold the fulminate. Guns using these were called detonators or tube locks. Manton's detonator patent was dated 1818. From that date, almost every prominent gunsmith in England and many on the Continent worked on some system of percussion ignition, either for converting existing flintlock guns or for use on new ones. Ideas were pirated, the patentee often not the actual inventor. Conflicting claims were made, then as now hard to unravel.

The tube lock was still being used as late as 1860. The last of this type of ignition to be made in quantity was the Consol system as used by Austria to convert flintlock muskets and pistols. These enclosed the primer tube in a little metal box with a loose striker on the lid. This was struck by the hammer. The tube itself differed from others in having a small wire attached for handling.

The ignition device commonly called a percussion cap had its beginning around 1816 and is still being made in approximately its original form. This is simply a small copper cup, the larger musket size having a flange, which makes it resemble a miniature top hat. This cap, which has priming composition inside, is placed on a perforated projection from the breech, which has been called a chimney, a cone, or, more generally, a nipple. It seems likely that both nipple and cap were British inventions of about 1816, but the first known patent is Prélat's, in France, in 1818. Joshua Shaw was granted a United States patent in 1822, although he maintained that he first had the idea in 1814, but other Englishmen also claimed the idea as their own – among them Durs Egg, Hawker, Purdey, and Manton. Shaw developed some of the first machines for making caps and supervised their installation at the Frankford Arsenal in Philadelphia.

There were other primer systems as well, some of them widely used. Edward Maynard invented a magazine capping system, which was standard for all United States service small arms from 1855 to 1861. He placed a row of fulminate pellets in a tape formed by two strips of paper, stuck together, then varnished. This tape was fed under the hammer mechanically in the act of cocking and firing. Richard S. Lawrence developed tiny wafers which held priming between layers of metal foil. These, known as disc primers, were used extensively in percussion Sharps arms.

This marked the beginning of cartridges containing primers as well as powder and ball. Then the primer moved inside with a variety of designs – rim-fire, pin-fire, teat fire, and others (see CARTRIDGE).

The detonating mixtures used in these primers varied considerably. The basic and original one was fulminate of mercury, which usually had some abrasive substance added for more certain ignition. Other compositions were based on potassium chlorate as a source of oxygen, with a suitable fuel, and usually a gum binder and an abrasive such as ground glass. These last were really very fast burning friction-sensitive mixtures, whereas the fulminates were detonating compounds. That is, their ignition was practically instantaneous and relatively more violent. Eventually, both these types of composition were combined to produce the most effective mixture of all. Mercury fulminate alone not only gave somewhat uncertain ignition, but tended to deteriorate under hot, humid, storage conditions such as are encountered in the tropics.

All the systems thus far mentioned were separate primers used to ignite black powder charges. Of these, one of the most significant was that patented in 1829 by Clement Pottet. His was a cartridge quite similar to that made earlier by Pauly but including a percussion nipple in essentially its final form.

The American Civil War occurred at a time when a variety of adequate cartridge designs made breechloaders and even repeaters practical for military use. The war gave a tremendous impetus to invention along the lines of both cartridges and weapons, the two logically coming along together. The United States Army's Frankford Arsenal, originally a powder magazine and cap supplier, naturally became involved in cartridge design and especially in developing manufacturing processes. The first really good breechloaders used rim-fire ammunition. The manufacturing techniques then known limited these to rather short copper cases, weak at the rims. This deficiency prevented making good long cases as needed for the smaller caliber arms desired by the military. Frankford began a long series of experiments with center-fire designs, intended to provide more strength, and later to allow reloading. The first group of cartridge types to reach a satisfactory stage of development for service use had their priming inside, where it was held in a small vented cavity in a bar, cup, or disc. This piece of metal acted as the anvil against which the percussion mixture was struck, through the relatively thin base wall. Although these priming holders might be considered primers in the sense of this article, they differed from the rest in being permanently attached within the cartridge case. As such cartridges could not be reloaded, a search began to produce a priming system which would be leak-proof and could be reloaded.

Among the short-lived systems of that period were those of Meigs, Allen, Martin, and Milbank. The Meigs primer used a small cup upset inside the case then filled with composition and partly closed together over it. The Milbank primer was inserted into a tapered hole through the head of the cartridge, and opened directly into the powder space. Its flared head kept it from going in too far, and provided support. The Allen primer was much like a blank caliber .22 cartridge, positioned by its rim. It was principally used in shotgun shells. The Martin head – a government type – was folded to form an inside primer pocket for anvil and composition, which was crimped down to hold the contents firmly. The Meigs and Martin types could not be reloaded.

In 1866 Hiram Berdan patented a center-fire cartridge which used a replaceable primer. The primer pocket was formed by a tubular rivet passing through the cartridge head. The rivet had a small projection in its base against which the primer was struck, and a small flash hole through which the flame passed. The cap was much like the percussion type, but relatively wide and shallow. A similar cartridge had been made previously at Frankford Arsenal, where the Commanding Officer stated that Berdan first saw it on a visit. Government developments were not usually patented. Berdan made an improvement in 1868 which eliminated the separate pocket, forming it by punching a cavity in the cartridge head. The punch had a depression in its face which left a corresponding bump in the bottom of the pocket for the priming to hit against. Such a solid anvil or strike point has always been essential for sure and uniform ignition. In a few years, the Berdan system predominated in the United States.

Meanwhile in England, Colonel Edward Boxer, Superintendent of the Royal Laboratory at Woolwich, produced a different type of primer for the Snider rifle cartridge. His cartridge used a primer cavity much like Berdan's original form, but instead of incorporating the anvil into the case, he put it in the primer. A tiny bar or trivet of metal was placed on top of the composition and crimped there. Similar designs had been tried at Frankford Arsenal, but never used in quantity. The Boxer type, not having the bump in the center of the pocket but having its flash-hole there, could be knocked out easily by inserting a thin punch through the hole.

Oddly, the American Berdan primer eventually became the predominant type in the rest of the world, while the British Boxer type became the only kind used in the United States, probably because of the great interest in reloading there. Since the Second World War, the American-preferred Boxer primer has been standardized by the NATO countries for military small arms cartridges. In England, incidentally, primers are still called caps.

Shotgun shells, unlike other types, have only thin metallic heads covering compressed paper. For strength they use a brass cup to hold the primer, very like the original

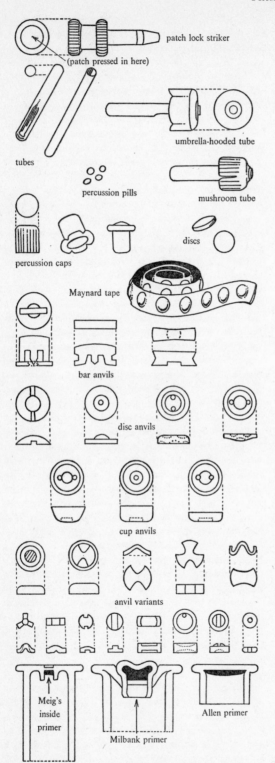

patch lock striker

(patch pressed in here)

tubes

percussion pills

umbrella-hooded tube

mushroom tube

percussion caps

discs

Maynard tape

bar anvils

disc anvils

cup anvils

anvil variants

Meig's inside primer

Milbank primer

Allen primer

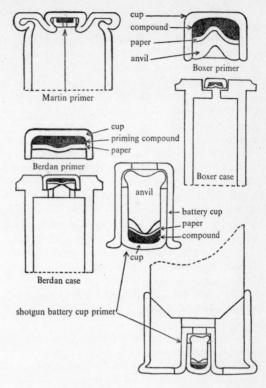

Martin primer

cup
compound
paper
anvil

Boxer primer

cup
priming compound
paper

Berdan primer

Boxer case

anvil

battery cup
paper
compound

cup

Berdan case

shotgun battery cup primer

Various priming agents

Berdan separate-pocket type but using the Boxer anvil. These are called battery cup primers.

In the 1890's, when smokeless powders began to displace black powder in ammunition, the old priming compositions began to give trouble. Smokeless powders required stronger primers, hence more composition. Pressures were greater and the heavy coating of burnt powder residue common to older guns was eliminated. These changes combined to point up deficiencies in the old primer mixes. When mercury fulminate ignites, free metallic mercury is released. This reacts with the brass cartridge case making an amalgam which is weak and brittle and which attacks the brass progressively. As most governments desired to salvage and reload fired cases, this effect of mercury was most undesirable. For this reason, the United States government did not use mercury in small arms primers after about 1900.

The combustion temperature of early smokeless powders was quite high. Rapid deterioration of barrels was blamed on the new powders but this was only in part justified. The real culprit was the potassium chlorate used as the basic primer ingredient after fulminate became unpopular. The effect of the chlorate had been obscured in black powder guns in two ways. First, the barrels had been protected by heavy deposits of fouling. Second, the accepted way to clean such fouling had been to scrub it out with water. With smokeless powders, shooters no longer had to contend with the heavy fouling and so just wiped out and oiled the bores after firing. Bore rusting was then blamed on smokeless powder, and many "powder solvents" came on the market, with only partial success.

Potassium chlorate decomposes when a primer is fired, forming a chloride. This has a property much like that of common table salt; it tends to absorb water, to the extent that in a humid atmosphere it will dissolve itself. When a gun is fired, this salt is driven into the very pores of the barrel by the great pressure. It happens that this chloride, like ordinary salt, is not soluble in oils, which are the substances commonly used to clean and preserve firearms. While covered by an oil film, the salt cannot pick up moisture, but as soon as the oil begins to dry or run off, the trouble begins. The answer was simple – just clean with hot water. But shooters either did not know this or did not take the trouble, and so many barrels were ruined.

During the present century, Germany has taken the lead in developing non-mercuric and non-corrosive primers. Early efforts involved lead azide, red phosphorus, and other substances, but the most successful new composition is based on lead styphnate. This was developed in Germany and was in quite general use in 1960.   B.R.L.

Logan, Herschel C., *Cartridges*, Huntingdon, W.Va., 1948.

Winant, Lewis, *Early Percussion Firearms*, New York, 1959, and London, 1961.

See also: BERDAN, HIRAM; BOXER, EDWARD MOUNIER; BOXER CARTRIDGE; CARTRIDGE; NIPPLE PRIMER; PERCUSSION SYSTEM.

PROOF MARKS

It is probable that from the earliest days of firearms some attempt was made to prove that a gun was safe to fire before it was put into the hands of the user. The account books of the city of Basle, Switzerland, record the trial of a gun as early as 1375, and later entries show that a special plot of land was reserved for the purpose outside the city walls. No details are given of the process of proof applied but it seems likely that, as now, an extra strong charge of powder was set off to confirm that the barrel would easily withstand the normal charge.

By the sixteenth century, many of the city guilds of northern Europe exercised some control over the manufacture of firearms, as they did with other arms and armor. Each city had its special control mark which was struck on the barrel, and sometimes on the lock, of a gun, alongside the name or mark of the maker. Nuremberg was represented by its coat of arms under the letter N; Amsterdam by a shield bearing a crisscross pattern under a crown; Augsburg by a pine cone; Essen by a sword; Suhl by the letters SUL; and so on. What is not clear is whether these marks were proof marks indicating a physical test of the gun, or merely view marks showing that the gun had passed a visual inspection.

During the seventeenth century some form of test firing, either in an official proofhouse or on the gunmakers' premises, was in operation in nearly every European country. At first, these tests were simple. The barrels were examined for flaws and gauged for correct dimensions. Having passed this "view," they were laid horizontally on a wooden frame and a strong proof charge was fired. The trouble was that a gunmaker might file down or alter his barrel after proof, with more thought for its appearance than its safety. The authorities did their best to stop this. The gunmaker might be required to file smooth the breech end of the barrel on which the mark was struck, or even be refused proof if the gun was not sufficiently finished. The custom of making two tests of a barrel was gradually introduced. In the second half of the nineteenth century it was universal. The first test, or provisional proof, was carried out on rough barrels in the course of manufacture, while the final, or definitive, proof was reserved for completed guns fully finished but "in the white," i.e. before bluing. As stronger powders and new cartridges were invented, however, proof became more complicated and various supplementary tests were found necessary. Marks on a sporting gun will often record the type and strength of powder used, the gauge of the barrel, the length of the chamber and the degree of choke (in a shotgun). Military arms were subject to even stricter survey, and they usually bear a number of government, proof and inspector's marks not only on the barrel but on the various metal parts and on the stock. It is impossible to describe all these marks in a short space, and the reader is referred to the bibliography for further details. The history of proof in the main manufacturing countries can likewise be summed up only briefly.

Great Britain

Before the English Civil War, few firearms were made outside London, and the control of the view and proof of handguns was the responsibility of those City companies who were concerned with metal work – the Armourers and the Blacksmiths. Both companies appear to have proved guns at their halls, the Armourers stamping their barrels with a crowned A and a P, and the Blacksmiths with a crowned hammer. In 1638 the gunmaking members of the companies broke away and formed a separate company of their own. With the authority of a Royal Charter, they began proper proof tests and in 1657 erected a proofhouse just outside the city walls, where they stamped guns with the mark of a crowned GP (gunmakers' proof) and a crowned V (for view). They were concerned mainly with sporting and trade guns; military guns came under the jurisdiction of the Board of Ordnance. During the Commonwealth, military arms were proved on the Spitalfields Artillery Ground, and two government marks, a St. George's cross and an Irish harp, were introduced. After the Restoration, a new proofhouse was built on the river wharf outside the Tower of London, and the marks became the royal cipher and the rose and crown. In the reign of William III the rose and crown mark was replaced by a crossed-sceptres mark.

At the end of the seventeenth century, the manufacture of firearms had spread beyond London and its suburbs to Birmingham in Warwickshire. The gunmakers built their own private proofhouses, and a number of proof marks consisting of some combination of the letters V and P were brought into operation. Not many arms were made or assembled in Ireland. Irish gunmakers normally used Birmingham-proved barrels, but a few guns in existence bear an Irish harp proof mark, probably struck in Dublin. Gunmakers who were not freemen of the Gunmakers Company could prove their guns at the Company's proofhouse, where they were struck with a special mark of a crowned F (for foreigner), or they could take their barrels to the Ordnance proofhouse on Tower wharf, where the crossed-sceptres mark was struck twice to denote the Tower Proof. The last two marks were adopted by the Birmingham gunmakers in 1813 when they set up their own proofhouse, the letters V (view) being added to one, and BCP (Birmingham Company Proof) to the other. A Gun Proof Act of 1855 made it compulsory for every gun sold or used in England to be proved at London or Birmingham or at one of the Ordnance factories.

France

The French gunmaking industry was at first centered on Saint-Étienne, and in 1665 military guns being made there were described as being proved with a triple charge. The first rules of proof in France were laid down in 1729 but applied only to military arms. New rules were introduced in 1766 when inspectors were instructed to put their initials on satisfactory barrels together with the last two numbers of the current year. These inspectors' marks were abolished in 1782, and the same decree made official the crossed-palms mark being used by the gunmakers of Saint-Étienne. In 1810 Napoleon made compulsory the proof of all firearms manufactured in the French Empire. Military arms were to be made only at government factories and marked with the letter E for *éprouvé* (proved), with or without a crown. All those towns producing commercial weapons were to come under the control of a proofmaster, his mark being the town's coat of arms, but only Charleville and Souilhac appear to have complied with this. Saint-Étienne insisted on using the crossed-palms mark with the addition of the letters SE (replaced by a crown in 1824), and Paris adopted the letter E reversed and P in an oval. Although compulsory proof was abolished in 1885, a proper proofhouse was built at Paris in 1897, and its marks, together with those of Saint-Étienne, are now recognised in other countries.

Belgium

In the sixteenth century the gunmakers of Liège, the arms center of Belgium, were members of the various guilds such as the Smiths and Carpenters. Laws governing the carrying of firearms were published, and in 1621 the minutes of the Metal Workers Guild refer to a proof of guns. It was not until 1672, however, that the first proof laws were promulgated. These intended that a public proof place should be established in Liège under the control of a proofmaster who would apply the mark of the "perron" or tower (part of the city's arms). This tower mark had been in use before, but the Liège gunmakers did not approve of their business being conducted in public and, in spite of re-issues of the act in 1689 and 1735, the proving of arms was conducted wherever and whenever the gunmakers thought fit. As late as 1802, the authorities were still trying to prohibit the use of private proofhouses. In 1810, however, Liège, now part of the Napoleonic empire, came under the 1810 edict. The recalcitrant gunmakers were soon brought to heel. A proofhouse was built and a new proof mark was established, consisting of the letter E, used by the other French cities, and below it the letters LG (for Liège) over a star, all enclosed in an oval. Between 1815 and 1830 Liège found itself in the kingdom of Holland, and it was the Dutch government's turn to try and impose order, which it did by issuing new rules of proof in 1818. In 1849, with Belgium now an independent kingdom, a new decree considerably tightened the whole system of control. Provisional proof marks, an EL in script, and inspectors' marks were introduced, and in 1853 a stylised version of the tower mark was designed for marking percussion guns and breechloaders after assembly. In the same year the inspectors' marks were changed to a letter of the alphabet under a crown, but as these were easily confused with other countries' marks, the crown was replaced in 1877 by an asterisk. This form of inspector's mark, together with the tower and ELG mark, is still in use.

Austria-Hungary

The great gunmaking center of the Austro-Hungarian Empire was Ferlach in Carinthia. The *Ferlacher Genossenschaft*, or "co-operative," of gunmakers was founded in 1577 and held what was virtually a monopoly of the trade until 1815. After the Napoleonic wars the business declined, and the opening of the Imperial Arsenal in Vienna in 1842 was a further blow. But it was at Ferlach that the first rules of proof (though they were optional) were promulgated in 1882. These were made compulsory in 1891, and five controlling proofhouses were established at Ferlach, Prague, Weihert, Vienna and Budapest. The main marks were: for provisional proof, a combination of the letter E with the first letter of the name of the town, and for definitive proof, a coat of arms – except in the case of Budapest, which had a triangle with the number 11 inside. After the dissolution of the empire in 1919, these marks were kept by the same towns, then situated in Austria, Hungary and Czechoslovakia.

A selection of proof marks

1. *Amsterdam*
2. *Antwerp*
3. *Augsburg*
4. *Barcelona*
5. *Birmingham, Gunmakers' proof mark, after 1813*
6. *Birmingham, Gunmakers' view mark*
7. *Denmark and Norway, reign of Christian IV*
8. *Denmark and Norway, reign of Christian V*
9. *Denmark and Norway, reign of Frederick IV*
10. *Denmark and Norway, reign of Christian VI*
11. *Denmark and Norway, reign of Frederick V*
12. *Eibar*
13. *Essen*
14. *Kongsberg*
15. *Leyden*
16. *Liège*
17. *Liège*
18. *London, Gunmakers Company, view mark*
19. *London, Gunmakers Company, proof mark*
20. *London, "Foreigners" mark*
21. *London, Board of Ordnance*
22. *Maestricht*
23. *Nuremberg*
24. *Paris*
25. *St-Étienne*
26. *St-Étienne*
27. *Suhl*
28. *Suhl*
29. *Utrecht*
30. *Vienna*

Spain

Spanish gun barrels were always renowned for their quality, and from the beginning of the sixteenth century there must have been some form of proof at the various manufacturing centers. The gunmakers of Madrid and Barcelona often placed the mark of the arms of their respective towns next to their own elaborate marks, but this does not necessarily signify that any proper proof was effected. The first definite record of a public proofhouse is at Eibar in 1844. It was an unofficial establishment, and proof was entirely voluntary. It was not until 1915 that official proofhouses were authorised and the proof of firearms made compulsory. A peculiarity of this Spanish proof was that it was in the hands of the military, who, if the occasion demanded it, would carry out the operation at the gunmaker's factory. The main Eibar proof mark was a pair of crossed guns, which was incorporated in a shield in 1929 and became stylised as a St. Andrew's cross in 1931. The old Barcelona mark was continued until 1935.

Scandinavia

In Denmark the most important arms factory was at Kronborg, where all military arms were made. The government mark, or acceptance mark, consisted of the royal cipher (a C or an F, according to whether the king was a Christian or a Frederick), sometimes with an R (for *rex*) and the appropriate number surmounted by a crown. Of the Norwegian marks, the majority are those of the arms factory at Kongsberg, whose control mark was a capital K under a crown. The Swedish government factory was at Jönköping, but no definite proof mark can be identified, although in the first half of the eighteenth century it appears to have been an O with three prongs at the top.

Germany

Although it is possible to identify some of the marks used by German cities in the control of gunmaking during the seventeenth and eighteenth centuries, the first datable proof mark is that of the royal Prussian proofhouse at Solingen (an SP under an eagle in an oval) in 1867, and it was not until 1891 that the first German proof laws were passed. They were based on the British and Belgian rules, but were considerably complicated by the German system of gauging barrels and by the fact that different strengths of proof powder were in use. The main proof mark was the German eagle supported by a number of subsidiary marks of a letter under a crown, e.g. U for *Untersuchung* (inspection), and G for *Gezogen* (rifled). These rules were simplified and made workable under a system introduced in the main proofhouses at Zella Mehlis and Suhl during 1911–12 and confirmed by new laws in 1939.

Italy

Since the seventeenth century the gunmakers of Brescia have been famous for their gun barrels, but nothing is known of any proof effected by them. In 1910, at the first International Conference of Proofhouses, Italy was represented by a delegate from the private proofhouse in Brescia. In 1924 proof was made compulsory. At this time the official proofhouse functioned in two parts, one at Brescia and the other at Gardone Val Trompia. Their respective proof marks were a lion rampant and a pair of crossed guns, both in a shield and surmounted by a crown, before 1951, and a star in a wheel afterwards.

America

Commercial firearms have never been the subject of proof laws in the United States, and no public proofhouses exist, but the majority of makers prove all guns intended for export and a few, notably Winchester and Colt, prove every gun they make. United States government inspectors are responsible for the testing of military arms at the various factories, and their marks, usually in the form of their initials, are a valuable aid in the dating of guns, particularly those of the nineteenth century.　H.L.B.

Blackmore, Howard L., *British Military Firearms, 1650–1850*, London, 1961.

Englehardt, Baron A., "The Story of European Proof Marks" in *The Gun Digest*, Chicago, 1953–62.

Goddard, Calvin, "Proof Tests and Proof Marks" in *Ordnance*, 1934.

Harris, Clive (editor), *The History of the Birmingham Gun-Barrel Proof House*, Birmingham, 1946.

Polain, A., *Recherches sur l'épreuve des armes à Liège*, Liège, 1891.

Reynolds, E. G. B., *The Lee-Enfield Rifle*, London, 1960.

Støckel, Johan F., *Haandskydevaabens Bedømmelse*, Copenhagen, 1943.

PUCKLE GUN

See: REVOLVER.

PUMP ACTION

A popular term describing repeating firearms activated by a horizontally operating slide action. Another popular term, trombone action, is a more accurate description.

The gun is operated by moving the sliding forearm below the barrel backward and forward. This action unlocks the breech bolt, extracts and ejects the fired shell, retracts the firing pin, transfers a live shell from the magazine to the chamber of the barrel, and relocks the breech bolt behind the shell.

Slide actions appeared as early as 1854 in Alexander Bain's British patent for a repeating gun. Two other versions were patented in England in 1866 by Joseph Curtis and William Krutzsch. In France, M. M. Magnot patented a slide action in 1880. In America, Christopher Spencer and Sylvester Roper received patents in 1882 and 1885. John Browning's patents of 1888 and 1890 were the basis for Winchester's revision of the slide action rifles and shotguns which have been so popular with American sportsmen. C.R.G.

Illustration: page 181.

Blackmore, Howard L., *British Military Firearms, 1650–1850*, London, 1961.

Smith, Walter H. B., *The N.R.A. Book of Small Arms*, Vol. 2 (*Rifles*), Harrisburg, Pa., 1960.

Williamson, Harold F., *Winchester, the Gun that Won the West*, Washington, D.C., 1952.

PUNT GUN

A firearm, usually single-barreled, for firing charges of between 6 oz. and 1½ lb. of shot at parties of duck or geese sitting on, or near, the water. The gun is attached to a specially designed punt, or boat, by a breeching rope running through the stem block. The boat, therefore, takes the recoil, not infrequently moving backwards through the water. Punt-gunning is now illegal in the United States. In Britain, guns were limited, by the Protection of Wild Birds Act, 1954, to an internal diameter at the muzzle of 1¾ inches.

In the early days, punt guns were muzzle-loading, being fired first by flint and then percussion locks. Some of the latter are still in action. In the late 1800's punting became fashionable among rich amateurs and demand produced breech-loading guns, several of which are still in use today. The best known makers were Holland & Holland and Thomas Bland, both of London. Bland still occasionally make six-ounce screw breech guns, and also a double four bore designed so that both barrels can be fired at once with a lanyard. The piece then throws a total charge of six ounces.

Punting has produced some notable literature and some great names. The father of the sport, as far as amateurs are concerned, was Colonel Peter Hawker, squire of Longparish in Hampshire, in the early 1800's. His punting experiences are recounted in his *Diaries* and *Instructions to Young Sportsmen*. Hawker's big double gun is now in the museum of the Birmingham Proofhouse. It was unique in that one barrel fired by percussion and the other by flintlock. The idea was that the flintlock, being slower to ignite, would fire its charge a fraction later than the percussion barrel, thus catching the birds as they rose, wings open and vulnerable. On the cover plate of the gun is engraved the fact that it accounted for 14,000 fowl. Other famous punters included: Abel Chapman, who took his punt to the marismas of southern Spain and wrote about his experiences in *Wild Spain*; John Guille Millais, author and illustrator of *Wildfowler in Scotland* (and son of the famous Victorian Royal Academician); and Sir Ralph Payne-Galwey, author of *Wildfowler in Ireland* and books in the Badminton Library series.

Many shooters believe that punting is "murder." It is, in fact, the most arduous and least efficient means of harvesting wildfowl. The difficulties of stalking within sixty yards for a shot, and of making the shot itself with the slightest ripple on the water, are immense. There is also considerable danger in handling such a small boat bearing 70–120 pounds of gun in open water. Punters often go weeks without a shot. A good shot would be twenty duck, an excellent one forty, but these things happen perhaps once a season. Shots of over 100 duck have been made, but very rarely. Black powder is used in both breech- and muzzle-loaders. Cartridges for the former are hand-loaded, a paper tube being glued to a brass base, and a .32 revolver blank inserted as a primer. Shot is generally BB and seldom smaller than No.1. Punts are sometimes single-handed, but more often double. The gunner gives aiming directions and shoots, the punter "sets to fowl" when lying prone and working a long single scull astern. It is cold and tricky work. C.W.

Illustration: page 281.

Willock, Colin, *Gun Punt Adventure*, London, 1958.

R

RAMPART GUN

See: SWIVEL GUN.

RANGE

See: BALLISTICS.

REMINGTON, ELIPHALET

Eliphalet Remington was born on October 27, 1793, in Suffield, Connecticut, but most of his life was spent in central New York State, where he moved with his parents at the age of six. According to tradition, Remington's career as a gunsmith began at the age of sixteen when he

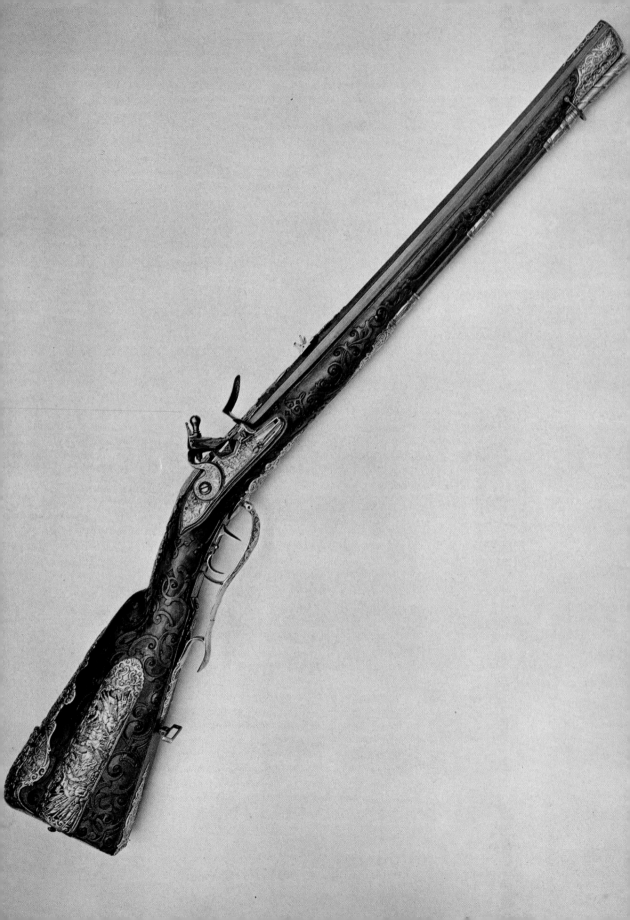

Plate 6

Flintlock rifle, one of a pair made for the Elector Charles Albert of Bavaria, later Emperor Charles VII (ruled 1726–1745). The mounts of gilt copper and silver are decorated with scenes from his life and with his portrait bust. His monogram is inlaid in silver on the barrel. The gun is the work of Joseph Nies of Mindelheim, near Munich; it illustrates the robust taste of the German Baroque gunmakers. South German, *ca.* 1740.

Collection of Lord Astor of Hever.

forged a gun barrel from scrap iron and took it to a professional gunsmith for finishing. The smith encouraged him to make more barrels, and soon this activity consumed all his time. By 1828 he was making complete guns. About this time also, Remington recognized the advantages of a location on the new Erie Canal, and he purchased a tract of land there. A community known as Remington's Corners developed around his shops, but at his insistence the name was changed to Ilion.

In 1845 Remington assumed an unfinished government contract for Model 1841 rifles. Thereafter he obtained contracts for more rifles, Jenks carbines and Maynard locks. In 1859 he brought out his revolver, which soon won popular approval for its strong frame and simplicity of design. The Civil War brought larger contracts and greater expansion of the armory, but Remington died on August 12, 1861, leaving the business to his three sons.

Eliphalet Remington made no striking innovations in firearms design himself. His contribution to firearms history lay in the foundation of a concern which constantly sought gifted designers and encouraged them to produce a fine series of arms under the Remington name. Some of them, such as the revolver and the rolling block rifle, have ranked among the best in the world for their type and period.   H.L.P.

Illustration: page 48.

Hatch, Alden, *Remington Arms in American History*, New York and Toronto, 1956.
Karr, Charles Lee, Jr., and Karr, Caroll Robbins, *Remington Handguns*, 3rd edition, Harrisburg, Pa., 1956.

REPEATING ARMS

From the time man began to use firearms, he has attempted to produce arms that could fire successive shots as rapidly as possible. This development has progressed with the means of igniting the charge and with improvements in combining the ball, charge and primer. In the beginning, with the slow match as a means of ignition, the simplest repeating system was an increase in the number of barrels; some such guns were mounted on carts, and others were grouped together as stationary defense pieces. Another primitive repeating system was one in which successive charges were loaded into the same barrel from the muzzle and ignited either through touchholes opposite each charge or fired with special bullets which transmitted the flame from one discharge to the next (see CHAMBERS SYSTEM; ESPIGNOLLE). Dubbed the roman-candle system, the latter device reappeared with every improvement in the method of igniting the charge down to the advent of the metallic cartridge.

The development of mechanical ignition systems permitted more practical repeating arms. The revolving-cylinder principle was one of the first to appear in hand and shoulder arms (see PEPPERBOX; REVOLVER). It was the simplest, safest means of holding a supply of loose powder and balls, but imaginative gunsmiths sought other methods of feeding reserve loads into the barrel chamber, and the true magazine repeater appeared.

One of the earliest forms of the magazine repeater is believed to have developed in the early seventeenth century, and is named after the Florentine gunmaker Michele Lorenzoni. In this system there are two magazines in the butt, one for powder and one for the ball, and another magazine attached to the lock for priming powder. These components are conveyed to the chamber of the barrel by a cylindrical breechblock rotated by a lever on the left side of the breech (see LORENZONI REPEATING SYSTEM).

The other principal magazine repeater of the period was the Kalthoff system, named after a family of German gunmakers (see KALTHOFF). In the Kalthoff system the ball magazine is under the barrel, while the powder magazine is in the butt. A carrier attached to the pivoted trigger guard is used to deposit the components in the barrel chamber. Kalthoff guns were probably the first military magazine rifles. About a hundred flintlock rifles of this pattern are believed to have been issued to marksmen of the Danish Royal Foot Guards and used in the siege of Copenhagen in 1658. No other magazine gun was as fast and safe as the Kalthoff, but it had disadvantages that limited its use. It was expensive, and its delicate mechanism required the services of a highly skilled gunsmith in its construction and use. It was also susceptible to powder fouling, a problem that plagued all designers of repeating arms using black powder.

The Lorenzoni and Kalthoff magazine systems were copied and variations were made by many others. Notable among these was Harman Barne of London, who designed guns for Prince Rupert and Charles II. In England the Lorenzoni magazine system also appeared in the flintlocks of Abraham Hill and John Cookson, constructed in the late seventeenth century. A century later, the system was still being used by H. W. Mortimer of London. In America, Lorenzoni's system was made in Boston in 1756 by another John Cookson, whose name has also been used to identify the system.

Until the development of the metallic cartridge, in which the ball, powder and priming were combined into a single unit, it was not possible to develop a practical magazine action for common use. As long as these basic components were loaded separately, the safest and simplest repeating systems remained multi-barreled and revolving-cylinder arms. Both were used extensively.

Multi-barreled designs reappeared in the forms of side-by-side barrels, over-and-under barrels with one or two locks, and clusters of barrels.

The revolving cylinder system was the most popular repeating system used. In its basic form it consisted of a chambered breech holding five to seven charges and rotated by hand to align each chamber with a single barrel. One of the most unusual applications of this principle was the "Defence" gun patented by James Puckle of London. It was mounted on a tripod and employed a many-chambered breech revolved by hand and ignited by a flintlock. Puckle provided two breeches for his gun: one chambered for square bullets for use against infidels, and one chambered for round bullets for use against Christians. A more practical application of the revolving-chamber action appeared in the flintlock revolver made by Elisha Collier of London in the early nineteenth century. Collier's revolver was based on an earlier design by Captain Artemus Wheeler of Boston, who had been unable to interest the United States Navy in his plan.

With improvements in the ignition system, the roman candle principle of superimposed loading reappeared. About 1818, in America, Lewis Jennings combined this system with a sliding flintlock which was pushed forward on a track until it was opposite the uppermost flashhole, and then moved backwards with each shot. In England, guns using this system were made by Henry Mortimer, and are reported to have had a very loyal following. Towards the middle of the nineteenth century, the Walch revolver and Lindsay's double-shooting pistol and musket appear to mark the end of superimposed loading.

In the percussion cap era, the revolving-cylinder principle was to emerge as the only repeating action with any practical value as a military weapon – and then it was largely confined to handguns. The most successful of all revolvers was the Colt. Samuel Colt combined the Collier principle with the percussion cap and provided an ingenious mechanism of his own whereby the chambered breech was unlocked, rotated, and locked again with a chamber in line with the barrel. All this was accomplished by cocking the hammer, which was then ready to strike a percussion cap at the rear of the chamber.

The success of the Colt revolver inspired the development of a series of weird revolving-cylinder actions that were actually produced and used. John Webster Cochran's United States patent of 1837 called for a radially bored cylinder revolved horizontally. This turret system was revived many years later as a practical magazine for the Lewis machine gun. The Porter system, patented in the United States in 1851, was a vertically revolving cylinder which placed the charges in line with the bore – and the shooter. This was particularly dangerous when there

were flashes from one chamber to another, which often occurred in firearms loaded with loose powder and ball or paper cartridges.

The pepperbox was a close competitor of the revolver. It was a logical extension of the primitive multi-barreled system, consisting of a cluster of three or more barrels, each fired by a single hammer. In some, the barrels were revolved by cocking the hammer. In others, the double-action principle was introduced: pulling the trigger rotated the barrels and cocked the hammer, which was released when the trigger reached its rearmost position.

Another type of multi-barreled action was one in which a number of barrels, usually four to six, were mounted vertically, often in pairs. These barrels were stationary and were fired by a moving striker. The British Rigby type, a percussion gun, had a manually revolved striker attached to the hammer. The American Sharps, a four-barrel, rim-fire cartridge pistol, also had the striker attached to the hammer, but it was revolved by the cocking action of the hammer. An improved example of the Sharps type is the early British Lancaster four-barrel cartridge pistol. The Lancaster had four firing pins which were struck in succession by a striker activated by the trigger. A variant of the above types is the Marston three-barrel repeating pistol. The barrels were mounted vertically over each other, and were fired by a striker moved upwards by the cocking action of the hammer. An odd variant of the multi-barreled repeater appeared toward the end of the percussion era, although for the most part using pin-fire cartridges: this was the harmonica pistol action. It consisted of a row of barrels that moved laterally under the hammer as the double-action trigger was pulled. This system was also used as a magazine in a repeating rifle designed by Jonathan Browning, father of John M. Browning.

Two of the most important developments in magazine repeating firearms during the percussion era, however, can be dated by Walter Hunt's United States patents of 1848 and 1849. The earlier patent was for a cylindro-conical projectile with a hollow base to hold a powder charge. The powder was sealed by cork and pierced with a small hole to admit the flash from a separate primer. In 1849 Hunt patented a gun with a tubular magazine containing a coiled spring to force the bullet towards the chamber. He placed the magazine under the barrel and named it "Volitional Repeater." This was the basic design for what was to develop into the Winchester repeating magazine action. In the same year that Hunt designed his rifle, Lewis Jennings obtained a patent for a simpler arrangement of Hunt's magazine, and later Horace Smith and Daniel Wesson made major improvements. One of Smith & Wesson's modifications was in Hunt's bullet, when they filled the base of the bullet with a priming compound instead of gunpowder. This eliminated the necessity for a separate priming magazine, for the priming could now be ignited by a firing pin passing through the breech. In actual use, however, the modified cartridge proved to be a liability, for it was weak and corroded the barrel. The problem was solved by Benjamin Tyler Henry, who in 1860 designed a .44 rim-fire metallic cartridge that was very successful, and for a time the improved gun was known as the Henry rifle. In 1866 the Henry was improved by Nelson King's side-gate loading system and renamed Winchester after the president of the newly organised company.

The Winchester action was simple and efficient. To load, the shooter inserted fifteen rim-fire cartridges into the magazine through a gate in the side of the frame. A strong spiral spring kept them under pressure. A simple forward-and-back movement of the trigger-guard lever carried the cartridge from the magazine to the barrel chamber and cocked the hammer.

A contemporary of the Henry-Winchester rifle, and the only other repeating magazine arm that showed any promise, was the Spencer. It was an excellent gun with a lever action that fed cartridges from a tubular magazine in the butt.

It was sturdier, simpler and cheaper than the Henry-Winchester, but held only seven rounds in its magazine, and the hammer had to be cocked for each shot. In the post-Civil-War era the Spencer could not compete with the Winchester, and in 1869 the company was dissolved.

Repeating firearms with tubular magazines proved themselves on the battlefields of the American Civil War and on the Western plains. The lesson was repeated in 1877, when at Plevna the Turks, armed with Winchesters, slaughtered the attacking Russians. European military observers were quick to notice the changing trend, and a number of tubular magazine repeaters were adopted. The lever action was dropped in European military arms in favor of the popular bolt action introduced by the German Dreyse rifle. The Swiss adopted the Vetterli in 1866 and the Italians followed in 1871. This was a bolt-action copy of the Winchester repeating action, complete with side-gate loading. A similar rifle designed by Früwirth was adopted by Austria for the gendarmerie in 1869. The French government tested the Vetterli-Gras combination in 1874, and in the same year issued the Kropatschek to its marines. Mauser combined his bolt action with a tube magazine under the barrel, and the arm was adopted by Germany in 1884. In the same year, Sweden adopted the Jarman tubular repeater. France in 1886 adopted the Lebel system, which combined the tubular magazine with the revolutionary smokeless-powder cartridge.

The tubular magazine in the butt was applied to a number of other systems. In the United States, the Ward-Burton was seriously considered by the army in 1872. The Hotchkiss system of 1882 was also adopted for trials. In Europe, Mannlicher designed a bolt-action magazine rifle with four tubes in the butt, which saw limited service in Germany.

The tubular magazine, however, was soon to be replaced by a revolutionary new magazine. In 1879 James Paris Lee, an American, introduced the vertical box magazine, which eliminated the weak springs, the space problem and the danger of bullet distortion found in many tube magazines. Lee placed his box magazine directly below the bolt, and it was adopted for the United States Navy in 1879. Within a decade it had been widely adopted in Europe, with Mannlicher developing an almost identical device.

In 1885, Mannlicher combined his vertical box magazine of 1881 with a special loading clip. This cartridge clip was a convenient device for preparing in advance complete magazine loads to be inserted with a single motion. This was the basis for practically all cartridge clips in use today. With this device the magazine repeater had reached full development. Only minor improvements in action, such as the perfection of the new sliding lever or pump action, remained. Major advances would lie in the field of automatic arms.   C.R.G.

Illustrations: pages 169–84, 214, 337, and endpapers.

Greener, William W., *The Gun and Its Development*, 9th edition, London, 1910.

Peterson, Harold L., *The Treasury of the Gun*, New York, 1962 (*The Book of the Gun*, London, 1963).

Smith, Walter H. B. and Joseph E., *Small Arms of the World*, 6th edition, Harrisburg, Pa., 1960.

See also: AIR GUN; ARISAKA RIFLE; AUTOMATIC ARMS; BAR PISTOL; BERTHIER RIFLE; BOLT ACTION; BROWNING, JOHN M.; CARCANO RIFLE; CHAMBERS SYSTEM; COLT REVOLVER; COMBINATION WEAPON; GAS GUN; GRAS RIFLE; HARMONICA GUN; HENRY RIFLE; HUNT, WALTER; KALTHOFF; KRAG, OLE H.; KRAG RIFLE; LEBEL RIFLE; LEE, JAMES P.; LEE RIFLE; LEMAT REVOLVER; LEVER ACTION; LORENZONI REPEATING SYSTEM; MANNLICHER; MANNLICHER, FERDINAND RITTER VON; MAUSER; MAUSER, PETER PAUL; MOSIN-NAGANT RIFLE; PALM PISTOL; PEPPERBOX; PUMP ACTION; REVOLVER; ROSS RIFLE; SPENCER, CHRISTOPHER M.; SPENCER CARBINES AND RIFLES; SUICIDE SPECIAL; TURRET GUN; VETTERLI RIFLE; WALCH REVOLVER; WEBLEY, PHILIP AND JAMES; WINCHESTER.

REVOLVER

A revolver is a firearm in which a series of barrels or a cylinder with a series of chambers revolves around a central axis so that each barrel or chamber in turn comes before the firing mechanism. It can be a handgun, a long gun or even a machine gun. Common usage today tends to restrict the term revolver to those guns with a cylinder revolving around an axis parallel to the bore. Those arms with revolving barrels are called pepperboxes; those with other forms of cylinders are known as radial-cylinder or turret guns. This is a useful distinction, and is followed in this encyclopedia.

The concept of guns with revolving barrels or cylinders apparently developed early in the sixteenth century. In Venice there is preserved a matchlock pistol with three revolving barrels which is almost certainly the *schioppo da serpa con tre cane* listed in a Venetian inventory of 1548. A matchlock long gun with a revolving cylinder probably dating from the middle of the sixteenth century was recorded by Essenwein in *Quellen zur Geschichte der Feuerwaffen* in 1871. A number of wheel lock revolvers have survived, and in the Tøjhusmuseet in Copenhagen are two snaphance revolvers believed to have been made by Hans Stopler of Nuremberg. One of them is dated 1597. Thereafter surviving examples multiply rapidly.

Two problems faced all makers and designers of revolvers. Separate ignition had to be provided for each chamber in turn. The cylinder had to revolve easily, yet each chamber had to line up exactly with the breech of the barrel and lock securely in that position until the gun had been fired.

Ignition systems in revolvers generally paralleled those most commonly used for standard firearms. It was necessary, in the early specimens, however, to provide a separate priming pan for each chamber. In the case of flintlocks complete frizzens were needed as well. A number of these frizzens protruding from the periphery of a cylinder made a gun difficult to carry, and this led to the retention of the snaphance system with a stationary steel mounted on the barrel for use in revolvers well after it had disappeared for most other uses. The pan covers also needed to fit tightly, both to keep the powder from falling out when they were on the underside of the cylinder and to prevent the flash of one pan from igniting several others. It was not until the advent of the percussion system that thoroughly satisfactory ignition could be obtained without danger of powder spilling or unnecessary protuberances, and it was not until the adoption of the metal-cased cartridge that the danger of one explosion setting off several others was completely eliminated.

The problem of aligning chamber and barrel was even more complicated. Various devices with locking levers and springs were tried. Some were not really locked in position at all. Often a spring arm was used which settled lightly in a notch to indicate that the cylinder was in the proper position but did not actually secure it there. James Gorgo, an English gunsmith of the late seventeenth century, tried to evade the issue completely by fastening a funnel arrangement to the breech of the barrel to catch the ball as it emerged from the chamber and deflect it into the bore, but this was dangerous, inefficient, and destroyed almost all hope of accuracy.

It remained to another Englishman to solve the alignment problem more successfully and become one of the first men in history to attempt to market the revolver on a large scale. James Puckle, a notary public of London, patented such a gun in 1718. It was a large revolver, mounted on a tripod, with interchangeable cylinders holding varying numbers of charges. These cylinders were turned by hand, and there was a crank at the back by which they could be screwed up tightly against the barrel for each shot while the coned mouth of each chamber fitted into the countersunk breech of the barrel to form a reasonably tight and properly aligned joint. One surviving specimen, believed to be an experimental model, is ignited by a match. The other two surviving examples are both flintlock. Special cylinders with rectangular chambers were available for firing square bullets against infidels while the normal cylinders for round balls were deemed efficient against Christian enemies.

Despite his imaginative designs and active promotion, Puckle's gun did not prove a popular success. He demonstrated it at Woolwich in November 1717, but Ordnance disapproved. A stock company was formed, and public demonstrations were held. The *London Journal* reported on one of these in 1722 when the gun was fired sixty-three times in seven minutes in the midst of a rainstorm, an amazing feat for the period. Still there were few buyers. Two of Puckle's guns were taken on an expedition to the islands of St. Lucia and St. Vincent in 1727, but no record of their performance has been found. The company failed, and the gun disappeared.

Numerous gunsmiths in England and on the Continent produced flintlock revolvers in the succeeding years of the eighteenth century, but it was nearly a century after Puckle's invention that the first reasonably practical revolving firearm was introduced. The inventor of this arm was Captain Artemus Wheeler of Concord, Massachusetts, and he obtained a patent for his gun on June 10, 1818. It was a flintlock with a fixed frizzen and a priming magazine that filled each pan automatically as it was closed preparatory to firing a shot. Presumably it had a mechanism for automatically rotating the cylinder, although this device is missing from the two surviving specimens in the United States National Museum. An attempt was made to interest the United States Navy in the new pistol, and when this failed, Wheeler apparently gave up all active interest in either manufacturing or marketing the weapon.

This was by no means the end of the Wheeler revolver, however. Within weeks of the granting of the patent, Elisha Collier, of Boston, Massachusetts, sailed for England with a sample of the pistol and obtained an English patent in November, while Cornelius Coolidge, also of Boston, took a model to France and obtained a patent there. The relationship of these two men to Wheeler has never been completely explained. In applying for the English patent, Collier claimed that the device had been partly communicated to him by a foreigner living abroad but insisted that he had made improvements, possibly including a different priming magazine and an improved joint between the chambers and the barrel. Actually, this was Puckle's system in reverse with the breech coned and the chambers countersunk. Attempts to interest the British Ordnance in 1819 and 1824 were unsuccessful, but civilians proved more susceptible. Both pistols and long guns were manufactured, first in flintlock and later in percussion. Collier himself later claimed that he had sold £100,000 worth of rifles, shotguns and pistols. This may have been something of an exaggeration, but sufficient quantities were sold to classify it as a successful revolver and to fix it firmly in the public mind as the Collier system, while Wheeler is almost completely forgotten.

The percussion system, developed as a result of Alexander John Forsyth's work, offered a form of ignition that could make the revolver a truly practical arm. No longer was there any need for priming powder that might fall out or explode with a stray spark. The motion of closing the pan before each shot was eliminated so that the gun could shoot faster, and a more streamlined silhouette was possible so that it would fit better in a pocket and could be drawn out without catching.

Gunsmiths all over the world quickly set out to take advantage of the new system. Both pepperboxes and cylinder revolvers began to appear in quantity. The percussion Colliers were the first of the true revolvers, but there were others within a few years. Many of them were the work of unknown designers and never became commercial successes, but Peder Rasmussen of Denmark developed a series of revolvers in the 1830's, and Jonas Offrell of Sweden patented a highly original version in 1839. It remained for the American, Samuel Colt, however, to perfect and market a revolver that would mark the beginning of a new age in firearms, and even he failed financially and was forced to cease operations for a period of years.

According to tradition, Colt conceived the design of his weapon on a sea voyage in 1830 when he was a youth of sixteen. It was 1835, however, before he obtained an English patent and 1836 before he was granted an American one. The leading feature of Colt's claim was the automatic rotation of the cylinder when the hammer was cocked. This was not absolutely new. John Dafte, the English gunsmith, had achieved the same results with flintlock revolvers in the seventeenth century, and some of the Collier revolvers had also rotated automatically. Colt's system, however, was simpler, stronger, and surer, and his new gun was eminently practical.

Colt offered the public a wide variety of revolvers from which to choose. Even during his first years of operation he produced three different models of handguns with variants in each, as well as revolving rifles, shotguns and carbines. When he resumed manufacturing again in 1847, after his first failure, he produced a new and larger military revolver. Soon it was followed by a plethora of other models, big and small, and special adaptations were always available for customers who were willing to pay for them.

Success brought imitation, and soon a host of other makers began to manufacture revolvers. Some copied Colt products as closely as possible. Others added innovations and improvements. As long as the Colt patent remained in effect, however, it restricted the activity of these designers to some extent. Many clung to hand-revolved cylinders. Radial cylinders were tried, and some even resorted to clockwork mechanisms to provide mechanical rotation.

In England a significant advance was made by Robert Adams who patented a large double-action percussion revolver in 1851. All Colt revolvers had been single-action, requiring the shooter to cock the hammer manually for each shot, then release it by pulling the trigger. In Adams' double-action pistol, a single pull on the trigger first cocked the hammer and then released it, making for a faster-firing weapon. The Adams revolvers also boasted a solid frame which the inventor maintained made them stronger than the Colt, and their larger calibers, ranging up to .50, gave them greater stopping power.

Meanwhile, the metal-cased cartridge had begun to make its presence felt in the revolver field. The French were the first to try such weapons on a large scale with pin-fire cartridges, Lefaucheux's to start with, then Houiller's improved version. Elsewhere revolvers were developed to fire most of the other early cartridges. There were even Dreyse "needle-fire" models.

The first really successful cartridge revolver, however, was designed by Horace Smith and Daniel B. Wesson of the United States and used their own rim-fire cartridge. An essential feature of their pistol was a cylinder with the holes bored all the way through it which had been patented in 1855 by Rollin White. Smith & Wesson acquired the rights to this cylinder in 1856 and produced their first revolvers in 1857, promptly after the expiration of Colt's patent. Their control of this cylinder gave them a virtual monopoly on practical cartridge revolver design in the United States until 1869. It was a tremendous advantage, and the partners made the most of it in developing markets and improving their designs. Other makers were forced into attempts to evade the Rollin White patent. They devised cylinders that loaded from the front or side or which used teat-fire or lip-fire cartridges. There were divided cylinders, and sliding tubes. Some worked reasonably well, but none were really successful.

After 1869, the field was open once again. The Colt Company brought out its famous single-action Model P in 1873. Known variously as the Peacemaker, Frontier Model, Single-Six, or one of a host of other titles, it became the most popular revolver in the American West, and it was manufactured for a longer period than any other revolver in history. Production continued from 1873 until 1941. The Second World War brought a hiatus in manufacture, but because of popular demand it is once again in production.

It is interesting that a single-action revolver such as the Colt Peacemaker should have remained widely popular for so long a period. The faster-firing double-action weapons had been perfected long before and had been widely accepted in Europe. Robert Adams' percussion double-action revolver of 1851 has already been mentioned. His brother, John, developed a double-action cartridge model in 1867 which was promptly adopted by the British Army, and there were Tranters and Webleys in a variety of patterns as well as several lesser makes. In France some of the Lefaucheux pin-fires were double-action, as were the Perrin and Raphael cartridge revolvers which followed. Austria adopted a double-action revolver invented by Leopold Gasser in 1870, and other makes and models proliferated throughout the Continent. By 1882 almost all major European nations had adopted a double-action cartridge revolver as an official sidearm.

In the United States the acceptance of the double-action arm was much slower. Marksmen maintain that more accuracy can be obtained by firing a pistol single-action than double-action, and it may be that Americans laid more emphasis on accuracy than on speed. Some of the percussion revolvers of the Civil War, such as the Savage and the Starr, had been double-action, but they never achieved great popularity. The Colt company did not introduce a double-action cartridge model until 1877, and it was 1880 before Smith & Wesson marketed their first double-action arm.

With the double-action cartridge models, revolvers reached the height of their practical development. There were some attempts during the closing years of the nineteenth century to apply systems for automatic loading and cocking to them, which made use of both gas pressure and recoil force. None of these designs proved really satisfactory, however, and the British Webley-Fosbery recoil-operated revolver of 1901 was the only one ever to be manufactured commercially. It enjoyed a vogue of some ten years, then disappeared. Both single- and double-action revolvers, however, remain in wide use.   H.L.P.

Illustrations: pages 41, 171–6, 182, 212–13, 320 (plate 8), and endpapers.

Bennett, G. E., and Blackmore, Howard L., "The Walch Revolver" in *Journal of the Arms and Armour Society*, Vol. 1, No. 8, London, 1954.

Blackmore, Howard L., *British Military Firearms, 1650–1850*, London, 1961.

Dowell, William C., *The Webley Story*, Kirkgate, Leeds, 1962.

George, John N., *English Pistols and Revolvers*, Onslow County, N.C., 1938.

Gluckman, Colonel Arcadi, *United States Martial Pistols and Revolvers*, Buffalo, N.Y., 1939.

Karr, Charles Lee, Jr., and Karr, Caroll Robbins, *Remington Handguns*, 3rd edition, Harrisburg, Pa., 1956.

McHenry, Roy C., and Roper, Walter F., *Smith & Wesson Hand Guns*, Huntingdon, W.Va., 1945.

Parsons, John E., *Smith & Wesson Revolvers*, New York, 1957.

Peterson, Harold L., *The Treasury of the Gun*, New York, 1962 (*The Book of the Gun*, London, 1963).

Serven, James E., *Colt Firearms, 1836–1960*, Santa Ana, Cal., 1954.

Smith, Walter H. B. and Joseph E., *Small Arms of the World*, 6th edition, Harrisburg, Pa., 1960.

See also: ADAMS, JOHN; ADAMS, ROBERT; COLT, SAMUEL; COLT REVOLVER; COMBINATION WEAPON; LEFAUCHEUX; LEMAT REVOLVER; SMITH, HORACE; SUICIDE SPECIAL; WALCH REVOLVER; WEBLEY, PHILIP AND JAMES; WESSON, DANIEL B.; WHITE, ROLLIN.

RICHARDS, WESTLEY

Westley Richards, who was the eldest son of William Westley Richards, a leading Birmingham and London gunmaker, was born on August 8, 1814. He made his first real mark on contemporary firearms development during the Crimean War when, at the request of the government, he joined Whitworth in investigating the best design of rifled barrels for small arms. Being persuaded that the ideal barrel was of small bore, polygonally rifled, he became a strong critic of the government's reluctance to abandon large-calibered arms.

A greater claim to fame followed a few years later, in 1859, when the merit of his monkey-tailed capping breechloader was officially recognised. Though he gained the distinction of producing the first breechloaders regularly issued to British infantry, for various reasons comparatively few of these arms were manufactured. Before ill-health compelled his retirement from business in 1872, he had been responsible for the perfecting of the top-lever system for sporting guns, the production of a most successful falling-block center-fire military breech-loading rifle, the systematic development of the solid drawn brass cartridge case, and numerous experimental breech-loading mechanisms for ordnance.

Under his chairmanship, the firm, which still bears his name, made 170 New Bond Street a mecca for all categories of rifle and sporting gun enthusiasts. The firm produced the Anson-Deeley hammerless action, the Deeley-Edge match-rifle mechanism, and very many other important innovations. He died on May 27, 1897.   C.H.R.

Taylor, Leslie B., *The Westley Richards Firm, 1812–1913*, Stratford-upon-Avon, 1913.

See also: WHITWORTH, SIR JOSEPH; WHITWORTH RIFLE.

RIFLE MUSKET/RIFLED MUSKET

This class of long infantry arm was generally introduced in 1851, with the decision of England, France and some German states to arm elements of their infantry with muzzle-loading arms having the expanding-ball system, yet retaining musket characteristics familiar to their troops. Previously, rifled infantry weapons were shorter arms, restricted in their use either to light infantry or to riflemen.

The British gave these new weapons the classification Rifle Musket. Their first design was a clumsy adaptation of the Minié projectile to the traditional .75 caliber Brown Bess form. Fitted with a French-pattern rear sight, the 1851 design showed great superiority over the musket, but was still inferior to weapons developed on the Continent. They therefore developed in 1853 a new design of .577 caliber, having bore characteristics of the *à tige* arm developed by Saxony but retaining the Minié principle. With an improved ball, this first pattern showed marked effectiveness in combat during the Crimean War, but the weapon was not to be perfected until shortly

afterwards when "progressive" rifling was employed, reducing the depth of the grooves from the breech to the muzzle. The Pritchett bullet was then introduced. Variations, designated Short Rifle Muskets, were designed at first for sergeants of infantry, and later for rifle regiments. There were many makers and several patterns in England. Some were also made in Belgium and Spain. In spite of their almost complete lack of interchangeability of parts, these arms became the principal muzzle-loading weapons in Europe, until they were altered to become breechloaders on the Snider system about 1865.

United States development started in 1855 on a .58 caliber rifle musket similar to the Enfield first pattern, but with progressive rifling and a ball designed by James H. Burton. A short, heavier-barreled version, designated simply as the Rifle, was also designed for the use of flanking companies and Mounted Rifles. Although there were later to be several models and many contractors, a remarkably high standard of interchangeability of parts was maintained.

At the same time, existing stocks of .69 caliber muskets were called in and rifled according to the same system. These were frequently designated rifled muskets, and thereby influenced the nomenclature for all long muzzle-loading rifled arms of domestic manufacture and of foreign makes imported at the outbreak of the American Civil War.

During that war these rifle muskets and rifles proved terribly effective and caused such changes in tactics that the distinction in length between the long and short muzzle-loading weapons ceased to be significant.

By the end of the war, in 1865, all classes of muzzle-loading weapons were eclipsed by the increased effectiveness of new breech-loading and repeating arms, and United States Ordnance determined to alter all rifle muskets to a breech-loading system invented by E. S. Allin of the Springfield Armory.   R.L.M.

Illustrations: page 105.

Barker, Lieutenant Colonel A., "The Rifle in the British Service" (part 1 of 5) in *The American Rifleman*, Washington, D.C., April 1956.

Blackmore, Howard L., *British Military Firearms, 1650–1850*, London, 1961.

Fuller, Claud E., *The Rifled Musket*, Harrisburg, Pa., 1958.

Mordecai, Alfred, *Military Commission to Europe in 1855 and 1856; report of Major Alfred Mordecai of the Ordnance Department* (Senate Executive Document No. 60), Washington, D.C., 1860.

Peterson, Harold L., *The Treasury of the Gun*, New York, 1962 (*The Book of the Gun*, London, 1963).

See also: ALLIN, ERSKINE S.; BURTON, JAMES HENRY; CARABINE À TIGE; MINIÉ, CLAUDE-ÉTIENNE; RIFLES AND RIFLING.

RIFLES AND RIFLING

Rifling comprises a series of spiral grooves cut into the bore of a gun to impart a spinning motion to the projectile. A firearm with such grooves is, therefore, a rifle.

Not long after handguns had assumed a form suitable for the use of rifling, the first experiments appear to have been made in this direction. Exactly where and when rifling was first tried is impossible to determine with accuracy. One traditional account places the discovery at Leipzig another attributes the idea to August Kotter of Nuremberg, and yet a third gives the credit to Gaspard Kollner of Vienna. All that one can state with confidence about the earliest use of rifling is that it probably dates from the end of the fifteenth century or the beginning of the sixteenth. Against the oft-quoted tale that the oldest form of rifling was straight-grooved and simply a means of reducing friction between bullet and bore in a fouled barrel, must be placed the fact that the notion of rotational stabilization was already well known.

There are quite a number of rifles surviving from the second half of the sixteenth century, but certainly nothing to show that they were intended for anything more serious than sporting purposes. Possibly the earliest military use of the rifle was by the Danes about 1611. By 1631 the Landgrave of Hesse had a troop of riflemen, and a little later the Elector Maximilian experimented with a restricted issue of similar arms. The French under Louis XIII and XIV also tried a small-scale issue, but neither they nor any other nation managed to demonstrate the advantages of the rifle sufficiently to encourage its more general employment. On the other hand, it was clearly an easy step in time of need to make use of sporting rifles for sniping purposes.

There was nothing unduly mysterious about the theory behind the rifle's superior accuracy. In 1742 Benjamin Robins, a member of the Royal Society, expounded the whole theory of rifling in a most able treatise. And, not long after his endeavor by argument and scientific fact to prove the superiority of the rifle for military use, others demonstrated its military potential in a much more poignant fashion.

If too much is not made of the point, it is true to say that the American War of Independence marked the beginning of the reasonably successful use of the rifle in warfare, though there are records of its occasional appearance in British service from as early as 1754. The War of Independence was still a conflict in which the smoothbore musket was the decisive arm, but it was equally a struggle in which the riflemen fighting on both sides showed that they could constitute, by themselves, a serious threat to the enemy if measures were not taken to counter their skirmishing activities. On one side were American hunters with their long, accurate Kentucky rifles, and, on the other, riflemen drawn principally from the Hesses, Hanover and Denmark with shorter jaeger rifles. The two areas in which the rifle had been brought to a fair degree of perfection were thus matched against each other. Whatever else emerged from the War of Independence, it certainly demonstrated that the British Ferguson breech-loading rifle was better, in most respects, than either kind of muzzle-loading rifle.

After this convincing proof of their utility, it might have been expected that rifles would come into more general military use. However, there were a number of factors preventing this. The principal objection raised against the rifle's more frequent employment was its extreme slowness of fire, the inevitable result of the difficulty of loading to perfection. After loading his powder charge, the rifleman was then obliged to place the greased patch squarely upon the rifle's muzzle. Next, ensuring that the ball, sprue scar downwards, was in the center of the greased patch, he had to ram it, gently so as not to distort it, into its correct position just in contact with the powder charge. Ezekiel Baker, whose rifle was adopted by the British government in 1800 for the newly raised Rifle Corps, reckoned that one round a minute was a reasonable rate of fire. Though Baker's rifle was frequently criticized, it served usefully in the Peninsular War and remained in issue to the Rifle Corps until replaced by the Brunswick in 1838.

The rifle was considered so imperfect as a military arm that Napoleon personally withdrew it from issue to the French skirmishers. In spite of this instance, there is considerable evidence to suggest that, in an emergency, riflemen were not quite as helpless as they might at first appear to have been. In the retreat from Burgos to Valladolid in 1812, the king's German Legion, armed principally with rifles, completely defeated French cavalry attempts to rout them. Similarly, at Montmirail, 230 Prussian riflemen utterly foiled French cavalry endeavors to cut them down. Yet there could be no question of the more general introduction of the rifle as long as it remained a weapon slow to load and requiring a specialist to operate it well. It was left to the French to suggest a way out of the quandary facing those who would see the rifle more acceptable as a military arm.

In 1826 Captain Gustave Delvigne proposed a form of rifle in which the chamber was of a smaller diameter than the rest of the barrel. Thus, on loading, the ball, so sized that it was a very easy fit in the bore, came to rest on the shoulders of the powder chamber. It was then a simple matter to expand the ball to take the impression of the rifling by two or three blows of the rammer. There were obviously many objections to the new system. The ball was deformed by the blows necessary to achieve this expansion. The powder chamber itself could easily become so fouled by continuous firing that it was unable to accommodate the whole charge. In this case, not only would the ramming cake the powder but the necessary degree of expansion would not be imparted to the ball itself. In spite of these objections, which were at least partly due to the French government's insistence upon a spherical ball, the Delvigne rifle performed so satisfactorily in Algeria that its great military potential was definitely acknowledged.

The first Delvigne arm of chambered breech design was formally adopted by the French in 1842. Delvigne tackled the problem of the ideal military rifle as scientifically as possible, and laid the foundations upon which he and his later associates, Pontcharra, Thouvenin, Minié and Tamisier, were to continue to build. At Vincennes, Delvigne experimented with elongated projectiles as early as 1830. More than that, from the same period he advocated the use of hollow cylindro-conoidal bullets expanded by the action of the powder gases and not by manual means. All these features, that were later to become so widely popular, were recapitulated in his additional patent of 1841. Moreover, Delvigne's original form of rifling, of 4 grooves making one turn in $6\frac{1}{2}$ feet, was not only adhered to in the French service but, so far as the pitch was concerned, copied by the British and retained, in spite of its unsuitability to the later English cylindro-conoidal projectile, until the end of the era of the muzzle-loading rifle.

With the removal of official objections to the use of cylindro-conoidal bullets, the way was clear for Colonel Thouvenin, in 1844, to propose the adoption of a *tige*, or pillar breech. This new modification, in which a short pillar served as an anvil against which the projectile might be expanded, was adopted by the French in 1846. To minimise distortion to the bullet, the head of the ramrod was countersunk to conform with the shape of the nose of the projectile. For use in this new rifle, Captain Claude-Étienne Minié of the *Chasseurs d'Orléans* proposed a solid cylindro-conoidal bullet with an ogival nose. A single deep cannelure, or groove, served both as an aid to the manual expansion of the bullet and as a receptacle for the lubricant. The pillar-breech or *tige* system, in spite of many practical drawbacks, was extensively copied in Great Britain and many Continental countries.

In 1849, Minié produced a cylindro-conoidal bullet incorporating an iron base cup designed to expand the bullet by the action of the powder gases formed by the explosion of the charge. Though it was this form of projectile that was eventually adopted in England in the Pattern 1851 rifled musket – sometimes known as the Minié rifle – the French found that a cylindro-ogival solid projectile with three deep cannelures of the design of Captain Tamisier was at least as effective if shot from the pillar-breech rifle. Indeed, their Pattern 1846 rifled musket was deemed a suitable arm for the infantry in general, and by the 1860's the smoothbore musket was considered obsolete as a military weapon by all the major nations. It is particularly interesting to note that this addition of the base cup to the Delvigne bullet was Minié's only really original contribution, and equally that it was so imperfectly worked out that in later English trials truncated cone plugs were found infinitely superior. In America, James Burton's bullets dispensed with the plug and relied entirely upon a properly designed cavity. Unlike the original Minié projectile of 1849, the English version was never cannelured. Lubrication was effected by a mixture of grease and wax coated on the paper covering the cylindrical portion of the body of the bullet. The British Pattern 1853 rifled musket was also constructed on the Delvigne-Minié principle, though the bullet was not cannelured and expansion was assisted by a clay or boxwood plug. Three grooves were used in place of the earlier four, but in England it was finally determined in 1863 that the ideal form of rifling for a large-bore military rifle was Lancaster's oval-bore system.

Lancaster's elliptical rifling, which was first tried officially in England in 1852, was by no means novel. The Russian, Johan Georg Leutmann, advocated it in 1735. Beaufoy, writing about 1807, referred to it as an old invention, and in Denmark N. S. Jessen experimented with it a few years later. There were others also, but certainly no other person exploited its potential as thoroughly as this English maker. Thought of by many as two-groove rifling with the grooves merging into the lands, the principal advantage possessed by this system was its comparative freedom from fouling. It did in fact find sufficient official support to be adopted in 1855 for the carbines of the Royal Engineers, and sufficient favor with Lancaster's many customers to be used on a wide variety of sporting and target arms.

Though no one wanted to return to the clumsy two-grooved Brunswick with its belted ball, it occurred to a number of people that a polygonal form of grooving with a mechanically fitting projectile might be equally effective. Once again the idea was of considerable antiquity, but the honor of rationalizing the details of the system belongs to Sergeant Major Robert Moore, R. A. In 1843 he suggested to the Board of Ordnance that a pentagonal or hexagonal barrel rifled with one turn in about twenty inches and firing a hardened lead or iron projectile was the ideal form for a military rifle. Unfortunately, he did not have the financial or engineering resources vital to ensure the success of his proposals. Isambard Kingdom Brunel, the famous civil engineer, independently suggested a similar system, but it was left to Sir Joseph Whitworth to patent and exploit its possibilities. In association with Westley Richards, who acted as his firearms adviser, Whitworth applied his great technical skill and knowledge to the problem placed

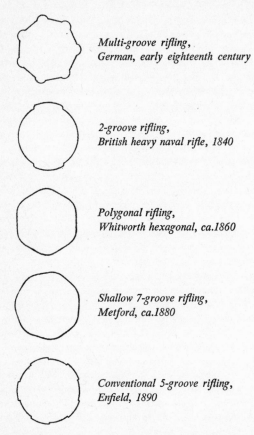

Multi-groove rifling,
German, early eighteenth century

2-groove rifling,
British heavy naval rifle, 1840

Polygonal rifling,
Whitworth hexagonal, ca.1860

Shallow 7-groove rifling,
Metford, ca.1880

Conventional 5-groove rifling,
Enfield, 1890

before him by Lord Hardinge, the Commander-in-Chief, namely, to discover the most perfect form for a military rifle barrel. Neither Westley Richards' rifles on this principle, with their octagonally bored barrels, nor Whitworth's, using an hexagonal form, were ever officially issued on a wide scale to British regiments. The reason for this was that they were obsolescent before they had passed the experimental stage. Official acceptance of improved cartridge design outmoded Westley Richards' system, but Whitworth's muzzle-loaders were beaten in a fair test by Metford's new system of bullet and rifling introduced in 1865.

To William Metford must go the credit for bridging the gap between precision muzzle- and breech-loading rifles. His rifles first swept the board as muzzle-loaders, and then, following their introduction in 1871 as military breechloaders, they completely dominated all British shooting until almost the end of the century. Metford, a civil engineer like Whitworth, undoubtedly made a greater contribution to the development of rifles and rifle design than any other individual in this period. Briefly, Metford's success depended upon limiting friction between the bullet and the walls of the barrel to the minimum possible. He found that paper-patched hardened lead projectiles fired from barrels rifled with grooves of extreme shallowness produced the very best results. He was also very particular that the wad, and the bullet itself, should be so shaped that there was an absolutely effective fire check to the burning powder gases. His bullet, which was self-expanding by its own inertia, was so shaped that the rear portion of the cylinder was all that was actually gripped by the rifling. His later arms were rifled with seven grooves of segmental form and progressive pitch so that, as he claimed, "equal increments of rotation" were imparted to the bullet "in equal times." Rifle contests with teams from overseas in the late 1870's and early 1880's gave proof that Metford's rifles were internationally, as well as at home, second to none.

When, in 1888, it was decided to introduce the .303 into British service, Metford was asked to lay down the necessary specification for barrel and bullet. This he did so successfully that scarcely any deviation from his recommendations was found advisable, and, though the introduction of cordite in 1891 eventually rendered his segmental grooves obsolescent, he could still point out that the so-called Enfield five-groove rifling was almost precisely what he had advocated thirty years earlier.

Ballistically, modern military rifles differ but slightly from those introduced by the Great Powers in the last decade of the nineteenth century and the first of the twentieth. A pitch of about one turn in 9–11 inches, a groove depth of .005 to .008, a caliber of between .256 and .311, a cupro-nickel- or steel-jacketed bullet: all these are most familiar features. Since 1895, time and place have counted but little in basic design. Differences that do exist are chiefly in breech closure, firing mechanisms, and traditional forms of stocking and furniture. However, it must not be forgotten that there are many other types of rifle in daily use, from the indoor .22 with its 40-grain lead bullet, to the giant double-barreled big-game rifle firing a projectile of massive proportions. Wherever one turns, in fact, from air rifles to target pistols, some form of rifling is to be found, since shotguns, flare pistols and a few other specialized weapons are almost the only arms still relying upon a smoothbore barrel.

C.H.R.

Illustrations: pages 102–5, 133 (plate 3), 252 (plate 6), and endpapers.

Deane, John, *Deane's Manual of the History and Science of Firearms*, London, 1858, and Huntingdon, W.Va., 1946.

George, John N., *English Guns and Rifles*, Plantersville, S.C., 1947.

Greener, William W., *The Gun and Its Development*, 9th edition, London, 1910.

Ommundsen, H., and Robinson, Ernest H., *Rifles and Ammunition and Rifle Shooting*, London and New York, 1915.

Peterson, Harold L., *The Treasury of the Gun*, New York, 1962 (*The Book of the Gun*, London, 1963).

See also: ARISAKA RIFLE; BAKER, EZEKIEL; BAKER RIFLE; BALLARD, C. H.; BALLISTICS; BERTHIER RIFLE; BICYCLE RIFLE; BRUNSWICK RIFLE; BULLET; CARABINE À TIGE; CARCANO RIFLE; FARQUHARSON RIFLE; FERGUSON RIFLE; GARAND RIFLE; GRAS RIFLE; GREENER, WILLIAM; HALL BREECH-LOADING ARMS; HENRY RIFLE; JAEGER RIFLE; JESSEN, NIELS STAAL; KENTUCKY RIFLE; KRAG RIFLE; LANCASTER, CHARLES W.; LEBEL RIFLE; LEE RIFLE; MARTINI-HENRY; METFORD, W. E.; MINIÉ, CLAUDE-ÉTIENNE; MINIÉ BALL; MOSIN-NAGANT RIFLE; PILLAR BREECH; PLAIN RIFLE AND PLAINS RIFLE; RICHARDS, WESTLEY; RIFLE MUSKET/RIFLED MUSKET; ROSS RIFLE; SCHUETZEN RIFLE; SNIDER RIFLE; TARGET RIFLE; TSCHINKE; VETTERLI RIFLE; WHITWORTH, SIR JOSEPH; WHITWORTH RIFLE; WINCHESTER.

ROCKET GUN

Rocket gun is a term used to designate hand-held launchers for rockets used by infantry. Incendiary rockets were used in the East from early times, but so little is recorded of their effect that one presumes that their main purpose was to frighten the horses of cavalry. In 1657, the fort at Bital surrendered when a rocket fired by the besiegers fell in an explosive-filled pit. In 1783-84, a mission sent by Tippoo Sahib to the Sultan of Turkey took him a variety of gifts but "none were so much admired as the Rockets." In India in the same year, a few rocketeers threw the Mahratta cavalry into confusion even though the rockets used were small 8-inch tubes of 1.5-inch diameter. At Seringapatam in 1792, the troops of Cornwallis' army suffered "a good many wounded ... chiefly by rockets." Seven years later an eye-witness wrote of Indian rockets "of uncommon weight," one of which killed three men and wounded four more.

Soon afterwards, General Desaguliers attempted unsuccessfully to make large war rockets at Woolwich, to be followed by Sir William Congreve who, in 1808, designed the first efficient military rockets to be seen and used in Europe. The chief value of rockets was that one or two men could discharge missiles equivalent in power to those projected by the heaviest cannon of the day. To Congreve the rocket was "the soul of artillery without a body." Beginning with the idea of an incendiary rocket, he widened the scope of his system to include explosive and shrapnel rockets. In 1806, eighteen boats shot two hundred rockets into Boulogne, and in 1807 Copenhagen was similarly attacked, with successful results in each case. As the rockets provided their own means of propulsion, the rocketeers needed only to rest them in a tube or trough at the correct elevation and pointed in the correct direction before lighting the fuse.

Apart from Congreve's heavy rockets, which were used by the Royal Artillery, experiments were carried out in Britain with light, infantry rockets. A series of gun launchers for these, in the Tower of London Armouries, all appear to date from between 1810 and 1820. Little is known about their origins at the present time, but presumably they were in the process of development when the Napoleonic Wars ended and the cost of research no longer seemed justified. The Armouries' rocket guns fall into two distinct types, those intended to be fired from the shoulder like a musket and the hafted variants fired like long mortars.

The name Alock appears on the lockplate of two of the apparently more primitive second group which have, respectively, long steel and copper tubes set on a wooden haft with a spear point at the butt. The spear could also have been used for the defense of the firer when the haft was reversed, but it was primarily intended as a firm base for the haft when stuck in the ground. The lock is set at the rear of the tube and is fired by a sliding latch connected to it by a two-foot wire rod. The fuse is lit directly from the flash in the pan.

Two other launchers by Alock are very close in design to a third, engraved TOWER on the lock plate. All three are equipped with a standard musket or carbine lock fastened near the upper end of a musket-like stock to which the firing tubes are fitted like gun barrels. Two have long hinged backsights. A sloping ramp at the muzzle of the third is its only sight.

Two more rocket guns are fitted with copper tubes of large diameter set on musket butts with a standard lock that connected with the rocket fuse through a train of powder in a separate parallel tube. For ease of carrying, the flash guards with which these are fitted can be removed from one and retracted on the other. When in place to protect the firer from the rocket flame they are locked by a spring catch. This flash guard seems such an indispensable feature that it is difficult to understand its absence from the Alock designs.

Although the rocket, fired from more conventional launchers, was used in a number of campaigns, it achieved no real military popularity until the Second World War, when it sprang to the forefront as a most effective shock weapon for land, sea and air use. At that time the hand-held infantry launcher returned in the form of the "bazooka," a 2.36-inch launcher developed by the United States Ordnance in 1942.   W.R.

Illustration: page 281.

Congreve, William, *A Concise Account of the Origin and Progress of the Rocket System*, London, 1810.
Scoffern, J., *Projectile Weapons of War and Explosive Compounds*, 3rd edition, London, 1858.

ROSS RIFLE

The Ross rifle was developed during the last decade of the nineteenth century by Sir Charles Augustus Frederick Lockhart Ross, ninth Baronet of Balnagown, and was first manufactured in quantity in 1897 by Charles Lancaster of London. This early model was a straight-pull bolt-action rifle with an external hammer.

In 1901, following service in the Boer War as a major of Lovat's Scouts, Ross took several rifles which were made for him by Joseph A. Bennett of Hartford, Connecticut, to Canada for submission to the Minister of Militia. They were described as a modification of the Model 1890 Austrian Mannlicher, the principle of the mechanism being identical. A contract was signed on March 27, 1902, but the plant Ross constructed at Quebec was not in operation until 1903 and the first completed delivery to the militia did not take place until August 1905, although 1,000 Mark 1 rifles were supplied to the Royal Northwest Mounted Police in the summer of the previous year.

All Ross rifles are of the straight-pull bolt-action variety. Locking of the action was accomplished by a turning bolt head with lugs engaging the receiver. The Model 1905 had solid lugs which were horizontal when locked, while those on the Model 1910 were of the interrupted screw type and were vertical when locked. Many alterations were made during production, but the designation "Mark II" persisted until five stars and over eighty changes had been added.

Sir Charles developed the particularly accurate .280 Ross cartridge, a match target version of the .303 British and a sharp-pointed copper-tube bullet.

The following rifles were produced by Ross:

SPORTING

Model	Caliber	Remarks
1897	.303 British	Made by Chas. Lancaster, London, England
1900	.303	Made by Jos. A. Bennett, Hartford, Connecticut
1902	.370 and .375	
1903	.370	
"R" 1905	.303 British	
"E" 1905	.303 British and .35 W.C.F.	
"Deer Stalker" 1905	.280	
1905 Match	.280 and .303	
M-10	.280	
E-10	.303 and .35 W.C.F.	
1911	.22 r.f.	

MILITARY

Model	Remarks
1903 Mark I	
1903 Mark I	Adapted for Royal Northwest Mounted Police
1905 Mark II	
1905 Mark II*	
1905 Mark II**	
1905 Mark II***	
1905 Mark II****	
1905 Mark II*****	
1910 Mark III	
1911 Caliber .22 r.f. Cadet	
1912 .280 military target	

All military models were made in .303 British caliber, except models 1911 and 1912.

Manufacture of the Ross rifle was discontinued in 1917.   S.J.G.

Official History of the Canadian Forces in the Great War, 1914–1919 (General series, Vol. 1), Ottawa, 1938.
Phillips, Roger, "The Gun That Canada Built" in *Gun Talk*, Vol. 2, No. 1, Regina, Saskatchewan, 1962.
Sharpe, Philip B., *The Rifle in America*, New York, 1938.

RUSSIAN FIREARMS

The history of Russian firearms is one of the least studied and documented of any in the world, and few basic sources are available.

Imperial Russia had always been an absolute monarchy until the twentieth century, and all Russian arms development must be examined in the light of this.

Since ownership and usage of arms was prohibited to the bulk of the populace until very recent years, Russian firearms development has largely occurred by and for the military. Only the nobility, a small fraction of the total population, were ever permitted privately owned firearms, and individual craftsmen were long discouraged from gunmaking, unlike those of western Europe.

From the reports and letters of early English and European travelers, we know that Russian armies under Ivan IV (1547–88) were equipped with firearms, but only with artillery, of foreign or hand-made domestic manufacture, not with individual small arms. The average Russian soldier carried a pike, crossbow, or short Mongol-type horseman's bow; only a few regiments of fusiliers or *streltski* had matchlock muskets.

The first Russian armory was not established until 1595, when Tsar Boris Godunov (1595–1605) located an arms factory at Tula, some 110 miles south of Moscow. It is doubtful that the Tula armory initially made small arms; it was probably established primarily to produce cannon. For over two centuries this armory, using local iron from an ironworks established in 1636, provided all of Russia's native ordnance. Imports were certainly considerable, but we cannot estimate actual quantity.

Some sporting arms, often ornate and of high quality, were produced by Russian gunmakers, probably as early as the seventeenth century, and examples of such arms survive today in Russian museums. Ignition types seem to be basically north-European and Baltic, not Asiatic, except in the Caucasus and along the Turkish border. The writer has never seen any existing Russian firearms earlier than the various flint types. It must always be remembered, of course, that the Renaissance, which indirectly resulted in so many elaborate and beautiful examples of early European arms, as well as fairly rapid technical and mechanical development, never occurred at all in Russia. Imperial Russia remained essentially a medieval nation until the mid-nineteenth century, with elaborate and ornate arms produced in fairly small numbers.

Under Peter I (1688–1725), the Tula armory was greatly expanded, in 1705 and again in 1714, largely to meet the needs of the war with Sweden. Tsar Peter was a strong francophile, and, as part of his lifelong effort to make Russia into a modern European nation, filled the Imperial court with French advisers who sowed the first seeds of Russian industrialization. As in much of Europe by 1720, flintlock military arms began to replace a vast variety of older weapons, and, through French influence, the new arms produced at Tula strongly resembled the early French patterns. As before, native developments were negligible – arms designs and most other Russian technology came from western Europe.

With Russian industrial progress completely dependent on a strong ruler, the next period of expansion at Tula occurred during the late eighteenth century under Catherine II (1762–96). The earlier French influence of Peter's reign had waned; Catherine, given to military adventures, surrounded herself with German and Prussian advisers who reorganized and modernized the Russian army, and, of course, Germanized armaments, equipment and tactics.

In 1807 a new armory, actually at first an ammunition factory, was established by Alexander I (1801–25) at Izhevsk in eastern Russia, now in the Udmursk Autonomous Area of the R.S.F.S.R. With the Napoleonic Wars making foreign sources of ammunition and arms increasingly less dependable, Russia had at last decided that native production was the only practical solution.

Because of Catherine's German advisers and Alexander's foresight, the Russian army, when it faced Napoleon in 1812, was the equal of any army in Europe, in small arms at least, for the first time in the nation's history.

After 1825, during the reign of Nicholas I, the situation was reversed. Old arms, captured foreign arms, and new Russian arms alike were issued, making the ordnance and supply situation chaotic. Parading became more important than readiness for battle; many arms actually in the hands of the troops were unserviceable because of lost parts, worn out from over-polishing, or hopelessly antiquated. Tula Armory in 1842 had a capacity of 15,000 arms per year, but the Imperial Army refused to consider the new percussion arms being adopted all over Europe.

Except for a few rifle regiments, the Crimean War pitted Russian infantry carrying worn out flintlock smoothbores against European armies equipped with new percussion rifled muskets. The result, of course, was disastrous for the Russians.

Unable to buy new percussion arms in hostile Europe, Russia turned in the end to the United States, and the Imperial Army's first breechloading arms were American designs, later made at both Tula and Izhevsk.

Up to the mid-nineteenth century, Russia's contribution to world firearms development, technical, mechanical, and artistic, was insignificant; Russian arms followed whatever was current in Europe.

After 1860, Russia's military small arms came to be the effective equal of any in the world, yet the over-all technological base remained archaic. Hence Russia's forced campaign, over the last century, to catch up with the rest of the world.

Tula and Izhevsk, both sizeable cities, are still Russia's primary arms-making centers. Other recent but probably less important armories are widely diversified, and still others are either kept secret or simply unknown in the West, as are also any existing detailed histories of Russian firearms.   D.B.W.

Smith, Walter H. B. and Joseph E., *Small Arms of the World*, 6th edition, Harrisburg, Pa., 1960.

See also: AUTOMATIC ARMS; MOSIN-NAGANT RIFLE.

S

SAFETY DEVICE

A contrivance to prevent the accidental discharge of a firearm or accidental damage or injury when a gun is properly fired. The first and simplest safety device was the trigger guard, introduced on matchlock guns of the sixteenth century and surviving until the present on all but a few firearms, the notable exceptions being guns and pistols made in Scotland on traditional lines (see SCOTTISH FIREARMS). Some later matchlock guns are fitted with a turning catch such as is found on certain crossbows of the same period. When turned, the catch locks the trigger. This safety has been described, without proof, as the invention of the Emperor Maximilian I.

Early representations of wheel locks in the sketchbooks of Leonardo da Vinci and in the Löffelholz manuscript show no form of safety catch, and one would be surprised to see one on such early designs, but some sixteenth-century French wheel locks have a safety bolt that acts directly on the trigger. On wheel locks dating from the second half of the sixteenth century and the beginning of the seventeenth century, a safety bolt is found on the lockplate or on the screw plate on the opposite side of the stock. In both cases it acts on the end of the sear, preventing it from moving and so letting the other end disengage from its notch on the wheel. The simplest method of making the wheel lock safe was not to set the dog lock on the wheel or the pan cover, but to leave it forward or back in the rest position.

Similarly, on the early snaphance lock the user needed only to push the separate steel forward, away from the pan, for the lock to be quite safe. In the Scandinavian version of the snaphance lock of *ca.*1600-1660 the steel can be turned outwards through 90° away from the barrel to a safe position. Some snaphance locks were made

with a catch or "dog" at the rear of the lockplate. The dog hooks into the tail of the cock and requires a positive act by the shooter to move it to allow the cock to fall. These "back ketches," or dog catches, survived into the eighteenth century, even after the introduction of a reasonably safe half-cock bent on the tumbler, and they are occasionally found on percussion locks. This half-cock safety was achieved in the Scottish lock by a short sear-like peg that projected through the lockplate in front of the cock which engages behind it. Similar projecting half-cock pegs are found on the so-called miquelet locks.

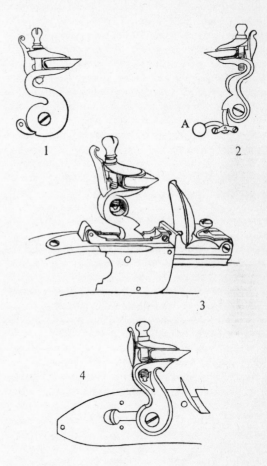

1. *Small dog catch engaging the base of the cock, ca.1700*
2. *Manton's gravitating stop, after the patent drawing of 1812. As the gun was raised towards the vertical, the weight (A) pushed the catch under the toe of the cock to prevent it from falling.*
3. *Sliding safety bar to lock both the cock and the steel*
4. *Sliding safety bar to engage the tumbler*

With the advent of the true flintlock, the number of safety devices multiplied rapidly. Most popular was the safety bolt which engaged a notch cut in the tumbler and thus prevented movement of the cock. This device had appeared by the middle of the seventeenth century. In one early example of it the rear of the lockplate is formed of two thin plates. The outer plate slides back and forward under finger pressure to lock or unlock the tumbler. Some sliding safety bolts fitted to quality weapons are finished so carefully that they are difficult to see. The normal bolt is narrow, set into a groove on the lockplate, usually directly behind the cock, and slid forward and back by pressure on a raised lump. They were most popular during the second half of the eighteenth century. Other sliding bolts were made to engage the cock directly, and these were especially popular on pistols with an enclosed lock and the cock in the center. Another sliding safety involved the entire trigger guard, which could be slid forward to engage a notch cut in the trigger itself, thus holding it motionless.

In 1795, Sir George Bolton patented a lock with a special bolt to take the place of the normal sear, designed to prevent accidental firing when loading military rifles which needed a heavy blow from a rammer to force the ball home. The British Board of Ordnance was not interested.

Joseph Manton patented an automatic "gravitating stop" in 1812, in an attempt to eliminate the danger inherent in carelessly loading a cocked muzzle-loading gun. Whenever the muzzle pointed up at an angle of 80° or more, a catch automatically engaged the cock and held it. It was not well received, as a little dirt or rust jammed it, and when it was working smoothly it made high shots impossible. Many guns originally fitted with the stops have had them removed.

A crop of ingenious safeties sprang up in the nineteenth century. John Hale's patent of 1845 showed a catch operated from the small of the butt. If this was not gripped by the trigger hand when shooting, the action remained safely locked. Variations of this grip-safety, in addition or as an alternative to the more usual sliding catches, have continued in use for some automatic pistols until the present day. It is a standard fitting, for example, on many Colt automatic pistols where it is supplementary to the thumb-operated safety. Shoulder arm safeties were operated by the left hand gripping a catch on the fore-end, or, as in Greener's butt safety bolt, the pressure of the butt against the shoulder. The most complex series of safety inventions was patented by a Scottish minister of the church, John Somerville, in 1824. These included a small key on the fore-end which could be used to lock the gun in the safe position, rather in the manner of a motor car ignition key.

With the full development of modern shotgun actions, makers installed automatic safeties operating on the triggers and/or an intercepting safety stop to prevent the sear being jarred out of the bent. On modern military rifles, the safety almost invariably locks the bolt mechanism.   W.R.

See also: DOG LOCK; SCOTTISH FIREARMS.

SAINT-ÉTIENNE

Saint-Étienne, situated nearly forty miles south of Lyons, is referred to for the first time in a decree of 1195. Its development has been due to rich coal deposits in the vicinity which enabled the metal industry to develop rapidly.

The manufacturers of Saint-Étienne began to produce arquebuses at a fairly late date; a document of 1582 refers to only five craftsmen specializing in these weapons. Yet the manufacture of side arms had been practised for a long time, since the skill of the workers in forging iron, and the presence of the coal, had given the engineer Virgile, ordered by Francis I in 1515 to create a royal arms manufactory, the idea of choosing Saint-Étienne. This city became one of the centers supplying the Royal Arsenal of the Bastille (founded in 1665), and a "Commissioner for the manufacture of arms for the service of His Majesty" was given supervisory responsibility for it.

In 1717 a service was organized to inspect the newly created factories which supplied arms to the army. On May 12, 1717, the Duke of Maine, supreme commander of the artillery, was instructed to appoint artillery officers, ". . . upright, intelligent and alert, for the permanent superintending of the manufacture of arms for the King at Maubeuge, Charleville and Saint-Étienne."

Nevertheless, arms production at Saint-Étienne, carried on in numerous small workshops, working in isolation and without co-ordination, was far behind the quality at Charleville. Methods of production had to be overhauled; General de Montbéliard of the Royal Artillery Corps was appointed to examine the situation. He suggested to the individual armorers that they should merge into one company and develop a manufactory on which the king would confer the title of Royal Manufactory, with all the privileges which that of Charleville already enjoyed. The purchase of premises to house the new concern was dated June 13, 1764.

The introduction of machinery necessitated a complete change of buildings, since, before this, the work there had been done by hand. A drill ground measuring some thirty acres was chosen for the site and the inauguration of the new factory took place on April 28, 1866, on the occasion of the installation of new steam machinery.

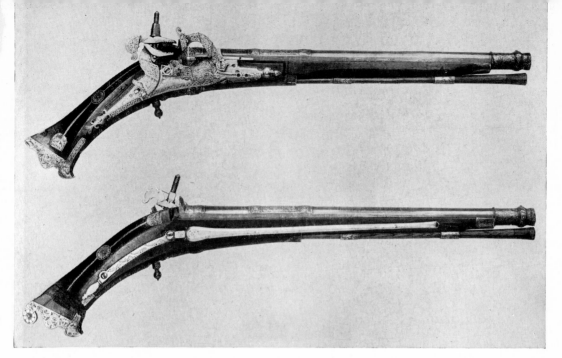

Pair of Scottish snaphance pistols with fishtail butts, the locks stamped IL.
probably for James Low of Dundee; dated 1602. *Tøjhusmuseet, Copenhagen.*

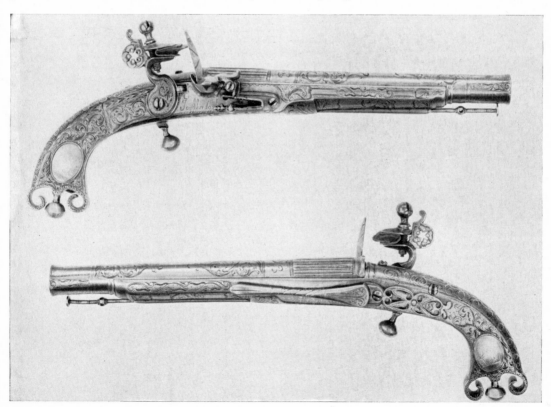

Pair of typical eighteenth-century Scottish pistols made by John Murdoch of Doune, *ca.*1760.
Armouries, Tower of London.

Scottish powder horn of 1683. *Glasgow Art Gallery and Museum.*

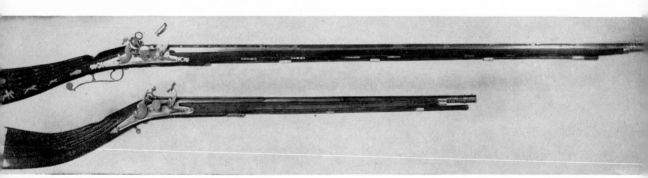

Scottish guns of the seventeenth century. *Collection of the Countess of Seafield, Cullen House.*

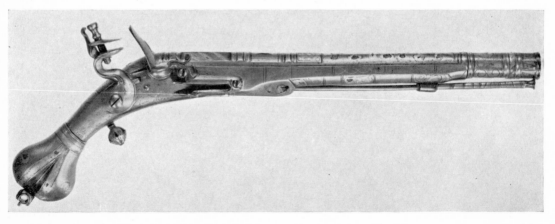

Scottish heart-butt pistol made by John Burges of Elgin, *ca.*1705; the stock and barrel inlaid with panels of engraved silver. *Armouries, Tower of London.*

Scottish gun made by John Stuart, dated 1703.
Collection of R. T. Gwynn.

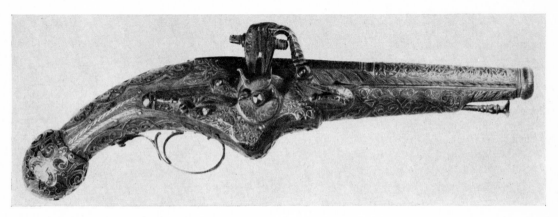

One of a pair of Ripoll wheel lock pistols, *ca.*1620–25.
Archeological Museum, Madrid.

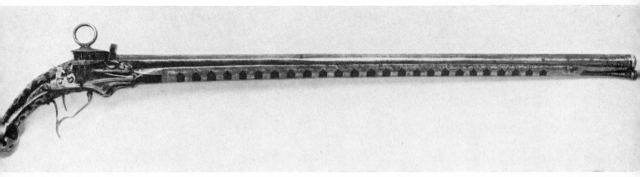

Ripoll *pedrenyal*, second quarter of seventeenth century.
Ripoll Museum, Ripoll, Spain.

Miquelet pistol made by
Pedro de las Heras of
Salamanca, *ca.*1675,
the barrel, lock, and
furniture chiseled with
foliage in low relief;
retains original
knuckle pad.
*Collection of
James Duncan Lavin.*

Ripoll miquelet pistol,
second half of
eighteenth century.
*Collection of
James Duncan Lavin.*

Madrid miquelet pistol,
lock *a la moda*, made by
Diego Alvarez, *ca.*1765.
Museum of the Army, Madrid.

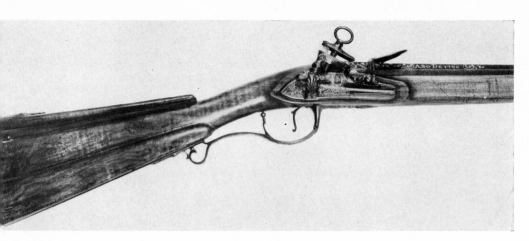

Miquelet gun made by Antonio Navarro, Madrid, 1786,
the barrel damascened with gold against a blued and stippled ground.
Museum of the Army, Madrid.

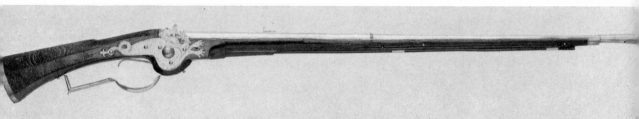

Early air gun with barrel reservoir, dated on barrel 1645, made by Hans Köhler, Kitzing.
Danish National Museum, Copenhagen.

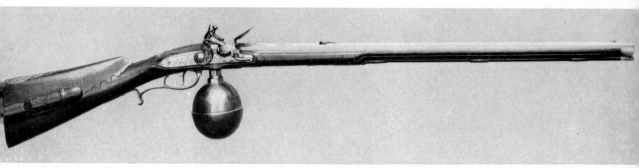

Air gun with globe reservoir, made by Johan Christian Jahn, Weringerode, *ca.*1750.
Tøjhusmuseet, Copenhagen.

Austrian air gun made by Joseph Contriner, Vienna, *ca.*1810; copy of the Girardoni air rifle Model 1780.
Tøjhusmuseet, Copenhagen.

Bronze percussion alarm gun,
to give warning of the opening of a door.
Collection of Dr. W. R. Funderburg.

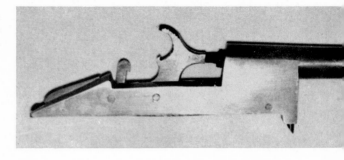

Sundial alarm gun.
Collection of Robert Abels.

Drop alarm gun.
Collection of
Lewis Winant.

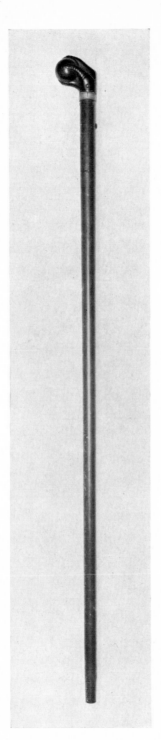

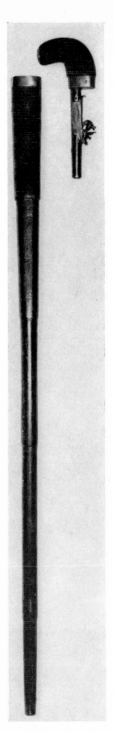

John Day cane gun.
Collection of
John L. Barry, Jr.

Remington cane gun with
claw and ball handle.
Collection of Frank R. Horner.

Flintlock cane gun.
Collection of
Dr. W. R. Funderburg.

American flare pistol of the
Civil War period, Army Model.
Collection of Francis A. Lord.

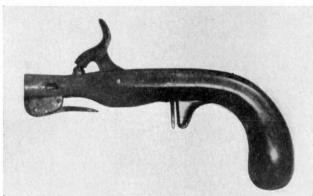

American flare pistol of the
Civil War period, Navy Model.
Collection of Francis A. Lord.

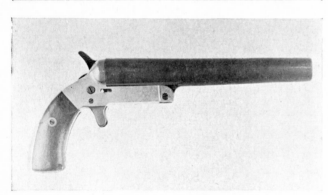

U.S. signal pistol of
the First World War, Mark III.

British signal pistol of
the First World War.

British Webley & Scott signal pistol,
Mark I, 1918.

English long fowler, mid-seventeenth century.
Curtis Museum, Alton, Hants.

English short fowling piece, mid-seventeenth century.
Curtis Museum, Alton, Hants.

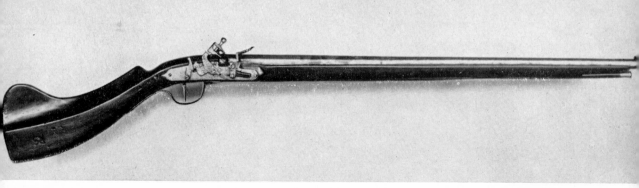

Detail of the locks and breech of a flintlock sporting gun by Joseph Manton, London, *ca.*1810. *Armouries, Tower of London.*

Manton double-barreled flintlock fowling piece. *Winchester Repeating Arms Company.*

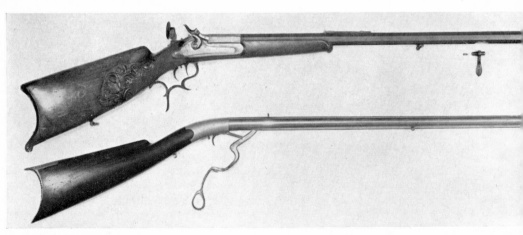

Two gallery guns: German *Zimmerstutzen* and American Forker indoor rifle. *Collection of Lewis Winant.*

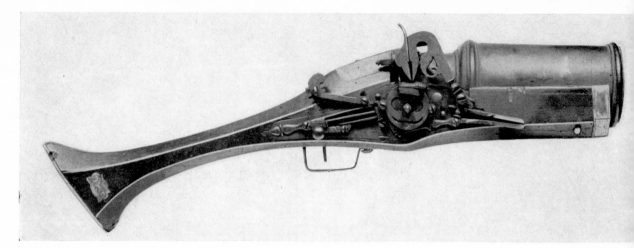

German wheel lock grenade launcher, late sixteenth century.
British Museum.

Saddle with grenade launcher, *ca.*1700. *Tøjhusmuseet, Copenhagen.*

Tinker's mortar carbines; the lower carbine shows the butt open to
load the cup, the stand lowered. *Armouries, Tower of London.*

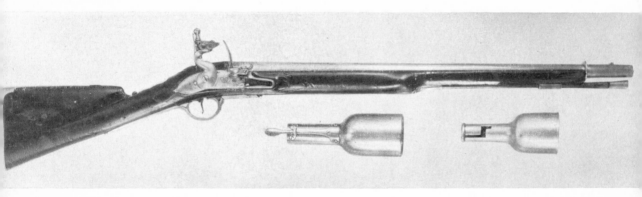

Grenade carbine, dated 1740 and marked "Roy^l Artillery", with cup detached. The left-hand cup,
from a gun by Wooldridge dated 1739, has a spring-clip fitting. *Armouries, Tower of London.*

A punt gun. *Photograph by John Hedgecoe, courtesy "The Observer."*

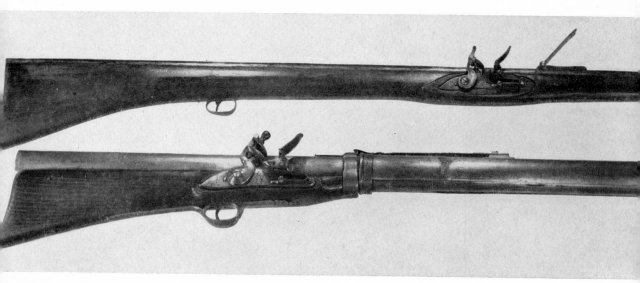

Rocket guns made to be fired from the shoulder, London, *ca.*1815. *Armouries, Tower of London.*

Eighteenth-century naval swivel gun of brass, 1½-inch bore.
Armouries, Tower of London.

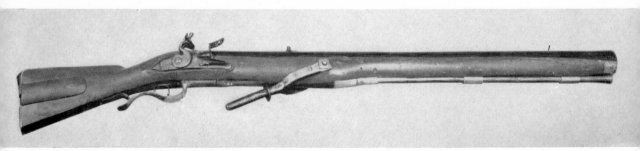

American swivel rifle, or amusette,
made at the Rappahannock Forge, Virginia, between 1775 and 1780.
West Point Museum Collections.

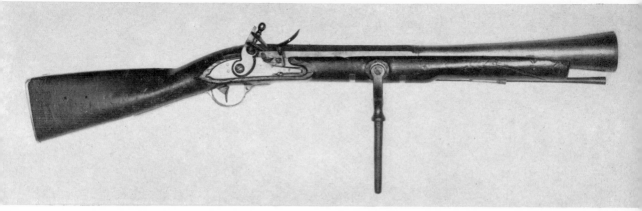

American blunderbuss on a swivel, made by T. French, Canton, Mass.

Chambers swivel gun. *Arms Museum, Liège*.

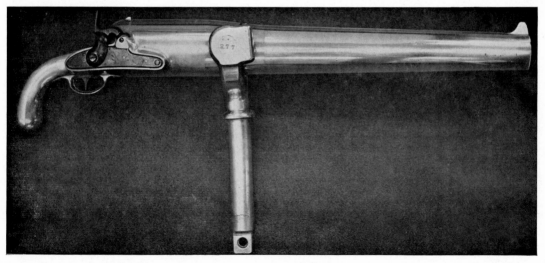

Boat swivel gun made in 1858 at the Navy Yard, Washington, D.C.;
percussion lock as on the standard U.S. musket Model 1842.
Marine Corps Museum, Quantico, Va.

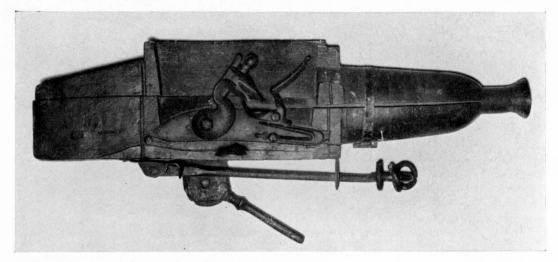

Flintlock trap gun. *Collection of Robert Abels.*

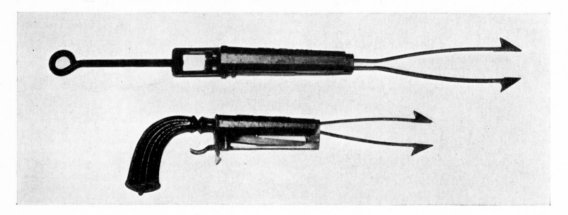

Reuthe trap guns. *Collection of Eddie Reider.*

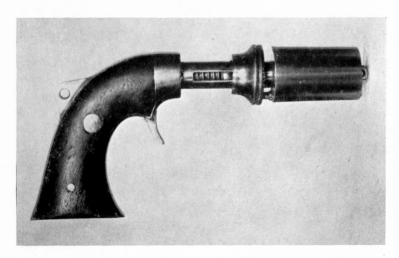

Reuthe game-getter.
Collection of Lewis Winant.

After the Second World War, the national arms manufactory of Saint-Étienne devoted a part of its capacity to the manufacture of sporting weapons, and it is now, in fact, the only center in France to do so.   CL.B.

SALOON GUN

See: GALLERY GUN.

SCANDINAVIAN SNAP LOCK

In the middle of the sixteenth century, the snap lock makes its first appearance in the Scandinavian countries, the earliest being 1547 (Sweden), 1562 (Norway) and 1565 (Denmark).

There are two main types of snap lock in these countries, called – not quite satisfactorily – the Swedish and the Norwegian types. The most conspicuous difference is that on the Swedish type the upper jaw of the cock is mortised, and later dovetailed at the back into the very short neck, while the Norwegian type has an upper jaw ending in a guiding pin through a hole in the lower jaw. A third type, which may have developed from the Swedish type, is the Baltic lock in which the upper jaw is formed as a leaf wrapping the neck of the cock.

The Swedish snap lock is generally believed, although this is not proved, to have come from North Germany, maybe at first in the form of arms support from Lübeck to the Swedish rebel leader Nils Dacke in 1542. At any rate in about 1550, snap locks were being made by a number of gunmakers in Sweden, both Swedes and immigrant Germans.

Probably the oldest surviving example is a snap lock gun in the Royal Armory, Stockholm, which for several reasons is connected with a royal order for thirty-five snap lock guns in 1556. In this, as in all Swedish snap locks prior to about 1650, the mainspring is placed on the outside of the lock plate, working from beneath on the spur of the cock. The fore-end of the spring acts on the steel, which is separated from the now missing pan cover. No doubt this was of the swing-out type found on other Swedish snap locks. The jaws of the cock are rather long with short lips bent slightly downwards.

Among the details developed on locks of the Swedish type are a triangular bridle covering the spur of the cock, and a sort of extra pan cover growing out of the reinforced lower rim of the steel. Full cock is established by the end of the Z-shaped sear protruding through the lock plate over the spur. Inside the lock plate the sear is located between two studs, or, more often, in a U-shaped mounting. Later the sear is divided into two members, a spring with a lug protruding through the lock plate, and a sear proper removing the lug when the trigger is pressed. As the steel can be laid forwards, thus making the lock safe, there is no half cock.

In the seventeenth century, a variation has a steel attached to the pan cover like the steel of a flintlock, but so that the steel proper may be turned at a right angle to the barrel, thus making the lock safe without uncovering the powder. While the older Swedish snap locks have a cock with jaws at right angles to the neck, the whole cock later became curved. By about 1650 most

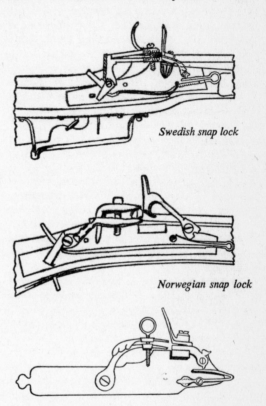

Swedish snap lock

Norwegian snap lock

Baltic snap lock

snap locks of the Swedish type had interior mainsprings, acting downwards on the toe of a tumbler connected with the cock. Locks with steels of the swing-out type and with steel and pan cover separated are equally often found. At the same time the lock plate, which originally was almost rectangular, became more curved, and, at least on locks made by gunmakers in the towns, often with a pronounced concave lower edge.

The snap lock was very popular in Sweden during the entire seventeenth century, while the wheel lock played only a very unimportant role. Even sporting guns of high quality ordered in Paris by Swedish noblemen were occasionally made with snap locks of the Swedish type, normally unknown to the French gunmakers. As late as the first half of the eighteenth century, snap lock guns were made by the town gunmakers in Sweden, although the flintlock became more and more predominant. In the country, and especially in the north of Sweden, the snap lock was in use long into the nineteenth century, and on some small islands in the Baltic even after 1900.

On Swedish snap lock muskets from the Thirty Years' War, locks both with swing-out steel and with separate steel are found. On most models the jaw screw was formed as a ring. As late as 1688, a snap lock musket was introduced in the Swedish Army. This Model 1688 had steel and pan cover in one piece, as did the ordinary flintlock. The mainspring, also serving as spring to the steel, acted downwards upon the toe of the cock. Half cock was made by a projecting stud under the toe, full cock by a square projection over the spur.

The Swedish snap lock was also made in the Norwegian and Danish border provinces. A special type was developed in the Danish-Swedish borderland of North Scania. The most conspicuous feature of this was a cock's comb with an intricate perforated pattern on the back of the upper jaw, and very often also a star-shaped bridle over the spur, decorated with corresponding perforations. Frequently the combined mainspring and steel spring had a bend round the foremost lock plate screw, a feature also now and then found on Swedish early seventeenth-century locks.

The Swedish-type snap locks found in Norway may be of Swedish manufacture, although it is more probable that they were made in Norway. Very few of them have any maker's signature or dating, but no doubt they were made at least as late as those in Sweden.

On the other side of Sweden, too, the Swedish-type snap lock was copied. The locks made in Finland, then a part of Sweden, differ only in having the cock screw placed further back than on the Swedish locks. In the Baltic provinces, which also belonged to Sweden until 1721, the special variation called the Baltic lock was made. Its cock has been discussed in the beginning of this article. Generally, the lock plate was of the wheel lock type, ending at the back in a leaf. Late examples (from the second half of the eighteenth century) were very curved. The steel was almost always of the swing-out type.

Just as the Swedish type did, the Norwegian-type snap lock also probably came from Germany, where snap locks with the same construction of the upper jaw of the cock are occasionally found, mostly dating from the last quarter of the sixteenth century. It is significant that the first mention of the snap lock in Norway refers to guns sold by the corporation of German merchants in Bergen. As Norwegian troops throughout the seventeenth and eighteenth centuries in most cases got their equipment from the central arsenal in Copenhagen, which was used by both the Danish and Norwegian armed forces, the Norwegian snap lock may also have been influenced by the type used in Denmark.

Besides the form of the cock, two other features are characteristic of the Norwegian-type snap lock. One is a sort of fence on the pan, developing in a shell pattern. In late town-made guns this shell may appear as a cartouche. The other feature is a special form of the sear. Like the Swedish, this sear is two-membered, but the branch of the sear acting upon the sear spring is shaped like a ring. The sear does not pivot around a vertical pin but is kept in position by a tiny bridle. This last feature is not found in all locks of the Norwegian type. The steel could be either the swing-out type or the type separated from the pan cover, with a preference for the latter.

The peasants of Norway, being woodsmen, soon took a liking to the snap lock which was then produced by clever country blacksmiths or even by the peasants themselves. Already in 1591 the commandant of the castle of Akershus ordered fifty long guns with snap locks "of the type which is now used in this realm," and a little later the national defense forces were permitted to serve with snap lock guns instead of wheel lock guns, because they were more used to the former. Owing to the conservatism of the peasants, there was hardly any development of the snap lock throughout the seventeenth and eighteenth centuries. The existing specimens include only a very few town-made snap lock guns, probably because in the towns the flintlock soon gained the upper hand over the snap lock. Among the Lapps of the far north of Norway, however, snap lock guns survived, almost to our own day, frequently transformed into percussion locks.

In Denmark, as mentioned above, the snap lock is known to have existed from the same time as in the other Scandinavian countries. Although it never acquired the same popularity as the wheel lock and later the flintlock, we find it frequently mentioned in literary sources. Of about 18,000 guns in the Copenhagen arsenal in 1609, one third were snap locks, while there were only very few of these fifty years later. It is, however, a curious fact that we do not have any snap lock gun from that time which can be proved to be Danish. Some few guns with stocks that seem Danish have early snap locks of the Swedish type with the jaws almost at right angles to the neck of the cock. Several of them have a curved finger-grip in one piece with the upper jaw, a feature not known on any proved Swedish snap lock. But what the Danish snap locks really looked like is still an open question.

A.H.

Illustrations: page 39.

Lenk, Torsten, "Nordiska snapplåsvapen. En orientering" [Scandinavian snaphance arms. An orientation] in *Svenska Vapenhistoriska Sällskapets Skrifter*, edited by Nils E. Hellsten, 2nd series, Vol. 2, Stockholm, 1952.

SCENT-BOTTLE LOCK

See: PERCUSSION SYSTEM.

SCHEEL, F. W.

Frederik Wilhelm Scheel, Norwegian officer and gun-designer, was born in 1795 at Stavanger, Norway, and died in 1876. In 1814 Scheel was commissioned in the Norwegian Army as an infantry officer, but soon transferred to the artillery, where he eventually became a lieutenant colonel.

In 1837 Scheel was made a member of a Royal Commission to propose new firearms for the Norwegian Army. The commission, after some consideration, recommended that the new weapons should be rifled breech-loading guns with percussion ignition. In answer to these demands, Scheel constructed a pistol which he presented in 1838. In this pistol he had worked together details from other different constructions. From the American Hall rifle, which he had read about in *Travels in America*, by Bernhard, Duke of Saxony, he took the upward movement of the breech. This was first moved backwards by means of an eccentric on its axis, as used by the Danish gunmaker Löbnitz. The lock was an underhammer construction, taken from the Swedish Whitelock experimental rifle. Later this lock was modified by the Norwegian gunmaker Gregersen, who placed the mainspring as a sort of guard around the cock.

Some rifles were made, with these details of construction, and in 1842 some one hundred rifles were put to a practical test by an infantry battalion. Shortly afterwards the Scheel rifle Pattern 1842 was adopted as the general arm of the whole Norwegian Army.

The Pattern 1842 was a strong and simple weapon, not very gas-tight but still moderately accurate. At a distance of two hundred els (approximately 140 yards) there were 70% hits in a figure of a standing man. The caliber was 16.8 mm., the paper cartridge containing a round ball and about six grains of powder. Most of the rifles were made at Kongsberg, the government gun factory.

In the following years a number of minor alterations were made – the introduction of a cylindro-conical ball in 1848 and the reduction of caliber to 11.7 mm. in 1860. When the Norwegian Army went over to a metal cartridge rifle in 1867 (the Remington), the best Scheel rifles were adapted to this new cartridge.

With the Scheel rifle, Norway was the first country to introduce a breech-loading percussion rifle for use by the entire army.　　　　　A.H.

Illustration: page 44.

Skaar, Fritz C., "Den norske Haers Kammerladnings-gevaerer" [The breech-loading guns of the Norwegian Army] in *Vaabenhistoriske Aarbøger*, edited by Arne Hoff, Vol. 4, Copenhagen, 1943.

See also: BREECHLOADERS.

SCHUETZEN RIFLE

The Schuetzen rifle is a specialized form intended for offhand target shooting according to well established rules. The earliest date which can be assigned to the formalized shooting which became known as the Schuetzen Festival is in the fifteenth century. The custom survived in Central Europe until about the beginning of the last century, after which America took the lead. Schuetzen shooting, as an active sport, did not survive the First World War.

Shooting was done in the offhand fashion, without artificial support. In the earlier days, when many guns were shot from rests, this was no doubt a difficult matter.

Rules similar to the European ones appear to have been in force at the Kentucky rifle shoots which represented the earliest American from of the European custom. Formalized American shooting festivals commenced around the middle of the last century, with the first national meeting being dated 1866. The Germanic character of the sport survived, and many Teutonic names were associated with it.

The Schuetzen rifle is very heavy and generally too clumsy for other uses. The octagonal barrels average well over an inch across the flats, are in the vicinity of thirty-two inches in length, and have thick and deep butt stocks, bringing average gun weights to twelve pounds. Weights up to sixteen pounds have been encountered. Stocks were fitted to the users, for which reason they appear to be uncomfortable to anyone of other dimensions.

The use of a stemmed palm rest was optional but expected. Either ball-ended rests or functionally shaped ends were used. The balance of the weapon dictated the position of attachment to the forestock.

Another characteristic feature of the Schuetzen rifle was the weight at the muzzle. In instances this was increased by the temporary attachment of metal, producing so unique a balance that, once appreciated, it proved ideal for the offhand type of stance required by the rules.

Inasmuch as such weights were not permanently attached, they do not appear on surviving specimens.

Schuetzen matches were noted for the individuality of the equipment. Shooting was slow and deliberate, as was necessitated by the careful charging of the muzzle-loaders. Any rifle was acceptable; any form or weight was allowed; any charge was permitted, whether black or smokeless powder or any combination of these, and the bullet weight and design were optional with the shooter. Calibers ranged from about .32 to as high as .45. The result was a heterogeneous assembly of equipment, with duplication well-nigh impossible.

Apart from the rules regarding safety and progression of shooters, another is worthy of note. No shooter was allowed to place the butt of the rifle, when aiming, under his coat, vest or suspender. This followed the rule, first noted in the great prize shoot at Zurich in 1472, that the gun, when fired, was not to be supported by any strap in the sleeve or around the neck.

Targets were clearly identified in the program of the National Schuetzen Bund of America, dated 1898, and were quite standard over the years of the sport.

The Stich Target Germania consisted of a twelve-inch disc with a six-inch bull's-eye. Only hits in the bull's-eye were counted.

The Honor Target Columbia, otherwise known as the German ring target, consisted of 25 concentric rings, spaced three quarters of an inch apart, with the inner ring $1\frac{1}{4}$ inches in diameter. Values commenced at 1 in the outer ring, progressing to 25. The 12-inch bull's-eye had values from 18 to 25.

Man targets and the American Standard were also employed. Local meets, which were not as elaborate as the national ones, generally used only ring targets. Shooting ranges were generally at two hundred yards.

Without doubt German immigrants brought their target rifles with them to America; and similar weapons were produced there, with improvements, to meet the demand. Local gunsmiths supplied the greater part of the need, particularly in the Ohio River basin and in the Great Lakes region, where even small towns often had their makers.

Three recognizable forms of Schuetzen rifle are known: muzzle-loaders, muzzle-breech-loaders, and breechloaders. The muzzle-loader, being the original type, and widely made, was probably the best known for many years and survived actively to the end of the Schuetzen era. The remaining two types gained in popularity, but were the products of a limited number of manufacturers. Recognized and identifiable models became available but, though factory products, were still subject to the whims of the customer. Custom assembly of standard parts and the addition of special barrels were common.

Certain barrelmakers added their elements to otherwise commercial breech parts.

The muzzle-loader is characterized by the presence of a false muzzle. After loading, the false muzzle was removed and the shot fired. Shooting was, accordingly, quite slow and deliberate.

As breechloaders, basically of the Ballard design but with manufacturers' patented variations, became popular, the muzzle-breech-loader appeared. Such a rifle was charged at the breech with a powder-loaded cartridge. The bullet was loaded with a false muzzle, as previously. Harry M. Pope is recognized as the most famous maker employing this system. His rifles have never been surpassed.

As the traditionally formal Schuetzen shooting gradually declined and other techniques gained popularity, the true breechloader was accepted, although the appearance of the newer products continued to suggest the old system. Manufacturers became still more limited in numbers and products were definitely standardized. Among the last of the makers who produced this breechloading form of Schuetzen rifle one finds the names of Ballard (produced by Marlin), Winchester, Stevens, Bullard, Remington, Sharps, and others. So-called target rifles which date within the last half century are not true Schuetzen weapons, but instead follow structural form and shooting techniques of a more recent date.

E.G.W.

Illustration: page 107.

Smith, Ray M., *The Story of Pope's Barrels*, Harrisburg, Pa., 1960.

See also: TARGET RIFLE.

SCOTTISH FIREARMS

No example survives of a wheel lock or matchlock gun of Scottish origin, but it is known that they were used from the frequent documentary references to muskets in Scotland fitted with *rowet*- and *lunt*-works. The words originate from the French *platine à rouet*, meaning a wheel lock, and the German *Luntenschloss*, a matchlock. Both were largely superseded for civilian use before 1600, by the first version of the Scottish snaphance lock, but the less costly matchlock lingered on as a military arm with one prime advantage so far as the king was concerned. By keeping available stocks of match in his arsenals the king could control, by the issue or withholding of match, the amount of shooting that went on in his continually troubled country. Between issues, the militia, which formed the greater part of the available military force, retained its muskets, which were harmless without supplies of match.

The earliest surviving examples of Scottish guns and pistols are fitted with the distinctively Scottish form of snaphance lock which was in use at least by the last quarter of the sixteenth century. This lock had the common feature of a separate pan cover and steel, the cover being connected by a rod to the tumbler. On firing, the rod pushed the pan cover forward before the flint struck fire on the steel. The end of the pan carried a small circular or hexagonal fence or shield which was frequently engraved with the date of manufacture. These dates can be accepted only with reservations, as many surviving pieces are fitted with detachable pans held in position on the lockplate by one or two screws. The reason is seen in several guns and pistols that have their pans burnt or corroded through. A second hazard can be seen in one gun whose fence has been fractured at the notch which serves as a stop for the peg on the outer edge of the pan cover. If the cover was returned too sharply, it might easily break the fence. In the early Scottish snaphance lock there is no half-cock position. At full cock the nose of the sear projects through the lockplate and engages a hooked spur at the base of the cock. In slightly later versions, the hooked cock gave way to one with a rounded base with either a pierced slot or a shallow recess to receive the nose of the sear.

This mechanism continued in use until about 1685, by which date the more advanced form of the snaphance lock was used throughout Scotland. In the second type, which seems to have seen service from about 1647 to just after 1700, to judge by existing firearms which use the system, the sear still worked horizontally but now engaged a notch in the tumbler. The steel was still separate from the pan cover, and the lock lacked the bridle which would have made it more efficient.

Pistols fitted with the early form of lock are found in a variety of materials and styles. The earliest examples have wooden stocks with flat butts of the type described by collectors as a "fishtail butt." These terminate in a scrolling butt cap of brass or silver, engraved with traditional rosettes, leaf scrolls, scale and cable patterns. Several early single pistols and pairs have stocks of sheet brass made both in the fishtail shape and in the clumsier type of a few years later which has an oval pommel faceted, engraved and occasionally pierced. All have belt hooks, even the longest which were awkward to handle because of their weight and length. One pair, of notable quality, is dated 1614 and fitted with pommels which unscrew to allow a rod to withdraw from the butt. This can then be supported against the shoulder like a carbine butt. Throughout the seventeenth century pistols were made in pairs with right- and left-hand locks. At the beginning of the century the triggers, which never had trigger guards, were shaped like a short baluster, to

flatten later into an oblate spheroid formed of two shells of silver or other metal soldered or brazed along their joint.

Towards the middle of the seventeenth century, the least attractive type of Scottish pistol was developed. Slab-sided, with two scrolling "horns" of steel at the butt, it was the immediate predecessor in style of the most typical Scots pistol of the following two centuries. Screwed into the butt between the horns was a touchhole pricker that remained a standard feature on all Scottish pistols from then until they ceased to be used even as accessories to Highland dress. Several writers have suggested that these slab-sided pistols evolved from the slender, graceful, fishtail type, but it is difficult to trace more than a distant relationship.

About the same time, the English influence on Scottish arms design was responsible for the introduction of the combined steel and pan cover. The earliest example is on an over-cleaned all-steel pistol dated 1665. Fitted with a dog catch and with no half-cock bent on the tumbler, it is of the northeastern "heart butt" type, which forms quite a substantial proportion of the seventeenth-century Scottish pistols that survive. A few of these are signed in full on the lockplate, and a number, such as one in the Tower Armouries by John Burges of Elgin, bear the maker's town as well as his name. The rarest pistol of this group is by the very fine maker John Stuart, and has a wooden stock and silver mounts. It dates from ca.1700 and has a fully developed Scottish lock.

Contemporary with the earliest snaphance pistols is a type of distinctively Scottish gun of which only two examples appear to have surived until the present day. One of these was once owned by King Louis XIII of France (1601–43) and is now in the Tower Armouries. The other was made for a famous Scotsman, Sir John Grant of Freuchie (1596–1637), whose initials, coats of arms and title are engraved on its silver butt cap and on a silver plate on the barrel. The brass lockplate of the Grant gun is engraved on the fence with the date 1635, but this is probably the date of a replacement pan, as it is very similar to the Tower gun which is dated 1614 on both lock and barrel. The guns are also stamped with the initials of their makers, both of whom worked in Dundee at the same time.

The stocks of these two pleasantly proportioned guns are of Brazil wood (*Guilandina echinata* Lam. Spreng), an expensive, red, close-grained wood which was popular with the gentry of Scotland for fine gunstocks. Pistols of the same period are also found with Brazil-wood stocks. The guns are both inlaid with silver in rather crude ornament. That on the Grant gun includes an equestrian figure, animals, fish and the coat of arms of Dundee. The town was well known for its firearms as early as 1600. An inventory of that year refers to a gun similar to both of those described above and calls it a gilt piece "wt the lairds arms that come out of Dundie stockit wt brissell." Other woods popular in Scotland included walnut, which was frequently referred to as "wanet trie" in contemporary accounts.

Both the Tower and the Grant guns have full-length fore-ends and butts that slope downward slightly before curving upwards toward their butt caps. The stock shape is rather angular in section with the butt narrow from side to side, giving a long, rectangular cross section. Each has a trigger guard – rare on any Scottish weapon – to protect the short baluster trigger. The slightly later Grant gun has a series of shallow flutings carved on the butt, a feature which was emphasized on later guns and rifles made in Scotland.

After Sir John Grant's gun, there is a gap of some years before the next dateable Scottish gun on record. In common with many Scottish firearms, it carries the arms and initials of its original owner, James, fifth Earl and first Marquis of Montrose, who was hanged and dismembered as a traitor in Edinburgh on May 21, 1650. The breech is engraved with the partly illegible date 16—. The early snaphance lock bears the maker's initials "IS" under a crown of three points. The major difference between the Grant and Montrose guns is that the latter has the fully developed stock with a considerable curve to the butt which is carved with a series of deep flutes close to its upper edge. Just behind the lock on top of the stock is a cut-out notch for the right thumb, a feature that begins on the earliest Scottish gun and, although uncommon abroad, runs on to the last of seventeenth-century make. From the Montrose gun onwards, none has a trigger guard; many have flared muzzles, brass or silver inlaid panels on the barrels, and butt caps of brass or silver made in the form of shallow rectangular boxes to fit over the butt.

The finest Scottish long arm to survive belonged to a grandson of Sir John Grant, Ludovic Grant (?1650–1716), whose initials and coat of arms appear on the barrel of a superb silver-mounted rifle of .79 inch caliber, dated 1667 on the barrel and 1671 on the lockplate. The stock is carved with shallow interlace and fern patterns, and the silver mounts are exceptionally fine, engraved with simple but effective floral ornament.

The only known Scottish breechloader of this period is also a rifle, with a simple turn-off action. The lockplate is engraved with the initials "GS" of the maker, probably Guilielmus (i.e. William) Smith of Grantown, and the date 1686. This rifle of .68 caliber is of unusually heavy construction.

The last recorded Scottish gun that retains any of its national characteristics is dated 1703 and signed on the lockplate "John Stuart." The gun has almost the lines of a contemporary English fowling piece, but there is still the suggestion of a curve to the butt, below which is a small floral carving in the Scottish tradition.

At the same time as the gunmakers of Scotland were turning out their highly individual productions, the "horners" were making a type of powder horn that was no less easily recognisable as Scottish. A considerable number of these survive, all made from curved, yellow-gray cow or bull horn flattened after soaking in hot water and decorated with engraved geometric designs, scrolls, coats of arms and foliage of great complexity. The finest are extremely well executed. Many are dated between 1650 and 1750, which may be taken as the peak period of the craft of making and of the art of decorating them. Additional engraving sometimes includes the names of the owner and the maker, and long mottoes in English or Gaelic are not uncommon. The variations in size show that they were made in proportions for use with guns or with pistols. Few of the surviving horns retain their mounts, which consisted of a pewter, brass or silver nozzle and a plug of the same material, occasionally made in the form of a thistle and retained by a thong or a slender chain. On the upper edge of the flask were two or three small loops to take a shoulder cord.

Bandoliers were also used in Scotland in the seventeenth and early eighteenth centuries, the small chargers being made from a variety of materials and slung from a narrow crossbelt. Few of these have survived, since, unlike the horns, they had little or no aesthetic value and there was not much about them to which a "history" could be attached.

By 1690, the fully developed Scottish pistol could be said to have arrived in common use, the direct descendant of the slab-sided, ram's horn butt pistol of the middle of the century. It retained a more elegant version of the butt shape, the flaring faceted muzzle, the belt hook, the pricker and the general lines of its predecessor, but was shorter and more heavily ornamented. Its new lock had a combined steel and pan cover and an improved action in which the peg at the tail of the horizontally operating sear engaged the tumbler at full cock. At half cock the elongated nose of the sear projected through the lockplate to engage the breast of the cock. Many pairs of pistols survive with left- and right-hand locks of this type from the eighteenth and early nineteenth centuries, most of them *armes de luxe* with carefully executed engraved and silver inlaid ornament and with silver escutcheons with their owners' arms and mottoes on the barrels or the butts. The names of their makers and their town of origin are almost invariably found on the lockplates, among them Cadell, Murdoch, and Christie of Doune in Perthshire. This little village achieved such fame for the quality of the arms produced there that many collectors speak of "Doune" pistols as though the makers of Dundee, Stirling, Edinburgh, Leith and many other towns never existed. Close in style to these "typical" pistols is a group that seems to have been made mostly by Thomas Murdoch of Edinburgh, that resembles them in every respect other than that they have hemispherical ends to the butts instead of the ram's horn terminals. The rounded ends allow a neater shape also to the actual grip.

In 1757, in addition to the muskets and bayonets carried by the other ranks and the halberds of the sergeants, the soldiers commanded by Colonels Simon Fraser and Archibald Montgomery were issued with pistols. These troops belonged to the newly formed Highland Battalions of Foot. By 1762, however, the pistols issued to the Highlanders were no longer of native make but came from the workshops of Birmingham.

Two different types of Birmingham military pistols are known to have been issued. The more traditional form is retained in the belt hook and the ram's horn butt of a series of all-steel pistols which are engraved on the lockplate with the name of the Birmingham maker Isaac Bissell. Their 8-inch barrels bear the initials of the Royal Highland Regiment. The second type, mentioned in documents of 1788, is less ornate and the gun metal butt terminates in a kidney shape with flattened sides. The steel barrels of this group usually bear the stamp of John Waters, also of Birmingham. By February 1795, Highland regiments no longer carried these pistols that were described at one time as "coarse popguns, resembling more the tin toys of a bazaar than the weapons of an army."

The great days of the traditional pistol made by masters of the gunsmith's craft were virtually over from the day pistols were no longer issued to Scottish troops. The traditionally styled pistols that survive in considerable numbers from a later period are largely ornate presentation pieces, sometimes exquisitely made but impractical, and those made to enhance Highland dress. The steel stocks lost something of the freedom of an earlier age, and on some the butt, or even the entire stock, was of copper gilt with applied decoration of silver or enameled plaques. One pair which was presented to the Prince of Wales in 1800 is of blued steel inlaid with gold floral sprays. This pair, which has the additional luxury of gold and silver touchhole prickers, was made by the Edinburgh makers Innes and Wallace, who by this date were making high-quality guns and pistols in the style then current in England. One superb cased set of their small traveling pistols with carbine stock and accessories is equal to the best of its type made in Britain. The Prince of Wales's gift seems to have been, like other examples, a very special exception to their general run of

practical work. But presentation orders were not enough to keep the Scottish gunmakers in business, and they were fortunate that the Prince of Wales's visit to Edinburgh in 1822 caused a romantic tidal wave of interest in Scottish antiquities, costume and culture. This in turn led to such a demand for plaid brooches, dirks, skean dhus and, naturally, pairs of pistols, as had not been seen since the Rising of 1745. The craft of the Allisons and the Stuarts, the Murdochs and the Campbells, was gone for ever, to be replaced by ill-proportioned knick-knacks. At the end of the story one finds only nickel-plated percussion-lock monsters, sold by jewelers and outfitters.

Scottish gunmakers continued to make top-grade shotguns and rifles and to be closely concerned with the development of small arms, but they could not long compete against the close-knit gunmakers' community of Birmingham and the well advertised, if exaggerated, reputation of the London houses. In recent times, production has been virtually limited to custom-made shotguns and rifles made to the special order of a small but discriminating clientele.   W.R.

Illustrations: pages 269–71, and endpapers.

Whitelaw, Charles E., "Treatise on Scottish hand firearms" in *European Hand Firearms of the Sixteenth, Seventeenth and Eighteenth Centuries*, edited by Herbert J. Jackson, London, 1923.

See also: FARQUHARSON RIFLE; FERGUSON RIFLE; FORSYTH, ALEXANDER JOHN.

SCUPPET

See: ESCOPETTE.

SELF-LOADING ARMS

See: AUTOMATIC ARMS.

SEMI-AUTOMATIC ARMS

See: AUTOMATIC ARMS.

SET TRIGGER

The set trigger was a device for increasing the delicacy and surety of the trigger in the discharge of a firearm. In the earlier firearms of snap-matchlock, wheel lock, and flintlock type, the mainspring employed was frequently very powerful. It was necessary to hold the considerable force of this spring in check with absolute surety, yet to be able to release it, at the instant of firing the arm, with-

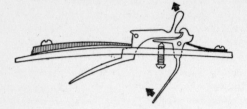

Simple set trigger mechanism from a wheel lock gun

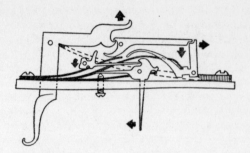

Compound set trigger mechanism consisting of a primary mechanism with one intermediate lever and a simple secondary mechanism

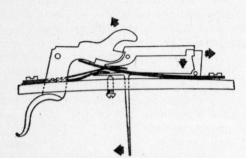

Set trigger mechanism with one intermediate lever, from a seventeenth-century wheel lock rifle

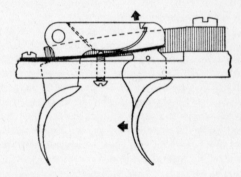

Double set trigger mechanism from a modern Mauser hunting rifle

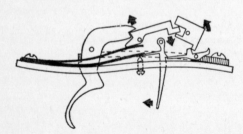

Set trigger mechanism with three intermediate levers

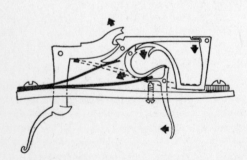

Set trigger mechanism with three intermediate levers

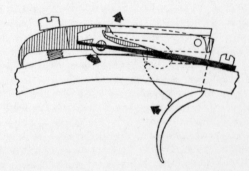

Single set trigger from an early nineteenth-century percussion pistol

out applying so much force as would deflect the weapon from an accurate aim. The set trigger was developed concurrently with, and similarly to, the release action of the sporting crossbow. It first appeared as an independent mechanism, separately removable from the weapon, about the middle of the sixteenth century. Mechanically it is similar to a percussion-type gunlock. A hammer is forced forward by a strong spring; it is pulled back by hand, against the action of this spring, until it is caught and held by a catch which itself moves under the impetus of a weaker spring. Pulling back on the catch releases the hammer which, under the impetus of its spring, flies forward and delivers a powerful blow. In firearms this blow is delivered against the trigger of the gunlock, giving to that trigger a sharper and quicker release than could ever be given it by the finger alone.

In order to reduce the pull necessary to release the set trigger mechanism, resort is had to various devices. Intermediate levers may be employed between the hammer and the catch; some set triggers have as many as three. Each additional lever, while increasing the cost, complexity, and delicacy of the apparatus, also increases its sensitivity. In some late wheel lock rifles the set trigger mechanism is compound: one set trigger operates upon the wheel lock discharge mechanism, but has no part protruding; a second complete set trigger mechanism operates not upon the lock but upon the release catch of the first set trigger.

The earlier set triggers were always double; that is, two triggers protruded below the stock of the gun. The shooter pulled back one of them to arm the mechanism; a light pull on the second would then release the set trigger mechanism which in turn would activate the gun lock and discharge the gun. The length of pull of this firing trigger was made adjustable by a screw in the base plate of the set trigger mechanism.

With the later wheel locks, the mainspring was so strong that it was impracticable to release the lock except by the set trigger, but with flint and percussion discharge mechanisms it was often found convenient to arrange a set trigger mechanism so that the firing trigger could release the gunlock either with or without the use of the set trigger. A long pull on the firing trigger would fire the gun in the ordinary way. But if the setting trigger were pulled first, the set trigger mechanism would be spanned and thereafter a very light pull on the firing trigger would discharge the piece. With later flintlocks, percussion locks and cartridge arms, set triggers were often made single, i.e. a single trigger functioned as both setting and firing trigger. When pulled straight back, it fired the gun in the ordinary way. When pushed forward, it spanned the set trigger device; thereafter, only a slight rearward pull was needed to discharge the piece. T.T.H.

Hoopes, Thomas T., "The Double Set Trigger" in *A Miscellany of Arms and Armor*, New York, 1927.

SHARPS, CHRISTIAN

Christian Sharps, born at Washington, New Jersey, in 1811, was apprenticed in the machinist's trade after a grade school education. Details of his early life are few, and the date when he took up gunmaking is uncertain.

In 1848, while living in Cincinnati, Ohio, he filed his first patent papers on his new dropping breechblock percussion rifle but there is reason to believe that he developed his design at the Daniel Nippes armory at Mill Creek, Pennsylvania. A small number of his arms were manufactured initially by the Massachusetts Arms Company and by Robbins & Lawrence of Windsor, Vermont.

In 1851 he formed the Sharps Rifle Manufacturing Company, a stock corporation, at Hartford, Connecticut, to produce his rifles at a royalty of $1.00 each. Sharps resigned from the firm in 1853, and was never again directly associated with it.

Going to Philadelphia in 1854, he formed C. Sharps & Company, which first produced his single-shot percussion pistol. A later development was his famous four-barreled pistol. The four barrels, bored from a solid block, slid forward to load .22 or .32 rim-fire cartridges.

Sharps entered into partnership in 1862 with William Hankins, riflemaker of Philadelphia, and produced the caliber .52 rim-fire Sharps & Hankins carbine. This is a different weapon from the well-known dropping breech percussion arm made by the entirely separate Sharps Rifle Manufacturing Company. Individual states and the Federal government bought an unknown (but sizeable) number of Sharps & Hankins carbines in the Civil War.

Following the war, the firm produced the successful four-barreled Sharps pistols at Philadelphia, probably until Sharps's death. He died at Vernon, Connecticut, on March 13, 1874, aged sixty-two. D.B.W.

Illustrations: pages 46, 178.

See also: SHARPS RIFLES AND CARBINES.

SHARPS RIFLES AND CARBINES

The Sharps Rifle Manufacturing Company of Hartford, Connecticut, was founded in 1851 by Christian Sharps to produce his dropping breechblock percussion arms. Sharps assigned the company his patents for a royalty of $1.00 per rifle. He managed the firm, but probably did not own a controlling interest, and resigned in 1853, severing all direct connection.

The Sharps plant was built at Hartford in 1853 and

managed by the Windsor, Vermont, firm of Robbins & Lawrence. As well as box-lock prototypes and sporting rifles, the firm produced the M1852 carbine, which had a sloping breech and brass furniture. A variation was the M1855, with Maynard tape primer. The M1852 and variations are probably most famous as the "Beecher's Bibles" sent from Massachusetts in 1856 to John Brown in Kansas.

When Robbins & Lawrence failed, about 1855, control of the Sharps company reverted to the stockholders, with R.S. Lawrence as plant manager.

The first of the vertical breech carbines was the M1859, an arm purchased in some numbers by the government. In 1863 it was simplified as the New Model 1863, the last of the Sharps percussion arms. The firm also produced a full-length military rifle with a bayonet.

During the Civil War the government purchased 9,141 rifles and 80,512 carbines of both 1859 and 1863 models.

The company entered a carbine in the 1865 army trials for breech-loading cartridge arms, but it was not adopted. Thereafter, many existing percussion carbines were converted to the new .50–70 cartridge and used by both the army and hunters.

The company brought out a varied line of cartridge sporting rifles, based on a converted military action, after the war. The gun market was saturated, however, and production was cut back, until in 1871 the Sharps plant was sold to the Weed Sewing Machine Company, with only a small part leased for arms manufacturing.

The Sharps Rifle Manufacturing Company was reorganized and refinanced in 1874 as the Sharps Rifle Company, and a simplified action was produced as the basis of a variety of sporting, target, and buffalo rifles. Beautifully made and finished, most of the 1874 rifles were probably manufactured almost on a custom basis, for many different cartridges.

In 1876 the Sharps Company moved to a new plant at Bridgeport, so that the 1874-type rifles are found with either Hartford or Bridgeport markings.

The Sharps Rifle Company brought out, in 1878, the hammerless Borchardt action designed by Hugo Borchardt, chief engineer at the Bridgeport factory. Made in a number of sporting models and a .45–70 military type, the Sharps-Borchardt, although a superb rifle, was shortlived.

In 1881, the company ceased production and the firm went out of business.   D.B.W.

Illustrations: page 46.

Smith, Winston O., *The Sharps Rifle*, New York, 1943.

See also: BREECHLOADERS; SHARPS, CHRISTIAN.

SHAW, JOSHUA

Joshua Shaw, who was born at Bellingborough, England, in 1776, and died at Bordentown, New Jersey, in 1860, is the man credited by many with being the inventor of the percussion cap. Shaw, after he came to America, undoubtedly produced many thousands of these igniters of gunpowder, but his claim to primacy of invention is no stronger than the claims set forth on behalf of several other men (see PERCUSSION SYSTEM). It is certain that Shaw was not the first patentee.

Joshua Shaw was the son of a farmer who died when Joshua was seven. At fifteen he was given seven weeks' schooling by an uncle and was then apprenticed to a sign painter. From sign painting he went on to become a moderately successful artist. He moved to America in 1817, apparently disappointed with his status in England. He arrived in Philadelphia aboard the "Electra" on the 13th of October of that year, bringing with him as a gift to the Philadelphia Hospital from his friend, Benjamin West, that famous artist's huge painting, "Christ Healing the Sick."

Shaw did some experimenting with percussion ignition in England shortly before he migrated to the United States. In his adopted country he continued to work on the problem, and, after establishing the two years' residence required by United States law, applied for a patent for a percussion cap. The patent was granted in 1822, despite the fact that France had, more than twenty months earlier, given patents for percussion caps to two Frenchmen, Prélat and Deboubert.

The Twenty-ninth Congress, after being given an incorrect report by F. W. Risque asserting that there was no patent, European or American, for a percussion cap, dated earlier than 1822, authorized a monetary award to Shaw. The exact amount of the award, made largely in consequence of Shaw's work for the Frankford Arsenal, was stipulated to be determined by the then Secretary of War, W. L. Marcy. Marcy conferred with the Ordnance Office and was told that $12,500 would be an ample sum. But Marcy took it upon himself to make the amount $18,000, and on May 4, 1847, Shaw collected that amount, receipting for the payment as "a full compensation for the past and present use of his invention."

Shaw's early years, from his own account, were years of hardship. His last seem to have been no better. In 1854, by which time he had become paralyzed, he claimed, in petitioning Congress for an additional award of $7,000, that he was "now old and infirm and reduced to poverty." The petition was not granted.

In his later years Shaw lived in Bordentown, New Jersey. He bought a house there in 1847, and died there on September 2, 1860, a year in which Mrs. Willetts, one of his two married daughters, petitioned Congress, again unsuccessfully, for $7,000 for relief. (It is recorded that Shaw married in Manchester while he was still working as a sign painter. Nothing more is known of his household.)

Shaw wrote many letters in the 1820's to the Franklin Institute and to the Frankford Arsenal, both in Philadelphia. In these letters he made it clear that he was primarily interested in painting and secondarily in the manufacture of percussion caps.

Shaw was the author of *Picturesque Views of America, 1820*, a rare book consisting of nineteen colored plates, each as painted by Shaw. This was published after Shaw's trip through the West with a United States government exploratory expedition. Shaw was also the author of the now extremely scarce *A Sketch or History of the Copper Cap, and Percussion Artillery Primer*, published in 1847 when he was living in Bordentown. Shaw also compiled the *United States directory for the use of travellers and merchants, giving an account of the principal establishments, of business and pleasure*, published in Philadelphia in 1822. In that directory is a listing, "J. Shaw, Philadelphia – Historical Landscape Painter."   L.W.

Blackmore, Howard L., *British Military Firearms, 1650–1850*, London, 1961.

Peterson, Harold L., *The Treasury of the Gun*, New York, 1962 (*The Book of the Gun*, London, 1963).

Winant, Lewis, *Early Percussion Firearms*, New York, 1959, and London, 1961.

See also: PERCUSSION SYSTEM.

SHOT

Sportsmen began to use shot in smoothbore guns early in the history of firearms. Buckshot, "swan drops," and small shot were being used in Italy about the middle of the sixteenth century. They had been used even earlier in England. One of the first shot-manufacturing plants was started in Paris, and soon afterwards the industry became established in England.

In the early days, individual hunters molded their own shot of the larger sizes, using multiple molds. Some of them cast several different sizes at once. Fine shot was made by chopping up sheet lead. Casting shot was a slow, laborious process. As early as the seventeenth century, individuals had made shot by pouring molten lead through a sieve and letting the drops thus formed fall into a bowl of water to cool and solidify. The shot tower refined this process, taking advantage of the natural law that causes drops of liquid to assume a spherical shape in free fall.

A shot tower has to be high enough for a melted lead droplet to have time to solidify before reaching the bottom. This requires quite a tall structure. Most of the old ones were made with bricks, like a tall chimney. Modern shot towers are usually incorporated into conventionally constructed steel-frame buildings, but are still relatively high for their cross section.

Lead for modern shot is alloyed. Pure lead is too soft. Besides producing irregular shot, the product would be easily deformed in loading and firing, with resulting loss of accuracy and poor patterns. A small amount of arsenic added to melted lead makes the drops form more spherically. Shot made from this alloy is known in the trade as drop shot. Adding some antimony makes the shot harder, with better performance. This kind is known as chilled shot. It is sometimes further improved by copper, nickel, or other hard plating.

The lead is carried to the top of the tower, then melted and poured through a sieve, just as in the ancient method. The sieve has holes corresponding to the size of shot to be made. As the melted lead falls through the sieve and down to the bottom of the tower, it forms into spheres, which have time to solidify before striking a water bath at the bottom. The shot is then graded for size, as there is always some variation. Several sizes usually result from each batch dropped. After grading for size, the shot are rolled down a smooth inclined plane. Any that are irregular in shape fall off at the sides and are remelted. The resulting uniformly graded shot is then sacked in convenient quantities, five- and twenty-five-pound bags being customary.

Although shot formed in a shot tower is good enough for most purposes, the only way to ensure absolute uniformity is to make the shot by some mechanical means, so as to be perfectly round and uniform in weight. This kind of shot will provide the best performance of any type available, and is preferred by trap, pigeon, and skeet competitors.

Though shotgun shells have been standardized in recent years as to bore and chamber sizes, there is still much variation in the numerical designation of shot sizes.

BIRD SHOT SIZES AND QUANTITIES

Diameter (inches)	Number per oz.	English size	French & German size	U.S. size
.03	–	–	–	Fine Dust
.04	4565	–	–	Dust
.05	2326	–	12	12
.06	1346	12	11	11
.07	848	10	10	10
.075	688	–	–	9½
.08	568	9	9	9

Diameter (inches)	Number per oz.	English size	French & German size	U.S. size
.085	472	8	–	8½
.09	399	7	8	8
.095	338	–	–	7½
.10	291	6	7	7
.11	218	5	6	6
.12	168	4	5	5
.13	132	3	4	4
.14	106	2	3	3
.15	86	1	2	2
.16	71	B	1	1
.175	55	BB	–	Air Rifle

BUCKSHOT SIZES AND QUANTITIES

Diameter (inches)	Number per lb.	U.S. size
.25	299	3
.27	238	2
.30	176	1
.32	144	0
.34	128	00
.36	112	000

B.R.L.

See also: BALLISTICS; BULLET MOLD; FOWLING PIECE; SHOT POUCH.

SHOTGUN

See: FOWLING PIECE.

SHOT POUCH

A small container meant to be carried by the hunter or his loader, made of any of a variety of materials such as leather, wood, horn, metal or a combination of these, and containing the shot with which he loaded his fowling piece, shotgun or punt gun. It was an important accessory to hunters using muzzle-loading firearms and was in use until the general acceptance of the self-contained brass and paper shot shell in the last quarter of the nineteenth century. Some primitive peoples in Africa and elsewhere still carry the shot for loading their modern flintlock fowling pieces in brass flasks.

Shot was carried in a multitude of ways – in one's hunting pouch, in the pocket, or in a soft or hard flask. Early powder and shot pouches of the sixteenth century were often made by the Guild of Pouch Makers, who also manufactured many other types of bags, purses and pouches, which dangled from the girdles and belts of the Middle Ages. Less wealthy shooters probably made their own. Pouches were often made to be carried upside down,

the theory being that this caused less pressure by the shot and was less likely to break open the seams or stitching; a preference for loading in this position may have been the real reason.

Early shot containers were apt to be more like the bags or girdle bags carried by huntsmen. These were of soft leather or buff leather, often contained items other than shot, and were carried about the waist. Some types are difficult to recognize because of both their means of manufacture and their origin. Early hard shot flasks looked much like wine flasks, were made of *cuir bouilli* (boiled leather) and decorated much like these early vessels. Unfortunately this common and perhaps often dual usage contributed to their quick disintegration and few of these early types are now extant. If is difficult to determine the true identity and age of many early shot flasks because the shapes and forms were and are similar both to powder flasks and to pouches utilized for other purposes.

Lever shot chargers are usually associated with the nineteenth century, but this form of container was made as far back as 1570 by a German, David Altenstetter.

The eighteenth century saw many innovations in shotgun ammunition, including new methods of making shot. Early shot had been made by rolling bits of lead between stone or metal plates until they had achieved some degree of roundness. Later shot was made by pouring molten lead into water. Neither of these methods produced really uniformly spherical shot, and the question of "pattern" as we know it today was of no great importance. Thus uniformity of shot charge and the means of measuring it were equally of no import. All this changed after 1782 as the result of the efforts of a plumber of Bristol, England, who in that year devised the shot tower. Molten lead was now poured down from a high tower so that it passed through a long, slightly cooling column of air before it hit the cooling water. During its descent it had time to become more or less spherical, at least much more so than in the previous methods of manufacture. With good shot now available, and some constancy of shooting now possible, the era of shot pouches, shot measures, shot chargers and shot belts began in earnest.

It has been said that the greatest development in ammunition has been in the manner of carrying it. The late eighteenth and nineteenth centuries provided innovations in both the shot belt and the shot pouch. Uniformity of shot and some degree of accuracy in shooting brought forth literally hundreds of shot measuring and carrying devices. Measuring gadgets were generally attached either to the pouch, which was now really a flask, or to the new shot belt. The pouch could be of soft leather or hard leather, the tendency being toward hard as the nineteenth century developed. Two forms of shot belt emerged, one

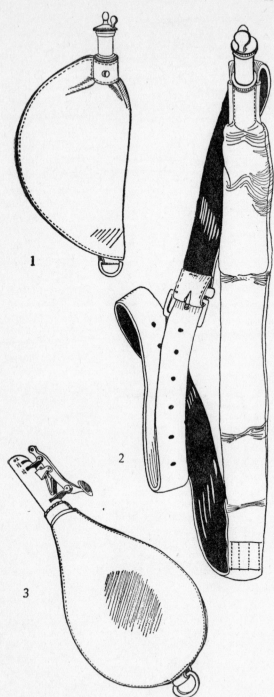

as a baldric hanging from the left shoulder to the right hip, with the charger at the lower end, the other as a belt around the waist. The latter was awkward to use, though, and so was never as popular as the more convenient shoulder belt. Colonel Peter Hawker, the famous nineteenth-century English gunner and sportsman, described the virtues of the lightness of the shot belt in 1846, but specified that the mouth of the charger should fit the muzzle of the shotgun, to avoid losing any shot. He preferred the belt to the pouch because of its lightness.

Double shot belts existed, which were naturally heavier. They were often made with two chargers and double capacity, sometimes with the chargers both at the same end, sometimes with them at opposite ends so as to even the load.

The shot belt was carried either right side up or upside down, with the charger usually of brass, for ease of manufacture, appearance, and corrosion resistance. The belt was made of various leathers, and usually rather soft. Black was a popular color, and russet even more so.

The shape most often associated with the shot pouch is that associated with the powder flask, the commonly known pear shape with myriad charger variations; indeed, apart from the difference in these chargers, the two look much the same. During the first three quarters of the nineteenth century, literally hundreds of charger patents were issued, in England, on the Continent and in the United States, most of the time for the same or similar body shape. Most of these fell into one of three categories: metal, usually brass, less often copper and zinc; brass, covered with leather; and plain leather. The metallic flask made for a good shape, but was apt to be noisy when loaded with shot, hence the preference for leather pouches which would not startle game when the hunter moved around. The development of steel dies for stamping out perfect metal shapes was responsible for the extensive use of metal flasks and pouches during the nineteenth century.　　　　　　　　　　　　　H.W.

Riling, Ray, *The Powder Flask Book*, New Hope, Penn., 1953.

1. *Soft pouch*
2. *Shot belt*
3. *Hard pouch with nineteenth-century measuring device*

SIGHTS

The first hand firearms, of the fourteenth century, were themselves so inaccurate that no more precise method of aiming was required than mere pointing at the target with the entire gun. Soon, however, their precision increased, thus necessitating sights of some kind. As early as 1450 we know of gun barrels equipped with a bead front sight and a standing back sight with a sighting notch.

The bead, originally of iron but during the sixteenth century more and more often of brass or, on luxury guns, of silver, was either screwed into the barrel or inserted from the side on a foot dovetailed into the barrel so that its position could be adjusted simply by giving a soft blow to the foot. At first the bead was usually placed at the extreme muzzle end; later, it was moved back a little, so that it was less exposed to being accidentally hit and knocked out of alignment.

The back sight, which was also sometimes inserted on a flat foot, was normally placed about twelve inches (approximately 32 cm.) in front of the eye, so that there was the best chance of seeing both the front and back sights clearly and simultaneously when aiming. When the sights were adjusted, a small control mark was normally engraved in the barrel and the foot of the sight to secure the right position. Mostly on rifles, the back sight as well as the sighting notch were also given one or more movable leaves, which were carried in a flat position but could be raised for aiming at greater distances, thus concealing the standard sighting notch. Another system giving the possibility of different aiming was found in Turkish barrels. Here the breech plug was provided with a rather high comb with a notch on top and two to four peepholes for the different distances. From Turkey the system spread to most of the Middle East and North Africa. Incidentally, it was also used on European military firearms in the nineteenth century, although with the holes on a movable leaf.

As early as about 1500, a back sight is found consisting of two panels placed parallel with the length of the barrel and with an interspace of about one fifth of an inch. Between the panels a piece of lead with a filed notch was located. In the second quarter of the sixteenth century these panels were often displaced by an angular or cylindrical tube in which was inserted a plate with either a notch or a peephole. On the angular tubes, the lid could be removed in order to facilitate the exchange of the inserted plate. On target-shooting guns in the Netherlands, from the seventeenth century, the tube was replaced by a solid block pierced by a peephole, sometimes also with an exchangeable peep plate. This entire back sight could be adjusted laterally by a screw.

Sometimes a long groove over the breech end of the barrel would lead the eye towards the back sight. This feature is often found on north German and Scandinavian barrels of the late sixteenth and early seventeenth centuries. Another kind of sighting auxiliary was the hog's-back barrel, where the entire barrel had an angular or pointed-oval ridge. This type, although of German origin, was mainly used in Denmark in the seventeenth century, while it reappeared in Germany in the eighteenth century, especially in Dresden. In a group of south German target-shooting rifles of about 1600, only the foremost three to four inches had a hog's-back, while the

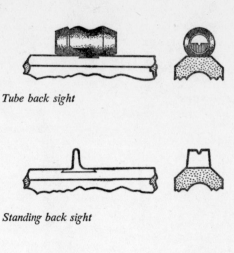

Tube back sight

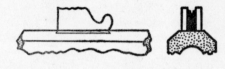

Standing back sight

Panel back sight

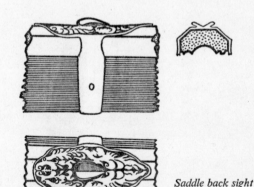

Saddle back sight

Back sight with comb and peepholes, from a Turkish rifle

rest of the barrel was of the usual hexagonal or octagonal form with a flat top. In gun and pistol barrels of the French seventeenth to eighteenth century fashion, the back sight was very often replaced by a long flat rib covering most of the length of the barrel.

When in the beginning of the seventeenth century shooting at flying birds was becoming more and more popular, a special open back sight for fast aiming was developed, probably in France. A standing back sight with a wide V-notch eventually became a buck-horn sight, which, again, developed into two flat wings set at an obtuse angle. Often the sight had a pointed fore-end, thus resembling a heart. From about 1660 these back sights were not inserted in the barrel, but fastened to a belt going round the barrel. Such belt back sights were very popular on fowling pieces until the middle of the eighteenth century.

At first military firearms were equipped with sights similar to the civilian ones, but from the late seventeenth century the back sights disappeared while the front sights took a rectangular form, and besides their original function also served to lock the bayonet by means of a zigzag slot in the bayonet socket. Later, a special bayonet stud for this purpose was placed underneath the barrel, and the front sight was usually formed as a rather large half-almond of brass. On muskets where the barrel was held to the stock by means of steel bands, as were the French, for example, the front sight was sometimes fixed to the foremost band. The inaccuracy of this system, if the band was turned a little off its proper position, soon led to its abolition.

Only military rifles, as they began to come into use in the second half of the eighteenth century, were better equipped with sights, having either a fixed back sight with one or two leaves, or a movable one, usually with an angular stem going down in a vertical recess in the stock just behind the tang. The different positions of this kind of sight were secured by a screw.

With the considerably increasing precision of the pillar breech and Minié rifles, and even more of the breech-loading rifles, from the middle of the nineteenth century, the necessity for better, and, especially, more detailed, back sights became more apparent. Most rifles therefore were equipped with sliding back sights of some kind, either just sliding along a raised stem or gallows or regulated by resting on a curved ramp giving the different elevations of the notch block. A special variation was the so-called arch back sight where a curved leaf with sighting notch in the end slides in an arched recess on the surface of the back sight block, arrested in the different positions by a screw. The arch back sight was used in Danish, Austrian and French military rifles about 1850. On the British Lee-Metford rifle of 1889 a special long-range sighting set was applied. The front sight was placed vertically on the left side of the stock and consisted of a dial with marks for the ranges 1,700 to 2,800 yards and a movable pointer with a bead. The back sight was a lever with a peephole, attached to the locking bolt.

On modern target rifles the front sight is usually a so-called ring bead, consisting of a bead on top of a pin, the whole in a ring with the bead as center. The back sight is a disc with a peephole mounted on a block with screws regulating both elevation and side position. A special form of this back sight is the Lyman sight where the disc is replaced by a ring. As the ring does not exclude so much of the surroundings of the target, it is easier to bring the target into the center with this back sight.

Special telescope sights are known as far back as the seventeenth century. They are first described in Francesco de Lana's book *Magister Naturae et Artis*, 1684. A more highly developed system is discussed in *Oculus Artificialis Teledioptricus*, by Johannes Zahn, Nuremberg, 1702, where the telescope has four lenses and, in between, a disc of plain glass with an engraved center spot. Several occasions occur during the eighteenth century where telescopic sights are mentioned. Thus King Frederick the Great of Prussia in his diary in 1737 notes that he had tried a rifle with telescopic sights at a target shoot. During the American Civil War and in the First World War, both sides used sniper's rifles with telescopic sights. In the latter conflict, further refinements were added, including mirrors, to permit the aiming of the rifle over a parapet without exposing the shooter.   A.H.

SILENCER

A silencer is a device for reducing the noise created by the discharge of a firearm. Normally this is accomplished by trapping the gases from the burning powder at the muzzle of the piece and slightly delaying their release. This is done very quickly, but the pressure peak of the escaping gases is lengthened sufficiently to eliminate or greatly reduce the sharp report which is caused when they burst forth all at once.

One of the earliest successful firearms silencers was invented by Hiram Percy Maxim of the United States, who obtained his first patent for such a device on March 25, 1908. At first, Maxim believed that it was necessary to impart a whirling motion to the gases, and his first silencers were made with passages designed to do this. Actually, all that is necessary is to slow the release of gases, and the exact manner in which this is done is unimportant.

Under certain conditions, a silencer can be very effective. If the muzzle velocity of the projectile is below the speed of sound, and if the breech of the firearm is tightly closed, the noise elimination is almost complete. A bullet

Plate 7

Pair of flintlock dueling pistols made under the direction of Nicolas-Noël Boutet, *Directeur Artiste* of the Imperial Factory at Versailles, for presentation by the Emperor Napoleon. Boutet is the most famed single master in the whole history of gunmaking, and the only one to use the title *Artiste*. The walnut stocks are inlaid with engraved silver, the locks encrusted with gold, the barrels blued and gilt and semé with gold stars. They were presented by the Marquis of Wellesley to the Prince Regent in 1810.

Royal Collection, Windsor Castle.

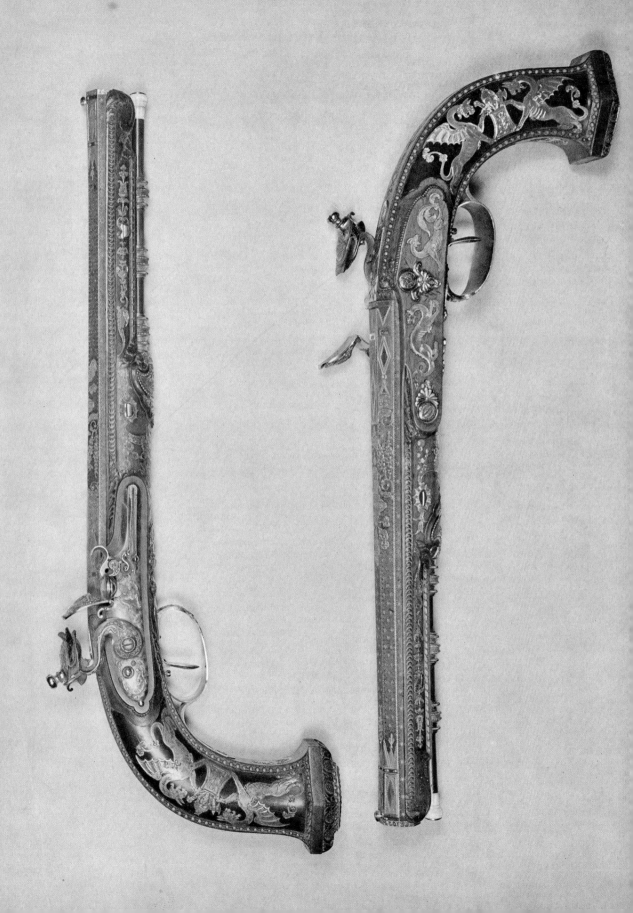

traveling faster than sound, however, creates a loud crack that cannot be controlled by a silencer since the noise is produced after it leaves the gun. Guns with leaky breeches, such as revolvers, cannot be effectively silenced because a certain amount of the gases escape through the joint between the cylinder and the barrel to produce a report. The breeches of some semi-automatic arms open while there is still considerable gas pressure in the barrel, and although the noise of these arms can be reduced, it cannot be eliminated.

Silencers have never been widely popular. The fact that such devices are really effective on only a limited number of arms, plus the fact that they tend to make a gun muzzle-heavy, have offset the advantages that they offer for most purposes. They have frequently been used on guns being tested in confined quarters, and some have also been employed for military purposes. During the First World War, for instance, a sniper model of the 1903 Springfield was produced with a Maxim silencer, and during the Second World War various nations employed silencers on small weapons for semi-military use. Because of the obvious advantages of silencers for clandestine activities, most countries today have strict laws governing their ownership and use.   H.L.P.

SINGLE-ACTION

Single-action is a descriptive term applied to a gun, normally a pistol or revolver, in which it is necessary to pull the hammer back manually in order to cock the piece before firing. This was the usual operation for firearms prior to the second quarter of the nineteenth century. At that time double-action pistols and revolvers began to appear in some quantity, but the single-action mechanism continued in use, and some arms, such as the English Beaumont-Adams revolver, were made so that they could be fired either way. The single-action is still preferred by many marksmen because it permits a lighter trigger pull than the double-action.   H.L.P.

See also: DOUBLE-ACTION; REVOLVER.

SLIDE ACTION

See: PUMP ACTION.

SMITH, HORACE

Expert machinist, inventor and arms maker of Norwich, Connecticut, later of the firm Smith & Wesson, Horace Smith was born in Cheshire, Massachusetts, on October 28, 1808. His association with Daniel B. Wesson began while both were employed by Allen, Brown & Luther,

riflemakers of Worcester, Massachusetts. On August 26, 1851, Horace Smith obtained a patent for a breech-loading firearm, Patent No. 8,317. With this patent as well as one for a Henry action, acquired from expert mechanic and inventor B. Tyler Henry, Smith, in partnership with Wesson, went into arms production of a repeating pistol – patented February 14, 1854, Patent No. 10,535 – retaining Henry as their plant superintendent. To attract working capital for expansion, in July 1855 they incorporated the firm under the name of Volcanic Repeating Firearms Company, to which Smith & Wesson turned over their patents as well as a new one of August 8, 1854, No. 11,496, for an improved cartridge.

Shortly after the firm's incorporation, Horace Smith left it to work in the gunsmith trade with his brother-in-law in Springfield, Massachusetts. Wesson remained with Volcanic until February 1856, when he left to work on the development of a cartridge revolver. He was successful, and about May 1, 1857, he sought out and joined his former partner Horace Smith in Springfield. There they leased a building and in October 1857 started the manufacture of a small .22 caliber revolver incorporating the novel feature of a metallic rim-fire cartridge using the Rollin White patent of a "cylinder bored end to end." The Smith and Wesson foresight in acquiring what became an outstanding patent for a weapon with chambers bored clear through the cylinder, even though originally unsuccessful because applied to a paper cartridge, gave them a virtual monopoly of the manufacture of revolving cartridge arms. By court action, and by the pressure of infringement suits, the firm successfully prevented the competitive manufacture of cartridge revolvers until 1869, when the Rollin White patent expired.

Over the years the firm acquired a world renowned and honored name in revolver manufacture and the name of Horace Smith has been preserved for posterity in "Smith & Wesson" of Springfield, Massachusetts.

Horace Smith himself retired from the firm in 1873 and died in Springfield, Massachusetts, on January 15, 1893.   A.G.

Illustrations: pages 174, 180.

Parsons, John E., *Smith & Wesson Revolvers*, New York, 1957.

See also: CARTRIDGE; HENRY, BENJAMIN TYLER; REPEATING ARMS; REVOLVER; WESSON, DANIEL B.

SMOKELESS POWDER

The term "gunpowder" is now used both for black powder (described under GUNPOWDER), and for smokeless powder. The propulsive gases are formed in the case of black powder by the burning of charcoal and sulphur by the oxygen in the saltpetre or potassium nitrate, KNO_3, in the mixture. The residue of potassium salts produces smoke and a deposit in the gun. Smokeless powder consists of materials in which the nitrate group NO_3 is actually in the molecule along with carbon and hydrogen, and the products are entirely gaseous, carbon dioxide, steam and nitrogen.

Smokeless powders consist of nitrocellulose with or without nitroglycerine and small quantities of other materials. Nitroglycerine was discovered in 1846 by Sobrero in Turin and is made by the action of a mixture of concentrated nitric acid and concentrated sulphuric acid on glycerine, C_3H_5 $(OH)_3$:

$$C_3H_5(OH)_3 + 3HNO_3 = C_3H_5(NO_3)_3 + 3H_2O$$

The sulphuric acid removes the water formed in the reaction. The chemical name of nitroglycerine is glyceryl trinitrate. The product, which is washed with water containing some alkali, is a colorless oil. It was manufactured by Alfred Nobel from 1862, and from 1867 absorbed in porous material as dynamite. Both are unsuitable for use in firearms since they are high explosives and would burst the piece.

Nitrocellulose, or guncotton, was discovered in the same year as nitroglycerine, 1846, by Schönbein in Basle and Böttger in Frankfurt. Cellulose exists nearly pure in cotton and less pure in wood. Its simplest formula is $C_6H_{10}O_5$, but the molecules are joined into long chains corresponding with the fibrous structure. It contains three hydroxyl groups, $C_6H_7O_2(OH)_3$ like glycerine, and on nitration with a mixture of concentrated nitric and sulphuric acids the fully nitrated product is cellulose trinitrate, $C_6H_7O_2(NO_3)_3$, containing 14.14 per cent of nitrogen. The nitration is always incomplete, and there are two main groups of products: (a) guncotton, containing 13 per cent or more of nitrogen, a high explosive used in blasting, insoluble in a mixture of ether and alcohol, and (b) nitrocelluloses containing from 10.8 to over 12.5 per cent of nitrogen, more or less soluble in a mixture of ether and alcohol and in nitroglycerine, used in making collodion, plastics, and smokeless powder (when it contains 12.5 per cent of nitrogen). Purified cotton waste or wood pulp is nitrated with the mixed acid in iron pots, and the product pulped, thoroughly washed, and molded by pressing.

Apart from powders containing nitrocellulose and mineral nitrates, which are used to some extent but leave a residue in the gun, smokeless powders fall into two main groups: (a) those consisting only of nitrocellulose, and (b) those containing both nitrocellulose and nitroglycerine in various proportions. The first kind was made by Vieille in France in 1886. He completely gelatinized

nitrocellulose with a mixture of ether and alcohol, rolled the product into thin sheets, cut these up, and removed the solvent by drying. The second type was invented in England in 1889 by Abel and Dewar, who produced cordite by gelatinizing guncotton with acetone and mixing with nitroglycerine and mineral jelly. In modern smokeless powders small amounts of stabilizers such as "centralite" are added.

A piece of smokeless powder burns from the outside, and the rate of burning is varied for use in different types of firearms by making the pieces of different sizes and shapes. For sporting pieces the powder is in grains or thin flakes. For military small arms the pieces are flakes, discs, or ribbon. For larger guns thick cords, cubes, cylinders or tubes, which may be perforated, are used.

J.R.P.

Marshall, A., *Explosives*, 2 vols, London, 1917–32.

See also: GUNPOWDER; NOBEL, ALFRED BERNHARD.

SNAPHANCE/SNAPHAUNCE

The term snaphance is applied by modern students to those forms of flint arms in which the steel and the pan cover are separate structures, rather than combined as they are in the true flintlock. Within this broad category are several types of locks. These include the Dutch form, which may be the earliest and which gave the type its English name; the Scottish version, which has many structural similarities to the Dutch in addition to the separate steel; and the Scandinavian and Italian types, which have no other structural relationship.

The Dutch snaphance appeared sometime before 1550. It is quickly recognized by its large S-shaped cock with the vise for holding the flint and the big disc usually fastened to the exterior end of the pan. The pan itself was normally made as a half-cylinder with a sliding cover. The steel was pivoted ahead of the pan and bore upon a V-shaped spring so that it could be at rest in two positions – either directly above the pan ready for firing or pulled well forward out of the way.

The internal mechanism was simple. The shank of the cock passed through a hole in the lock plate, and a lug called a tumbler was fastened to it as a bearing point for the mainspring. When the cock was pulled back, the tumbler rotated and compressed the spring. At the same time it permitted the nose of the sear to move laterally and project out through a hole in the lock plate to engage the tail of the cock, thus holding it in the cocked position until pressure on the trigger retracted the nose. When the trigger was pulled, the cock, freed from this restraint, was driven forward by the action of the mainspring against the tumbler. The flint in its jaws struck the steel a glancing blow and produced a shower of sparks to ignite the priming powder in the pan below. On most locks a plunger automatically opened the pan cover as the cock fell. In others it was necessary to open the pan by hand so that it would receive the sparks. There was no half-cock position since the gun was safe as long as the steel was left in its forward position.

The action of the cock in snapping forward sharply to strike the steel reminded the Dutch of the action of a pecking rooster. Thus they called it a *schnapp-hahn* or pecking cock. From this analogy the term *hahn* or cock came to be applied to the flint vise, and the steel was sometimes called the hen. This terminology was also adopted in Germany, Scandinavia, and even in England, though there the Dutch *schnapp-hahn* quickly became corrupted to snaphaunce or snaphance, the terms still used today. It should be noted, however, that the distinction made by modern students which confines the use of this term to those locks with separate steels and pan covers has no basis in contemporary usage. Throughout the late sixteenth and early seventeenth centuries, the name snaphance was applied to any form of arm with a striking cock, including even the French flintlock and the Spanish miquelet.

From the Low Countries the Dutch snaphance spread far and wide. It probably served as a pattern for the mechanism of the early Scottish and English snaphances. Its relationship to the Scandinavian snap locks is more problematical, but by far its biggest sphere of influence lay in Africa, especially in Morocco. As late as 1885 snaphances of the Dutch type were still being manufac-

Italian snaphance

tured there by native gunsmiths, centuries after the type had disappeared in Europe.

The Italian snaphance was a very different lock from the Dutch version, and there was probably no direct relationship between the two forms. The Italian snaphance developed much later than the Dutch. Most surviving specimens date from the late seventeenth and early eighteenth centuries. They are usually sophisticated and well made whereas the Dutch locks were usually very simple and often crude. The Italian locks boasted sears which acted vertically in the manner of the French flintlock in contrast to the horizontal sear of the Dutch. The only resemblance between the two, in fact, lies in the separation of steel and pan cover.   H.L.P.

Illustrations: pages 171, 269, and endpapers.

Lenk, Torsten, *Flintlåset, dess Upkomst och Utveckling*, Stockholm, 1939.

Peterson, Harold L., *The Treasury of the Gun*, New York, 1962 (*The Book of the Gun*, London, 1963).

See also: AFRICAN FIREARMS; FLINTLOCK; SCANDINAVIAN SNAP LOCK; SCOTTISH FIREARMS.

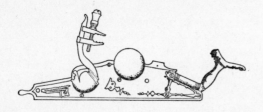

Dutch snaphance

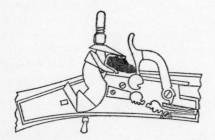

Scottish snaphance

SNIDER RIFLE

The Snider rifle was the first breechloader generally issued to the British Army. The design was submitted by Jacob Snider of New York in 1864, and won the government competition for the cheapest and best means of converting the muzzle-loaders then in general use. Basically, it consisted of a simple, flip-open breechblock, hinged on the right-hand side of the action, and containing a striker to transmit the blow of the hammer of the original percussion lock to the cap of the center-fire cartridge. In later models, a simple catch to lock the breechblock in position was considered necessary.   C.H.R.

Illustration: page 47.

George, John N., *English Guns and Rifles*, Plantersville, S.C., 1947.

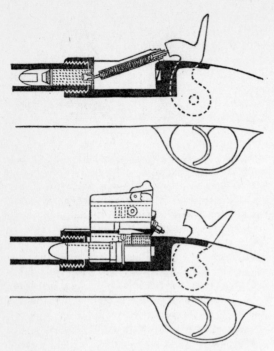

Snider rifle breech action – closed (above) and open

Majendie, V. D., and Browne, C. O., *Breech-loading Rifles*, London, 1869.

See also: BREECHLOADERS.

SPANISH FIREARMS

Firearms on the Iberian peninsula were first recorded in 1342, when the chronicler of Alfonso XI of Castile described the use of cannon by the Moors defending the besieged city of Algeciras. They appear frequently in subsequent literature, and existing medieval examples show that they differed little from the guns of the rest of Europe. Handguns, too, were of universal style, and by the end of the fifteenth century arquebuses were being made throughout Spain, principally in Biscay and Málaga.

The wheel lock was introduced from Germany early in the sixteenth century. The oldest extant piece is a small saddle arquebus of Augsburg manufacture purchased by the Emperor Charles V in that city in 1530. A self-spanning wheel lock arquebus dated 1546, apparently made near Montserrat in Catalonia, seems to indicate that this mechanism was also manufactured on the Peninsula at an early date. Its south-German style, however, makes it as likely that it is the product of an itinerant German gunsmith as that of a Spaniard.

The earliest known Spanish maker of wheel locks is Cristóbal Frisleva of Ricla, active during the third quarter of the sixteenth century. In the absence of surviving guns by his hand, he is known only through contemporary inventories.

After establishment as the capital in 1561, Madrid became the center of Spanish firearms manufacture. Wheel locks made there after the third quarter of the century show that the Spanish gun had assumed a character of its own while maintaining a distinctly German flavor.

Probably the most striking characteristic of Spanish wheel lock guns is their extreme simplicity. Even when made for royal use by such renowned makers as the Marquarts or Juan Salado, they were almost devoid of ornamentation. Arquebuses were generally small (pistols were uncommon until the beginning of the seventeenth century), and existing examples as well as contemporary inventories show that they seldom exceeded six palms in length. Barrels were invariably octagonal at the breech and round toward the muzzle, transition being made with a turn or decorative ring; they were normally mounted with front and rear steel sights. Although according to written sources rifling was known and used, it is not found on surviving arms and seemingly never achieved popularity in Spain. Barrels were usually pin-fastened to full stocks of cherry, walnut, or pear. The slight downward curve of the butt was broken at the small only by an indented thumb rest. Instead of a butt plate, a small L-shaped steel plate protected the heel. The trigger guard was rectangular with a small spur.

The wheel lock itself consisted of a flat, roughly lozenge-shaped plate, rounded at the rear and mounted flush with the stock. Its centrally mounted internal wheel was protected by a raised wheel cover made integrally with the plate. The V-shaped cock spring was externally mounted by its short lower arm. The cock was characterized by the peculiarly ovoid shape of its jaws, the upper of which was fixed. There was no manual safety.

Towards the end of the sixteenth century, Ripoll, in Catalonia, began to emerge as Spain's second great gun-manufacturing center. Although the wheel lock did not appear there until *ca.*1590–1600, its design harked back some fifty years. The Ripoll lock plate was raised, beveled and mounted to the stock by three screws. The wheel was disproportionately small and accentuated the deep drop of the plate that provided for the action of the mainspring. In contrast to the Castilian lock with its sliding pan cover, the Ripoll pan cover pivoted and the upper cock jaw was movable. This lock, in its earliest form, was fitted almost exclusively to an exceptionally long pistol known locally as a *pedrenyal*.

Ripoll pistols are characterized by their peculiar ornamentation, all parts being decorated *en suite* with chiseled arabesques even to the stocks, usually sheathed in steel or brass. Barrels were pin-fastened; the tang screw was an extension of the trigger guard, usually made with a spur. Belt hooks were common.

The wheel lock *pedrenyal* lasted until *ca.*1615. Its barrel, between two and three palms long, octagonal at the breech with no abrupt change to round towards the muzzle, was sometimes fitted with a rear sight. The stock terminated in a small fishtail butt. Later wheel lock pistols had shorter barrels with no sights; the transition from octagonal to round was made with a half-ring or indentation. Their locks were usually equipped with manual safeties, and their trigger guards were normally without the spur. Instead of the fishtail, their butts were spherical, the hallmark of the Ripoll pistol until the nineteenth century.

The snap lock was known in Spain at least as early as 1580, but there is no evidence that the conventional miquelet lock appeared much before the second quarter of the seventeenth century. Almost immediately, it replaced the wheel lock in Madrid and Ripoll.

In Madrid, except for the change of ignition, the gun remained generally the same. However, barrels were lengthened to as much as six palms, then shortly after became standardized at approximately one yard. Pin fastenings were replaced by barrel bands. Gold-lined touchholes were known by 1644, and sights when used were of iron. A fluted gunstock was introduced before 1650 and quickly superseded the plain stock, but the earlier heelplate was retained. Pistols varied little in style from their European counterparts.

With the change of dynasties in 1700, French influence invaded the court bringing an entirely new style to the Madrid gun, which began to be made with stock, mounts and a modified miquelet lock in imitation of the French flintlock. This influence did not extend beyond the capital, and even there traditionalists continued to order guns made in the Spanish manner. Decoration was standardized; locks and mounts were finished bright, and on finer pieces were often decorated with designs chiseled over a stippled ground. Barrels were blued, inlaid with gold at the breech and fitted with gold spider sights at the muzzle. The rear sight was often incorporated into the rear barrel band. Madrid gunsmiths prided themselves on their ability to produce and often decorate an entire gun. Their names or marks are usually found on barrel, lock plate and trigger guard.

In Ripoll, the earliest snap lock must have appeared late in the first quarter of the seventeenth century. A miquelet variation with a dog catch and a deep drop to the lock plate similar to that of the wheel lock, it is found only on the *pedrenyal* but does not appear to have been intended to convert this gun to flint. Although similar in construction to the wheel lock and undoubtedly built

around older barrels, the miquelet *pedrenyal* was distinct in always having a spherical butt. The style lasted hardly more than a decade.

Shoulder arms followed the earliest Madrid pattern, until in the first half of the eighteenth century the toe of the butt began to be elongated, giving a boot-like appearance to the buttstock, a style that became popular throughout the provinces. However, the fluted stock was introduced here as early as in Madrid and was manufactured to a small extent.

But for the change to the miquelet lock, pistols continued in the style of the later wheel locks. Variations were made in the stock, one of which approximated to a miniature gun butt, but the spherical butt remained the most popular. Ripoll pistols of the eighteenth century were generally fitted with belt hooks and worn on *xarpas*, or bandoliers, which were made with small loops for this purpose.

Unlike the gunsmiths of Madrid, those of Ripoll were divided into locksmiths, barrelsmiths and stockmakers; the two former usually marked their products on the battery and breech.

Early in the nineteenth century, the French-type flintlock began to achieve great popularity throughout Spain, and might seriously have threatened the miquelet lock had it not been for the adoption of the fulminate system which by 1820 was in common use. Both the fluted and boot-shaped stocks gave way to the common European gunstock. Keys replaced the traditional barrel bands and European style began to dilute the Spanish flavor. The year 1825, which saw the death of Isidro Soler, the last great Spanish gunsmith, may also be chosen to mark the death of Spanish gunsmithery.   J.D.L.

Illustrations: pages 271–3.

Buttin, Charles, "L'Arquebuserie de Ripoll" in *Armes à Feu et Armes Blanches*, 1914.

Martínez de Espinar, Alonso, *Arte de Ballesteria y Montería*, Madrid, 1644.

Neal, W. Keith, *Spanish Guns and Pistols*, London, 1955.

See also: MIQUELET.

SPANNER

"Spanner" is used generically to mean a wrench of any kind, more specifically (in America) to refer to a special wrench for loosening a packing gland or similar threaded ring. In the history of firearms, it is used principally to denote the instrument required to prepare for firing any discharge mechanism of the wheel lock type.

In its simplest form, it consists of a handle terminating

SPENCER, CHRISTOPHER M. – SPENCER CARBINES AND RIFLES

in a steel plate pierced with a square hole. This hole fits on the squared arbor of the wheel. When the handle is moved, the wheel rotates against the pull of the mainspring, until it is caught by the sear mechanism, and held until released by the trigger.

Wheel lock spanners often had an expanded head pierced with several square holes of different sizes, permitting them to be used with more than a single firearm. The addition of a projection at the end of the handle made the spanner usable also as a screwdriver for dismounting the lock. In addition, the spanner was sometimes modified to serve as a powder measure or priming flask as well.

T.T.H.

Illustrations: pages 344, 347.

SPENCER, CHRISTOPHER M.

Born in South Manchester, Connecticut, on June 20, 1833, Christopher M. Spencer was a machine tool designer and patentee of the celebrated Spencer repeating shoulder arms of the Civil War, patented March 6, 1860, No. 27,393. These arms were later improved by the addition of a magazine cut-off devised by Edward M. Stabler of Maryland. The arm was made largely in carbine form for cavalry use, though over twelve thousand Spencer rifles were also acquired by the Ordnance Department during the war. Spencer was the founder of the Spencer Repeating Rifle Company, of Chickering Building, Boston, Massachusetts. During the war Spencers were also made by the Burnside Rifle Company of Providence, Rhode Island. The parent Spencer Company was active from 1861 to 1869. The Company went out of business on September 12, 1869, when the plant was sold by auction and most of its assets acquired by the Winchester Repeating Arms Company.

Brigadier General George D. Ramsey, Chief of Ordnance, reported to the Secretary of War on April 5, 1864, on the subject of repeating arms: "Colt's and Henry's rifles and the Spencer rifles and carbines are the only arms of this class in the service ... Spencer's is the cheapest, the most durable and most efficient of these arms."

Captain D. E. Hurd, of the Ordnance Department, stated: "Due to the use of the Spencer rifle by a part of General Geary's troops at Gettysburg, a whole division of Ewell's Corps was repulsed by inferior numbers." In the campaign in the West, a regiment armed with Spencers was considered more than a match for a division armed with the conventional muzzle-loaders.

But regardless of the wartime success of the Spencer arms, the practical evaporation of domestic demand after the war – following the wartime expansion of the small arms industry – drove the industry into diversification,

the production of machine tools, screw machines, bicycles, sewing machines, precision measurement and other metal products, and the Spencer Repeating Rifle Company failed. Spencer, in about 1870, became associated with Charles Billings, who had worked at Colt's and Remington's in the Civil War, working on the short-lived Roper repeating arms of the Roper Repeating Arms Company, of Amherst, and later of Hartford. When Roper failed, Spencer turned to the machine tool industry, where he introduced a lathe cam control by which operation of the lathe became automatic. In association with Billings he became interested in drop-forging and became one of the pioneers in die-forging of metals in complicated shapes. He died at Hartford, Connecticut, on January 14, 1922.

A.G.

Bruce, Robert, *Lincoln and the Tools of War*, New York, 1956.

See also: FOWLING PIECE; REPEATING ARMS; SPENCER CARBINES AND RIFLES.

SPENCER CARBINES AND RIFLES

Spencer carbines and rifles are rim-fire repeating arms of the American Civil War period, with tubular magazines holding seven cartridges in their buttstock. These cartridges were fed to the breech by a compressed spring in the magazine tube. Downward operation of the trigger guard dropped the breechblock, extracting the fired shell, and moved a cartridge out of the magazine into the breech. Closing the lever pushed a cartridge into the chamber, ready to be fired by a conventional side hammer. The rapidity of sustained fire was improved by the Blakeslee patent cartridge box which contained six to thirteen tin tubes, each holding seven cartridges, loadable as a unit.

The carbines, principally in caliber .52, were made with 22-inch barrels rifled with 3 grooves, total length 39 inches. Rifles with a total length of 47 inches were also made, taking the regulation triangular bayonet. The arms were the invention of Christopher M. Spencer, of South Manchester, Connecticut, basic patent No. 27,393, March 6, 1860. During the Civil War they were made by the Spencer Repeating Rifle Company of Boston, Massachusetts, and by the Burnside Rifle Company of Providence, Rhode Island. The Ordnance Department procured 77,181 Spencer carbines to equip cavalry and 12,471 rifles. Perhaps as many more were purchased by state governments and individuals.

A.G.

Illustrations: pages 181, 214.

Bruce, Robert, *Lincoln and the Tools of War*, New York, 1956.

Gluckman, Colonel Arcadi, *United States Muskets, Rifles, and Carbines*, Harrisburg, Pa., 1959.

See also: REPEATING ARMS; SPENCER, CHRISTOPHER M.

SPRINGFIELD

United States government small arms manufactory developed at Springfield, Massachusetts, on the site of a Revolutionary War arsenal and powder magazine established in 1777. Started principally as an ammunition manufactory and gun carriage repair shop, the plant expanded its facilities to the repair of small arms and ordnance. By 1790 the stock of muskets available to the government from former Revolutionary imports had fallen to a dangerous level, and since further imports were not available from France, which was beset with domestic difficulties, or from England, then at war with France, Congress in 1794 directed the establishment of two Federal armories for the manufacture of small arms: Springfield in the north and Harpers Ferry in the south.

The pattern adopted was the French flintlock musket Model 1763, which had been in service during the Revolution, having been acquired by gift or purchase from the French and found satisfactory. This model, with minor improvements, served until 1844, when it was superseded by the percussion-ignition system. Production began in 1795, during which year 245 muskets were made laboriously by hand. However, production facilities were improved rapidly with the aid of newly invented machinery, such as triphammers for welding barrels, barrel-turning lathes, and Blanchard lathes for turning the walnut stocks, until by 1830 annual production reached 16,500 muskets. In addition to the muskets the Armory made pistols and cadet arms. It furnished pattern arms and inspection gauges, and it trained inspectors for the inspection of contract arms being made by private armories.

In all, 471,346 flintlock muskets were made at the Springfield Armory from 1795 to 1844, when production changed to caliber .69 smoothbore percussion muskets of which 171,940 were made by 1858, when the caliber .58 rifle musket was adopted. Of these rifled arms, 840,549 were made at the Armory between 1858 and 1865. The end of the Civil War found the government with hundreds of thousands of obsolescent, if not obsolete, muzzle-loaders on hand. Many of these were converted to breechloaders under the direction of Erskine S. Allin, the Armory master armorer. His trap door system served, with minor improvements, until 1892 as a rugged, dependable, single-shot black-powder arm, well known as the Springfield 45–70.

With the invention of smokeless powder, the Armory in 1892 undertook the production of a slightly modified Danish magazine arm, the Krag-Jørgensen, which lasted until 1903, when an improved, clip-loading, modified Mauser patent rifle was adopted, which, widely known and famed as the accurate "Springfield," served throughout the First World War. Production of over a thousand a day was achieved by October 1918. In the 1920's the Springfield Armory developed and produced the Garand semi-automatic rifles of the Second World War, and since then has developed a new weapon, the M-14, to take the NATO cartridge.

At this time, the Armory not only produces small arms but is an arms research and development center for practically all arms used by the United States Army, such as machine guns, mortars, recoil-less rifles and other weapons used in infantry support. A.G.

Illustrations: pages 47, 105.

Gluckman, Colonel Arcadi, and Satterlee, L. D., *American Gun Makers*, Harrisburg, Pa., 1953.

STOCK

The gun stock is the frame, normally of wood, which provides a means of holding the arm properly while securing the various elements of the gun in proper relationship to each other. In the days before the revolver and the self-loading pistol, handguns were stocked as well as shoulder arms; for the purpose of this article, however, the evolution of the stocks of long arms only is considered, for these developed according to use and function, while the shape of pistol butts was often determined primarily by aesthetics.

Shape and Development

The stock is a part of the gun which, being shaped according to its function, has altered in shape according to demand through the ages. During the infancy of the gun (*ca.*1350–*ca.*1500) the stock was intended only to facilitate the shooter's handling of the gun, and it was generally shaped as a wooden stick, simply lengthening the barrel.

Types of stock were the stick-shaped stock, which was fixed to the rear end of the barrel by means of a socket or spike, and the contemporary beam-shaped stock. The barrel of the latter was at first fastened to the stock by means of sheet-iron rings nailed to the stock. Later it became customary to fasten the barrel by means of sprigs.

After *ca.*1500 the stock acquired a new function: to secure the gunlock. Only the beam-shaped stock was

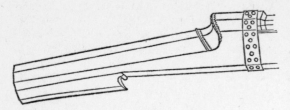

Beam-shaped stock, late fifteenth century

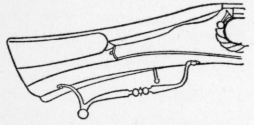

Early German stock, mid-sixteenth century

suited to this purpose, and it later developed into the German stock. During the first decades of the sixteenth century the square, clumsy shape of the fore-stock disappeared. Before 1550 the butt developed a flat cheekpiece on the left-hand side. During the last years of the sixteenth century this was often lengthened down below the butt like a plate. The back of the butt shows an even, not particularly deep, fall from the rear end of the barrel to the heel of the butt. This made it possible for the shooter to aim pressing the gun to his right cheek, which was the firing position at that time. Therefore, the patch box – when one was added – had to be placed on the right-hand side of the butt, and this type became common about 1580.

About 1600, a characteristic change of the butt took place. Its upper edge developed a sharp fall just behind the breech of the barrel, and the comb of the butt continued to the rear almost horizontally. In this way the thumb was removed from the line of sight. As the butt was rather narrow, the downward-lengthened cheekpiece now became the rule.

This last-mentioned shape of the German stock remained practically unchanged until this kind of stock was abandoned. This coincided with the disappearance of the wheel lock. After 1650 the German stock quickly became less common, and before 1700 it had almost disappeared. During its last fifty years it was almost exclusively used for rifles.

The above-mentioned types of stock were not intended to support the gun against the backward force of recoil. However, when they could be used, it was simply due to the fact that the charge and caliber were adjusted to the weight of the gun. The heavier the gun the larger the

caliber and charge that could be used without uncomfortable recoil.

This fact proved to be of importance to the development of the military stock. The demand for penetrating and stopping power for soldiers' guns became greater during the sixteenth century, and thus the charges and calibers had to be increased. In this way the force of recoil was also increased. The effect of this was counteracted by increasing the weight.

The weight increase affected the stock in such a way that its butt was extended backwards and bent downwards. This type of stock may be named the Castilian or Spanish stock, since it was probably developed in Spain. Such a stock made it possible to swing the heavy gun up into the firing position. In the case of comparatively light guns of this type, the rear part of the gun was pushed down with the right hand, while the left hand pressed up the fore-stock. The butt of heavy guns was pressed under the armpit or towards the right side of the chest. This type of stock was very common in European armies from 1550 to 1580.

However, increasing the weight of the guns was not the only way to make it possible to use greater charges and calibers. The stock could also be shaped in such a way that the rifleman could support it and so that the gun did not kick, even though it was subjected to considerable force of recoil. The outstanding feature of the musket stock is its anti-recoil quality. It may easily be seen from the butt of the musket that it is intended to give rear support, for on top of the downward-bent butt of the Castilian stock a high, thin comb has been fitted for this purpose. At the same time the foot of the butt was cut almost vertically and was therefore comfortable to place on the chest. To hold the gun it was necessary that the thumb could reach up and round the high butt. This is the reason for the deep thumb groove cut in the comb of the butt.

The advantage of this stock is obvious. For guns of the same weight, it becomes possible to use bigger

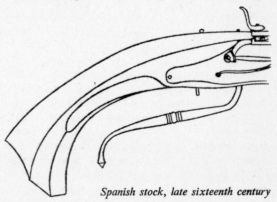

Spanish stock, late sixteenth century

charges, or bigger calibers, or both. The greater range and penetration of the musket gave it military superiority.

Where and when the musket stock was invented is an open question. But it must at least be taken for granted that the Spaniards used it during the first few years of their war against the free Netherlands. Thus there is reason to believe that the shape was developed during the decade 1570–80, and it is very likely that the Duke of Alba was the first to understand the great military value of the musket stock.

In its earliest forms, the musket butt was rather sharply curved downwards, short and fairly clumsy. This meant that the rear point of support against the chest lay rather low compared with the axis of the barrel. The trouble with this, however, was that the gun muzzle was raised considerably when the shot went off; this caused much disturbance in the old days when the powder burnt slowly. But already before 1600 the musket butt had developed its classic form; high, thin and with a slight fall. This form was preserved as long as the matchlock musket was used, that is, for nearly a hundred years. The musket butt, incidentally, was the same, no matter whether it was fixed to the heavy guns for which forked rests were used, or to the light guns fired freely from the chest.

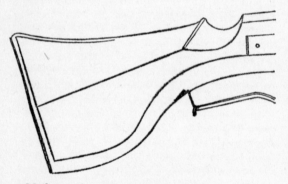

Musket stock, mid-seventeenth century

The musket soon influenced the sporting gun, which until then had been equipped with a German stock. When using a stock supporting the rear part, the gun could be made lighter without losing its effectiveness. In this way flying shots were made possible, too. Finally, the chest or shoulder support was an advantage when aiming.

It seems that it was in France that they accepted the new type of sporting gun with the greatest zeal. We therefore call this type of stock the French stock. Its rapid spread in France is probably due to its connection with the invention of the flintlock in 1610–15 by the Frenchman,

Marin le Bourgeoys. The matchlock and flintlock have one common feature which makes them suitable for mounting on musket stocks – a narrow lock plate.

The French stock differs from the old musket stock in its superior workmanship. Shortly after 1625 its forms became rounder, both the under side and the comb of the butt, and a short small, or wrist, was developed from the thumb groove. The whole stock had a soft and round form. Seen from the side the butt was rather large, with heel and toe almost perpendicular. The foot of the butt sloped back and up, and was intended for support against the rifleman's chest.

In about 1650 the stock was modified to some extent, as the heel of the butt was made round. At the same time the butt became a little narrower and flatter, and there was a tendency towards diminishing the fall of the butt so that its foot became almost completely vertical.

The tendency to raise the butt is undoubtedly due to the fact that support against the chest was now abandoned, and it was moved up to the shoulder. Therefore, during the period 1675–1700 it was found practical to make a shoulder rest by developing a strongly protruding heel. The older kinds of this heel were clumsy and ball-shaped (1675–1725); later it became more pointed and elegant. The shoulder rest has never since left the gun stock. At the same time the wrist was made a little longer and the connection with the comb was marked by a groove.

As was natural, the French stock was transferred to the military gun, and thus replaced the musket stock. However, this does not seem to have happened until the change in arms from matchlock musket to flintlock musket took place, i.e. *ca.*1675–1700. From then on the French stock was practically supreme. And, as it satisfied all the practical demands which could reasonably be made concerning gun stocks, it has remained unchanged since then, at least until the special stocks of the Second World War.

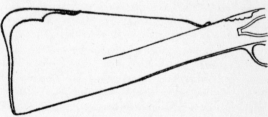

French stock, late seventeenth century

Special Shapes

Besides the main types mentioned, characterizing the development of the stock, a few diverging forms should be mentioned and fitted into the main scheme.

The tschinke (wheel lock rifle) is typologically connected with the Scandinavian Gjønge-guns (snaphance rifles). The butt is characterized by its resemblance to a cow's hoof or a deer's hoof, or something similar. The fall is such that cheek support gives an excellent aim. As the rear butt fall is gentle, but has a pendant cheekpiece, it belongs to the German stock type, from the period immediately before 1600. The tschinke went out of fashion about 1650.

The petronels are very distinctive with their sharply downward-bent butt fitted with a backward-turned foot intended for support against the chest. This support cannot be necessary for the recoil as the butt cannot possibly stand a heavy pressure. It must be due to a desire for firm support during aiming, and therefore the petronels must be taken as transitional forms between the Castilian and the French stocks. They date back to the period 1560–1600.

Kentucky rifles in their fully developed form are distinguished by, among other things, their stocks, which are vertically rather narrow, and turned downward a little more than normal, with a deep crescent-shaped shoulder rest constituted by a pronounced heel and toe. As these rifles have a very long barrel they are preponderate in front. The firm, deep shoulder rest may serve to remedy this.

Half-stocks are possibly connected with the appearance of the screw-off guns of 1660–80, or with the contemporary break-open breechloaders. But although we know of half-stocks from the 1680's, they do not become common until about 1725 when the light barrels also appear. They seem to have been particularly popular in the first half of the nineteenth century, but in fact they have been much used since ca.1725.

Decoration

This subject applies primarily to sporting guns, and only they will be mentioned below. As almost all stocks were made of wood, the possibilities for decoration were limited to the inlaying or covering of the wood, besides, of course, carving. These ways of decorating have varied from country to country and time to time.

The stocks of the wheel lock guns, most of which were made in central Europe, were decorated with inlays of bone during the whole of the sixteenth century. The bone pieces were often ingeniously arranged in patterns of lines and dots, sometimes so closely that the wooden stock almost disappeared. After ca.1580 a new material appeared, imported mother-of-pearl. Wheel lock guns, especially from the countries near Germany, were decorated with mother-of-pearl – for instance, in Italy, France, England and Bohemia. From 1610 to 1620 decorating became less and less frequent, and by about 1650 bone

inlaying had gone completely out of fashion. It must, however, be added that the abundant mother-of-pearl and bone decorations were kept on the characteristic tschinkes as long as they were in use, that is, until ca.1650. Other ways of decorating have also been attempted. For instance, we know of stocks from ca.1570–90 which were completely covered by carved bone plates, or by etched, engraved or embossed tin plates. In Italy, about 1600, special decoration of iron filigree was developed which lasted for many years and was also used on weapons with French stocks.

The stocks of the flintlock guns which originated in France were far more sober in their decorations. Stocks were almost bare, apart from a few luxuriously decorated weapons, until 1675. There might be a small inlay (bone, silver, or something similar), a small carving or an ornamental mounting, and nothing more. It was the barrels and locks mainly which were decorated. The best stocks, however, were often of exquisite materials.

In the next forty-five years (until ca.1720) the decorating of stocks became more common in France. The luxurious types of butt had inlays of silver, but rarely very closely arranged. The mountings were made more ornamental than before, and after ca.1700 they were of brass, often gilded, or of silver, sometimes gilded, instead of iron. Carvings were also used, usually only as light twinings along the groove of the comb of the butt, round the rear ramrod pipe and at the ends of the trigger guard.

These decorations have lasted ever since. Their shape has altered with fashion (French Regency style, rococo, Louis XVI, English Regency, etc.), but the decorations have nearly always been discreet. Carving was very popular during the English Regency period, when the long small of the butt was often made as an animal's head under the butt. The English Regency period also stuck to the cross cutting (checkering) of the small, which the previous generation had already introduced and which was never abandoned.   F.A.

Askgaard, Finn, "Hovedtraek i gevaerskaeftets udvikling" [general development of the gunstock] in *Vaabenhistoriske Aarbøger*, Vol. 10, Copenhagen, 1960 (with a summary in German).

Askgaard, Finn, "To studier over danske 1600-tals gevaerer" [two studies in Danish guns of the seventeenth century] in *Vaabenhistoriske Aarbøger*, Vol. 8, Copenhagen, 1956 (with a summary in French).

Hayward, J. F., *The Art of the Gunmaker*, 2 vols, London and New York, 1962–64.

See also: AFGHAN STOCK; AFRICAN FIREARMS; ASIATIC FIREARMS; DECORATION OF FIREARMS; JEZAIL; PETRONEL; SPANISH FIREARMS; TSCHINKE.

SUBMACHINE GUN

The advent of the Second World War and its demand for increased fire power by the individual soldier led to the development of the submachine gun. The British Sten, the Australian Austen and the United States Thompson and M3 were examples of the more dependable types.

Most of these weapons embodied simple blowback actions and were chambered for cartridges from caliber .45 to 9 mm. They were fitted with skeleton stocks and weighed from 6 to 9 lb. with magazine capacities of 25–32 cartridges. They operated at cyclic rates of 500–600 rounds per minute at a maximum effective range of 200 yards.   G.M.C.

Illustrations: pages 204–5.

Smith, Walter H. B. and Joseph E., *Small Arms of the World*, 6th edition, Harrisburg, Pa., 1960.

See also: AUTOMATIC ARMS; MACHINE GUN.

SUICIDE SPECIAL

The name Suicide Special, to gun collectors, is quite recent, as is collector interest in the arms themselves. The term, apparently first coined by Duncan McConnell in an *American Rifleman* article of February 1948, has, actually, two definitions. Broadly applied, as it is by many collectors, the name Suicide Special encompasses a myriad cheap, low-quality American pocket revolvers made for mass sale during the second half of the nineteenth century. It can include single- or double-action, center-fire or rim-fire, and solid-frame or break-open revolvers, usually types of indeterminate ancestry which do not fit conveniently into any collector category.

Specialists and serious collectors of Suicide Specials define the term much more narrowly, and it is this definition which is preferred. True Suicide Specials, single-action pocket revolvers with spur triggers, have solid frames which do not break for loading. The cylinders are held in place by a center pin which can be withdrawn from the front of the frame and used as an ejector. Invariably nickel plated, the revolvers are often crudely engraved, and are generally marked with a trade name, but not usually a manufacturer's name, on the frame or barrel.

While all Suicide Specials conform basically to the above description, the scope of variation is little short of fantastic. Most of the many trade names were manufactured in a variety of models, ranging from plain nickel finishes to extremely elaborate engraving, with grips of wood, hard rubber, ivory, or pearl, with both round and octagonal barrels in lengths from two to twenty

inches, and in four basic calibers, commonly .22 and .32 rim-fire, uncommonly .38 rim-fire, and rarely .41 rim-fire. Occasionally, long-barreled types are found with attachable shoulder stocks.

Otherwise identical revolvers may carry different trade names, and dissimilar revolvers by different makers may have the same trade name. Some Suicide Specials, such as the common Hopkins & Allen Blue Jackets, were produced in a series of several models. Blue Jacket No. 1 is .22 rim-fire, as is the larger frame No. 1½. Blue Jacket No. 2 is .32 rim-fire, No. 3 is .38 and the rare .41 model is No. 4.

A list of observed Suicide Specials trade names follows, excluding unconfirmed and doubtful names: Aetna, Alaska, Alert, Alex, Alexia, Alexis, Allen, America, American Boy, American Eagle, Aristocrat, Aubrey, Avenger, Bang Up, Big Bonanza, Bismark, Blood Hound, Blue Jacket, Blue Whistler, Bonanza, Boys Choice, Brutus, Buffalo Bill, Bull Dog, Bull Dozer, Bulls Eye, Capt. Jack, Centennial, Challenge, Champion, Chicago Ledger, Chieftain, Clipper, Columbia, Columbian, Comet, Commander, Conqueror, Constant, Continental, Cowboy, Cowboy Ranger, Creedmore, Crescent, Crown, Czar, Daisy, Dead Shot, Defender, Defender 89, Defiance, Despatch, Diamond, Dictator, Dispatch, Double Header, Dreadnought, Eagle Arms Co., Earlhood, Earthquake, Eastern Arms Co., Elector, Electric, Empire, Empress, Encore, Enterprise, Excelsior, Express, Faultless, Favorite, Favorite Navy, Forehand & Wadsworth, Frontier, Garrison, Gem, Governor, Great Southern, Great Western, Guardian, Gypsy, Half Breed, Hard Pan, Harrington & Richardson, Hartford Arms Co., Hecla, Hero, Hinsdale, Hood, Hopkins & Allen, Imperial, International, Jewel, Joker, King Pin, Kittemaug, Knockabout, Lakeside, Leader, Liberty, Lifelong, Lion, Little Giant, Little John, Little Joker, Little Pet, Little Scott, Lone Star, Long Range, Long Tom, Marquis of Lorne, Metropolitan Police, Midget, Mohawk, Mohegan, Monarch, Monitor, Mountain Eagle, Murderer, My Companion, Napoleon, Nero, New Baby, New Little Joker, Newport, New Secret Service, No. 3, Non Pareil, Non-XL, Norwich Arms Co., Norwich Falls, O.K., Optimus, Orient, Our Own, Panther, Paragon, Paralyzer, Parole, Pathfinder, Patriot, Peace Maker, Peerless, Penetrator, Pet, Phoenix, Pinafore, Pioneer, Prairie King, Premier, Princess, Protector, Protector Arms Co., Ranger, Rattler, Red Cloud, Red Hot, Red Jacket, Reliable, Retriever, Robin Hood, Rob Roy, Rover, Royal, Russian, Russian Model, Ryan, Ryan's New Model, Safeguard, Savage, Scott, Scott Arms Co., Scout, Secret Service, Senator, Smoker, Smokey City, Southron, Spitfire, Splendor, Spy, Star Leader, Sterling, Striker, Success, Swamp Angel, Terror, Tiger, Tower's Police, Tramp's Terror, True Blue,

Tycoon, Union Jack, U.S. Arms Co., Veiled Prophets, Venus, Veteran, Veto, Victor, Victoria, White Jacket, White Star, Wide Awake, William Tell, Winfield Arms Co., Winner, Wonder, XCD, XL, XLCR.

In spite of their high-flown names, Suicide Specials, cheaply manufactured for a mass market, emphasized exterior splendor and sales appeal at the expense of interior design, workmanship and materials. Deceptive short cuts were common. The Robin Hood series, for example, has smoothbore barrels with false rifling arranged as three deep notches at the muzzle, which is indicative of the quality of most Suicide Specials.

Prices were low and competition intense. Mail-order firms maintained a huge sales volume at insignificant prices, so that every man, woman and child, with judicious saving, could own a pocket revolver. Merwin, Hulbert & Company in 1888 offered a Robin Hood revolver "absolutely free" with the purchase of one of their caliber .44 army revolvers. In 1890 the same firm advertised "the celebrated Liberty" for $1.10. Prices went as high as $10.00 for engraved types with special grips; in fact, ivory or pearl grips often cost more than the revolvers themselves. It was such, however, as the 60 cent Blue Jacket advertised by Merwin, Hulbert & Company in 1887 and Sears, Roebuck & Company's 68 cent Defender, that created a market for millions of Suicide Specials.

Fairly simple in design and construction, Suicide Specials could be turned out in quantity by small manufacturers, mostly in New England, with cheap labor and a minimum of capital equipment. Some makers made nothing but Suicide Specials; others had a full line of arms. Most were small and financially unstable, and only a few were thriving. Only two of some twenty or more makers, Harrington & Richardson and Iver Johnson, are still in business today.

A listing of known makers of Suicide Specials follows; again, those unconfirmed are not included. Other companies found listed in catalogues and advertising were often not manufacturers at all, but rather sales outlets or subsidiaries of other firms.

Bacon Manufacturing Co., Norwich, Connecticut
Bliss & Goodyear, New Haven, Connecticut
Chicago Firearms Co., Chicago, Illinois
Continental Arms Co., Norwich, Connecticut
Eagle Firearms Co., New York City
E. L. Dickinson & Co., Springfield, Massachusetts
Enterprise Gun Works, Pittsburgh, Pennsylvania
Forehand & Wadsworth, Worcester, Massachusetts
Great Western Gun Works, Pittsburgh, Pennsylvania
Harrington & Richardson, Worcester, Massachusetts
Hood Fire Arms Co., Norwich, Connecticut
Hopkins & Allen, Norwich, Connecticut

Iver Johnson Arms Works, Worcester, Massachusetts
Lee Arms Co., Wilkes-Barre, Pennsylvania
Lowell Arms Co., Lowell, Massachusetts
Meriden Arms Co., Meriden, Connecticut
Rupertus Patent Pistol Manufacturing Co., Philadelphia, Pennsylvania
Ryan Pistol Manufacturing Co., Norwich, Connecticut
United States Arms Co., New York City
Whitney Armory, Whitneyville, Connecticut.

D.B.W.

Illustration: page 116.

Deyrup, Felicia, *Arms Makers of the Connecticut Valley*, (Smith College Studies in History), Northampton, Mass., 1948.

Gluckman, Colonel Arcadi, and Satterlee, L. D., *American Gun Makers*, Harrisburg, Pa., 1953.

Webster, Donald B., Jr., "Suicide Specials" in *The Gun Report*, March 1956.

Webster, Donald B., Jr., *Suicide Specials*, Harrisburg, Pa., 1958.

SWIVEL GUN

Charles James's *Military Dictionary* (4th edition, London, 1816) defines: "Swivel, a small piece of ordnance which turns on a pivot or swivel." In the usual context it refers to a small cannon, the trunnions of which are permanently mounted in an iron yoke. The trunnions are free to move in the yoke so the gun may be elevated or depressed in aiming. The lower part of the yoke is termed the pivot, and this fits into a hole bored in a timber. In this manner a swivel gun may be swung in any direction and aimed freely. The yoke and pivot would be strong enough to sustain the recoil of the gun.

As swivel refers to a method of gun mounting, a swivel gun may be any gun weighing about twelve pounds or more, fitted with a yoke or swivel for mounting the piece. Blunderbusses, muskets, and rifles may all fall within the swivel-gun classification if equipped with this fitting, and all of these forms were made for both land and sea service. Normally, however, during the eighteenth and nineteenth centuries, such swivel-equipped guns for land service were designated as "wall pieces" or "rampart pieces." The Americans made use of large, stocked, swivel-equipped rifles termed "rifle-amusettes" during the War of Independence.

General Lallemand in his *Treatise on Artillery* (English translation, New York, 1820) describes the guns intermediate between cannon and small arms as *Demi-Cannon*:

"I have given this name to those fire-arms that have perhaps less relation to pieces of cannon, than to the common musquet, yet are not so easy to serve as it is. In this class may be marked the *Harquebuss* on a swivel, the *Rampart Gun*, and the *Repeating Musket* of the Americans.

The Harquebuss, which nearly resembles the amusette of Marshal Saxe, had a barrel like that of a musket, but naked, longer, and more reinforced; its ball weighed half a pound or more, and its range at an elevation of 4 degrees was 1,000 yards. This weapon was mounted upon a wooden frame, and had a handle fixed to the breech, to point it by. It is no longer used, but might, as well as the rampart gun, be employed in mountain warfare.

The Rampart Gun, or Wall Piece, is a large musket that was anciently much used in the defense of fortresses. Its barrel is 5½ or 6 feet long; its ball from 10 to 14 to the pound; its horizontal range 450 yards; it weighs about 50 pounds; it is carried upon a wooden frame, by means of a sort of fork, placed about ⅜ of its length from the butt. (No more of these are now manufactured)."

Rampart guns as here described were apparently manufactured in some quantity in both France and England during the first half of the eighteenth century. The French arms were of .75 inch caliber with 46-inch barrels, and many of the English had a one-inch bore and 54-inch barrel. Some of the latter are in the Tower Armouries.

Rifled variants of the rampart gun appeared on the American scene in 1776. Colonel Fielding Lewis wrote to General George Washington on February 4: "I propose making a rifle next week to carry a quarter of a pound ball. If it answers my expectation, a few of them will keep off ships of war from our narrow rivers and be useful in the beginning of an engagement by land."

Evidently, experiments with the above rifle led to manufacture of a number of this type of arm at the Rappahannock Forge in Virginia. Major General Charles Lee wrote to General Washington on May 10 from Williamsburg, Virginia: "I am likewise furnishing myself with four-ounced rifle-amusettes, which will carry an infernal distance; the two-ounced hit a half sheet of paper 500 yards distant."   J.C.M.

Illustrations: pages 282–3, 349.

Lallemand, Henri Dominique, *A Treatise on Artillery*, English translation by James Renwick, New York, 1820.
Peterson, Harold L., *Arms and Armor in Colonial America, 1526–1783*, Harrisburg, Pa., 1956.

See also: AMUSETTE.

TARGET RIFLE

Target rifles fall into three general groups: offhand or Schuetzen; Creedmoor or long range; and bench rest. These three group classifications originated in the last century but are still as descriptive today, the principal difference being that the offhand rifle is today called a Free or International rifle, while we generally call the long range rifle just that. A few years ago this latter type was generally referred to as the Wimbledon rifle. Bench rest target rifles are still called by that name.

The exact date of the emergence of the target rifle as a distinct type is not known. The first rifles were apparently used mainly for hunting. Smoothbores were the primary guns for shooting matches during the early years, and rifles were either banned or consigned to special events to avoid mixed competition. After 1560 such special events became more and more common until, by 1600, they were standard throughout central Europe, with the target often a 3½-foot disc at a range of some 800 feet. Shooting was done offhand without any form of support, the origin of the Schuetzen style of competition.

Once the flintlock ignition had been generally accepted, there were few improvements until the nineteenth century, when the percussion system, metallic cartridges and improved breech-loading systems paved the way for the highly developed target rifles which are the primary subject of this article.

About 1853 Sir Joseph Whitworth introduced his "Fluid Compressed Steel" for gun barrels. Many of the best British and American barrelmakers adopted this steel for their barrels. In the United States, Morgan James, H. V. Perry, Horace Warner, N. S. Brockway, and others, used this steel in fabricating the barrels of their bench rest rifles. These were percussion-cap pieces firing a cylindro-conical slug with heavy charges of black powder. They were heavy-barreled rifles with false muzzles, using a cross paper patch and a bullet starter. They also had good set or hair triggers and finely adjustable sights which usually consisted of a hooded pin-head front and a vernier peep rear. These fine bench rest rifles gained some popularity in the northeastern states but almost none elsewhere.

The invention and development of the Sharps rifle paved the way for the single-shot breechloader. The paper and linen cartridge used by the early Sharps soon gave way to a brass cartridge with self-contained primer. By the 1870's these metallic cartridges were made quite large and powerful and suitable for long-range accurate target shooting.

Almost forty variations of the famous Sharps breech system were still being manufactured in Europe when the Second World War began, but in America, where the Sharps originated, only one variation of it, the Stevens, persisted after 1920.

Some very heavy-barreled rifles were built on Sharps, Remington or Ballard breech-loading actions. These used false muzzles, cross paper patches and bullet starters similar to the heavy slug rifles produced earlier by Warner, Perry, Brockway, etc. These breechloaders were generally .40 and .45 calibers.

So, by the mid-seventies, three patterns of target rifles were fairly well developed.

The first, the Schuetzen or offhand rifle of the Swiss and German shooting societies, with fine set triggers, vernier sights, palm rests, and Swiss or prong butt plates, grew naturally out of the muzzle-loading, percussion ignition pieces earlier used by these clubs. These graceful and beautiful target rifles were generally in .32 and .38 calibers. In the middle and late seventies, the .40 calibers were fairly popular, but by the early 1880's the smaller bores of .32 and .38 were much more popular. The most popular and accurate Schuetzen rifles were made by Marlin (the Ballard), Sharps, Remington, and the Massachusetts Arms Company (the Maynard).

The second type were contemporaries of the offhand rifles and were the long range or Creedmoor target guns. These were long-range rifles, shot prone, developed to conform to the rules of the newly organized National Rifle Association. These rules specified barrels of not over thirty-four inches in length, single triggers of not less than three pounds pull, and a total rifle weight of not over ten pounds. These rules and usages resulted in a gracefully tapered long-barreled rifle with a windage-adjustable hooded front sight, generally with a spirit level contained therein, and a vernier rear sight mounted on the tang of the action or on the heel of the stock. These vernier rear sights were adjustable in thousandths of an inch to register the small changes necessary when shooting at ranges of 600–1,000 yards. These rifles represented the very highest development of the target rifle and were generally .40, .44, or .45 caliber, with the latter two calibers soon becoming standard, with long paper-patched bullets and heavy charges of black powder. The most popular long range rifles were made by Sharps and Remington, and an American rifle team armed with these two makes of rifles defeated a British team at Creedmoor Range on Long Island, New York, in September 1876. Other long range rifles were the Ballard, Maynard, Wesson, and Peabody-Martini, and these enjoyed popularity later.

The third type of target rifle was the heavy-barreled, bench rest rifle previously mentioned, but the use and popularity of this latter type never became as widespread as that of the offhand and long range types. The reasons for this limited popularity may or may not have been the heavy weight and rather ungainly appearance of the bench rest piece, plus the fact that it could not have been fired offhand as easily as the Schuetzen or Creedmoor styles.

It is interesting to note that the development of the long range rifle in England paralleled that of this type in the United States, while the true offhand or Schuetzen target rifle was never very popular there. The Schuetzen, however, was extremely popular on the Continent, and retained that popularity there longer than anywhere else.

Target rifles of these three general classifications are still being manufactured and used today. In the United States, Remington and Winchester both produce long range target rifles and limited quantities of International Free or Offhand rifles. These still utilize the heavy barrels, set triggers and hook or prong butt plates of the old Schuetzens.

The long range types retain the fairly long barrels and prone stocks, and both long range and offhand types sport micrometer sights capable of very fine adjustments.

It may be due to the romance of times long past, but it seems to the present writer that the target rifles of yesteryear were much easier on the eye in many ways than those made today. The older pieces have a symmetry and grace lacking in our modern ones.

There is probably not very much difference in performance between the modern and the older models, except in the bench rest categories. The modern (usually custom-built) bench rest rifle is capable of, and delivers, day after day, in matches throughout America, results on the target that have never before been equalled, let alone surpassed. These rifles will group their shots reliably in three quarters of a minute of angle and in some cases in or under a half-minute of angle. It does not seem possible these groups can be tightened any more, but perhaps, nevertheless, the future will see even smaller groups. The human factor is largely discounted by the bench rest used so that any improvement will come from better cartridge components, no doubt.   J.J.G.

Illustrations: pages 107, 338.

Grant, James J., *Single-Shot Rifles*, New York, 1947.
Grant, James J., *More Single-Shot Rifles*, New York, 1959.
"Stonehenge" [John Henry Walsh], *The Modern Sportsman's Gun and Rifle*, 2 vols, London, 1882 and 1884.

See also: KENTUCKY RIFLE; RIFLES AND RIFLING; SCHUETZEN RIFLE.

TOWER

In its long history, the Tower of London has served many functions – fortress, palace, prison, jewel house, royal mint, record office, etc. From the sixteenth century it was also the headquarters of the Board of Ordnance, responsible for the supply of arms to the armed forces. Inside the walls worked and lived the members of the Board and their staffs, and on the river wharf outside was a group of workshops for smiths and armorers under a Master Furbisher. In 1682 an Ordnance proofhouse was built on the wharf, and until the end of the eighteenth century all government arms had to be brought to the Tower for proof. At first the Ordnance maintained several storehouses in the Minories, but in 1690 a Grand Storehouse was erected near the White Tower. Apart from its store of arms and materials, it contained workshops and the famous Round Table where arms were viewed and tested. The normal Ordnance system of manufacture was for locks, barrels, and other parts to be made in Birmingham and then sent to the Tower where they were viewed, proved and stored, later to be issued to the London gunmakers for setting up into complete firearms. Arms made in this fashion were engraved on the lock with the word "Tower." The contractors were often late with their deliveries and, in 1805, the Ordnance decided to manufacture its own arms. The Armoury Mills, Lewisham, were converted to produce barrels and locks, and the Tower was turned into a small factory for their assembly. This arrangement proved unsatisfactory, and in 1816 both branches were transferred to Enfield. In 1841 a great fire destroyed the Grand Storehouse, and the Ordnance began to disperse its stores. Manufacture was concentrated at Enfield, administration was conducted from offices in Pall Mall, and the Tower gradually assumed the status of a minor depot. Today, it houses the most important collection of arms and armor in the United Kingdom.   H.L.B.

See also: PROOF MARKS.

TRADE GUNS

Next to edged metal tools, flintlock trade guns were probably the most important articles of trade introduced to the savage tribes of Africa and the Americas by Europeans. Use of firearms greatly facilitated living by the chase and profoundly affected tribal warfare and politics.

The first trade guns were cheap versions of the muskets or fowling pieces already in European use, but distinctive models tailored to the demands of the trade were developed as the business increased. In North America, the English, Dutch and French colonists all began selling "firelocks" to the Indians during the first half of the seventeenth century. By 1650 the Indians had demonstrated a marked preference for the long slender flintlock arquebus of light caliber which was manufactured for export in Liège and the surrounding Low Countries.

Careful examination of numerous gun remains found on Iroquois village sites in western New York indicates that the barrels of seventeenth-century trade guns averaged 4–4½ feet long with calibers from .50 to .60. Small heelplates or cast full butt plates were used, and other items of stock furniture were of simple patterns done usually in sheet brass and less commonly in iron. Such trade guns were much lighter and less powerful than the contemporary muskets and fowling pieces used by the European settlers.

By 1700 trade guns were being sold directly from French and English trading posts around Hudson's Bay, the Great Lakes, the Illinois country and the Appalachian Mountains region. An even greater distribution was meanwhile being achieved by traveling white traders and by inter-tribal commerce with more remote areas. The few surviving specimens of this period are generally light, plain fowling pieces of 28 to 22 gauge (about .56 to .61 caliber) with barrels 3½–4 feet long and plain fittings of iron or brass. After 1700 the earlier heavy, undercurved, or fat belly, style of stock gave way to the more graceful drooping type of stock now often called a "handrail butt."

Very little is known about the makers of French trade guns, and few identified specimens exist for study. Limited documentation of early eighteenth-century English trade gunmakers is available, and the known suppliers to the Hudson's Bay Company in that period included Joseph Buckmaster, Thomas Green, John Hawkins, John Jones, Humphrey Pickfatt, Charles Pickfatt, John Smart, John Williams and Richard Wilson. The Wilson family made Hudson's Bay guns for over a hundred years.

Sometime about the middle of the eighteenth century, English trade guns for the North American Indians are known to have appeared in a standardized pattern which became popularly known as the northwest gun. This pattern was distinguished by a side or screw plate of cast brass in the form of a scaly sea-serpent or dragon, a plain iron trigger guard with exceptionally large bow, a flat brass butt plate, ribbed brass ramrod guides and a full stock of walnut or maple. The caliber was approximately 24 gauge or .59 caliber. Barrels were part-octagon and were 3–4 feet in length. Short northwest guns with 2½-foot barrels first appeared about 1798 and gradually became popular as emphasis in the Indian trade shifted to the prairie regions.

After France ceded Canada and eastern Louisiana to Great Britain in 1763, British traders became the acknowledged leaders of the fur trade in North America. Most of the guns and other important trade goods later used by traders in the United States were either manufactured in England or copied in America from English patterns. Thousands of northwest guns were manufactured in Birmingham and London for sale to British and American trading firms and wholesale dealers in Indian trade goods.

Early northwest guns, without identifying viewers' marks or trading company marks, are known to have been made by Grice and Wilson and are believed to have been sold from Montreal or New York. Numerous examples of the 1790–1815 period exist which are stamped with a view mark showing a sitting fox, or fox-like animal, in a circle of 0.35 to 0.40 inches in diameter. This stamp was regularly placed on the lock plate below the pan, and on the top flat of the barrel a few inches from the breech. Since this circle marking appears on guns of the period during which the Northwest Company of Montreal was in operation, and since none of the makers of these guns are known to have made guns for the Hudson's Bay Company, it is generally assumed to be the mark of the Northwest Company or one of its derivative companies like the "Mackinaw Company" of Michilimackinac.

The fox-in-circle view mark

Many of the guns with this mark also carry British government view marks and are believed to have been purchased for the use of Indian allies in the War of 1812. Known makers of northwest guns with fox-in-circle view marks include Ketland, Grice, Whately, Wheeler, Dawes, Rolfe, Morris and Willetts.

A superior type of Indian gun which resembled the northwest gun appeared in the Great Lakes country during this same period and was apparently also used to arm Indians friendly to the British cause. This type has a three-foot part-octagon barrel of .60 caliber, lightly engraved brass fittings, a full stock of selected walnut, a fine sporting flintlock with roller frizzen spring, and a silver medallion with a feathered Indian head on the wrist of the stock. With few exceptions, the known specimens have fox-in-circle markings, British government view marks, and a crown with broad arrow on the lock plate. These guns do not have the serpent or dragon side plate, and all of them appear to date from the period

1790–1815. Known makers of this type include Ketland, Galton, Morris, Moxham, Rolfe and Sutherland.

Some early northwest guns were marked on the locks with small stampings of a fox in relief which may have been early view marks for the Hudson's Bay Company and the Northwest Company. About 1790 the marking known as the Tombstone Fox appeared, and after 1821 it was widely used on northwest guns. This mark is a deep rectangular stamping, approximately 0.2 by 0.4 inches, with a rounded top, enclosing a tiny sitting fox over two initials in relief. In the Hudson's Bay Company mark of this type, the initials are "EB".

The tombstone fox

Another fox-in-circle, or "sitting fox," mark was stamped on the butt stocks of some trade guns sold by the American Fur Company and the Hudson's Bay Company during the period 1830–80. On these stock marks the fox generally faces left whereas it faces right in the fox-in-circle lock and barrel mark noted above.

The "sitting fox" trade mark of the Hudson's Bay Company

Makers of northwest guns for the Hudson's Bay Company after its union with the Northwest Company in 1821 included: William Wilson, Edward Bond (later E. & W. Bond), Thomas Barnett & Sons (later John Edward Barnett & Sons), William Parker (later Parker Field & Company), Edward Brooks & Son, and I. Hollis & Son. Both plain and fine guns of this type were made. Orders for flintlocks continued until about 1887. Percussion northwest guns were first ordered by the Company

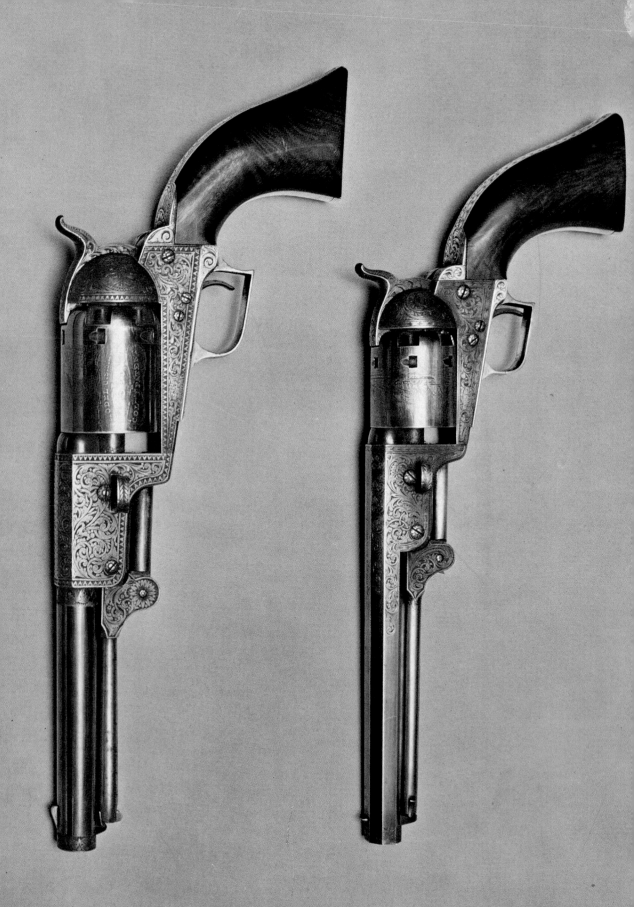

Plate 8

Second model Colt Dragoon revolver (left) and model 1851
Colt Navy revolver. They are decorated in the preferred
fashion for production arms of the mid-nineteenth century.
The iron parts are blued and engraved with profuse floral
scrollwork confined in most areas by formal borders. The
brass backstraps and trigger guards are silver plated, and
the plain grips are made of select varnished walnut. Both
pistols, cased *en suite*, are believed to have been presented
to H.R.H. Prince Albert by Samuel Colt.

Royal Collection, Windsor Castle.

in 1861 and were supplied to Canadian posts until after 1900. Light percussion double- and single-barreled shotguns gradually replaced the northwest guns and were sold under the Company's name until 1936.

Trading firms in the United States imported most of their flintlock northwest guns from such English makers as Ketland, Barnett, Lacy & Company, Sargant Brothers and W. Chance & Son. Most of these guns imported after 1820 carried tombstone-fox marks with the initials "IA". Other initials were sometimes used and in a few cases the mark was omitted altogether. Belgian guns were also imported by American firms in some quantity. They were generally of inferior quality and rarely bore the names of their makers. View marks, however, were often stamped on the Belgian northwest guns either in the tombstone style or in the earlier fox-in-circle style.

Henry Deringer of Philadelphia made northwest guns for the United States government under several contracts between 1814 and 1844. Most of Deringer's guns have an eagle on the lock plate, but no view mark. The Henry Rifle Works at Boulton, Pennsylvania, made northwest guns on several occasions for the American Fur Company in the period 1815–50. Two other prominent Pennsylvania gunmakers – Tryon and H. E. Leman – made thousands of trade guns for the United States government and for private trading companies in the period 1840–60. The Leman view mark was a tombstone fox with initials "P.A."

Typical mid-nineteenth-century northwest guns were made with barrels ranging from 30 to 42 inches in length, the flat brass butt plates were attached by screws instead of the earlier square nails, and the butt stocks were branded with a fox-in-circle mark about half an inch in diameter. The popularity of trade muskets in the United States declined rapidly after 1860 and the few trade guns used in the Indian wars of the eighteen-seventies were confined to some later products of Leman, W. Chance, and the Liège makers, together with a scattering of Hudson's Bay guns traded by Red River half-breeds.

In addition to northwest guns, American traders also regularly sold Pennsylvania rifles in limited quantities to the Indians. The majority of these rifles were of the conventional Kentucky pattern made by Jacob Dickert, Christopher Gumpf, Peter Gonter, John Guest, Frederick Goetz, Henry Gibbs, Jacob Fordney and other well known Lancaster riflesmiths. Henry Deringer of Philadelphia made several thousand plain flintlock Indian rifles for the United States government. J. J. Henry and his son James supplied rifles to the American Fur Company in three patterns: the regular Lancaster model, a plain walnut-stocked type known as the English Rifle, and a scroll-guard maple-stocked model called the New English Rifle. Later Indian rifles were made by Tryon

and Krider, but the most prolific maker in the 1850–75 period was Henry E. Leman of Lancaster, who made thousands of short, sturdy flint and percussion rifles for Indian traders and the United States government.

The early gun trade in South America was not so extensive as that of North America because the Spanish conquerors did not favor the arming of the natives in their colonies. Light, small-gauge single- and double-barreled shotguns with long barrels became popular with the Brazilian Indians, since small calibers were adequate for the game ordinarily encountered in the dense jungle. Portugal purchased so many light guns in Liège for export to its colonies that a special scale of proof for 32-gauge guns was adopted by the Liège proofhouse in 1810. Guns of this type were made quite extensively in Birmingham and Liège well into the twentieth century. Some of the fancy Belgian guns for this market had stocks carved with the heads of Indian chiefs.

The demand for slaves, first in Spanish colonies and later in British possessions, encouraged early trade in Africa, and guns were naturally in demand for hunting and tribal warfare. A company of English adventurers received a Royal Charter for the African trade in 1662, and by 1685 they had a regular gunviewer at work. Little is known about the details of the early African trade guns, but contemporary makers for the domestic market were contemptuous of their vile quality. Liverpool became an important center for the slave trade, and a gunsmith there named John Parr is known to have dealt extensively in such arms in the 1770's.

The British African Company apparently adopted an elephant with howdah as its view mark, and it was generally stamped on the lock only. The elephant was a popular symbol of Africa, and the Liverpool Exchange Hall in the eighteenth century was decorated with "busts of blackamoors and elephants" as a tribute to local wealth gained in the African trade.

English guns for Africa eventually fell into two types – "male" and "female" – whose names dated from their earliest intended use in the slave trade. The "male" guns were refurbished or assembled muskets of fair quality from London dealers. The "female" guns were cheap long-barreled trade guns from the shops of Birmingham.

The barrels of the latter were as much as five feet long and the stocks often followed the undercurved or fat belly butt style of ancient buccaneer muskets. Patterns varied with the tastes of the native rulers in Lagos, Nigeria, Dahomey and elsewhere who supplied the slaves and other native merchandise. Stock decorations often included red paint, brass tacks, mirrors and cheap carving. By 1775 the price of a slave had risen to at least two guns, but the trade was still profitable, for the guns could be bought in Birmingham for three dollars apiece. Manufacture of these late British trade guns continued into the twentieth century, long after their original use in the slave trade had ended.

Belgian factories also made thousands of guns for the African trade, and such manufacturing continued up to very recent years. Nineteenth and twentieth century Belgian models included not only the long light "female" guns and the heavy flintlock muskets, but also long 10-gauge "buccaneer guns" and other special types. The Belgian makers utilized war surplus from any source when it was available. In 1900 alone, 50,000 surplus American Civil War percussion muskets were shipped there for conversion to flintlocks for the African trade.

Spanish and Portuguese traders introduced guns of Spanish manufacture to some parts of Africa. By 1780, Spanish gunmakers had developed a special type of trade gun flintlock which closely resembled the miquelet lock in outward appearance. These guns were eventually supplanted by cheap Belgian imitations having similar locks with miquelet-style cocks and frizzens and stocks of traditional fluted "Madrid" style or the under-cut "Catalan" style. The last of these Belgian Spanish-style African guns were very crude, with cheap stampings to imitate engraving on the barrels, locks and fittings, and red-painted stocks of soft wood.   C.E.H.

Illustrations: pages 214, 216.

Hamilton, T. M. (compiler), "Indian Trade Guns," *The Missouri Archaeologist*, Vol. 22, December 1960.
Hanson, Charles E., Jr., *The Northwest Gun* (Nebraska State Historical Society Publications in Anthropology, No. 2), Lincoln, Neb., 1955.
Mayer, Joseph R., *Flintlocks of the Iroquois, 1620–1687*, (Research Records of the Rochester Museum of Arts and Science, No. 6), Rochester, N.Y., 1943.
Parsons, John E., "Gunmakers for the American Fur Company" in *The New York Historical Society Quarterly*, New York, April 1952.
Russell, Carl P., *Guns on the Early Frontiers*, London, and Berkeley and Los Angeles, Cal., 1957.

See also: INDIAN GUNS.

TRAP GUN/TRIP GUN

"Trap," as here used, has nothing to do with the sport of trapshooting; it refers to devices designed to shoot automatically at men or animals that come into the line of fire. Many of these trap guns are set off by the tripping of a wire or cord. In that its discharge tells anyone in hearing that it has been fired, a trap gun is also an alarm gun (see ALARM GUN).

A trap gun that had a man and not an animal as its intended victim was widely used in England before and after 1800 when poaching was an accepted way of life. A pin loosely fitted on the under side permitted the gun to rotate. Discharge was effected when a line running out from a ring attached to a rod under the stock was drawn taut. The feature of this invention – utilized in many later small-animal traps – was the fastening to the rod of several lines to ensure that the rotating trap would be lined up with the victim at the moment when it was set off. Each line was fastened at its far end to an object fixed close to the ground. The lines were radii covering a small arc of a circle. As a line tightened when a poacher tripped over it the trap rotated just enough to ensure the victim's being in the line of aim. It was possible to elevate or depress the muzzle of this trap, as it was in many of the later animal traps.

About 1800, the vocation of grave robbing was often more lucrative than poaching, and these "spring guns," as they were called, were frequently set up in graveyards to discourage the resurrectionists. This variety of man-trap gun was outlawed in England in 1827.

A "Trap for Capturing and Destroying Wild Animals" was patented in the United States by a certain Reuthe in 1857. It was manufactured in large quantities and had big sales. The Reuthe trap had two barrels which fired simultaneously when two barbed springs, held together in a tube between the barrels, were released. These barbs were baited and flew out and apart when an animal seized and pulled on the bait.

Another American percussion-cap trap gun was the "Game-getter." Australians liked it for hunting kangaroos. This, like the Reuthe trap, was held in place by a cord or wire running back to a tree or post and discharged when an animal took bait held close to the muzzle by a short cord. The Game-getter fired six shots simultaneously from a cylinder. It was unlike the Reuthe trap in that it had no barbs, and in that it had a pistol-grip. It was concealable on the person and usable for self-defense or murder. It could be fired either by a pull on the rod protruding from the muzzle, or by pressure on the trigger.

The twentieth century brought the Taylor Fur-getter, a breechloader firing modern cartridges. Both light .22 and heavy 10-gauge models were popular. A supporting screw, or heavy pin, was driven into a platform, or into firm ground. Discharge was effected by a pull on a baited rod running out in line with the barrel.

The gun that has perhaps been of greatest interest to collectors of trap guns is the French all-metal "Chicken Thief." This was made both in flint and in pin-fire. The Chicken Thief is a pocket pistol with a clamp at the butt to permit fastening to a firm support. A pull on a string run out from a bar under the barrel would fire the gun. The invention was not designed primarily to shoot robbers of hen roosts, but to be clamped in a room pointed at a door or window through which an intruder might enter.

L.W.

Illustrations: page 284.

Logan, Herschel C., *Hand Cannon to Automatic*, Huntingdon, W.Va., 1944.

Winant, Lewis, *Firearms Curiosa*, New York, 1955, 2nd edition 1961, and London, 1956.

TSCHINKE

About sixty miles southwest by west of Krakow, near the Czechoslovak border, is the town of Cieszyn, formerly known as Teschen. Here there developed during the first half of the seventeenth century a peculiar type of light hunting rifle which, from the name of the town, became known as a tschinke. Originally a wheel lock, the type was continued into the flintlock period. It is characterized by light construction, a small bore, and a butt stock extremely short and narrow, shaped rather like the hoof of a deer and hence known as a "hind's-foot" stock.

In the wheel lock tschinkes, the mainspring, wheel arbor and chain are all on the outside of the lock plate. The sear mechanism is internal and is unusual in that the first sear operates contrary to the usual way. In the ordinary wheel lock, the sear is pushed by the sear spring into engagement with a depression in the wheel, and is forced out of this engagement by the superior power of the mainspring when the secondary or supporting sear is withdrawn from contact with the tail of the primary sear. In the tschinke, on the other hand, the sear spring acts to keep the primary sear out of engagement with the wheel. When the lock is spanned, therefore, the sear does not automatically spring into position; instead, it must be forced into engagement by pressing on a push-rod attached to the sear. This makes the preparation for firing more laborious, but, since there is no drag of the sear against the starting of the wheel's rotation, it gives a faster action to the lock and a faster and surer fire.

The small hind's-foot stock was not placed against the shoulder, but was held against the cheek of the shooter. The caliber of the tschinke usually ranged from .25 to .38. It was subject to considerable variation, but averaged much smaller than other contemporary firearms.

T.T.H.

Illustration: page 38.

TUBE LOCK

The tube lock was one of the early developments in percussion ignition. The famous Joseph Manton must be given credit for its invention, in 1818. In use, a copper tube, usually open at both ends, filled with fulminate, was crushed by a blow from the hammer. Usually, the tube lay horizontally on an anvil and was struck on its midsection, but in some locks the blow struck an exposed end. A tube of the open-end variety, when struck in the middle, would spurt flame at both ends – and perhaps disquiet a shooter standing alongside. Consequently, some of these horizontally placed tube primers were supplied with one end capped, so that all the flame of detonation would be directed to the touchhole. Men using tube lock guns often carried the tiny tubes in small dispensers, from which a single primer could be quickly detached. The dispenser dangled from a button or from a cord hung around the neck. Percussion caps were later carried in the same way.

L.W.

Blanch, H. J., *A Century of Guns*, London, 1909.

George, John N., *English Guns and Rifles*, Plantersville, S.C., 1947.

Hawker, Colonel Peter, *Instructions to Young Sportsmen in all that relates to Guns and Shooting*, London, 1844.

Logan, Herschel C., *Hand Cannon To Automatic*, Huntingdon, W.Va., 1944.

Marks, Edward C. R., *The Evolution of Modern Small Arms and Ammunition*, London, 1898.

Pollard, Captain H. B. C., *A History of Firearms*, London, 1926.

Winant, Lewis, *Early Percussion Firearms*, New York, 1959, and London, 1961.

See also: MANTON, JOSEPH; PERCUSSION SYSTEM; PRIMER.

TULLE

Tulle, principal town of the department of the Corrèze, France, appears to have grown up round a monastery founded in the seventh century. By the end of the seventeenth century, its population numbered 5,000.

The manufacture of arms dates from this period. In 1690 a master cannonier, Michel Pauphille, who belonged to a family of arquebusiers long established in the town, received a commission from the Intendant General to manufacture cannon for the arsenal at Rochefort. Pauphille's workshop thrived to such an extent under the royal patronage that it had to expand. However, the master cannonier lacked sufficient capital to expand his business and to include the manufacture of guns as well as that of cannon. He went into partnership with Fenis de Lacombe, the public attorney at Tulle, who supplied him with the necessary capital to found a factory.

In 1692 this factory exployed 200 workers, recruited

mainly from Saint-Étienne and later from Liège. Making constant progress under the management of M. de Fenis's descendants, it became a royal manufactory in 1777. The First Empire marked the highest point of its activity; the firm employed 700 workers and was capable of producing 12,000 weapons a year.

Production at Tulle was at all periods of a consistently high quality. Maritz, the inspector general, includes the following remarks in his report of his tour of inspection in 1763: "One notes that the Tulle cannon and guns are made of the softest Périgord iron and that they are smelted with charcoal, which does not damage the iron as coal does. It is recommended that a requisition be made to this firm for two thousand guns. It should be given preference over Saint-Étienne for the manufacture of high quality guns, which shall be made of iron which is not brittle."

In 1816 the company passed into the ownership of the state.   CL.B.

TURRET GUN

In military and especially in naval parlance a turret gun is a cannon housed in a turret that, usually, can be revolved. In small arms terminology a turret gun is one having a cylinder with the chambers radiating from the center, as spokes radiate from the hub of a wheel.

The "Monitor" of the American Civil War had a revolving turret. That warship was called by many "a cheese box on a raft." Its turret did resemble a cheese box, and it also reminded one of a popular old-time form of spring-mousetrap – squat, round, with openings spaced evenly around its cylindrical surface. Some collectors called Cochran rifles "mousetrap guns."

Of the few early turret guns that were even moderately successful, the percussion Cochran and the percussion Porter received the most acclaim. (There was general rejection, coming largely from the knowledge that when any such gun was fired it also had one bullet in the cylinder pointing directly back at the shooter – and there was always the danger that all charges might go off together when any form of percussion revolver was fired.) John W. Cochran obtained an American patent in 1837 for his percussion cap underhammer turret gun, but Cochran was probably more successful in Europe than in America with his inventions. Cochran guns, which exist both in pistols and in rifles, have horizontal turrets that are turned manually. Two Cochrans, incidentally, that are exactly alike would be hard to find.

A few percussion-cap, horizontal-turret guns, not Cochrans, were produced with the ball placed in a chamber at right angles to the gunpowder chamber to lessen the possibility of a multiple explosion.

Parry W. Porter's rifle (two or three Porter pistols exist), patented in the United States in 1851, has a vertical turret. Movement of the trigger guard down and up cocks the hammer and simultaneously revolves the turret.

On all vertical turret guns, the turret obstructed normal aiming. On the Porter, the sights were set well to the left, and aim was taken along the side of the barrel rather than over the top.

The *Système Noel* pistol was a percussion vertical-turret pocket arm. This weapon was side-hammer and double-action; its turret turned when the trigger was pulled.

Another, and more interesting, European turret gun was the Genhart, patented in France in 1844. This employed a horizontal turret and was made both in shoulder arms and in pistols. Genhart turret guns fired unusual metal cartridges (now even scarcer than the guns) which made use of the Manton tube-primer principle. Whereas the Noel is side-hammer and its turret turns when the trigger is pulled, the Genhart is underhammer and its turret requires manual turning. The Genhart turret was quickly removable. A man who carried several spare turrets, loaded, could do a lot of shooting in a short time.

The commonest turret pistols are the squeezer pistols usually known as "protectors." These fired special small center-fire cartridges. They were a French invention, patented and marketed in several European countries, and in the United States in 1883. *Le Protector Revolver de Poche* was held in the palm of the hand, with the barrel thrust out between the first and second fingers, and fired by tightening the fist. The turret was hidden between two covers (caps) and would drop out for reloading when one of the caps was unscrewed. The squeezing pressure turned the turret and drove a firing pin against a cartridge primer.

From American Civil War days until shortly before the First World War, large turret guns were in disrepute and were regarded as impractical relics. Then the Lewis gun was invented by Colonel Isaac N. Lewis of the United States Army. That gun handled military cartridges (30/06 at first, mostly .303 British later) loaded into a revolving turret. The turret capacity of this gas-operated light machine gun was increased from forty-seven cartridges in the earliest models to ninety-six in the last models.

Eventually the Lewis gun had great success when mounted in airplanes, but at first it was regarded only as a ground weapon, and as such it became a favorite with the United States Marines. As a ground weapon, it was supplied with a light tripod or with an even lighter folding mount. Later, for aircraft use, the Lewis was furnished with various mountings.

The earliest illustrations of a Lewis gun picture it, fitted with a tripod mount at the muzzle, being carried at the ready by an advancing infantryman. A soldier preferred taking the prone position when shooting a Lewis gun, but any soldier in good condition could shoot it offhand. Complete with tripod and magazine the gun weighed perhaps 30 lb, which was less than some elephant guns.

A test of the gun for possible use by fliers was made in the United States in 1912. In that test it was held in the lap of its operator, with its muzzle resting on the cross-bar which supported the feet both of the pilot and of the gunner on the Wright pusher airplane. This first strafing practice from an aircraft put bullets in a target lying on the ground, and Captain Chandler, the commanding officer at College Park, just outside Washington, who made the unofficial tests in person, was greatly pleased with the results. But, as often happens, approval was not immediate. The United States did not approve the Lewis gun until long after its usefulness had been proved by the nations of the Triple Entente, and after the gun had been produced in thousands by the Birmingham Small Arms Company.

The Lewis gun, firing newly invented Buckham incendiary bullets, is to be thanked for the fact that during the First World War England was able to prevent any great damage being inflicted on London by the bombs dropped from Zeppelins – something she was, of course, unable to prevent during the Second World War, when bombs were dropped from airplanes. Fighter airplanes of the First World War could not quite reach the heights at which dirigibles could fly, but they could get close enough underneath to riddle the hydrogen-filled bags with bursts from their Lewis guns. Colonel Chinn, in *The Machine Gun*, states that Lewis guns are credited with ten of the twelve Zeppelins brought down over London.

During and soon after the First World War, one or two other turret machine guns were developed for use in aircraft, but none matched the performance of the Lewis gun.   L.W.

Illustrations: pages 178, 337.

Chinn, Colonel George M., *The Machine Gun*, 4 vols, Washington, D.C., 1951–55.

Logan, Herschel C., *Hand Cannon to Automatic*, Huntingdon, W.Va., 1944.

Sawyer, Charles Winthrop, *Our Rifles*, Boston, Mass., 1920.

Winant, Lewis, *Firearms Curiosa*, New York, 1955, 2nd edition 1961, and London, 1956.

See also: AUTOMATIC ARMS; LEWIS, ISAAC NEWTON; MACHINE GUN; PALM PISTOL.

U

UNDERHAMMER GUN

Underhammer guns are, exactly as the name implies, guns with the hammer on the under side of the barrel. Early accounts also refer to them as "understrikers" and "undercocks." The principle of placing the hammer on the under side of the barrel was employed on both handguns and long arms. Such arms included single-shot, multi-shot, and revolving firearms.

The oft-repeated question as to why the hammer was placed in this unusual position can be answered briefly as follows: (*a*) to lessen the danger from flying particles of metal from the metal percussion caps; (*b*) to provide a less obstructed view for sighting the gun; (*c*) to afford simplicity of construction; (*d*) to provide a streamlined arm which could be carried with ease in a boot, belt or pocket.

Mechanisms were for the most part extremely simple. Often the trigger guard also served as a mainspring. Some arms employed a coiled spring, while others utilized a U-spring, or a straight or curved spring to activate the hammer. Although the majority of the underhammers are single-action, it is not unusual to find one working on the double-action principle, where a pull on the trigger also cocks the hammer.

Triggers were of the usual types found on conventional arms: straight, folding, ring and button. Calibers ranged from the small bore used for firing pellets with only a bit of fulminate, up to the large bore of shotgun size. Barrels, round, octagon, or round and octagon, were rifled or smoothbore as necessary for their intended use. Their length varied from three or four inches, on the pocket models, to eighteen or twenty inches, on the buggy rifle size.

Underhammers equipped with a bullet starter are rather scarce. Those by William Billinghurst of Rochester, N.Y., are the best known as fine target arms. Sights on the guns differed little from those found on other guns of the period. A few of the fine target pistols were equipped with telescope sights.

Some makers produced underhammer pistols in pairs, though these are also scarce, especially if cased with accessories.

By far the greater number of underhammers were muzzle-loading and percussion, but some which utilize metallic cartridges are found, as also are some using needle-fire ignition. There is a small quantity of underhammers which use the "pill-lock" system of ignition. Instead of a percussion cap such arms used tiny pellets of fulminate, held in place in the touchhole by some form of paste binder.

Grips on the handguns varied from the bird's-head, western, saw-handle and right-angle, to unusual ones, such as those on the French Delvigne and the Day bludgeon pistol. Maple, walnut and ebony were used in the making of stocks. All-metal grips are also encountered from time to time. Some, too, were ornamented with silver or ivory, silver inlays being either of fine wire or solid patches. Brass and German silver were extensively used in mountings for the guns. Fluted grips are believed to have been used principally by French and Belgian gunsmiths; rarely, if ever, have they been seen on American underhammers.

Though not frequently encountered, underhammer pistols equipped with a detachable extension stock are known. Such guns are of the buggy rifle type and were used primarily for hunting and target shooting. These guns were, as a rule, of better workmanship than some of the pocket arms.

Buggy rifle was another name given to pistols with extension stocks or with an unusually long barrel. Such guns could easily be carried in the horse-drawn buggy of their day. They were ideal for hunting, target shooting, or, if need be, for defense. With an extension stock, the buggy rifle provided a convenient gun for any game which might appear.

The name "pocket rifle" was another descriptive name applied to underhammers, as well as to some of the conventional arms of the day. It was an arm with or without an extension stock and with a shorter barrel than the buggy rifle. It could be carried in its owner's pocket or in a separate holster.

Multi-shot underhammers included double-barrel, over-and-under, revolving-barrel, pepperbox, revolving-cylinder and harmonica types.

Underhammer pepperboxes were patterned after the prevailing styles of the time, and in both single- and double-action. The number of barrels varied, from the six-shot of the American types, to the sixteen and more of Continental European production. Distinguished by their beauty of decoration are the French and Belgian pepperboxes of the Mariette system. The barrels of these guns were separate units instead of having the chambers bored in one block or cylinder of steel, as was the usual method.

Of unusual style are those repeating or multi-shot pistols employing a flat, horizontal cylinder in which the chambers radiate out like the spokes of a wheel. The best known of these are the Cochrans of American manufacture.

The principles of operation, style of ornamentation and the individuality of the long arms followed those of the handguns. Most remarkable of the long arms were the cane guns. Such guns were made in two styles – one a whole unit, and one which when broken down in parts would supply its owner with both handgun and walking cane. The John Day cane gun was the one produced (in England) for the greatest length of time. Patented in 1823, it was still being produced some thirty years later – an unusual length of time for such a dual-purpose arm.

Five countries are known to have experimented with and considered the use of the underhammer principle for military arms – England, France, Denmark, Norway and the United States. Of the five, England appears to have been the only one which did not actually adopt this arm for service with troops. Though tests were made with Baron Heurteloup's Koptiter Lock Underhammer around 1836–39, there is no record of anything more than tests. Denmark adopted an underhammer pistol – a rather heavy breech-loading percussion arm. France tested an underhammer musket using a pin-fire cartridge, but it is not known to what extent it was used by the services. During the Civil War the United States adopted, and purchased, several hundred of the Greene underhammer rifles for the use of troops in the field. While not martial arms in the sense that they were adopted by the military, it is known that men on both sides of that conflict did occasionally use underhammer pistols, for specimens were later picked up on the battlefields.

The actual origin of the underhammer principle is obscured by the mists of time. It is known, however, that the placing of the cock under the barrel dates back into the flintlock period. Specimens of such guns made on the Continent and in America do exist, though they are quite scarce. It was not until the advent of the percussion system of ignition that the underhammer guns came into their own.

First produced on the Continent and in England, the "understrikers" found more than passing interest in America. Their utter simplicity appealed to the early gunsmiths, for here was a type of gun which could be fabricated in its entirety in their own shops. Never mass produced, but rather individual arms made for the pleasure of the gunsmith or for some friend, many of them do not have any mark of identification. Thus they will always pose a problem as to where, when and by whom they were produced. Others are fully marked with the maker's name, in some instances together with the name of a dealer or agent.

Granted that the European pieces did show more finished craftmanship, nevertheless their American counterparts achieved more definite public appeal and acceptance. From available data it appears that the most active period of the underhammers was from about 1835 to about 1860, and that the area of greatest production was the northeastern part of the United States. It was here also that the greatest variety of types were fashioned.

More or less discarded for nearly a hundred years, the underhammer guns are staging a revival among present-day target shooters. Today many muzzle-loading rifle shooting matches in the United States include under-hammer entries, and it can be said that they are giving an excellent account of themselves. Many of the guns used in such matches are being built by present-day gun-smiths, but it is not at all unusual to find shooters using one of the guns produced by a gunmaker of a hundred years ago.   H.C.L.

Illustrations: pages 41, 337–8.

Logan, Herschel C., *Underhammer Guns*, Harrisburg, Pa., 1960.

V

VERY PISTOL

See: FLARE PISTOL.

VETTERLI, FRÉDÉRIC

Frédéric Vetterli was born in 1822 at Wagenhausen, a little village in the canton of Thurgovia in eastern Switzerland.

After serving an apprenticeship with the arms manufacturer Schalch at Schaffhouse, he left to extend his knowledge. He worked first at Lahr, a German town near the Black Forest, subsequently at Paris, Saint-Étienne and London. He then returned to Switzerland, to join the Société Suisse pour l'Industrie (established in 1853) at Neuhausen. A contract, signed June 24, 1864, appointed him to the newly formed arms department (created in 1860), which owed its remarkable development to his skill and experience.

Together with many other inventors in Europe and the United States, Frédéric Vetterli had tried since 1847 to solve the problems of the breech-loading rifle. His work at Neuhausen and his ingenuity enabled him to create the weapon that was to be adopted by the Swiss government. His designs were accepted and the Technical Commission, nominated by the Federal Council to study a new type of rifle, chose his model, which was officially accepted by the decree of March 6, 1868.

Frédéric Vetterli did not leave Switzerland again, and died in 1882.   CL.B.

See also: VETTERLI RIFLE.

VETTERLI RIFLE

On December 20, 1866, the Swiss government decided by federal decree to adopt the repeating rifle for its army. This was a theoretical decision only, since no model had been presented to the Army Technical Commission, who were entrusted with the thorough examination of the designs submitted to them. Their studies resulted in the communication of the Federal Council of March 6, 1868: "In pursuance of the Federal decree of December 20, 1866, the repeating rifle recommended by the Expert Commission, the Vetterli rifle (which combines the mechanism of the American Winchester and the Prussian rifle), will be introduced as the regulation rifle."

The first order was for 119,000 pieces; delivery must have been slow, since up to the end of May 1872 – that is, four years after the decision – the army had only 48,368 rifles at its disposal.

The principal dimensions of the model known as the "1869" are as follows:

Total length: 1,300 mm.
Length of barrel from breech box: 822 mm.
Bore: 10.4 mm., 4 grooves in rifling.
Sighting range: graduated to 1,000 mm.
Weight: 4,500 gm.
Cartridge: Boxer system; total weight 30.60 gm., of which 20.40 gm. is for the missile and 3.75 gm. for the powder.
Breech plug system: double movement cylinder.
Bayonet: blade measuring 480 mm.
Number of cartridges it can contain: 13.
Initial speed: 480 m.
Maximum range: 2.800 m.

The Swiss armament was completed by a junior rifle (Communiqué to the cantons May 6, 1870) and by a carbine (decision of February 27, 1871).

This weapon, which was intended for the carabiniers (top marksmen), was shorter than the rifle: 1,200 mm. instead of 1,300 mm. It was equipped with a Thury double trigger system.

The dragoon companies were equipped with a shorter weapon still (February 20, 1871); this measured 930 mm., with a magazine for six cartridges. A few details of the Vetterli were modified, resulting in the models of 1871, 1878 and 1881.

The carbine was modified in 1881.

The Vetterli system was adopted by Italy (infantry rifle Vetterli-Vitali Model 1871/87 and infantry rifle of the marine Vetterli-Bertoldo Model 1871/72). In Switzerland the Vetterli rifle and carbine were used by the troops until their replacement by the rifle Model 1889 of Colonel Rodolphe Schmidt, of which the most notable feature is the rectilinear movement of the breech.   CL.B.

Illustration: page 182.

See also: VETTERLI, FRÉDÉRIC.

VOLCANIC ARMS

See: HENRY, BENJAMIN TYLER; REPEATING ARMS; WINCHESTER.

VOLLEY GUN

From the earliest days of firearms the possibility of firing more than one shot at a time was an attraction for gun-makers and inventors. In the fourteenth century, cannon with groups of barrels discharging all their shots together were popular, but their weight was a great disadvantage. Combinations of medium-size barrels were often mounted on wheels or in carts and were known as organ batteries or death organs. The crude handgun was sometimes made with three or more barrels, and a seven-barreled handgun was listed in a 1435 inventory of the Bastille. Because of difficulties in construction, most of these guns were ar-ranged to fire their barrels separately. As the manufac-ture of firearms improved, however, the volley gun became a more practical proposition. A sporting gun, dated 1612, in the Tower of London, has seven barrels bored from one piece of metal and designed to fire as a volley. Guns of this type, ignited by matchlock, wheel lock or flintlock, and with combinations of barrels up to a dozen, were made so that they could be fired from the shoulder without too much discomfort.

The combination of seven barrels seems to have been most popular, but whether this was from convenience or because of some mythological significance is hard to tell. It was a volley gun with seven barrels that was to achieve most distinction. In 1779, James Wilson offered the Board of Ordnance in London a "new Invented Gun with seven barrels to fire at one time." Two were made with rifled barrels, and after a satisfactory trial were recommended for use in the "tops" of naval vessels. Wilson was awarded £400, and the manufacture was placed in the hands of the London gunmaker, Henry Nock, who had made the prototypes. It was not an easy task. The seven barrels were made separately and brazed together, with a breech plug to each of the outer six. The center barrel was thread-ed so that it could be screwed to a plug or spigot, hol-lowed out in the form of a bell. This chamber, which was connected to the touchhole, fired the central barrel, and its ignition was carried to the outer barrels by six radial channels. There was a tendency for these interior channels to become clogged after a few rounds, so that the gun had to be dismantled for cleaning. Difficulties experienced in loading resulted in the barrels being made with smooth-bores, and because of the tremendous recoil the powder charge was reduced. Although the operation of the gun was made easier, much of its effectiveness as a long range weapon was thus destroyed. Nevertheless, between 1780 and 1788 some 655 volley guns were produced at a price of £13 each, except for the original two rifles which cost £15 each. The Nock guns were used by Howe's fleet at the relief of Gibraltar in 1782, but it is doubtful whether they ever became popular because of the fire hazard caused by their discharge in close proximity to the sails of ships.

The naval volley gun was about three feet long and weighed 12 lb., which was too heavy for a sporting gun. With their bore and weight reduced, however, the seven-barreled guns enjoyed some vogue among the sporting gentry. A handsome silver-mounted seven-barreled gun and pistol made for George III by Nock are in the Windsor Castle Collection, and other similar guns were made by Durs Egg, Ezekiel Baker and H. W. Mortimer. Although this combination of seven barrels was most popular, the only limit to the number of barrels was the weight factor. The great champion of the volley gun was the famous sportsman Colonel Thomas Thornton. In his collection of guns he had a twelve-barreled gun and one with a double set of seven barrels, which weighed $11\frac{1}{2}$ lb. The latter, with its special loader, is now in the Liège Arms Museum.

Most volley guns were made on a more modest scale, the size of the pistol in particular being limited by its weight. A considerable number of flintlock pistols were made with two, three or four barrels, but only a few fired all the barrels together, the majority employing some breech action which enabled one shot to be taken at a time. Pistols with more than four barrels normally em-ployed the volley principle, but specimens of them are rare. There was one type of four-barreled volley pistol, how-ever, which became popular in the last quarter of the eighteenth century. This was the duck's-foot pistol, so called because its barrels splayed out from a common breech. Bulky and dangerous, it was intended for guards and ships' officers against mobs. An even more dangerous weapon was offered to the Board of Ordnance in 1842 by J. Lillycrap: a soldier's belt bristling with pistol barrels designed to be fired five at a time.

The introduction of the percussion lock with its lighter and simpler mechanism encouraged the development of the revolver rather than the volley gun, but several fine percussion volley guns were made. A seven-barreled sporting rifle, made by Forsyth & Company, is now in the Tower of London, complete in its case with a brass powder charger, a boxwood false muzzle containing seven patched bullets, and a steel breech-plug wrench. With the percussion system still in its experimental stages, came the first cartridge breechloaders made by Samuel Pauly. As though to prove his locks capable of working on all guns, he produced a seven-barreled, breech-loading volley gun opened by sliding forward the fore-end and swiveling the barrel downwards at half-cock. The breech was loaded by a brass cartridge filling all seven chambers.

At the Great Exhibition of 1851 in London, firearms from all over the world were displayed, including many pepperboxes and revolvers. There was one volley gun, by the German gunmaker Ludwig Teutenberg, a seven-barreled rifle "particularly applicable for shooting wild fowl." The volley gun's ability to kill fowl at long ranges was now its only recommendation. An attempt by the American general, O. Vandenburgh, to introduce a new system of artillery which visualised clusters of up to 451 barrels firing musket bullets in unison met with little success. By the end of the nineteenth century the ordinary shotgun and rifle were adequate for most sporting purposes, and the multi-barreled volley gun became a curiosity. Probably the last ones made were those of the Belgian gunmaker Pieper which had seven rifled barrels firing .22 rim-fire cartridges from a Remington-type rolling breech.   H.L.B.

Illustrations: pages 184, 339.

Peterson, Harold L., *The Treasury of the Gun*, New York, 1962 (*The Book of the Gun*, London, 1963).

See also: NOCK, HENRY; REPEATING ARMS.

WALCH REVOLVER

The Walch revolver, patented in 1859, was designed to increase the fire power of the percussion revolver by means of double-loaded chambers. It had two hammers, and each chamber was fitted with two nipples; one leading to the rear of the chamber, as in a Colt, the other leading through a passage in the chamber wall to a point half way along the chamber.

A special bullet was covered by the patent. One type consisted of a half-ball joined to a circular plate of the same diameter by a small shank. Another consisted of two half-balls joined together by a similar shank. In both cases a recess was left between the two halves, and this was filled with a mixture of one part oil to three of soap. The bullet could be loaded with or without a wad, and on ramming it home, the mixture was forced out as the halves closed, sealing the rear charge from the flash of the forward charge.

Three models are known:

	Navy	*Pocket*	*Pocket*
Caliber	.36	.31	.31
Barrel	6″ octagonal	4½″ round	3¼″ octagonal
Total length	12¼″	10″	8½″
Frame	Iron	Brass	Brass or Iron
Triggers	Double	Single	Single
Shots	12	10	10

The pocket models, apart from the difference in size, had different mechanisms from the navy model. The latter had two triggers within a guard, and attached to the frame was a folding loading lever, similar to those fitted to Colt revolvers of the period. The pocket models were worked by an ingenious single trigger in a sheath guard, and were loaded by a separate brass rammer.

Apart from these production models, two other models are detailed in the illustrations to the patents. The production models have grips similar to the Colt, but with a slight spur curving back above the thumb. The patent models have Colt-type grips. In the patent models only one row of nipples was placed at the back, while the others formed a ring round the middle of the cylinder, each at a slight angle to the bore. The two hammers worked in the same plane, one having an extension piece passing through the other so as to reach over the top of the cylinder to reach the forward nipples.

To operate the production models each chamber was double loaded. Both hammers were cocked in one movement, the right-hand one falling on the first pressure of the trigger. The flash from the right-hand cap traveled through the passage in the chamber wall and fired the forward charge. On releasing the trigger and pressing again, the second hammer fell, firing the left-hand cap leading immediately to the rear charge.

The rarity of existing specimens seems to indicate a limited use.   G.E.B.

Illustration: page 175.

Bennett, G. E., and Blackmore, Howard L., "The Walch Revolver" in *Journal of the Arms and Armour Society*, Vol. 1, No. 8, London, 1954.

Smith, Sam. E., "Walch and Lindsay" in *The Gun Collector*, May 1950.

WALL GUN

See: SWIVEL GUN.

WEBLEY, PHILIP AND JAMES

Philip Webley was apprenticed to a gunlock-filer at the age of fourteen, and when he went into partnership with his brother James at Weaman Street, Birmingham, he was described in the 1835 directory as a percussioner and gunlock-maker. Not long afterwards, he married the daughter of William Davis, a gun implement and tool maker, and the two firms were amalgamated under the name of Philip Webley (late W. Davis). Philip appears to have concentrated on his father-in-law's side of the business, but, in 1853, James took out a patent for a percussion revolver and started a separate business under his own name at 14 St Mary's Row.

Most of the revolvers made by James were of the distinctive single-action type with a long spur hammer, described in an advertisement of 1856 as being furnished with a Minié rifle barrel and warranted to do execution at three hundred yards. The First Model, now much sought after by collectors, had a hinged barrel with a detachable rammer. This rammer was secured permanently to the barrel pivot in the Second Model. In the Third Model the barrel was screwed to the frame and was fitted with a patent Kerr rammer. All these models were made in holster, belt and pocket sizes and were of noticeably good quality.

Philip had also obtained patents for a revolver in 1853, but his was a self-cocking model with a rounded hammer. Although it had the advantage of a faster action, it was of poor finish and production was comparatively small. In fact, the Birmingham directories of this period continue to describe Philip as a gun implement maker. In 1857, however, the closing of the Colt factory in London encouraged the English gunmakers to greater efforts. Philip brought his two sons, Thomas William and Henry, into the business, the name being changed to Philip Webley & Sons. They wisely extended their trade to cover all kinds of arms – muskets, rifles, pistols, cutlasses, ships' axes, pikes, bayonets, etc. – and of course the famous W. D. range of bullet molds.

In 1865 Philip Webley & Sons endeavored to capture the revolver market with a single-action solid-frame revolver firing six rim-fire cartridges of .45 caliber. This was followed by a double-action model chambered to take the .577 Boxer cartridge – a formidable heavy pistol with great stopping power. In 1867 Webley's introduced an improved model of .442 caliber which, being adopted by the Royal Irish Constabulary, became known as the R.I.C. model. Made in a variety of heavy bores, it was officially adopted in Australia by the Queensland and Victoria governments and in South Africa by the Cape Mounted Police. A lighter model with a short barrel was issued to English police forces, and this, with a curved grip, became known all over the world as the "British Bulldog." In all these revolvers the cartridge had to be ejected and loaded singly, but the Webley-Pryse and Webley-Kaufman .45 revolvers of 1880 incorporated a breech action with automatic ejection. These formed the basis of the revolver with interchangeable parts which was adopted by the British Army and Navy in 1887 and was to be manufactured in vast numbers in the First and Second World Wars. Modifications of the army revolvers were the "W.G." (for Webley Green) model of 1889 designed mainly for target work, the Wilkinson Webley with refinements by the Wilkinson Sword company, and the Webley-Fosbery, a semi-automatic revolver invented by Lieutenant Colonel C. V. Fosbery. In 1897 Webley & Sons amalgamated with two other Birmingham gunmakers, W. & C. Scott & Sons and Richard Ellis & Sons, to form the Webley and Scott Revolver and Arms Co. Ltd. Between them they developed an automatic pistol which was issued to the Royal Navy and the Metropolitan Police. The present firm of Webley & Scott Ltd. continues to make guns of all kinds, including a series of air pistols and rifles introduced in 1924.   H.L.B.

Illustrations: pages 175–6.

Craig, C. W. Thurlow, and Bewley, E. G., *Webley, 1790–1953*, Birmingham, 1953.

Dowell, William C., *The Webley Story*, Kirkgate, Leeds, 1962.

WESSON, DANIEL B.

Daniel Baird Wesson, noted inventor and co-founder of "Smith & Wesson," was born in Worcester, Massachusetts, on May 18, 1825. Finishing his schooling at the age of eighteen, he served a four-year apprenticeship to the gunsmith trade in his brother Edwin's shop at Northboro, Massachusetts. Shortly after his brother's death in 1850, he worked for a while with his brother Frank, a gunsmith in Grafton, and then became superintendent of the Leonard pepperbox pistol manufactory. In 1852 Wesson took employment with Allen, Brown & Luther, riflemakers of Worcester, Massachusetts, where he became associated with Horace Smith, also an expert mechanic and inventor, who had obtained a patent for a breech-loading firearm, No. 8,317. With this patent, as well as one for a Henry action acquired from B. Tyler Henry, inventor of the Henry rifle, Wesson, in partnership with Smith, went into production of a repeating pistol patented by Smith & Wesson on February 14, 1854 (Patent No. 10,535), retaining Henry as their production superintendent. To acquire capital, they incorporated in 1855, under the name of Volcanic Repeating Firearms Company. Smith and Wesson turned over their patents to this company, among them a new one of August 8, 1854, No. 11,496, for an improved cartridge.

Wesson left Volcanic in February 1856 to work on the development of a metallic cartridge and particularly on a revolver to use such a cartridge. About May 1, 1857, he joined Smith, who had also left Volcanic shortly after its incorporation, in Springfield, and they resumed their partnership. They leased a building and started initially with the manufacture of a small .22 caliber cartridge revolver, including the innovation of a metallic cartridge using a patent of a "cylinder bored end to end" acquired from Rollin White. This patent, though at first unsuccessfully applied by White to paper cartridges, provided for the far-sighted Smith & Wesson a successful metallic cartridge revolving arms monopoly which they did not relinquish until 1869, when the patent expired.

Wesson retired in 1883 and died on August 4, 1906, at the age of eighty-one. The firm he founded grew to acquire world-wide fame and an honored reputation among hand arms users, and his descendants are still active in Smith & Wesson of Springfield, Massachusetts.

A.G.

Illustrations: pages 174, 180.

Gluckman, Colonel Arcadi, and Satterlee, L. D., *American Gun Makers*, Harrisburg, Pa., 1953.
Parsons, John E., *Smith & Wesson Revolvers*, New York, 1957.

See also: CARTRIDGE; REVOLVER; SMITH, HORACE.

WHALING GUN

Early in the history of whaling, attempts were made by the British and Scottish whalers voyaging to Greenland to devise a method of firing into the whale the barbed harpoon, which attached the creature by a line to the boat. These harpoon guns were in use early in the eighteenth century, and were originally fixed to the bow of the whaleboat. But it was soon demonstrated that the whale line thus fired had the effect of deflecting the harpoon from its true course, and attention was then turned to designing a gun for firing a bomb lance (i.e. a lance with an explosive head) instead of a harpoon. By 1731 the British whalemen in the Greenland fishery were testing such a crude bomb lance gun, but it was little used, and in 1771 a swivel gun for the purpose was introduced. In 1792 the London Society for the Encouragement of Arts, Manufactures and Commerce offered rewards for whales killed with a "harpoon gun." But most whalemen did not trust it, preferring the time-honored use of the hand harpoon and lance.

Soon after the War of 1812, another type of bomb lance was developed by a number of inventors, but with indifferent success. In 1822 a certain Joseph Hawkins was advertising in various newspapers a new type of weapon – a triangular, pointed, cylindrical javelin, fitted to the caliber of the swivel, containing an inner charge which was ignited by a fuse to explode in the whale's blubber, thereby driving the javelin deeper into the vital organs. This and the Congreve Rocket type of bomb lance were offered to whalemen, but never caught the fancy of these mariners. There was a good reason for this. The bomb, exploding in the vitals of the right whale, usually caused it to sink rapidly and thus be lost. Another type of bomb lance was invented by Robert Allen in Norwich, Connecticut, in 1846. Although it was the most practical that had yet been developed, two disadvantages prevented it from becoming popular: the lack of guiding wings, and the presence of the burning fuse at the rear of the cylindrical lance.

The shoulder whaling gun was an American invention. Before and after the Civil War, it was manufactured by several concerns in the United States. One of the first successful guns of this type was produced by C. C. Brand of Norwich, Connecticut, and manufactured by him for over three decades, with an improved design appearing on the market in 1852. This was a muzzle-loading gun, firing a bomb lance to explode in the whale. There were three calibers, ranging from $\frac{7}{8}$ of an inch to $1\frac{1}{4}$ inches, with guns measuring from 38 inches to 34 inches in length, the weight varying from 23 lb. to 18 lb. The ramrods were of hickory, with brass thimbles and screws. Three drams of powder were generally used in the propelling charge.

Two other shoulder whaling guns became popular with whalemen – the Pierce & Eggers gun and the Cunningham & Cogan gun. Both of these were breechloaders. S. Eggers, of New Bedford, Massachusetts, patented his gun in 1876. Made of heavy brass, with a skeleton stock and reinforced barrel, it weighed 24 lb. and was $36\frac{1}{2}$ inches long. Ebenezer Pierce adapted his bomb lance to this gun, but a Brand-type bomb lance could also be used. A Winchester cartridge was later used in the Pierce & Eggers gun, with the bomb lance being loaded separately. The Pierce bomb lance had the point end filled with black powder; the end screwed tightly, and would explode by concussion. The Cunningham & Cogan gun had a stock of cast iron and a barrel of steel, and the bomb lance and cartridge were combined. Patrick Cunningham was the inventor of the latter and it was improved by Bernard Cogan who manufactured it with the inventor.

The last to make shoulder guns and bomb lances in the United States was Frank Brown of New Bedford, who made them in his shop well into the twentieth century.

The shoulder gun was carried in a wooden box in the whaleboat, covered with a piece of canvas, and the stock was usually made fast to the forward hoisting strap to prevent it from being lost overboard. When fired from the shoulder, as an ordinary gun, this gun's recoil often "fired aft," so that the gunner would be knocked flat in the boat. In 1884 Pierce designed another type of shoulder gun with a breech release mounted on the breech itself, instead of inside the skeleton stock. Both kinds continued to be sold.

The first shoulder whaling guns fired bomb lances shaped to fit snugly in the gun barrel, with heads like javelins. Early Brand guns used bomb lances with rubber flanges on the tailpiece like feathers on an arrow. Later developments in the Pierce gun bomb lance had metal wings which sprang outward upon release from the muzzle and thus kept the flight true. The bomb fuse was ignited by a percussion cap, placed on the nipple of a fuse tube. It burned backward through the tube, to explode the magazine. A metallic hammer or plunger just under the head of the lance was held by a wooden pin. The breech-loading guns had the cartridge inserted after the lance had been placed in the barrel from the muzzle end. The concussion of the explosion of the charge in the cartridge when the gun was fired broke the pin and released the hammer or plunger which, upon impact with the whale, struck the percussion cap, exploded it, and ignited the fuse.

The darting gun was also an American invention. The first type was a muzzle-loading variety, and consisted of a stockless gun-metal barrel, fourteen inches long, with a breech lock and socket, affixed to a regular harpoon pole of wood. A harpoon, with whale line attached, was fitted loosely to the metal gun barrel by two lugs. When the weapon was thrown by hand, and the harpoon penetrated the whale's blubber deeply enough, a long wire rod projecting over the gun barrel was pressed back, acting like a trigger to fire the gun and send the bomb lance into the whale's body. The concussion of the lance entering the whale's body ignited a time fuse by means of a percussion cap. A lanyard, attached to the gun barrel, recovered it after the harpoon had fastened and the bomb had been fired.

In 1865 the darting gun was introduced by Captain Ebenezer Pierce to the Arctic whalers out of New Bedford, and it was used successfully the following year by Mate Leander C. Owen of the whaleship "Massachusetts" of New Bedford. By this time whaling in the Bering Sea and through the Bering Strait was being resumed with profit, and the new darting gun helped kill the bowhead whale before he could escape under the edge of field ice. Patrick Cunningham also designed a darting gun, which was first made for him by Bernard Cogan in the Sandwich Islands as early as 1875, on the same principle as Pierce's patent of 1865. Pierce later invented a breech-loading darting gun and made several improvements to the tripping or sliding rod mechanism. This rod, arranged to move in guides on the barrel, moved with the barrel when it was adjusted. A hinge connected it with the breech to permit the charge to be inserted. The latter was patented in 1881. Two types of these breech-loading gun barrels were designed by Pierce, both made of brass, one with a hinge which broke down like a shotgun, and the other a screw-barrel breech. A rubber-feathered bomb lance was patented by Pierce in 1886. The Cunningham lance was made of iron, with a malleable cast-iron point with three cutting edges. It had rubber wings, and was exploded by a time fuse ignited by a center-fire cartridge rigidly fixed to the lance and becoming a part of it.

An abortive attempt to use prussic acid, placed in a cavity within the harpoon head, took place in the 1830's, with European and American whalemen experimenting. But reports of the poisoned blubber causing death to men handling it soon discouraged efforts to kill whales by this unorthodox method. The Nantucket whaleship "Susan" had some of these acid-containing harpoons in 1833, but never used them. In 1861, a Scottish whaling firm used a large two-grooved rifle fitted with shells containing concentrated prussic acid and a small charge of powder fired by a ten-second time fuse. Captain William Adams reported using it successfully in May 1862, in the Davis Straits.

Another device introduced the idea of using electricity. Through a patent granted in 1852 by the United States Patent Office, it consisted of a wired harpoon to be used from a copper-sheathed boat, the electric current from a battery making a circuit from the generator through a wire to the harpoon, to be returned by the whale's body and the water to the boat.

Early in 1883, a whaling rocket was invented which consisted of a gun barrel mounted on a standard. This device was used for shore whaling on the northwest coast of America. The projectile contained a cast-iron shell and a rocket with a frame holding a shackle with a tow-line attached. When it was fired, the combustible material in the rocket-chamber created a gas which propelled it. Upon entering the whale the bomb-head exploded, releasing simultaneously a toggle and chain which held the frame and tow-line firmly in the whale.

William Greener, of England, designed the heavy Greener gun which, mounted on a swivel, was used successfully to fire the harpoon and became widely used.

But it was Svend Foyn, of Norway, who contributed most to the development of modern whaling methods. In 1865, Foyn designed a whaleboat gun, mounted on a swivel, which had an explosive head added to the harpoon. The bomb head was made of a hollow iron cap, filled with powder, screwed to the tip of the harpoon. The whale line was attached to the harpoon shaft. With this gun the finback whale, who was too fast to be caught by most whalemen in the traditional manner, was now pursued regularly, as were all "finners" or rorqual whales. Mounted in the bow of little steamers, the Foyn gun became standard equipment for Norwegian whalers, and in the 1870's and 1880's the Norwegians extended their industry. Early in the twentieth century, Captain C. A. Larsen, pioneering Antarctic whaleman, opened this part of the world to whaling and the Foyn gun was developed and used so that a fleet of "killer boats," each mounting a gun, killed the whales and towed them to a "mother ship" for processing and boiling out oil.

Modern whaling now has standardized this kind of fleet. Both muzzle-loading and breech-loading harpoon guns are mounted on the bows of the killer boats, balanced on a swivel. The barrel is some forty-five inches long, with a 3-inch bore. The harpoon is of finest tempered Swedish steel, six feet in length, and weighing some 100 lb. The head has four steel prongs which spring out after becoming embedded in the whale, when the line takes up the strain. At the harpoon's extreme head is a conical bomb, over a foot long, filled with gunpowder, which a time fuse explodes within a few seconds after the harpoon is in the whale. The whale line is attached to the shaft by an iron ring sliding inside the hollow formed by the shaft sides. The harpoon line, tied to its ring, fits snugly under the harpoon head, and upon firing runs out on a roller over the bow. The gun is fired within a range of twenty-five yards. A tube is inserted in the whale once it is killed, and air pumped into the body to keep the carcass from sinking. The harpoon shank is unscrewed, but the head is recovered later. Even with this powerful weapon, it is found that sometimes more than two harpoon shots are necessary to capture the largest of the creatures – the blue whale.   E.A.S.

Illustrations: page 340.

Brown, James Templeman, "Apparatus and Methods of the Whale Fishery" in *Fisheries and Fishing Industry of the United States*, edited by George B. Goode, Vol. 11, Section 5, Washington, D.C., 1887.

Scammon, Charles M., *The Marine Mammals of the Northwestern Coast of North America*, San Francisco, 1874.

Starbuck, Alexander, *History of American Whale Fishery*, Waltham, Mass., 1878.

WHEEL LOCK

When a mechanic sharpens a steel tool by holding it against a spinning emery wheel, sparks are produced. The wheel lock discharge mechanism for firearms utilizes the same principle, but does it like a cigarette lighter, in which the mineral is held stationary, while it is the revolving wheel which is of steel.

The origin of the wheel lock is somewhat obscure. Its invention has traditionally been ascribed to Nuremberg, but there now seems to be reason to think that the first wheel lock may have been made farther south, possibly in Italy or Hungary. The earliest dated specimen generally recognized is a pistol (No. K32) in the Royal Armory at Madrid, dated 1530. However, a combination crossbow and wheel lock pistol in the National Museum at Munich bears a coat of arms which was in use only between 1521 and 1526.

Both of these are fairly well developed wheel locks and it seems reasonable to believe that there must have been more primitive types at an earlier date. Such types, though undated, do exist, and it seems probable that eventually evidence will be found to give them a date close to the end of the fifteenth century. Documentary data also support this belief, notably the drawing of two wheel locks, actual or projected, by Leonardo da Vinci, which has been dated about 1508. Several of these primitive locks are, or were, in the National Museum at Budapest (Inv. No. 17/1906 A-E and one unnumbered specimen), where the writer saw them in a heap of metallic rubbish and called them to the attention of the authorities. One of these was eventually traded to the arms collection of the Austrian National Art Museum at Vienna. Similar locks are to be found on three combined pistols and crossbows, (Inv. Nos. Q1-3) in the Doge's Palace Museum in Venice, two hand-axe and pistol combination weapons in the same place (Inv. Nos. Q-7, 8), and on a combined war hammer and pistol in the Ferdinandeum Museum at Innsbruck (Inv. No. 1035), as well as several others.

Even these possibly earliest wheel locks have common characteristics with all – or practically all – the later wheel lock mechanisms. There is a pan fixed to the side of the gun barrel, with a touchhole leading into the chamber of the gun. There is a slot in the bottom of the pan through which protrudes the upper edge of a steel wheel. That wheel is carried on a shaft, or arbor, around which can wind a chain of three links. The third link ends in a toggle which fits into a hook at the end of a powerful mainspring. The end of the arbor is squared, so that it can be turned by an appropriate wrench or spanner. When this is done the wheel rotates until the chain is wound around the arbor, and the toggle is raised against the pull of the mainspring. In the side of the wheel towards the gun is a depression or hole. When the wheel has been wound up as far as possible, the nose of a sear, actuated by a sear spring, slips into that depression and holds the wheel fast until the pulling of a trigger, which acts upon the tail or mid-part of the sear, lifts the nose out of engagement with the wheel, which revolves as the mainspring pulls downward on the toggle, unwinding the chain.

There is a pivoted clamp called a doghead whose jaws contain a piece of iron pyrites, the spark-producing mineral. A spring, acting on a projection of the doghead shaft beyond its pivot, forces it into contact with the revolving wheel. There is also a pan cover which, when the pyrites is raised out of contact with the wheel, can be closed to keep the priming powder in the pan from falling out or being dampened by rain. When this cover is closed, the pyrites can rest on the top of it. As it is opened, the mineral is forced down into contact with the wheel. Iron pyrites was chosen as the mineral because it gives an excellent spark with less wear on the end of the wheel than flint would cause.

In the most primitive wheel locks the pan cover had to be opened by hand before the piece could be fired, but it was soon found possible to have this done automatically by arranging for a spur attached to the pan cover to be engaged by a lug on the rotating wheel arbor, or by a notch in the wheel itself. In the primitive locks the mainspring, wheel, wheel arbor and chain were all on the outside of the lock plate. Soon, however, it was found better to move most of them to the inside, where the mechanism could be protected by being encased in the wood of the stock. An exception to this custom is found in the rather late east German or Polish light sporting rifles known as tschinkes.

In the most primitive wheel locks the action was held, when in the spanned position, by a simple spring-actuated sear, the nose of which engaged a recess or hole in the wheel or a cam on the wheel arbor. This was soon found to be dangerous; the slightest wear on either might cause an accidental disengagement and premature discharge. An early and important invention was the double, or supported sear (cf. Budapest, no inv. no.). One sear engaged the wheel; a second engaged the tail of the first, blocking the nose from disengagement. The trigger of the firearm engaged the tail of this second, or supporting, sear, and, at the moment of firing, pulled it out of contact with the primary sear. The latter, having a rounded nose engaging a tapered depression, was under constant pressure to slip out of engagement and, with the supporting sear removed, it was now free to do so. (Again, the TSCHINKE is an exception.)

The presence of the supporting sear made possible another improvement; in many of the early wheel locks we find on the outside of the lock plate to the rear of the wheel a pivoted hook with a knob and spring. When this hook was swung to the rear it engaged a projection, through a hole in the lock plate, of the supporting sear, and blocked it from any motion whatever. Then the arm could not be fired even if the trigger was pulled. Before firing, it was necessary to swing this safety device forward, against the pressure of its spring, so that the supporting sear would be free to move. However, it seems that this safety too often appeared an unnecessary complication, and by the end of the sixteenth century it had become uncommon.

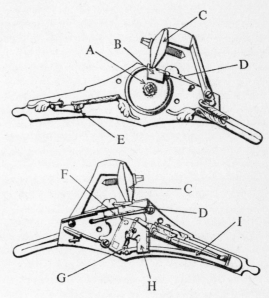

German wheel lock mechanism, ca.1565
A. *Wheel arbor*
B. *Pan*
C. *Dog head*
D. *Pan cover*
E. *Safety*
F. *Pan cover release*
G. *Chain*
H. *Bridle*
I. *Mainspring*

In many early wheel locks the wheel housing consisted of a plate over the face of the wheel, and a separate rim which shielded the edge of the wheel and extended to form the spring engaging the tail of the pyrites holder or doghead. The early doghead springs, then, were an extension of the wheel-housing ring. After the middle of the sixteenth century, however, they were usually separate, generally on the outside, but occasionally on the inside of the lock plate, in which case they engaged a cam on a rotatable doghead arbor.

The wheel housing itself was subject to many variations. At first, the parts covering the face and edge of the wheel respectively were separate; later, they merged. The earlier types had a housing more or less domed, the later ones were flat. In Italy, especially, the housing was often a skeleton one, consisting only of a bridle bar with a bearing for the wheel arbor and a small clip projecting below the wheel and turned upward to retain the edge. In later wheel locks the wheel housing was an integral part of the lock plate, which was usually slightly recessed to follow the shape of the wheel. The contour of this recess was followed on the exterior of the lock plate until the latter part of the seventeenth century, when the lock plate became quite flat.

It should be mentioned here that about the beginning of the seventeenth century there developed in France a peculiar variation of the wheel lock in which the mainspring was not attached to the lock plate at all, but was held independently in the wood of the stock.

A few minor improvements were added as the wheel lock spent its two centuries of service. There arose a rearward projection from the pan to reduce the danger of burning sparks of priming powder being blown back into the face of the shooter. The doghead developed a long projecting tail, to make it easy to turn it back for access to the pan or forward to put the lock in firing condition. The doghead jaws developed a flat plate on the outside to prevent chips of pyrites from being thrown out to the danger of the shooter.

There were also a certain number of anomalous wheel locks which require hardly more than mention in a general discussion such as this. In the Vienna arms collection is an extraordinary wheel lock, apparently made by a clockmaker, with a spiral instead of the normal flat mainspring. Other ingenious mechanics made wheel locks with gearing of two sorts. One type has the usual action but has the wheel arbor terminate, inside the lock plate, in a toothed wheel. A smaller toothed wheel engages the latter, and is mounted on a squared arbor to which the spanner is applied. This mechanism makes the winding up of the action easier in proportion to the ratio between the number of teeth on the two cog wheels. The other type has the mainspring and chain operate on an arbor bearing a cog wheel, while the ignition wheel is on a separate arbor actuated by a smaller gear. This offers no advantage in spanning, but the wheel, instead of rotating less than one full revolution, has a faster and longer movement in proportion to the radial difference between the two wheels.

More frequently found are wheel locks in which the doghead is linked to the wheel and mainspring assembly in such a way that by pulling the doghead away from the pan as far as it will go, then returning it to its original position, the wheel is automatically spanned, without the need of an external wrench. This is accomplished either by having a gear on the doghead arbor mesh with one on the wheel arbor, or by the use of a chain between and around the two arbors. There were also locks of the wheel lock type in which a complete wheel was replaced by a piece of steel shaped like a partial wheel (sector lock), or in which a straight-grooved bar was moved under the pyrites in a fore-and-aft direction (rasp lock), but these are in the nature of freaks, whereas the true wheel lock, for two hundred years, was a sturdy and reliable weapon in the hands of either soldier or civilian sportsman.

The appearance of the wheel lock brought changes in warfare and in social history as well. Pistols were now practical, and this brought a change in the armament and tactics of many cavalrymen, especially the German Reiters. It was now possible for a gun to be kept fully loaded and ready for instantaneous discharge, and this brought with it problems unknown with the earlier matchlock, in which the presence of a smoldering wick always indicated that a weapon was capable of being fired. In this connection, it is interesting that one of the first documents to mention a wheel lock is an account of an accident in which such an arm went off unexpectedly. The gun could now also be carried as a concealed weapon, and crimes of violence involving wheel locks became so prominent that rigid laws controlling their use were promulgated in many cities of Austria, Italy and England during the early 1500's. Finally, the booby trap or infernal machine with clockwork or spring release also became possible, and added one more facet to military and political life.

The wheel lock was a far more efficient and versatile weapon than the matchlock. Because of its complexity, however, it was also far more expensive, and greater skill was required for repairs. For these and lesser reasons, it never supplanted the matchlock as the standard weapon for infantry. Both ignition systems were used side by side, along with the various early flint arms, until the true flintlock superseded almost all other types, late in the seventeenth century.   T.T.H.

Illustrations: pages 35–8, 65 (plate 1), 84 (plate 2), 133 (plate 3), 177, 271, 341, 344, and endpapers.

Blair, Claude, *European and American Arms*, London, 1962.

Blair, Claude, "A Note on the Early History of the Wheel Lock" in *Journal of the Arms and Armour Society*, Vol. 3, No. 9, London, 1961.

Porter rifle, with vertical turret. *Collection of James E. Serven.*

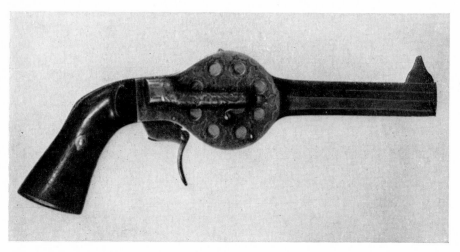

Noel turret gun. *Collection of Lewis Winant.*

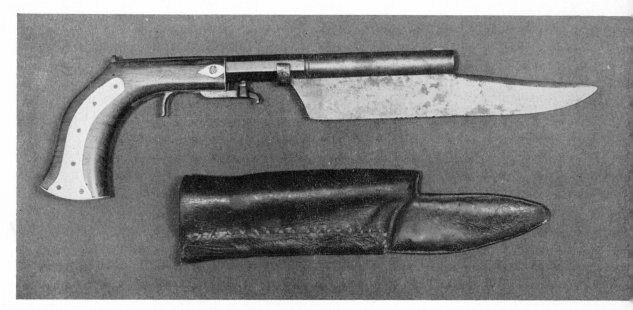

Very rare underhammer percussion cutlass pistol with scabbard, caliber .34, made by C. Oak & Son, Jacksonville. *Collection of Herschel C. Logan.*

Full stocked underhammer
percussion pistol, caliber .34,
made by J. Chase.
Collection of Herschel C. Logan.

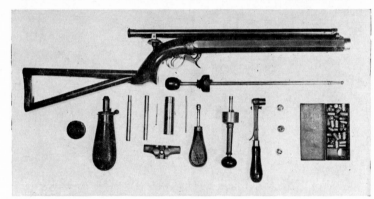

One of the finest of target
underhammer rifles, caliber .38,
made by W. Billinghurst,
Rochester, N.Y., with
accessories, shown out of case.
Collection of Herschel C. Logan.

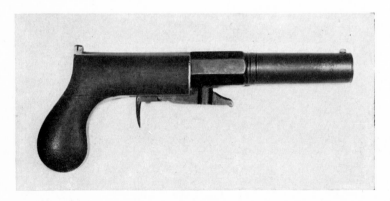

Underhammer pistol, caliber .34,
made by D. D. Sacket,
Westfield, Conn.
Collection of Herschel C. Logan.

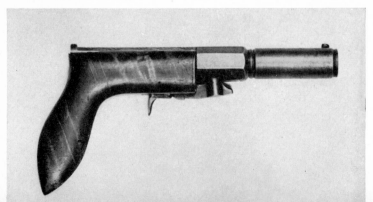

A typical New England under-
hammer pistol, caliber .31, made by
A. Ruggles, Stafford, Conn.
Collection of Herschel C. Logan.

Organ battery gun of the late seventeenth century,
with thirty-nine barrels on a rotating triangular block.
Zeughaus, Solothurn, Switzerland.

Duck's foot pistol, made by H. W. Mortimer, London.
Collection of W. Keith Neal.

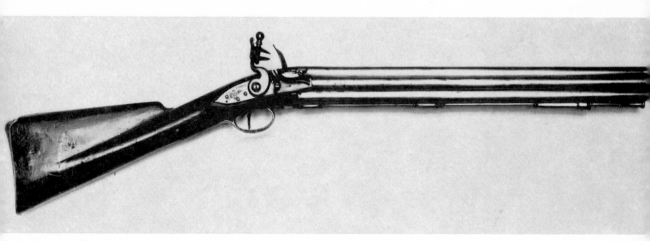

Seven-barreled volley gun, made by Henry Nock. *Armouries, Tower of London.*

The S. Eggers whaling gun; drop-breech type patented Feb. 12, 1878. *Mystic Seaport, Conn.*

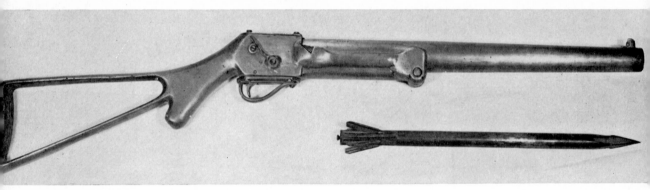

The Captain Ebenezer Pierce bomb-lance gun. *Mystic Seaport, Conn.*

Greener gun, usually mounted on bow of whaleboat. The gun illustrated is
an adaptation of the original British design. *Mystic Seaport, Conn.*

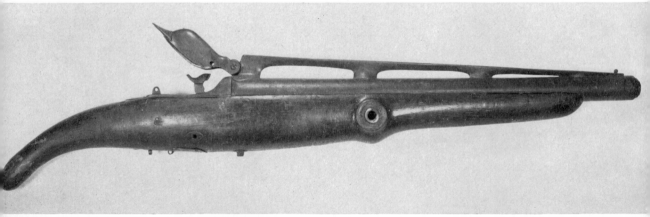

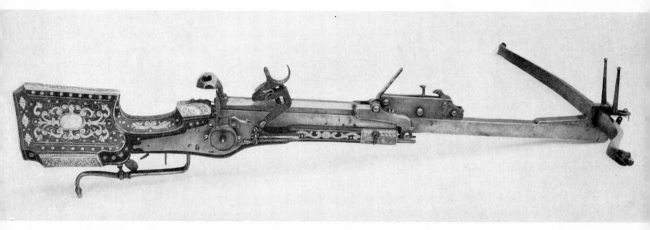

Combination wheel lock pistol and prodd, *ca.*1600. *Collection of Joe Kindig, Jr.*

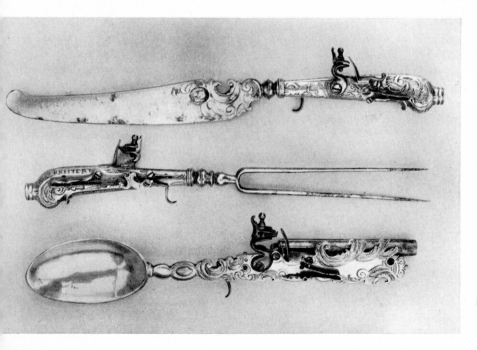

Knife, fork, and spoon pistols. *Collection of W. Keith Neal.*

Dolne apache pistol. *Collection of Eddie Reider.*

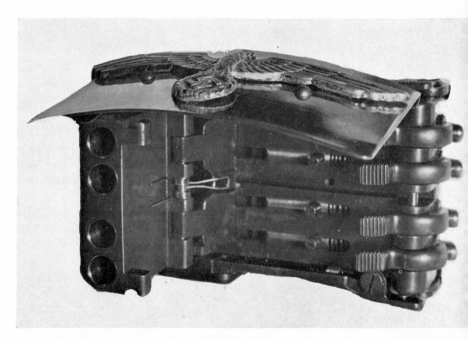

German four-shot battery and belt buckle, shown with belt plate raised.
Collection of Gordon Persons.

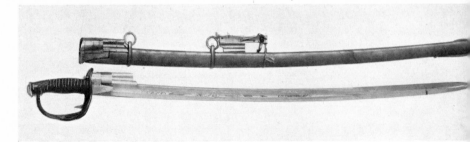

American pistol and sword combination patented by Robert J. Colvin, 1862.
Smithsonian Institution.

Double-barreled percussion knife pistol. *Collection of Lewis Winant.*

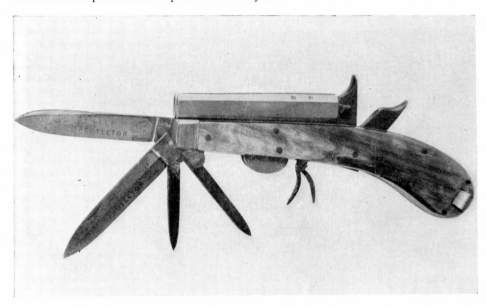

Elgin cutlass pistol. *Smithsonian Institution.*

Cased truncheon pistol. *Collection of Lewis Winant.*

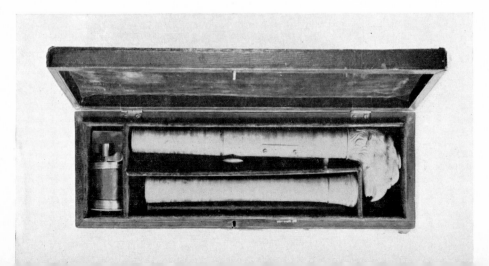

French set of armorer's tools,
made by Delpire, *ca.*1820.
Collection of Howard L. Blackmore.

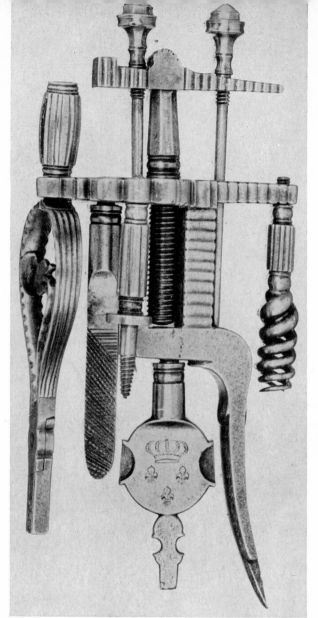

Wheel lock spanner.
Wallace Collection, London.

British flintlock musket tool,
with a ball drawer and lever
for a Baker rifle beside it.
Collection of Howard L. Blackmore.

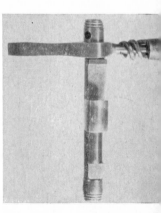

Combination tool for the
Enfield rifle.
Collection of Howard L. Blackmor[e]

English match-type powder tester
with brass body and walnut handle,
*ca.*1690--1700. This is the type
often referred to as
a "Queen Anne" tester.
Collection of Paul J. Wolf.

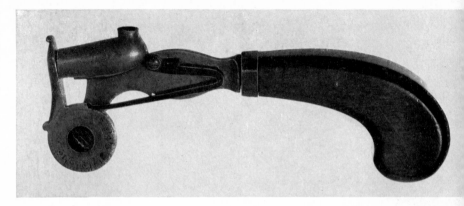

Miquelet powder tester with
mounts of pierced and engraved
brass, *ca.*1750; no signature.
Collection of Paul J. Wolf.

French flintlock powder tester,
first half of the eighteenth century;
the lock signed "J. B. Muit".
Collection of Paul J. Wolf.

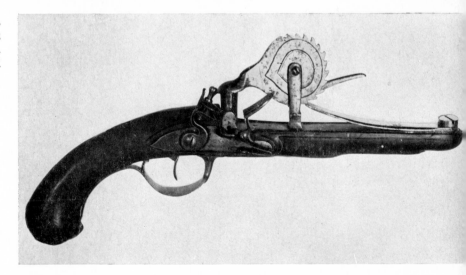

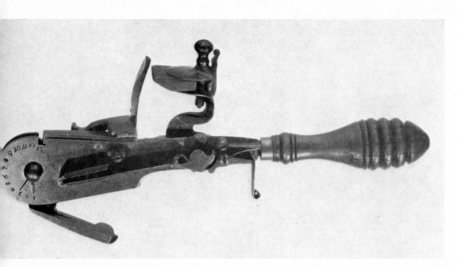

Powder tester with covered wheel,
no signature or other marks;
early eighteenth century,
probably Italian.
Collection of Paul J. Wolf.

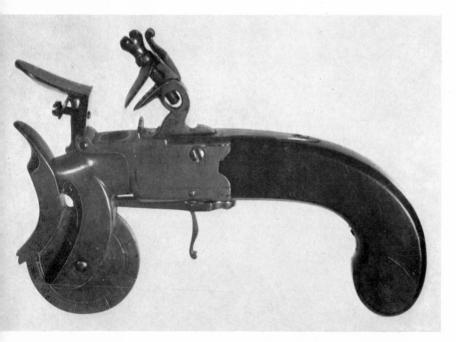

English flintlock box lock tester
with brass body, walnut stock,
and iron lock parts,
late eighteenth century.
Collection of Paul J. Wolf.

Match-type powder tester
on a wooden base;
seventeenth-century, probably Swiss.
Collection of Paul J. Wolf.

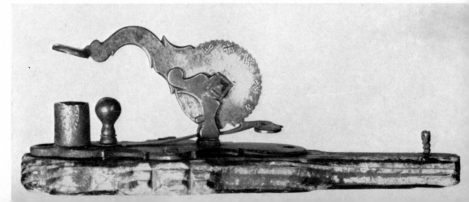

Dutch vertical ratchet powder tester on pistol stock, with flintlock ignition; late seventeenth century. *Collection of Paul J. Wolf.*

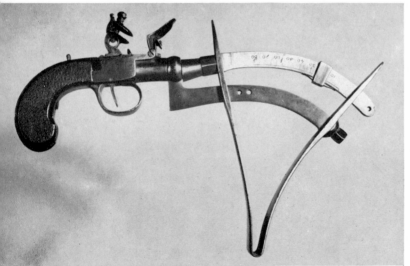

Flintlock V-spring powder tester, late eighteenth to early nineteenth century; not signed, but undoubtedly the work of Guillaume Berleur of Liège. *Collection of Paul J. Wolf.*

Combination powder tester, wheel lock spanner, and adjustable powder measure; early seventeenth century, possibly Italian. *Metropolitan Museum of Art, New York.*

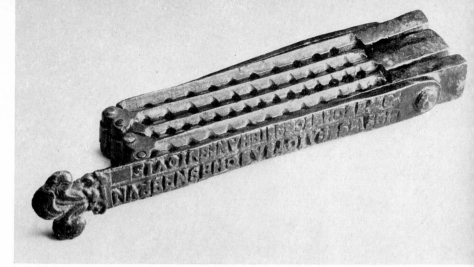

Multi-leaved French bullet mold of brass, late sixteenth century. *Collection of Harold L. Peterson.*

French seventeenth-century scissor-type bullet mold casting four balls. *Metropolitan Museum of Art, New York.*

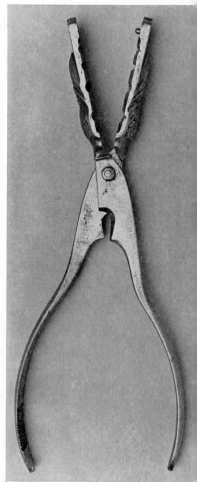

French brass bullet mold, early seventeenth century. *Collection of Harold L. Peterson.*

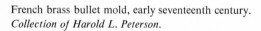

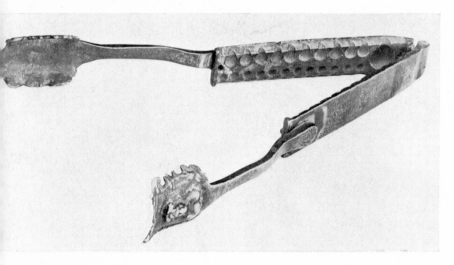

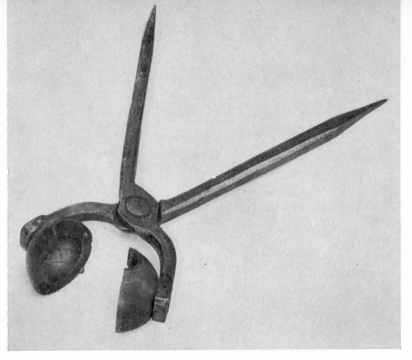

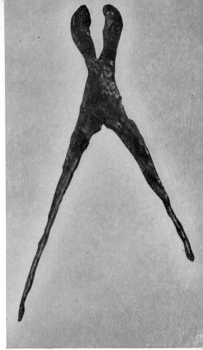

ABOVE
Scissor-type bullet mold
for swivel gun,
seventeenth century.
Collection of
Harold L. Peterson.

ABOVE RIGHT
Seventeenth-century
iron scissor-type bullet mold
with sprue cutter,
excavated at Jamestown.
U. S. National Park Service.

RIGHT
Brass bullet mold with four
cavities of different sizes,
dated 1760.
Collection of Harold L. Peterson.

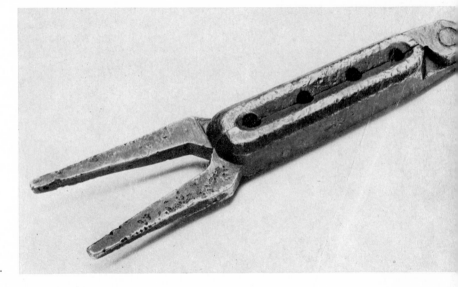

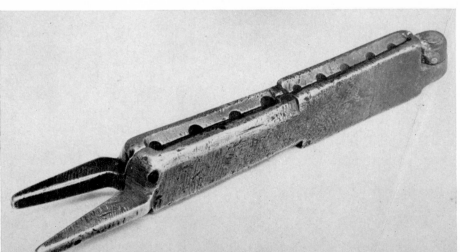

Brass bullet
mold casting
balls of four
different sizes
and two sizes
of buckshot,
mid-eighteenth
century.
Collection of
Harold L. Peterson.

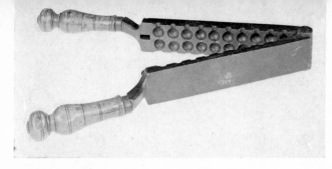

Mold for casting balls for
Brown Bess musket, marked BO and
British broad arrow, dated 1771.
Winchester Repeating Arms Company.

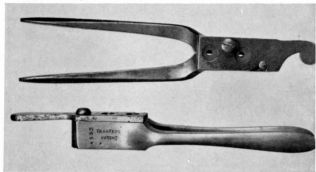

Tranter revolver bullet mold,
mid-nineteenth century.
Collection of James E. Serven.

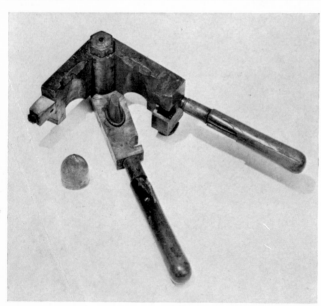

Mold for elliptical hollow-based
bullet, mid-nineteenth century.
Smithsonian Institution.

Soapstone bullet mold with
wooden frame, *ca.*1870.
Collection of Harold L. Peterson.

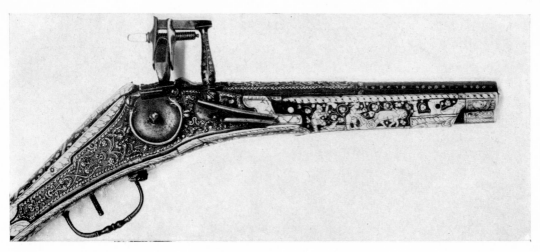

Detail of wheel lock pistol, the
silver encrusted ornament on lock
and barrel a later addition.
The barrel has been shortened
and the stock cut back.
Wallace Collection, London.

Tschinke, the incised ornament on
lock and barrel a later addition, and a
wheel lock rifle, the incised
and damascened ornament a later
addition, purchased from
Frédéric Spitzer.
Wallace Collection, London.

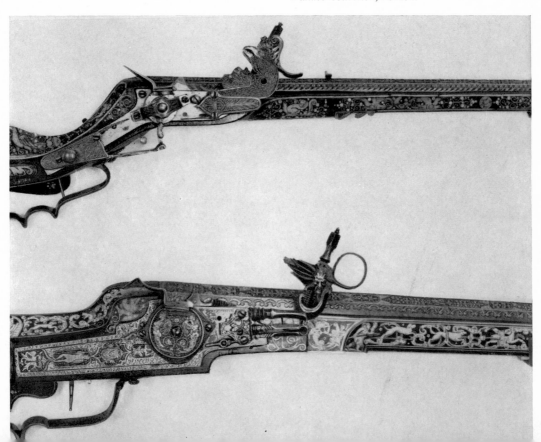

Detail of barrel of Saxon wheel lock pistol, the chiseled ornament
with the royal arms of France a nineteenth-century addition.
Victoria and Albert Museum, London.

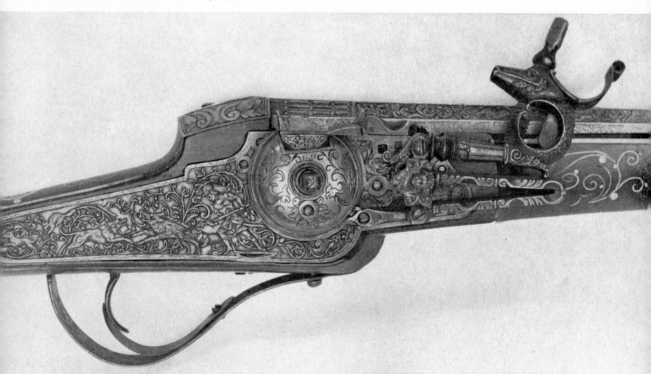

Detail of lock of Saxon wheel lock pistol. The gilt brass wheel cover
and the cherub's mask on the dog-spring bridle are original;
the chiseled ornament showing a Roman soldier hunting a wild boar
is a nineteenth-century addition.
Victoria and Albert Museum, London.

Hayward, J. F., *The Art of the Gunmaker*, 2 vols, London and New York, 1962–64.

Hoopes, Thomas T., "Das Frühste Datierbare Radschloss im National-Museum in München" in *Zeitschrift für Historische Waffen- und Kostümkunde*, Vol. 4, No. 10, 1934.

Peterson, Harold L., *The Treasury of the Gun*, New York, 1962 (*The Book of the Gun*, London, 1963).

See also: DECORATION OF FIREARMS; SPANISH FIREARMS; SPANNER; TSCHINKE.

WHITE, ROLLIN

Rollin White (1818–92), gunsmith and inventor, was born at Williamstown, Vermont, and learned his trade in the shop of an older brother. Employed at Colt's armory from 1849 to 1854 as a contractor on barrels and lock parts, he devoted his spare time to revolver improvements. His ingenuity led to several patents, taken out after leaving Colt's, the most significant claim being one of April 3, 1855, for "extending the chambers through the rear of the cylinder for the purpose of loading them at the breech from behind." A leather packing behind the charge, but pierced to admit ignition, was designed to prevent communication of fire between chambers.

Colonel Colt rejected the invention, but to Daniel B. Wesson, experimenting with self-primed metallic cartridges it was essential. In 1856 he obtained exclusive right to the feature of boring the chambers through, against payment of a royalty of twenty-five cents per pistol. Under this agreement White received nearly $70,000 from Smith & Wesson until the patent expired in 1869. Persistent infringement by other manufacturers in New England produced much litigation to which White devoted himself, the validity of the patent being finally sustained by a tie vote of the United States Supreme Court against the defense of prior invention abroad. In this suit, where White recovered $23,000 damages against Ethan Allen, the Lefaucheux patent of 1845 on pin-fire single pistols or pepperboxes was deemed inapposite to revolvers.

The inventor, prompted by Smith & Wesson, made valiant efforts to have his patent extended, but the Commissioner of Patents refused and a bill which would have permitted reconsideration was vetoed by President Grant in 1870. Grant acted at the instance of the Chief of Ordnance, who believed that the patentee merited no further reward for the altering of percussion revolvers to cartridge. Previously White had been paid for the conversion of some Remington army revolvers, and had also received fees on cartridge pistols made by the Rollin White Arms Company of Lowell, Massachusetts. The plea for extension was renewed in successive Congresses until 1877, but the intervening development of many types of breech-loading revolvers militated against it. Rollin White, in whom intransigence was a marked characteristic, never saw his own revolver designs fully executed. However, his single claim of 1855 to a bored-through cylinder afforded Smith & Wesson a virtual monopoly of the manufacture of metallic cartridge revolvers for over a decade.   J.E.P.

Parsons, John E., *Smith & Wesson Revolvers*, New York, 1957.

WHITNEY, ELI

Eli Whitney, inventor and manufacturer of New Haven, Connecticut, born on December 8, 1765, was famed for his invention of the cotton gin and his application of interchangeability of musket parts. He was the successful contractor, in 1798, for 10,000 muskets at $13.40 each.

In the summer of 1798, since the total production of the two national armories at Springfield and Harpers Ferry had just reached about 3,000 muskets each, Congress, apprehensive of strained relations with France and lack of arms for the arming of the militia, let contracts to twenty-seven contractors for 40,200 muskets of the Charleville, French Model 1763, pattern. Whitney was one of the twenty-one contractors to complete his contract. While others with smaller contracts were making their quotas practically by hand over a period of years, many being ruined by inexperience and rising costs, Whitney, with his larger contract, proceeded to apply his inventive genius to the design of machinery for making identical parts in quantities to gauges. Only when the identical parts were complete were the arms assembled. He was late in his deliveries, completing his contract in 1809, but his arms proved very acceptable, with parts largely interchangeable and including a number of improvements and refinements, some his own, some from the later French Model 1777.

The contract of 10,000 was followed by other Federal contracts for 33,000 additional muskets between 1812 and 1824, as well as contracts with states for their militia units. Eli Whitney died on January 8, 1826, but his armory continued to be operated by trustees, P. & E. W. Blake, and later by his son Eli Jr., when he attained his majority in 1842. The Whitney Armory made 17,600 Model 1841 percussion rifles to 1855, and made 15,001 rifle-muskets and 11,214 Whitney revolvers during the Civil War. The Armory ceased operations in 1888.   A.G.

WHITWORTH, SIR JOSEPH

Joseph Whitworth was undoubtedly the most celebrated mechanical engineer in nineteenth-century Britain. The discoveries he made form the very basis of all precise engineering. Amongst much else, he produced the first perfect plane, pioneered measurement to a millionth of an inch, and standardized measures, gauges and threads.

He was born in 1803, of humble parentage, and was not able to set up on his own until 1833. His first great triumph was at the 1851 Exhibition, three years before he made his first acquaintance with small arms at the invitation of the government. Once started, his interest grew; and the Whitworth rifle demonstrates the importance of his contribution to small arms manufacture. To their design he added little that was novel.

He spent much effort on improving ordnance and particularly on the quality of steel used in its construction. Indeed, this was probably the most important work of his later years. In 1869 he was made a baronet; though married twice, he had no heir. He died at Monte Carlo on January 22, 1887.   C.H.R.

"Memoir of Sir Joseph Whitworth" in *Proceedings of the Institution of Civil Engineers, 1887–88.*
Whitworth, Sir Joseph, *Miscellaneous Papers on Practical Subjects: Guns and Steel*, London, 1873.

See also: WHITWORTH RIFLE.

WHITWORTH RIFLE

The one common distinguishing feature of the Whitworth rifle, which enjoyed such fame in the early 1860's, was its hexagonal form of bore. Most Whitworth rifles were manufactured by the Manchester Ordnance and Rifle Company, though some were made entirely at Enfield. In caliber, most were nominally .451 and rifled with a 20-inch pitch, but there is an extremely rare variety with .564 bore and a 25-inch spiral.

Apart from his earliest experimental arms, Whitworth stuck closely to the single specification for his small-bores. His match rifles differ only in detail from each other and from his military arms. There is an official record of the construction of eight Whitworth breech-loading rifles, but it may be stated generally that the true Whitworth in almost all versions was a muzzle-loader.

The earliest experimental military Whitworths manufactured on an appreciable scale were those with 39-inch barrels made for the government trials of 1857 and 1858. In 1860 a small number of two military models, a heavy-and a light-barreled version, were prepared at Enfield and rifled at Manchester. The outcome of their successful trial against severe competition was the production at Enfield in 1862 of 1,000 Whitworths with 36-inch iron barrels.

This 1862 pattern proved itself quite promising, and

7,900 further rifles, known as "Short" Whitworths from their 33-inch steel barrels, were manufactured at Enfield in 1863. At the same time, 100 similar rifles were made by Whitworth at the Manchester Company's works. These were subsequently known as "Manchester" Whitworths. In 1864 seventeen regiments were issued Whitworths for prolonged troop trials. As military arms they proved highly controversial, but their early supersession by the Snider reduced the value of their trial to a check on the suitability of steel for rifle barrels. Although the Whitworth enjoyed some popularity as a sniping arm during the American Civil War, it was being eclipsed even in this direction by 1866. The advent of the Metford match rifle ended its long popularity with the target marksman.
                                              C.H.R.

Illustration: page 105.

See also: RICHARDS, WESTLEY; RIFLES AND RIF-LING; WHITWORTH, SIR JOSEPH.

WINCHESTER

Winchester is a name applied to a long line of firearms manufactured by the Winchester Repeating Arms Company of New Haven, Connecticut, since its organization in 1866. Most famous of the line have been the lever-action repeating rifles, but there have been other rifles also as well as shotguns, special weapons, and even a few experimental revolvers. The founder of the firm was Oliver F. Winchester, a shirt manufacturer turned financier, who had no practical knowledge of firearms or their manufacture. His understanding of corporate organization and finance, however, was excellent. Under his guidance a fine rifle was developed and a famous manufacturing company established.

Winchester's interest in gun making came gradually. In 1855 he purchased eighty shares of stock in the Volcanic Repeating Firearms Company organized to manufacture Smith and Wesson's improvement of the Hunt-Jennings Volitional Repeater. In 1857 the Company went bankrupt, and Winchester purchased its assets. He promptly organized a new stock company called the New Haven Arms Company and installed himself as president with a controlling 800 shares of stock. The firm continued to manufacture Volcanic arms, but with little financial success. Then, in 1858, Winchester set B. Tyler Henry to work on new ammunition and other improvements which led to the Henry rifle of 1860 and success for the company. In 1866 he reorganized the company once more and named it the Winchester Repeating Arms Company. Thereafter all arms manufactured by it were known as Winchesters.

The first of the new Winchester rifles was the Model

1866. In essence, it was the Henry, but with improvements by Nelson King. Most notable of these was a gate which allowed the cartridges to be slipped into the magazine from the breech instead of from the forward end and permitted a completely closed tube. A second model followed in 1873 which was designed for a longer center-fire cartridge and which abandoned the famous brass frame for one of iron. The Model 1866 remained popular and continued to be manufactured, however, and soon the Model 1873 developed infinite variations and calibers. With these two models the Winchester Company established itself firmly as one of the world's leading arms manufacturers, a position which it has retained ever since.   H.L.P.

Illustrations: pages 180–81, 214, and endpapers.

Madis, George, *The Winchester Book*, Dallas, Tex., 1961.
Parsons, John E., *The First Winchester*, New York, 1955.
Williamson, Harold F., *Winchester, the Gun that Won the West*, Washington, D.C., 1952.

See also: HENRY, BENJAMIN TYLER; HENRY RIFLE; HUNT, WALTER; REPEATING ARMS; SMITH, HORACE; WESSON, DANIEL B.

WINDAGE

See: BALLISTICS.

KEY TO THE ENDPAPERS

The endpapers and dust jacket show
a selection of guns from
the Tower of London Armouries.

1. English double-barreled officer's pistol with detachable shoulder stock, early nineteenth century.

2. English silver-mounted holster pistol, mid-eighteenth century.

3. Ferguson rifle.

4. Colt Dragoon revolver, second model.

5. Wheel lock pistol, the stock inlaid with engraved horn. German, late sixteenth century.

6. Remington double deringer pistol.

7. Brescian holster pistol, the walnut stock inlaid with panels of steel tracery, mid-seventeenth century.

8. Matchlock musket, the stock inlaid with engraved mother-of-pearl and brass wire. Dutch, early seventeenth century.

9. Scottish pistol, mid-eighteenth century.

10. Kentucky rifle, early nineteenth century.

11. Collier revolver.

12. Simeon North flintlock dueling pistol. American, early nineteenth century.

13. Winchester rifle, model 1873.

14. Scottish snaphance gun, second half of seventeenth century.

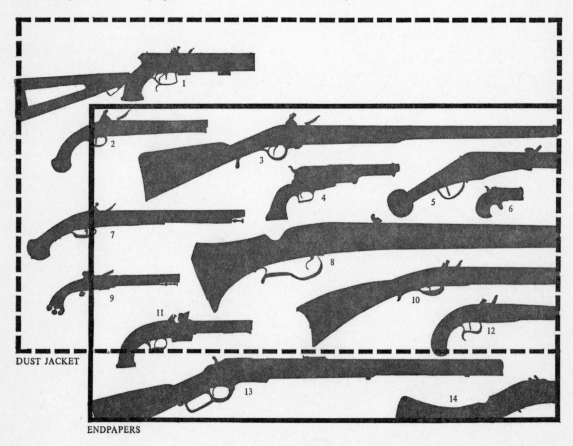

DUST JACKET

ENDPAPERS

ACKNOWLEDGMENTS

Color plates 7 and 8 are reproduced by gracious permission of Her Majesty the Queen. Permission to reproduce the other color plates was kindly given by W. Keith Neal (plate 1), the Trustees of the Wallace Collection (plate 2), the Trustees of the Victoria and Albert Museum (plates 3 and 5), R. T. Gwynn (plate 4) and Lord Astor of Hever (plate 6). The endpapers are reproduced by kind permission of the Master of the Armouries at the Tower of London. The subjects for the color plates and the endpapers were selected and captioned by J. F. Hayward, in consultation with the Editor and (for the endpapers) with A. N. Kennard. The color photographs for the plates and the endpapers were taken especially for this *Encyclopedia* by Bill Monaghan.

For advice on the selection of the black and white photographs, for prints and for permission to reproduce them, we are indebted to a great many individuals and institutions, in particular to William A. Albaugh III, Howard L. Blackmore, Claude Blair, Clement Bosson, the British Museum, the Curtis Museum (Alton, Hants), the Doge's Palace Museum (Venice), John S. du Mont, Egon Eriksen, the Glasgow Art Gallery and Museum, Craddock R. Goins Jr., R. T. Gwynn, Thomas Hall, Charles E. Hanson Jr., J. F. Hayward, the Hermitage Museum (Leningrad), Arne Hoff, Thomas T. Hoopes, G. B. Jarrett, A. N. Kennard, James Duncan Lavin, the Liège Arms Museum, Herschel C. Logan, John C. McMurray, the Marine Corps Museum (Quantico, Va.), the Metropolitan Museum of Art (New York), the Milwaukee Public Museum, Bluford W. Muir, the National Historical Museum (Stockholm), W. Keith Neal, the *Observer*, John E. Parsons, Harold L. Peterson, William Reid, Joseph E. Smith, the Smithsonian Institution, the Springfield Armory, Edouard A. Stackpole, the Controller of H. M. Stationery Office, the Tøjhusmuseet, the Tower of London Armouries, the Victoria and Albert Museum, the Wallace Collection, the Walters Art Gallery (Baltimore), Donald B. Webster Jr., the West Point Museum, the late Lewis Winant, the Winchester Repeating Arms Company, Paul J. Wolf, Eldon G. Wolff, and the Zeughaus (Solothurn, Switzerland). The black and white photographs are in most cases the copyright of the owners named in the captions. The photographs in the collections of the Tower of London Armouries and the Victoria and Albert Museum are Crown copyright.

The illustrations in the text, most of them commissioned especially for this book, were drawn by Albert Barber (rifles and rifling), Ronald Clark (ballistics, bandolier, bayonet, cartridge, Greener, gunflint, trade guns), John Edwards (jezail, stock), Blanche M. A. Ellis (capper, cartridge box, holster, nipple primer, porte tache, powder flask, primer, proof marks, shot pouch), James Duncan Lavin (miquelet), E. A. Mornard (Bourgeoys, false muzzle, flintlock, Gras rifle, Lebel rifle, Lovell, matchlock, muzzle brake, pillar breech, Scandinavian snap lock, set trigger, sights, snaphance), Harold L. Peterson (wheel lock), C. H. Roads (Farquharson) and H. Russell Robinson (dog lock, English lock, safety device, Snider rifle). Valuable advice and assistance in the preparation of the drawings was given by many individuals, in particular by Howard L. Blackmore, Claude Blair, John S. du Mont, S. James Gooding, T. M. Hamilton, Charles E. Hanson Jr., Arne Hoff, Thomas T. Hoopes, James S. Hutchins, Berkeley R. Lewis, William Reid and C. H. Roads.

If any owners of copyright material used in this book have inadvertently not been acknowledged, the publishers offer sincere apologies in advance and will gladly make due acknowledgment in any future edition.

INDEX

Page numbers in **bold type** indicate articles in the *Encyclopedia*. Page numbers of other text references are in roman type, and page numbers of illustrations are in *italic type*. An ampersand joining two page numbers indicates a continuous text reference divided by illustration pages. Page numbers of illustrations following the name of a place or person indicate illustrations of subjects associated with that place or person. Cross-references are for the most part those that arise within the index itself. For additional references to related topics, please refer to the lists following many of the articles in the text.